Nope, not here, mate.

Other books by Jude Southerland Kessler

Shoulda Been There, Vol. 1, **The John Lennon Series**
Shivering Inside, Vol. 2, **The John Lennon Series**
She Loves You, Vol. 3, **The John Lennon Series**
Should Have Known Better, Vol. 4, **The John Lennon Series**
Contributing Author to:
New Critical Perspectives on The Beatles: Things We Said Today
The Beatles in Context
The Beatles Get Back to Abbey Road

Read Jude's blog at
The Fest for Beatles Fans
https://www.thefest.com

Follow Lanea Stagg and Jude's radio show
"She Said She Said"
on Podbean, Spotify, I-Tunes, Facebook, and Instagram

Subscribe to Jude's free newsletter
https://www.johnlennonseries.com/

Meet Jude in person every year at
The Fest for Beatles Fans (New York Metro and Chicago)

Shades of Life

Part 1

Volume 5
in

The John Lennon Series

(Jan. - Aug. 1965)

Jude Southerland Kessler

jude southerland kessler

9 October 20

 # 111 / 250

Shine on

foreword by Bill Harry

Cover Art by **Rande M. Kessler**
Cover design by Tim Coulter

OntheRock Books

Penin Inc Publishing, LLC
Copyright © 2021 Jude Southerland Kessler

All photographs courtesy of the author and/or by permission

*Every reasonable effort has been made to contact
copyright holders and secure permissions.
Omissions can be remedied in future editions.*

Shades of Life/Part 1/Jude Southerland Kessler – 1ˢᵗ U.S. edition
Library of Congress Cataloging in Publication data

ISBN 978-0-9799448-6-4
Cover design by Tim Coulter
Original cover art by Rande Monroe Kessler

This book may be ordered by mail from the publisher
or downloaded on all e-book formats.

www.JohnLennonSeries.com

OnTheRock Books
Louisiana

Meet the Cover Artist...

Rande Kessler is a Renaissance man: a graduate of the U.S. Naval Academy; a deep-sea diver for the Navy; the former State Director for the Louisiana Small Business Development Centers network; a singer/songwriter (Top Ten Per-Cent in the Unisong International Song Contest), and a gifted artist. He was Louisiana's Caroline Dorman artist with a one-man show in the R.W. Norton Art Gallery, Shreveport, LA. Recently, he was the illustrator for a children's book by Thresa M. Schmitt, entitled *There Was a Sweater*. Kessler's work is also featured on the cover of *She Loves You*, Vol. 3, and the cover of *Should Have Known Better*, Vol. 4 in **The John Lennon Series**.

**To Mark & Carol,
Michelle Joni and Tilly Lapidos:**
*The Beatles created Beatlemania.
You created The Beatles Family
via The Fest for Beatles Fans.
Thank you for finding the way for thousands
of diverse people to truly "Come Together."
You are loved!*

**And as always to my bestie, Lanea Stagg,
and my husband "for 40 years!",
Rande.
Shine on…**

Acknowledgements

Rande Kessler, my talented husband who drew the cover sketch of John in 1965. He has lived with John for 44 years and works tirelessly to make sure John's story gets out to the world! Thank you for helping to edit the book whilst handling all the business aspects of publication as well. Thank you for being my partner in the monthly "Focal Points" webinars on John Lennon and the engineer for the "She Said She Said" podcast. And from me to you, thank you so much for picking up the "slack" around the house so that these books can be completed. I could not do this without you! I love you!

Lanea Stagg, the best friend a girl could ever have. In spite of a pandemic and the recent acquisition of a large, historic gym (The Pit Barbell Club) in Evansville, IN, Lanea, once again, took on the mammoth task of editing this work! As always, her editor's eye is matchless, as is the gift of her friendship!! The precious gift of her time and expertise cannot be repaid. Despite a mountain of other obligations, Lanea gave hours and hours to all aspects of this book while sustaining me as a friend. Love you, Lanea!

Bill Harry, who was so kind to, once again, write the Foreword for this book and who has been an integral part of **The John Lennon Series** from Day One. Bill, your authoritative Beatles books are always a valuable guide to me as I write, and you're never more than an e-mail away when I need help. It continues to be my great honour to call you "friend." My love to Virginia and to you.

Susie Duchateau, my sweet, savvy, and patient research assistant, who can find *anything*! Thank you for coming to my research rescue and for being my partner in our website, https://www.beatlesinterviews.net

Nicole Michael of "910 public relations," my outstanding PR agent and dear friend, who despite a busy schedule with *many* clients, always finds time to help me with webinars, podcasts, articles, and with new and innovative ways to get the word out about **The John Lennon Series**. She also listens to me vent…a lot…and prays for me. Thank you, Nicole!

Julia Baird, John's smart, creative sister, who has a place in my heart. Thank you for your friendship. You are in my heart.

Freda Kelly, who continues to inspire me to be a better person. I was blessed to interview Freda for my radio show, *The John Lennon Hour*, and to have her serve as the keynote speaker for my GRAMMY Museum of Mississippi Beatles Symposium in 2016. Freda sets the bar high! Across The Beatles World, she is admired, respected, and loved. Her friendship is a true blessing.

Louise Harrison, who gave me an interview in Kansas City, 1994, and then appeared on my radio show, *The John Lennon Hour*, in 2016. Her personal memories of those happy days with The Beatles in the Bahamas 1965 were so helpful in writing this book.

May Pang, for *always* being there when I needed support, an answer, a book review, or a kind word. I am so glad you touched John's life. Your love (and his for you) made him a better man.

Charlie Lennon, John's late uncle, who sat with me for hours in The Grapes, Liverpool, talking about the relationship between Stanley, Fred, and yourself...and about Fred's reluctance to reconnect with John. Charlie supplied family details that helped with the chapter of Fred's 1965 appearance at Kenwood in this book. Thank you, Uncle Charlie, and rest in peace.

Helen Anderson, for sharing your wonderful true stories about John through the years, and your heartfelt memories of your lifelong friend, Cynthia, during the timeframe of this book. You have been so gracious to help me from Vol. 1 on...thank you!

Elliot Easton, Rock'n'Roll Hall of Fame lead guitar player for the celebrated band The Cars and currently, The Empty Hearts. Elliot, you continue to amaze me! Your knowledge of The Beatles is in a league of its own! Thank you for your edits and guidance and most of all, for your friendship.

Dr. Angie McCartney and Ruth McCartney, two of the most positive, loving, and joyous ladies I know! Thank you for the 2020 interview on the "She Said She Said" radio podcast with co-host Lanea Stagg of **The Recipe Records Series** and me. You really made those days in the Bahamas with The Beatles come to life! It made that chapter so easy to write! My respect for you both is boundless.

Tom Frangione, the host of "Way Beyond Compare" and co-host of "Apple Jam" on The Beatles Channel, Sirius XM radio, who is not only a Beatles expert but the truest of friends. Tom, thank you for the 2020 interview on "She Said She Said," your extremely kind cover quote for this book, and most of all, for the bright light you shone on us all throughout the pandemic. In good times and bad, you make the world a better place.

Bill King, the creator and owner of the esteemed *Beatlefan* magazine, which is respected worldwide. I am extremely appreciative of your cover quote for this book, Bill. Thank you so much. Writing for *Beatlefan* has been one of my career's greatest honors.

Ivor Davis, who was the only reporter to travel with The Beatles on the entire 1964 North American Tour and who enjoyed a good portion of the 1965 North American Tour with The Beatles, including the night they met Elvis (which will be in Part 2 of this book)! Your true stories, insights, guidance, and most of all, your friendship have sustained me not only in the writing of this book but in some of the more difficult moments of the last three years. I'm so blessed to call you my friend.

Art Schreiber, who toured with The Beatles in 1964 and was one of John Lennon's close friends on the trek. Your many chats with me over the last few years have helped me understand John's personality better and to understand his relationship with Cynthia as well. Thank you, Uncle Arturo!

Larry Kane, who gave me a great interview about the 1964 and 1965 North American Tours…especially those days in the Bahamas, 1965, with the lads on the set of "Help!" Your three books have been extremely helpful throughout this series, and you have been so kind to Rande and to me for over ten years.

And very special thanks to my buddy, **Jim Berkenstadt,** author of *The Beatle Who Vanished* on the life of 1964 Beatle Jimmie Nicol, who sends me John Lennon information constantly, and who was truly there for me and my family in a very dark time during the 2020 pandemic. Jim, thank you for your wonderful cover quote and for the thousands of ways you've made me smile in a rough year.

A very special thank you and much love to my team of editors:

Rande Kessler, *who always finds time.* Thank you, honey!

Lanea Stagg, once again…who has sustained me in far more than this book, but who gave hours and hours to edit it whilst owning and managing a huge, busy gym, the Pit Barbell Club in Evansville, Indiana; co-hosting the "She Said She Said" podcast with me; and writing a new volume in your popular **Recipe Records Series** of rock'n'roll cookbooks! God bless you, my friend. God only knows what I'd be without you.

Al Sussman, a respected historian, the Executive Editor for *Beatlefan* magazine, and the author of *Changin' Times: 101 Days That Shaped A Generation,* which, of course, is enough to keep anyone extremely busy! And yet, you always find time to help me with articles and blogs…and the editing of this book. Thank you for the gift of your time and knowledge!

Janet Davis, an integral part of the editorial staff at the Beatles fanzine *Octopus' Garden.* Janet has been an expert panelist for years at the **Fest for Beatles Fans,** and she has served as editor for Sara Schmidt's upcoming book on the North American Beatles Fan Clubs, *Dear Beatle People,* as well as editor for Charles Rosenay's book, *The Book of Top 10 Horror Lists.* Janet spent *months* working non-stop on every line, space, and comma in this book. Janet, I can never repay such a gift. Thank you.

And thanks to my distinguished colleagues in research...

Mark Lewisohn, whose respected and trusted Beatles books are "right." Your books are, for all Beatles authors and fans, truly invaluable. On top of that, you are kind and generous to us all. Every Beatles author and researcher owes you a great debt. I certainly do. Thank you!

Richard Langham, Scott Freiman, and Jerry Hammack, who helped me with some of the recording studio chapters for this book. You are so *very kind* to share the gift of your time and expertise. Thank you all!

Sara Schmidt, author of *Happiness is Seeing The Beatles: Beatlemania in St. Louis* and the upcoming work, *Dear Beatle People.* Sara also created and manages the incredible, vetted website featuring true stories of people who have met The Beatles: https://www.meetthebeatlesforreal.com and has provided insights and events that I could find nowhere else. Sara, thank you for your superb research and for the wonderful photo of The Beatles in Paris for this book. Shine on!

Bruce Spizer, my friend and mentor, who generously helped me with the music and recording sections of this book. Your body of work, including *The Beatles for Sale on Parlophone Records* and *The Beatles' Story on Capitol Records, Vols. 1 and 2,* were indispensable in the writing of this book. I can always count on you.

Dr. Kenneth Womack, whose magnificent biographies of Sir George Martin (*Maximum Volume: The Life of Beatles Producer, George Martin, Vol. 1* and *Sound Pictures: The Life of Beatles Producer, George Martin, Vol. 2*) answered so many important questions, and whose elegant work, *Long and Winding Roads: The Evolving Artistry of The Beatles* answered all the others! Your work ethic continues to inspire me and challenge me. I'm amazed. (No "maybe.") Shine on!

Chuck Gunderson, author of the premier compendium on the North American Tours, *Some Fun Tonight!, The Backstage Story of How The Beatles Rocked America: The Historic Tours of 1964-1966, Vol. 1 and Vol. 2.* Chuck graciously worked closely with me on the chapter about Sid Bernstein and the plans for Shea Stadium, allowed me to use the Shea contract in this book, and always, always has time to be a friend.

Dave Bedford of *Liddypool, The Fab One Hundred and Four,* and *The Country of Liverpool,* who is continually answering my endless Scouse questions, helping me promote my books in his Beatles Bookstore, and as my friend, keeps me in his prayers.

Joe Goodden, whose excellent work *Riding So High* provided excellent insights on the LSD chapter and whose website, www.beatlesbible.com, is always spot-on!

Piers Hemmingsen, who helped me so much with the last book and is destined (sorry, Piers!) to be asked a zillion questions in Part 2 of this book. You are always so kind, so supportive. Thank you!

Tom Aguiar, creator and editor of *Octopus' Garden*, who has supported **The John Lennon Series** from Day One. Tom, Robin and you are dear friends. Thank you for encouraging me and keeping The Beatles "shining on" in your publication.

Pat Matthews of BeatlesARama radio who gave me my first radio show, The John Lennon Hour, and made me believe I could do it. Pat, your radio station set the trend for Beatles radio years ago, and we are all so grateful. You have encouraged so many of us in so many ways. Thank you!

And to my friends, who *must* get tired of John Lennon at some point, but who never show it...

Adam Forrest of BeatlesAgain.com and BeatlesNews on Twitter, who helps me get the word out about these books, and who is, day in and day out, my brother. Thank you for your love and care, Adam!

Esteemed Beatles Radio Show hosts (and friends) **Rod Quinn, George Noory, ChaChi Loprete, Steve Marinucci, Terri Hemmert, Elliot Goldstein, Anna Frawley, Dave Thurmaier, Ken Michaels, Dennis Mitchell, Robert Rodriguez, Ethan Alexanian, Kit O'Toole, David Ghosty Willis, Darren DeVivo, Allison Boron and Erika White, Meagan Pease, JC Haze, BeatlEdd, EP (Daniel Sam), Hudson Ranney, Don Jeffries, and of course, Joe Johnson and his PR expert, Donnie Gee** for supporting **The John Lennon Series** from its inception. You have been so kind to help me, always.

Sarah Howland, who, carrying out the mammoth task of sorting pre-sales, boxing, and mailing, spent uncountable hours helping me get *Should Have Been There* in the mail to all of you...and crazily signed on to do it again this time! But more importantly, your friendship brings a ray of sunshine into each and every week.

John and Sue (Suzie-Q) Trusty, who always encourage me to "keep calm and carry on," no matter what! Love you guys!

Andrea, Dwayne, and Cameron Hicks, who pray for me and for **The John Lennon Series** daily. That is the greatest gift. Love you all, my sweet friends!

And finally, to those who inspire me to write...

The people of Liverpool, who answer questions, give me encouragement, and always welcome me "home." Thanks especially to **Helen Anderson** for my one-of-a-kind John Lennon hat from https://www.helenandersondesigns.com I know why John loved you so much! You're uniquely wonderful.

My sweet children, **Cliff and Paige,** and my precious, perfect grandchildren, **Maverick and Tucker,** who know how much this means to me and always encourage me to write and sell! I love you all!

And, more than ever, to my beloved **TCA,** who always knows why. I love you yesterday and today!

And to YOU, the readers of *Shoulda Been There, Shivering Inside, She Loves You, Should Have Known Better,* and now, *Shades of Life, Vol. 1,* who give the precious gift of your time to read the books in **The John Lennon Series!** *You* have made the last 33 years of research completely worth it! Shine on!

And last but not least, thank you, Lord, for listening to all of my complaints over the last two years. I know, I know: "Take a sad song and make it better."

1 PICCADILLY CIRCUS
2 LEICESTER SQUARE
3 OLD COMPTON ST.
4 TRAFALGAR SQUARE
5 BUCKINGHAM PALACE
6 NEMS (HILL ST.)
7 NEMS SUTHERLAND HOUSE

(A) AD LIB CLUB
(B) PICKWICK CLUB
(C) THE SPEAKEASY
(D) REVOLUTION
(E) BAG O' NAILS
(F) PLAYBOY CLUB
(G) DE HEMS

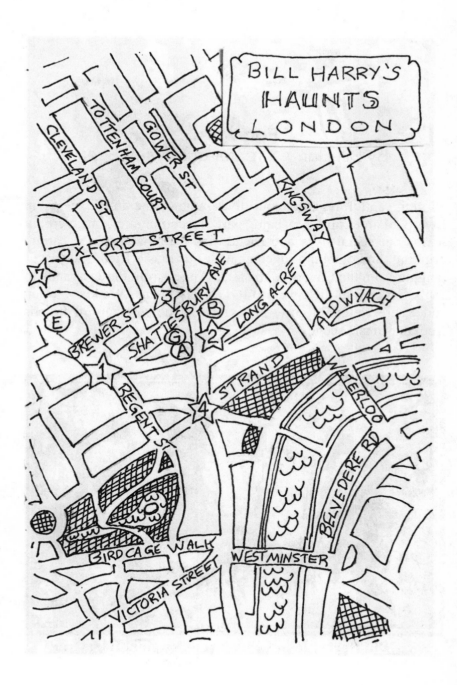

Foreword
By Bill Harry, Creator of *Mersey Beat*

Virginia and I regarded our lives among the music years in Liverpool and London as being part of a community. In Liverpool it was our social lives and friendships that encompassed eating, drinking, and clubbing together with our music friends at places ranging from the Cavern to the Blue Angel, from the Jacaranda to Joe's Café, from the Crack to the Roscoe Arms. We knew when and where we could go to always be in the company of friends from our music scene.

Bill Harry, John Lennon, and Virginia Harry
Photograph used by kind permission of Virignia and Bill Harry

The *Mersey Beat* office became an HQ for the scene with groups, managers, and photographers regularly dropping by. Ringo would

occasionally pop in while with the Hurricanes; John and Cynthia would come in and invite Virginia and me to join them for breakfast at the café down the road; various Beatles would pop in to help in the office, even answer the phone!

Brian Epstein was a regular visitor, too, and even brought Virginia a box of chocolate liquors on his return from Amsterdam.

Virginia Harry, 1965
in Swinging London
Photograph used by kind permission of Virginia and Bill Harry

In fact, Brian and Bob Wooler would often join me at the Roscoe Arms pub on the corner, and the most frequent get-together was at the Blue Angel.

Our flat in Mount Street was always a place where friends like Bob Wooler and Jankiel Feather would drop in for a chat, and we even put-up Moss and Syd out of the Rebel Rousers when they were in Liverpool. Within three years of John, Stuart, Rod, and I vowing to make Liverpool famous as "The Dissenters," the world was coming to our door.

The Blue Angel became a premier meeting place. I remember a long chat there with Beat poet Allen Ginsberg, playing the coin machine with Judy Garland, and phoning Mick Jagger in Southport, who then got in the van with the rest of the Stones and gave us a free performance. It was at the Blue that I got Brian Epstein to listen to Cilla Black singing 'Boys,' and he signed her up the next day. Hundreds and hundreds of stories and memories.

Funnily enough, I had asked John if he had a song they could give to Beryl Marsden, as I regarded her as the best girl singer on the local scene. He said she could have 'Love of the Loved.' A few days later he apologised to me and said Brian had refused to let him give the song to Beryl. Brian said he was the manager and would decide who their songs went to. He then made it Cilla's debut disc.

We were pleasantly surprised to discover a similar community situation in London — pubs and clubs, restaurants and parties where our musician friends used to frequent. One aspect of the London scene was the 'in' clubs, the places where the musical community met socially. When we settled into Charing Cross Road, at the side of Old Compton Street in Soho, we were at the heart of everything.

The first 'in' club involving the 'scene' was the Ad Lib Club on the fourth floor above the Prince Charles Cinema at No. 7 Leicester Place, although Virginia and I only visited it once before it was gutted by fire in 1966, just after we moved to London. This was the club where Ringo proposed to his Liverpool girlfriend Maureen Cox.

In 1965, John, Cynthia, George, and Pattie experienced their first LSD trip while they were at the club. They had attended a dinner party earlier that evening at the home of The Beatles' London dentist. Without their knowledge, he lined up four sugar cubes on his mantel and then put them into their coffee. After they'd drunk the coffee, he then revealed to them that the cubes had contained LSD.

Cynthia and Pattie became frightened but all left and initially attended the Pickwick Club to look in at Paddy, Klaus & Gibson, who were performing there. Then they set off for the Ad Lib. John recalled, "When we finally got in the lift we all thought there was a fire, but it was just a little red light. We were all hot and hysterical, and when we arrived at the floor, the lift stopped and the door opened, and we were all screaming."

The next 'in' club was the Scotch of St James in Mason's Yard. I remember when Virginia and I entered the main room where The Beatles and Stones, Marlon Brando, and American author James Baldwin were sitting. I spent most of my time chatting with Baldwin. Another time, when sitting with the Young Rascals, they were telling me how much they admired Paul McCartney. I excused myself, went into another room, then brought Paul in to join the Rascals for a chat. Sitting with Cynthia, she'd ask me if there was any form of artwork she could create, which I thought John might allow her to work on, as he was preventing her from working on her own, creatively.

The Pickwick Club at 15-16 Great Newport Street was an intimate place that Virginia and I began to frequent because the resident group was the Peddlers, a group I used to PR for. Paul would often drop in with Jane, and a Pickwick Club card autographed by John turned up at an auction decades later. Regulars included Michael Caine, Terence Stamp, and songwriters such as Leslie Bricusse and John Barry. This is also where Bobby Darin arranged to meet Virginia and me. He then took us to a famous Italian restaurant where he borrowed an acoustic guitar and sang '18 Yellow Roses' for us before inviting us to be his guests in London at the house he'd rented in Belgravia.

The Speakeasy at 48 Margaret Street opened on 15 December 1966 and was the main venue for groups and roadies in their evening hours.

General view of the bar, where journalists, managers, agents and pop stars can meet and talk in comfort. The dance floor is off to the right.

The Speakeasy Club, London, 1960s
Photograph used by kind permission of Bill Harry

At the time, I'd been made PR for the Speakeasy, Revolution, and Blaises clubs by Jim Carter-Fea, who ran them on behalf of owner David Shamoon. Groups who performed there included Mary Wells, Ben E. King, the Byrds – even a female Swedish topless group! NEMS held a party there for the Monkees, with The Beatles, Stones, Donovan, Lulu, Marianne Faithful, and others attending. I must admit to being embarrassed when Virginia and I entered the party section and George Harrison began to sing out my name and everyone followed him by singing along with him.

John, accompanied by Yoko in his chauffeured car, would give me and Virginia a lift down from the Speak to the Bag O' Nails.

The Bag O' Nails at 9 Kingly Street opened, also featuring top acts. One time, Virginia and I were sitting down at our table, and Paul was on the table next to us. He told us he'd just been to Liverpool and went to see Rory Storm's mum and sister, Iris. He mentioned that Iris (a former girlfriend of George and Paul) showed him a photograph of her and Virginia at school together. Just then, a friend of ours, Chas Chandler, came to Paul's table and introduced the girl he was with to Paul – it was his first meeting with Linda. Georgie Fame was on stage singing 'Sitting in the Park.' Paul then joined Chas and Linda and they then all went off to the Speak. Incidentally, in Mal Evans's diary he wrote "I ended up drunk at the Bag O' Nails with Paul McCartney and Neil Aspinall."

Paul McCartney and Bill Harry,
still mates years later
Photograph used by kind permission of Bill Harry

The Revolution in Bruton Place was probably our favourite club. Like the other clubs, it had artists and bands on every night. Several times they featured members of the cast of 'Hair' and Terry Reid, an artist I represented for Peter Grant. Terry was a great singer but turned down the role of lead vocalist with Led Zeppelin.

Acts who performed in the Revolution included Elton John, Delaney & Bonnie, King Crimson, Yes, the Grateful Dead, Billy Preston, Ike and Tina Turner, Eric Burdon and the New Animals, Ben E. King, and many others. It was also where the film stars went, ranging from Frank Sinatra to Brigitte Bardot.

Virginia was often thought to be a film actress. Every night when we were there, we'd be sitting chatting with various people including Brian Jones, Abi and Esther Ofarim, George Lazenby, and many others. We spent hours one night chatting with Judy Garland and Veronica Lake. I'd met Judy in Manchester and Liverpool and at the London after-show party for 'Maggie May' and also at the Speakeasy. She was something special. Among the various events we enjoyed was the filming of the Moon Landing which was screened at the club, a Tom Jones television show, and Pattie's modelling for a fashion show, attended by George.

After the Rev closed for the night, Virginia and I would go to the Playboy Club in Park Lane for breakfast – we could get steak and chips for 50p! We spent our time chatting with various people there, particularly Telly Savalas. He invited us to the studio where he was filming 'The Assassination Bureau,' but I had too much work on to take up the offer, and Virginia was working for an entertainment firm at that time.

Another club I worked on for Jim Carter-Fea was Blaises, in the basement of the Imperial Hotel at 121 Queen's Gate. They also presented hosts of artists including the Byrds, The Jimi Hendrix Experience, Ben E. King, and the Young Rascals. The club was featured in 'The Sorcerers,' a 1967 film starring Boris Karloff.

The Cromwellian at 3 Cromwell Road was another club that Virginia and I visited regularly. They had "Harry's Bar," run by

Harry Heart, and there were lots of jam sessions by Hendrix, Clapton, Chris Farlowe, and others. Artists who appeared at the club included Stevie Wonder, the Drifters, Patti La Belle, and Wilson Pickett. Regulars included Brian Epstein.

Apart from the evening clubs, there were drinking clubs in the afternoon such as the A&R Club and the Cottage and pubs such as the Coach and Horses in Poland Street and De Hems in Macclesfield Street. Sadly, such a community for popular music no longer exists.

**Virginia Harry, Bill Harry,
and Cynthia Lennon: Friends Forever**
Photograph used by kind permission of Bill and Virginia Harry

Author's Note:
What we'd all give to have had such magical experiences in Swinging London of the mid-Sixties! The accompanying map of London (1965-1967) shows the location of each of the clubs that Bill and Virginia Harry frequented with The Beatles, the Byrds, Ben E. King, the Stones, and so many others.

How many songs were inspired by these now-vanished haunts? How many shared ideas were trasnformed into compositions and hit songs? How many discussions prompted lyrics we still cherish? We thank Bill Harry for bringing this part of music history to life for us as only a "rock insider" could and for reminding us that songs are not only written only in mansionettes, flats, or studios...but also thrive where friends and fun abound!

In Shades of Life, Part 1, *you'll encounter The Ad Lib where Ringo proposes to Maureen, and you'll be present for the mad night which John, Cynthia, George, and Pattie experience in the Pickwick and the Ad Lib during their first LSD trip. It won't be the same as actually being there, as Bill was, but if you IMAGINE, you* might *come close.*

The Inimitable Bill Harry,
Creator of *Mersey Beat*
Photograph used by kind permission of Bill Harry

"But this is what I know about people…
they want someone to know how they got there.
Maybe they want to know that
when they dissolve into earth and water,
that last fragment will be saved,
held in some corner of someone's mind…
They want to leave their stories behind.
No one in all the world knows that better than I do."

Tana French
Broken Harbor

****

"He saw only what was not there
and missed what was right in front of him."

James Gray
Ad Astra

****

"Dissect history, and you'll see the words
that define it as a tale, a narrative."

Jodi Picoult
Vanishing Acts

Act 1:

Endless Rain Into A Paper Cup

John Lennon, September 1964
Public Doman, Vern Barchard Photographer

By the end of 1964, the sheen was wearing off
of Beatlemania, and the year that followed seemed
a lackluster repeat. John, however, slogged on,
determined to win despite the shades of life.

January 1965

Chart Toppers

"I Feel Fine" — The Beatles
"Come See About Me" — The Supremes
"Downtown" — Petula Clark

In the News

9 January: Capitol's *Beatles '65* goes to #1 and remains there for nine weeks.

12 January: On American TV, "Hullabaloo" debuted on NBC

15 January: *The Sound of Music* with Julie Andrews and Christopher Plummer is first shown in a "sneak peek" première in Minneapolis, MN.

16 January: The final episode of the TV hit, "The Outer Limits" is aired.

20 January: President Lyndon Johnson is sworn in for his first full term of office.
Alan Freed, the bold radio deejay who popularized rock'n'roll died, penniless.
The Byrds record "Mr. Tambourine Man."

24 January: Sir Winston Churchill dies.

John Lennon comments to songwriter Lamont Dozier, of Motown's main production team, Holland, Dozier, Holland: "You guys inspired us to do things!" And Holland responds with, "That's funny, you did the same for us!"

Friday, 1 January 1965
Odeon Cinema
Hammersmith, London

With charismatic brilliance that was designed to please the masses — and did — "the boys" leap-frogged into 1965. Since Christmas Eve, they'd been performing with feverish irreverence inside London's stylish 3,000-seat Odeon Cinema.[1] But its tightly-packed, plush, red velvet seats and mighty Crompton pipe organ[2] were but an ornamental frame around the animated Fab Four.

Undaunted by the lazy cold that dimmed London winters, Brian had slated no less than 38 holiday programmes between 24 December and 16 January, giving the boys only a slice of relief on Christmas Eve and 29 December, requiring only one performance on those two dates.[3]

"Ah," John intoned in his suave announcer's voice, "here we are — the boys from Liddypool — command-performin' twice nightly, in the insipidly labeled," he paused sardonically, "'Another 'Beatles' Christmas Show.'"[4]

"Well, we did have off Christmas Day, y' know," Paul shrugged insouciantly, "'n we've three Sundays off...in a row."[5]

"Yeah, right," John mauled his chewing gum. He balanced against the gritty backstage wall and fought to cram his foot into the fat snow boot required for their first skit. "Eppy's a regular Father Christmas, isn't he?"

"*You know* no one goes out much on a Sunday, Paul." George struggled with his snowsuit, annoyedly flipping back the furry hood. "Because if they *did go*, we'd have to be here, front 'n centre, performin' our fuggin' brains out, wouldn't we?"

"Sloggin' through this ludicrous, fuggin' pantomime!" John testily swiped the black furry hood from his face. He wrangled with the boot.[6]

"Straight from Eskimo-land," Ringo frowned, "because it's the *only* place we haven't visited this year!"[7]

"The only worthwhile part of this skit," John finally wriggled his foot into position, "is that when it starts, it means that Haslam's rendition of 'Yellow Ribbons' is happily over 'n done with for the night."

George snickered. They all agreed that Michael Haslam was one NEMS act that "would never see the light of day." Although Brian was firmly convinced that the lad would be "another meteor of success," The Beatles laughed behind his back.[8]

They were among many who believed that Epstein should have made a career out of representing The Beatles...and The Beatles alone.[9] But the NEMporer[10] found challenges irresistible; he always wanted "just one more" roll of the dice to see if fortune might smile on him again.[11] John, Paul, George, and Ringo, however, were impossible to duplicate.

"Yeah, well actually, it's '*Scarlet* Ribbons,' isn't it, John?" Paul couldn't help himself; he valued detail.

"Jadies and lents! Meet our very own Professor Messer!"[12] John swept a hand in Paul's direction. "Remarkably right...once again!"

"Look, John..." Paul lifted a chiding finger.[13]

"All right, you four," Neil popped into the dressing room, chucking a waxy sausage wrapper into the waste bin, "five 'r six minutes at most — then y'er on."

"Please sir, can we stroll down early, sir?" John smirked, "Y' know, to cadge a bit o' *showmanship* from that new Lancashire lad?"[14]

"Gerroff, Lennon." Neil bit off a smile. "Haslam's havin' enough trouble without *you* loiterin' in the wings, harassin' him."

"Well then, he's 'gotta get hold of himself,' then,"[15] John deadpanned. At the crafty use of Haslam's song title, George and Ringo sputtered outright. Even Paul spilled an unbidden grin.

"All right, all right, listen up!" Neil rapped on the door frame. He had only moments to explain. "We've devised a new tactic tonight to try 'n get your lines heard...or least *read*...by some o' the fans. We've done with those enormous, burdensome placards that we've been hoistin' for the girls to read...I mean, that was all too awkward — tryin' to switch 'em over so quickly, as it were."[16]

"Oh no," George sighed. "*Now what?*" He was never one for alteration.

"It's nothin' you'll have to worry about." Neil spat. "We'll be projectin' every word y' say tonight right onto the background behind your heads. So, just ignore it all 'n carry on, just as if there's nothin' there, y' know. The fans'll be able to read the lines, if they want…"

"They won't want." Ringo was right. "They only want to…"

"…rave on, it's a crazy feelin'…" John sang, wiggling his fingers madly and instantly morphing into a jittery, jangly Buddy Holly. "And-a I know it's got me reelin'!"[17]

"The fans don't like that skit, Nell." George tapped Neil's chest pointedly. "'N *we* don't like that skit!"[18]

"They don't even like brunette Elkie singin' her very jazzy Christmas song," John agreed. "What they want's a concert, son. What they want is *us* performin' for them! *That*'s what they paid to hear!"

And as usual, John was right. The fans had absolutely no interest in The Beatles pretending to be explorers searching for the Abominable Snowman.[19] They had even less interest in Elkie Brooks giving them Christmas "rock all."[20] They showed not a glimmer of notice when The Mike Cotton Sound performed Georgie Fame's latest hit, "Yeh, Yeh."[21] 'N the Yardbirds, frankly, annoyed them.[22] But most of all, the skit was a bust.[23]

The fans simply wanted The Beatles. They wanted John, Paul, George, and Ringo — wearing their instruments, singing their songs, bobbing up and down, and doing what they did best. Neither The Beatles nor their fans wanted a shred of anything else: one could well dispense with the other, irrelevant trappings.

The original iteration of
The Hammersmith Odeon, London
Photograph from Wikimedia Commons

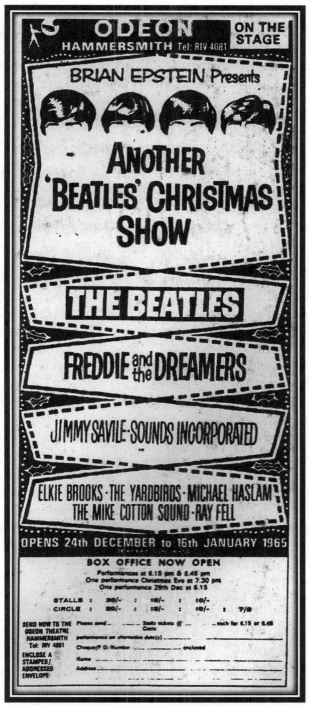

Poster for "Another 'Beatles' Christmas Show"

****

Brian had no idea why everyone was so ill-humoured and perturbed. For weeks last autumn — whilst The Beatles had been on the U.K. tour — he'd laboured alongside Tony Barrow, planning the ideal holiday variety show.

And truly, he grumbled to himself, *who doesn't love compère, Jimmy Saville? The man's indispensable on* Top of the Pops![24] *In fact, Tynes Television calls him "essential." And the Mike Cotton Sound?!* Brian shook his head. *They're well-sought after, across the board! I mean, not to overstate, but they've worked with Howlin' Wolf and Jimmy Reed...not to mention Muddy Waters.*[25]

The combo's recent transformation from a trad jazz group to a jazz-based rock'n'roll band had swiftly captured the respect of their contemporaries. The Mike Cotton Sound was at the top of their game, auditioning new members and choosing judiciously.[26] They'd even adopted an updated, rather Beatlesque style, and in doing so, they'd impressed the British music scene.

But inside the Hammersmith Odeon, Beatles fans were clearly indifferent to these innovative front men...as were Paul, George, Ringo, and particularly, John. In fact, Brian thought, the boys appreciated very little about the show as a whole...except, of course, their days off.

Even in their "best foot forward interviews," they seemed blasé about the grand Odeon affair.

In late November, for example, when Brian Matthew had chatted with the boys on *Top Gear,* spending several minutes speculating about the upcoming holiday programme,[27] the boys had responded with sufficient answers. But all Brian had heard was their ennui. Their polite responses had been edged in mild derision.

Brian Matthew: The final thing to talk about...
George: (Sitting forward eagerly) Yes...
Matthew: ... is the Christmas show.[28]
John: Ah, yes... (Slumping a little, as George leaned back as well) Jimmy Saville's on it, y' know.[29]
Matthew: I had heard! I had heard! (He grinned devilishly.) I was quite hurt, actually.
John: Oh well, we tried to get you, but you're too dear.

Brian: (Chuckling) That's one thing…that's one thing…
Ringo: (Eyes twinkling) Dear to us all!

**Brian Matthew, Host of BBC's *Saturday Club* and *Top Gear*
and frequent interviewer of The Beatles**
Photograph from Wikimedia Commons

Matthew: (Amused) That's nice. How lovely, Ringo. Can you tell us anything seriously about the show…or don't you know anything about it yet?

John: (Rapidly…from rote memory) Freddie 'n the Dreamers —
on! The Yardbirds — on! Elkie Brooks — on!
Paul: Mike Cotton Sound…
Matthew: (Overtalking the endless list of co-stars) Same as last
year?
George: (Trying to remember) Mike Cotton Sound…uhmmm,
ah, Jimmy Saville…
John: Ray Fell!
Paul: Sounds Incorporated!
John: (Backtracking to answer Matthew's last question: "Same
as last year?") It's goin' to be a bit better 'n last year.
Paul: Sounds Incorporated. In fact, they recorded the signature
tune.
Matthew: But what are *you* going to do? That's what I'm trying
to get at!
Paul: This very programme!
John: (Overtalking Paul) Well, we're goin' to do a coupla
sketches that are bein' written in the usual rubbishy
style…kiddin' 'n stuff.
Matthew: By John and Paul?
John: No, no, we're doin' the usual sketches, only a bit more
involved.
Paul: (Now repeating the company line) Y' know, we're just
havin' a laugh on the show…
John: (Scoffing) …a *larf* on the show!
Matthew: (Understanding, but smoothing things over) Yeah
well, I'm sure you'll have a fine time.[30]

There had been no eagerness, no excitement at all from the
boys. No: "We're actually *thrilled* to be workin' with the Mike
Cotton Sound!" No: "It's great havin' the Yardbirds along." Not a
single syllable to the good.

In fact, Brian mused, the topic of the Christmas programme
had been met with the same implied yawns that the group had
elicited to Matthew's query, "Do you get a little tired of being
Beatles?" Listening to the proceedings from the wings, Brian had
sighed. None of the lads had exhibited an ounce of gratitude for all
Tony and he had done to make the annual performance a ticket-
selling success. If anything, the boys had come off as discontented.
Unhappy.

"Well," Tony had tried to explain a few days later, "Try to see it their way, Brian. The boys could just do a *concert*, y' understand...just stand there 'n sing their songs, y' know. That's what they're tryin' to tell you...*that*'s what the fans really want. Those girls don't give a whit about costumes or...rhetoric...or cleverly planned patter from ol' Ray Fell, even if he *is* one of the greatest of comedians Merseyside! The fans want The Beatles...none of this other bit, unfortunately. And yes, I know how much *you* love it...the scenery, the show, the costumes...I mean, for you, it's fantastic! But for them..." Tony's eyes slid away.

And Barrow was right. Despite his prominence in the world of rock'n'roll, Epstein still longed to be a thespian. He'd been raised on the British tradition of jovial holiday performances that began well before Boxing Day and extended well beyond, and he wanted his boys to be part of that. He wanted their names in lights on the wide Odeon marquee. He wanted them to be magnificent stars of the London theatre scene. He wanted the boys to inhabit the dramatic world he'd always coveted.[31]

But The Beatles had no yearning for the smell of greasepaint or the glow of coloured footlights.

And what's more, after the whole of 1964, the boys were exhausted — "well-worn through," they'd said. Yet here they were, looking towards another United Artists film, another "World" Tour, another North American Tour, another U.K. Tour, another mountain of interviews as well as radio and television specials, and of course, two more LPs. The year ahead appeared very much like a replica of the year past.[32]

And although they were willing to attempt the much-demanded, insipid duplication, The Beatles needed a change of pace. They needed to breathe.[33] They needed to get back into the studio and make their music.[34] They needed inspiration. But their profound fatigue held little currency with Brian. He wanted them, successful. And to be successful, they had to work. John, most especially.

****

In the wake of the rather unanticipated success of *In His Own Write* (Well, John had guessed it would sell to fans, but never imagined it would be lauded by critics!), John had contracted, last spring, with Tom Maschler of Jonathan Cape Publishers to write a sequel in 1965.[35] And although his learnt aunt was thrilled at the prospect of her nephew's second book, she had nothing more to give him in the way of childhood or teenaged scribblings. John had depleted her stockroom of college poems and prose for the first volume.[36]

In desperation, John had cajoled his mate Bill Harry into helping him round up "any titbits anyone has 'round Liverpool," especially any work left behind with Stu and Rod Murray in his Gambier Terrace art college lodgings. But Rod, for his part, was reticent to help "that Lennon."[37]

"I'll be more 'n happy to give him back his *Daily Whatever* sketchbook, Bill," Rod had explained, "when 'n *if* he plays me the remainder of the fuggin' rent he owes me, on the unceremonious occasion o' his movin' out o' the flat all the sudden, like! I mean, look, Millie gave me Stu's part o' the rent, as it were. But John...well, he never followed through, 'n he *can*, without a doubt, these days, can't he?! But have I seen a pound from him? Not yet, have I!"[38]

So, Bill immediately rang Epstein with this information, giving The Beatles' manager Rod Murray's Liverpool address and imploring him to intervene on John's behalf. But as far as Bill could ascertain, no action had ever been taken to procure John's poetry and prose.

Rod had received nothing in the way of back rent, and John had received nothing in the way of his long-lost creations.[39] As things stood, there was missed communication and hard feelings on both sides.

And to make matters worse, several years earlier, when Bill and his wife, Virginia, had moved their *Mersey Beat* offices to a new Liverpool location, a full box of John's writings had been inadvertently mislaid. Although John had wept on Virginia's shoulder over the irreplaceable loss, his tears had restored nothing. The scores of precious scribblings were never again recovered.[40]

So, faced with the task of compiling a new book utterly from scratch — without any former texts to fill the pages — John felt pressured to write (or try to write) in every spare moment.[41] In fact, on 15 December, when the deadline for turning in his completed manuscript passed unheeded, John began to fret.[42] He despised failing at anything.

And it wasn't like he hadn't tried…

Last April, aboard the ramshackle Tahitian "yacht" that Cyn and he had shared with George and Pattie, John had amused them all with the cheeky tale of "Snore Wife and Some Several Dwarts." And one particularly sweltering afternoon in the ocean doldrums, he'd recruited George to help him concoct "The Singularge Experience of Miss Anne Duffield."[43]

When a *Daily Mirror* columnist named Cassandra brashly panned The Beatles, John was inspired to create the snarky "Cassandle." Joyfully lampooning the *Mirror* journalist as "a boring, owld gassbag" [sic], John feigned commiseration with Cassandle — whose awful job it was to review "*sleasy backward, bad, deaf monkeys parsing as entertainers, with their* [sic] *FLOPTOPPED hair, falling about the place like Mary PICKFORD.*"[44]

Then, during the stirring autumn national elections, John had smiled and scribbled, "We must not forget…The General Erection":

"*Azue owl gnome, Harassed Wilsod won the General Erection, with a very small marjorie over the Torchies….Sir Alice Doubtless-Whom was — quote — 'bitherly dithapointed' but managed to keep smirking on his 500,000 acre estate in Scotland with a bit of fishing and that.*"[45]

John had sought (and found) subjects everywhere, in all seasons, at all hours. In the three newspapers that he hungrily consumed each morning,[46] a daily advice column had inspired his cheeky "Readers Lettuce."[47] And backstage at the Odeon, whilst the others relaxed with "a cuppa" or took the occasional "spot o' kip," John was restlessly jotting on scraps of paper, worn envelopes, torn advertisements.

When he wasn't penning song lyrics, he was ginning out sardonic prose or bits of Lennonesque poetry. Often, the jibes were aimed directly at himself:

> "He's on a diet now you know
> From eating far too much
> They say if he gets fatter
> He'll have to wear a crutch." [48]

Most of the work was irreverent and extremely funny indeed — rattled off in spare moments under the duress of necessity. But sprinkled amongst the frivolity — carefully sequestered — there were moments of dark reflection that took even John's breath away. There were stark revelations about himself that he thought almost no one would suss out, and if they did guess, they'd only pause momentarily and then (all too gladly) move on. After all, relatively no one had questioned the lyrics to "I'm a Loser."

Hardly an eyebrow had lifted at the pitiable confession.[49] "This could hardly be autobiographical," the critics had all assumed. "Why, John Lennon has the world at his fingertips! He's practically king of everything!" No agonizing questions had been posed about John's self-confidence; no one had plumbed the shallow waters of his self-esteem.[50] They'd all just smiled and sung along.

No one wanted to know.

Now, John's horrid, recurring childhood dream of falling into a deep and inescapable hole merged with the heart-rending, untimely death of his Uncle George in the conclusion of John's rather lengthy piece, "The Wumberlog (or the Magic Dog)." As the meandering tale of a lonely little boy seeking his lost uncle wound to an end, a startling image emerged…a scene that finds the child and his uncle being buried alive, up to their necks, by an unfeeling, unruly mob:

> "Without a word, and spades on high,
> They all dug deep and low,
> And placed the boy into a hole

Next to his Uncle Joe."

John wrote furiously, his pen scritching across the rough newsprint and rapidly bleeding ink. Tugged into the world of the long-ago, John stood feebly, watching his childhood perish alongside his Uncle Ge'rge, watching faith and justice be swallowed up whole. He blinked, several times...but there it was again: the unspeakable sadness, the impossibility of recovery, of ever being the same again. John saw it all, unable to alter a thing.

" 'I told you not to come out here,"
His uncle said, all sad.
'I had to Uncle,' said the boy,
'You're all the friend I had.' "

All at once, John was fourteen-and-a-half...home from Scotland, facing his aunt at the Mendips kitchen sink. Mimi, peeling carrots.[51] Mimi, delivering the irreversible news. Mimi, maintaining a brave face in front of the boarders.[52] Mimi, expecting John to do the same...at least, until he reached his room.

And later...much later — too late, really — there was Julia knocking on his bedroom door. Julia, sitting on the bed. Julia, fighting to stave off John's hysteria;[53] Julia, battling to keep her son alive.

"With just their heads above the ground
They bade a fond goodbye,
With all the people shouting out,
'Heres [sic] mud into your eye!'
(And there certainly was.)"[54]

No one (John knew) would surmise the story behind the story. They'd think this just another ghastly ditty from "that bizarre Beatle's mind." Few would ever follow the dots. And those who could, wouldn't dare.

And so, he left the ghastly ending on the page for Tom Maschler to read...for Tom and all the others. And turning his attention to the illustrations, John sketched himself small and simple and hiding behind his Uncle Ge'rge — helpless hands raised in fruitless supplication.

Sources:

Lennon, John, A Spaniard in the Works, 52.
Lewisohn, Mark, The Complete Beatles Chronicle, 179, 180, and 183.
Lewisohn, Mark, The Beatles: Day by Day, 56-57.
Harry, Bill, The Ultimate Beatles Encyclopedia, 297, 466, 492, and 575.
Harry, Bill, The John Lennon Encyclopedia, 819 and 830-834.
Harry, Bill, The Encyclopedia of Beatles People, 73, 131, 155-156, 282, 293-294, and 344.
The Beatles, The Beatles Anthology, 176.
Miles, Barry, The Beatles' Diary, Vol. 1, 182 and 187.
Belmo, Scott and Marsh, Gary, The Beatles Christmas Book: Everywhere It's Christmas, 124-126.
Norman, Philip, John Lennon: The Life, 70-71 and 400.
Norman, Philip, Shout!, 23.
Davies, Hunter, The Beatles, 15-16.
Shotton, Pete and Schaffner, Nicholas, John Lennon: In My Life, 37.
Howlett, Kevin, The Beatles at the BBC: The Radio Years, 1962-70, 65-66.
Barrow, Tony, John, Paul, George, Ringo & Me: The Real Beatles Story, 74-75 and 140.
Goldman, Albert, The Lives of John Lennon, 180.
Hill, Tim, John, Paul, George & Ringo: The Definitive Illustrated Chronicle of The Beatles: 1960-1970, 178.
Riley, Tim, Lennon: The Man, The Myth, The Music, 276-277.
Riley, Tim, Tell Me Why: The Beatles, Album by Album, Song by Song, The Sixties and After, 120.
Coleman, Ray, Lennon, 240-242.
Coleman, Ray, The Man Who Made The Beatles: An Intimate Biography of Brian Epstein, 183 and 209.
Brown, Peter, The Love You Make: An Insider's Story of The Beatles, 165.
Jackson, Andrew Grant, The Most Revolutionary Year in Music: 1965, 159-161.
Buskin, Richard, John Lennon: His Life and Legend, 107 and 110-111.
Schultheiss, Tom, The Beatles: A Day in the Life, 127-128.
Turner, Steve, A Hard Day's Write: The Stories Behind Every Beatles Song, 64-65.
MacDonald, Ian, Revolution in the Head: The Beatles' Records and The Sixties, 99.

Spignesi, Stephen J. and Lewis, Michael, The 100 Best Beatles Songs: An Informed Fan's Guide, *207.*

Guesdon, Jean-Michel and Margotin, Phillipe, All the Songs: The Story Behind Every Beatles Release, *168.*

Bicknell, Alf, Beatles Diary, *26-27.*

Davis, Andy, The Beatles Files, *81.*

Schaffner, Nicholas, The Beatles Forever, *48.*

There is a good photo of all four Beatles in their "Abominable Snowman" costumes in Schaffner, p. 48.

http://stories-of-london.org/the-compton-apollo-hammersmith/
This is an excellent history of the Hammersmith Odeon theatre with superb colour photos.

https://www.allmusic.com/artist/the-mike-cotton-sound-mn0000112415
This is a good history of The Mike Cotton Sound.

https://www.independent.co.uk/news/obituaries/michael-haslam-36862.html This is a short biography of Michael Haslam, via his obituary.

https://www.discogs.com/Michael-Haslam-Gotta-Get-A-Hold-Of-Myself-This-Dream/release/9033345 This website provides Information on Michael Haslam's song, "Gotta Get A Hold of Myself."

https://www.youtube.com/watch?v=z_rSh770MCo You may listen to "Gotta Get A Hold of Myself" by Michael Haslam here.

https://www.beatlesbible.com/1964/12/31/live-another-beatles-christmas-show-6/ This is a good general overview of "Another 'Beatles' Christmas Show."

http://www.meetthebeatlesforreal.com/2014/12/the-cast-of-another-beatles-christmas.html This is a thorough discussion of "Another 'Beatles' Christmas Show" on Sara Schmidt's website. Great photos as well!

https://www.youtube.com/watch?v=uVpUXuD_54k
This video is the source for the interview in this chapter.
Or use this QR code:

Elkie Brooks from "Another 'Beatles' Christmas Show"
Photograph from Wikimedia Commons

[1] Lewisohn, Mark, *The Complete Beatles Chronicle*, 183, Miles, Barry, *The Beatles' Diary, Vol. 1*, 182, Hill, Tim, *John, Paul, George & Ringo: The Definitive Illustrated Chronicle of The Beatles, 1960-1970*, 178, and Belmo and Garry Marsh, *The Beatles Christmas Book: Everywhere It's Christmas*, 124.

[2] http://stories-of-london.org/the-compton-apollo-hammersmith/ The Hammersmith Odeon, an immense Art Deco building, was designed by architect Robert Cromie. This super theater (with more than 3,400 seats) was built for Israel Davis and the Gaumont British Theatres chain. In 1962, it was renamed the Hammersmith Odeon. Both of The Beatles' Christmas shows were held in this elegant London building. Excellent photos of the exterior and interior may be found on this website.

[3] Lewisohn, Mark, *The Complete Beatles Chronicle*, 179, Howlett, Kevin, *The Beatles at the BBC: The Radio Years, 1962-70*, 65-66, Harry, *The Ultimate Beatles Encyclopedia*, 492, and Riley, Tim, *Lennon*, 268.

[4] Belmo and Marsh, 125.

[5] Belmo and Marsh, 126. The boys were given days off on Christmas Day and Sunday, 27 December, as well as Sunday, 3 January, and Sunday, 10 January.

[6] You can see a photo of all four Beatles in their Arctic explorer costumes in Belmo and Marsh's *The Beatles Christmas Book,* 127. The expressions on the boys' faces speak volumes. There isn't a smile amongst them.

[7] Belmo and Marsh, 126 and Davis, Andy, *The Beatles Files*, 81. Direct quote from Ringo Starr.

[8] Belmo and Marsh, 126. Direct quote from The Beatles' press agent, Tony Barrow.

[9] Coleman, *The Man Who Made The Beatles: An Intimate Biography of Brian Epstein,* 183.

[10] Barrow, Tony, *John, Paul, George, Ringo & Me: The Real Beatles Story*, 74. Barrow states, "When word-wizard and Cavern Club resident deejay nicknamed [Brian Epstein] 'The NEMporer,' [Brian] was greatly chuffed. He went on to use the word NEMporer as the telegraphic address on NEMS Enterprises in London and as the name of his New York holding company, Nemporer Holdings. Eventually the NEMS office at 3 Hill Street in Mayfair was named Nemporer House. It was impossible to flatter Brian Esptein because he did that so capably for himself; he was his own most ardent fan."

[11] Coleman, *The Man Who Made The Beatles*, 183.

[12] "Professer Messer" is a Scouse term for a didactic or preachy person.

[13] Bicknell, Alf, *Beatles Diary*, 26. In his diary entry for 15 January 1965, Bicknell writes concerning The Beatles' relationships during the Odeon Christmas show, "There have been times when tempers have been strained, but generally everyone has gotten on well."

[14] Harry, Bill, *The Ultimate Beatles Encyclopedia*, 297. Twenty-four-year-old Michael Haslam, Harry tells us, hailed from Lancashire and was originally discovered by show business writer Godfrey Winn, who — dining with Brian Epstein — brought him to the NEMporer's attention.

[15] https://www.discogs.com/Michael-Haslam-Gotta-Get-A-Hold-Of-Myself-This-Dream/release/9033345 and Harry, *The Ultimate Beatles Encyclopedia*,

297. Haslam's first release on Parlophone was 1964's "Gotta Get Hold of Myself."
[16] Belmo and Marsh, 126.
[17] From the Buddy Holly hit "Rave On" written by Sonny West, Bill Tilghman, and Norman Petty. Holly was a huge influence on teens in Liverpool in the late 1950s. John would have known the words to many of his songs, including this significant Holly hit.
[18] Miles, *The Beatles' Diary, Vol. 1*, 182. Miles observes, "So excruciating was this section of the show, both for the group and their fans, that The Beatles resolved never to take part in a similar enterprise again."
[19] Harry, *The Ultimate Beatles Encyclopedia*, 492, Miles, *The Beatles' Diary, Vol. 1*, 182, Belmo and Marsh, 126. Harry says "Arctic." Miles says "Antarctic." Belmo and Marsh say "Antarctic" but place a "?" after that fact. Both Lewisohn in *The Complete Beatles Chronicle*, p. 179, and Belmo and Marsh, 127, supply photos of the lads in their costumes.
[20] Belmo and Marsh, 126.
[21] Harry, *The Ultimate Beatles Encyclopedia*, 492, Harry, *The Encyclopedia of Beatles People*, 228, Miles, *The Beatles' Diary, Vol. 1*, 182, and Belmo and Marsh, 126. Although Belmo and Marsh indicate that Georgie Fame *was present*, backed by The Mike Cotton Sound as he performed his hit, "Yeh, Yeh," both Harry and Miles say that the song was only performed by The Mike Cotton Sound. You can see on p. 26 of this book that Fame's name does **not** appear on the show poster. Bill Harry in *The Encyclopedia of Beatles People* lists the band members of The Mike Cotton Sound at the Odeon as being: Mike Cotton (trumpet), Stu Morrison (banjo), Dave Rowberry (keyboards...later, a member of The Animals), Derek Tearle (bass guitar), and Jim Ganforth (drums). To hear Georgie Fame's "Yeh Yeh," go to: https://tinyurl.com/y4regcaz
[22] Belmo and Marsh, 126 and Miles, *The Beatles' Diary, Vol. 1,* 182. To quote Belmo and Marsh, "The Yardbirds sang two songs. Yes, Eric Clapton was with the band then."
[23] Belmo and Marsh, 126 and Harry, *The Encyclopedia of Beatles People*, 73. According to Belmo and Marsh, Elkie Brooks opened the second half of "Another 'Beatles' Christmas Show." She stated, "I was doing this really lovely, jazzy version of a Christmas song...I was giving it rock all...[and the fans] were just saying, 'Get off! Get off, we paid to see The Beatles! We don't want you, you soppy tart, get off!'"
[24] Harry, *The Beatles Ultimate Encyclopedia*, 575. Harry notes that Saville was the Abominable Snowman in The Beatles' sketch mentioned in this chapter.
[25] https://www.allmusic.com/artist/the-mike-cotton-sound-mn0000112415, Harry, *The Ultimate Beatles Encyclopedia*, 466 and Barrow, 140.
[26] Harry, *The Encyclopedia of Beatles People*, 228 and https://www.allmusic.com/artist/the-mike-cotton-sound-mn0000112415 In 1964, when The Mike Cotton Sound made the transition from trad jazz to a rock'n'roll-based sound (in the wake of The Beatles' rise to fame), they auditioned new members. Two of the artists they rejected were Reginald Dwight (Elton John) and Joe Cocker.
[27] https://www.youtube.com/watch?v=uVpUXuD_54k

[28] https://www.youtube.com/watch?v=uVpUXuD_54k This is the first line of a portion of Brian Matthew's interview with The Beatles on *Top Gear*, which took place on 26 November 1964. I am not going to footnote every line but will footnote again on the last line of the interview.

[29] Harry, *The Encyclopedia of Beatles People*, 282. Harry points out the irony of Saville being selected to compère for "Another 'Beatles' Christmas Show" at the end of 1964, because a year earlier, when introducing The Beatles singing "Please Please Me" on *Top of the Pops*, Saville had wryly commented, "Well, here it is, the big new record from Liverpool's Beatles. I sure hope it pleases somebody out there, 'cause it sure isn't me!"

[30] https://www.youtube.com/watch?v=uVpUXuD_54k
This is the last line of a portion of Brian Matthew's interview with The Beatles on *Top Gear*, which took place on 26 November 1964.

[31] Coleman, *The Man Who Made The Beatles*, 209. In Coleman's book, Peter Bourne recalls, "I felt sorry for [Brian] because he was so frustrated in acting...I told him that Laurence Olivier got chucked out of the Central School of Acting and Rex Harrison, too." And Bourne concludes with, "He got the fame, he got the money, the extras, the frills, but he never really got what he wanted. That," says Bourne, "was 'to be there, on the stage, in the limelight.'"

[32] Lewisohn, *The Complete Beatles Chronicle*, 180 and Davies, *The Beatles*, 207. Lewisohn states, "This was a curious year for The Beatles, one in which they consolidated the successes and excesses of 1964 by virtually repeating everything already achieved."

[33] Bicknell, *Beatles Diary*, 26. Bicknell states in his 15 January entry, "I'm going to miss [The Christmas Show] I think, even though we need the break."

[34] Lewisohn, *The Beatles: Day by Day*, 57.

[35] Norman, Philip, *John Lennon: The Life*, 400.

[36] The Beatles, *The Beatles Anthology*, 176. John says, "The second book was more disciplined because it was started from scratch. They said, 'You've got so many months to write a book in.' I wrote *In His Own Write* — at least some of it — while I was still at school, and it came spontaneously. But once it became 'We want another book from you, Mr. Lennon,' I could only loosen up to it with a bottle of Johnnie Walker, and I thought, 'if it takes a bottle each night to get me to write...' That's why I didn't write any more."

[37] In the late 1980s and early 1990s, Rod was kind enough to answer some questions for me about John, his time in the Gambier Terrace flats with Rod and Stu, and John's "lost" drawings, and in every e-mail, Rod referred to John as "that Lennon."

[38] In the Foreword to Vol. 4 in **The John Lennon Series**, *Should Have Known Better*, Bill Harry wrote, "John was due to have a second book out to follow *In His Own Write*, but said, 'I just haven't got the time!' He told me that he'd lost his copy of *Mersey Beat* with his story of "Small Stan" in it, so I said I'd send him a copy to use in the new book. John told me that he wrote his poems and stories first, and when he'd collected them together, he sketched the illustrations for them.

John also mentioned he'd been looking for three years for a copy of his *Daily Howl* book. "I even went back to Gambier Terrace to see if I could find it," he told me. John explained that the *Daily Howl* was an exercise book full of his stories, poems, and cartoons. "And most of it wasn't very good – but it means a lot to me. I spent years fillin' that book up."

I was already familiar with the *Daily Howl* having written about it in early issues of *Mersey Beat*. In fact, several months before, I'd already found two of John's earlier poems, "The Land of the Lunapots" and "Tales of Hermit Fred."

"I'd appreciate it if you can trace where those poems came from," John said. "There may be some more of my writings there."

The two poems, I told him, had been brought into my office by a reader who told us she had some more of John's work. (After our day with The Beatles in Blackpool, I tried to get hold of the reader again, but without success.)

John and Rod [Murray] also had a lengthy conversation. I had spent time trying to trace John's work for him and had tracked down the flat where Rod was currently living. I asked Rod if he had any of John's works since he was the last to leave the Gambier Terrace flat.

Rod said he had found a copy of John's *Daily Howl* book and was willing to give it to John if he were given John's share of the rent that John still owed when he left. Stu's mum, Millie, had given him Stu's part of the rent, but Rod hadn't received anything from John. Upon finding this out, I had contacted Brian Epstein and said that Rod would give back John's *Daily Howl* in exchange for the rent money owed. I don't think Brian bothered."

[39] Harrry, Bill, Foreword to *Should Have Known Better*, Vol. 4 in **The John Lennon Series**. See footnote above for details.

[40] Coleman , Ray, *Lennon*, 152.

[41] Coleman, Ray, *Lennon*, 152. John is quoted as saying, "[Writing *A Spaniard in the Works*] was starting from scratch. The publisher said, 'You've got so many months to write a book in.' With the first book, I'd written a lot of it at odd times during my life." Coleman adds that John had almost a year to complete the second work from all new subjects and inspiration.

[42] Lewisohn, *The Beatles: Day by Day*, 56.

[43] Coleman, *Lennon*, 242.

[44] Lennon, John, *A Spaniard in the Works*, 60, Harry, *The John Lennon Encyclopedia,* 832, Riley, Tim, *Lennon*, 277, and Coleman, *Lennon*, 240.

[45] Lennon, John, "We must not forget…The General Erection," *A Spaniard in the Works*, 40, Harry, *The John Lennon Encyclopedia*, 831, and Riley, *Lennon*, 277.

[46] Coleman, *Lennon,* 25.

[47] Coleman, *Lennon*, 240.

[48] Lennon, John, "The Fat Budgie," *A Spaniard in the Works*, 19.

[49] Goldman, Albert, *The Lives of John Lennon*, 180 and Riley, Tim, *Tell Me Why*, 120. Goldman wisely comments, "The whole world listened to these songs, but nobody hearkened to them. The idea of John Lennon — the greatest winner in the pop sweepstakes — as a 'loser' was unthinkable…even the most discerning listeners [failed] to grasp the obvious meaning of Lennon's most explicit lyrics."

[50] Buskin, Richard, *John Lennon: His Life and Legend*, 111, Brown, Peter, *The Love You Make*, 46, and Riley, *Tell Me Why*, 120.

[51] Davies, Hunter, *The Beatles*, 15-16, Coleman, *Lennon*, 31, Norman, Philip, *Shout!*, 23, Norman, Philip, *John Lennon: The Life*, 70-71, Shotton and Schaffner, *John Lennon: In My Life*, 37, and Harry, *The John Lennon Encyclopedia*, 819. The story is told in detail in Vol. 1 of **The John Lennon Series**, *Shoulda Been There*, pp. 85-92. Here is John's own account of that day as told to Hunter Davies in *The Beatles*: "I remember coming home [from Scotland] the day Uncle George died. Mimi was crying over the carrots. She used to take in students at the time. They were sitting around looking sad, trying to look sad, but knowing they weren't going to get a proper meal and Mimi would be suffering for months. I didn't know how to be sad publicly, what you did or said, so I went upstairs." Then Davies adds, "Around the time of Uncle George's death, someone else had appeared on the scene who was becoming more and more important in John's life — his mother, Julia...she started coming around to Menlove Avenue, making sure first that John was around." (pp. 15-16)

[52] Coleman, *Lennon*, 31.

[53] Harry, *The John Lennon Encyclopedia*, 819.

[54] Lennon, John, "The Wumberlog (or The Magic Dog), *A Spaniard in the Works,* 51.

Friday, 8 January 1965
Kenwood
Weybridge, Surrey

Ken Partridge — his abashed smile covering a multitude of sins — vowed that Kenwood would soon be completed. "We're getting there...by degrees," the boyishly handsome interior designer sheepishly stated to John and Cynthia. "Just a few more days."

And then a few more. And then, several others.

But progress certainly hadn't halted out in Weybridge; Cynthia's mother, Lillian Powell, had been extremely industrious — filling her waiting moments with myriad shopping jaunts, "for this and that and the other, y' know!" She haunted local rummage sales, antique shops, and quaint, unpretentious, country salesrooms.[55]

Having settled into a picturesque Esher bungalow (for which John footed the bill and paid for the upkeep)[56] just miles from "Cynthia's place," Lillian Powell had briskly unpacked her bags and set to work. She'd appointed herself Kenwood's construction foreman and "*sous* decorator," as well as the Lennon household's official childcare expert. Overbearing and commandeering, Lillian bustled about, quizzing Partridge's workmen, cross-questioning Cynthia's every move,[57] and brimming over with unrequested "finds" — accessories "to make the house cosy, John. You know!"

But although everyone resented her interference, no one said a word. Silently, John despised the woman[58] who "plopped on the couch, stuffing glacé fruits into her mouth," the woman who made it clear that she'd never approved of him — had never trusted him, not one iota.[59] But in deference to his wife, who'd supported him without reserve for years, John never raised an eyebrow (much less his voice) in his mother-in-law's direction.[60] He saw all, but ignored most.[61]

Cynthia docilely walked in her mother's shadow. She did as she was directed to do. Only the decision to hire the former owners' housekeeper, Dorothy Jarlett, was Cynthia's own.[62] Every other pronouncement fell from the lips of Lillian Powell.

"I'm no match for her, luv," Cynthia sighed to John. "You know I'm hopeless when it comes to standing up to other people.[63] And Mum, least of all."[64]

John could only seethe; this constant drama was more than he could bear. He was too tired to arbitrate puerile domestic clashes. He was too weary to deal with Lillian Powell.[65]

And to compound John's discomfort, Cyn — in the wake of his lengthy tenure at home — had begun calling upon him to assist with domestic decisions. Lately, she'd purchased a rather enormous "scrubbed white" (or so she dubbed it) dining room suite, complete with twelve massive antique chairs.[66] And John could tell that she was fond of it and wanted his approval. But truthfully, to him the set looked ravaged, "as if it's been set on by fuggin' rabid dogs!" John had told her, honestly.[67]

And without a retort or even a rueful glance, Cynthia had walked away from him, retreating even deeper into the thick tapestry of silence she'd lately been weaving.

John swore…at her, at himself. And he wished himself back on tour again. Or back in the studio. Or back *anywhere*! Just not here…not until the house was reassembled and uncomplicated and safe to navigate again. Not until Lil was living her own life, miles away, in her own home.

But day after day, as the remodeling crept forward and Partridge tediously completed his work on the "ultra-modern" kitchen, "Lowl" (as John sardonically labeled his mother-in-law, mocking her Hoylake accent)[68] continued to hunt and gather, bringing home flowered chamber pots, fringed lamps, creased sepia photographs ("rare collectibles!"), and quirky memorabilia from World War II and the Boer War — weathered bits of Victoriana that were 1965's "latest trend."

She wedged the "treasures" gingerly into Kenwood's last unoccupied attic rooms, alongside Stu's two paintings that John had acquired from Millie Sutcliffe; alongside boxes of John's books; alongside the jukebox, guitars, Scalextric miniature racecar set, and table football game. And when every inch of space had been completely obstructed with a restored, antique copper fire extinguisher and a bright Edwardian umbrella stand, Lil began lining the narrow, adjoining hallway with nostalgic enameled signs for "Oxo" and "R. White's Lemonade." Lil snugged these fixtures up to mirrors and ginger jars and ornate tabletop clocks; she filled the entire upper floor with a vast menagerie of possessions.[69]

And just as feverishly, Cynthia searched daily for the elegant but illusive bedroom suite that John had requested. ("A super-king-size, hand-painted bed — massive, Cyn...ten feet long, at the very least!")[70] But nothing quite measured up to her husband's imagination, and Cynthia feared that she would only disappoint him in the end.

As the gurgling noise of Julian at play competed with scores of bellowing workmen, Lillian's self-centred babbling, and Cynthia's impenetrable silence, John began to regret that he'd ever abandoned London and Emperor's Gate. Rural living wasn't for him. It was chock-full of everything he'd always tried to avoid: regular hours, manicured gardens, kitchen appliances, required maintenance, family dramas, and a modicum of maturity. Somewhere along the way, his life had gone completely off the rails.[71]

Sources:

Lewisohn, Mark and Howlett, Kevin, In My Life: John Lennon Remembered, 36.
Lennon, Cynthia, A Twist of Lennon, 131.
Lennon, Cynthia, John, 150-151.
Norman, John Lennon: The Life, 382-384.
Brown, 166-167.
Coleman, Lennon, 103 and 106.
Spitz, Bob, The Beatles, 548.
Goldman, 192-194.
Trynka, Paul, The Beatles: Ten Years that Shook the World, 167.

http://kenwoodlennon.blogspot.com/ This is the official blog page for Kenwood, written and maintained by Sean Lennon. Rare photos.

https://blog.beatlesinlondon.com/kenwood-john-lennons-stockbroker-belt-residence/ This excellent article on Kenwood was written by Richard

Porter, who gives walking tours of The Beatles' London.

https://www.getsurrey.co.uk/news/nostalgia/john-lennons-kenwood-home-sale-11725799 This article was written by a fan who had met John when she was a teen. It affords a "virtual tour" of Kenwood.

https://www.independent.co.uk/news/obituaries/kenneth-partridge-interior-designer-whose-best-known-work-was-an-expensive-refit-of-john-lennons-a6774726.html This Independent obituary of Ken Partridge focuses mainly on his remodeling work at Kenwood and his relationship with John and Cynthia. Good photo of Partridge in his heyday included as well.

https://www.bing.com/images/search?q=kenwood+john+lennon+images&id=F8A4E7C48766B6312BEBA827BB0AEA8BC19C455C&FORM=IQFRBA This link provides many wonderful images of Kenwood both before the Lennons' renovation and after.

Cynthia, in her book, John, says that the renovation of Kenwood took nine months. That would have placed the Lennons in the re-designed home by May 1965. At this chapter's juncture, they would have been about halfway through the redecorating process.

**Young Cynthia Powell Lennon with her parents,
Charles and Lillian Powell**
Efforts have been made to contact the photographer for permission.

[55] Lennon, Cynthia, *A Twist of Lennon*, 131 and Norman, *John Lennon: The Life*, 388. Cynthia states, "My mother…couldn't resist buying us more and more junk…"

[56] Norman, *John Lennon: The Life*, 389 and Connolly, Ray, *Being John Lennon: A Restless Life*, 194. Norman points out that John also generously gave Lillian a weekly allowance of £30, "the same as Mimi received."

[57] Brown, 166.

[58] Norman, *John Lennon: The Life*, 288, Connolly, 194, and Spitz, 548. In *John Lennon: The Life*, John's cousin Michael Cadwallader states, "[John] couldn't stand her [Lillian]. Neither could Mimi." (p. 288) Spitz says, "There wasn't an ounce of love lost between John and Mrs. Powell, a spiteful, insufferable woman who had never forgiven him for impregnating her daughter and fulminated against her son-in-law every chance she got." (p. 548) Connolly adds, "[John] had never liked Cynthia's mother, Lil — nor had Mimi, who considered her intellectually and socially inferior."

[59] Goldman, 59 and Norman, *John Lennon: The Life*, 388-389. This is a direct quote from a visitor to Kenwood, according to Norman.

[60] Norman, *John Lennon: The Life*, 389. A visitor to Kenwood said that rather than complaining about Lillian, John "passed through without comment."

[61] Goldman, 192. Goldman accurately observes, "Nobody wanted to have a scene, so the animosity that Lil and John felt for one another was muted…"

[62] Lennon, Cynthia, *John*, 151, Norman, *John Lennon: The Life*, 384, and Goldman, 192. Goldman says that Jarlett "started off minding Julian for ten pounds a week and gradually took on the cleaning and cooking, the fan mail, in fine the whole management of the house…for the same ten pounds!" (p. 192) In *John*, Cynthia states, "[Dot] was a warm, competent woman in her forties who became indispensable to us. She was loyal and reliable and was a good friend to me when John was away for weeks on end." (p. 151)

[63] Brown, 166.

[64] Lennon, Cynthia, *A Twist of Lennon*, 131. Cynthia describes herself as "…the quiet little woman who wouldn't say boo to a ghost."

[65] Coleman, *Lennon*, 106. Coleman tells us that the very first meeting between John and Lillian went disastrously, and John left in a huff. Cynthia persuaded him to return, but Coleman says "[John] was destined never to get on well with Cynthia's mother, not even during the most joyful days of Beatlemania. When she lived at his Weybridge mansion, he regarded her as an intruder."

[66] Brown, 166.

[67] Brown, 166.

[68] Goldman, 192. Goldman accurately states that John called Lil "Lowl," "mimicking her Liverpool working-class pronunciation of 'Lil.'"

[69] Norman, *John Lennon: The Life*, 383.

[70] Norman, *John Lennon: The Life*, 383.

[71] Lewisohn, Mark and Kevin Howlett, *In My Life: John Lennon Remembered*, 36, Spitz, 549, and Trynka, Paul, *The Beatles: Ten Years that Shook the World*, 167. In Spitz's *The Beatles*, Paul McCartney — speaking of John in 1965 — says, "He'd tried to give Cynthia the traditional thing, but you kind of knew he couldn't. There were cracks appearing, but he could only paste them

over by staying at home and getting very wrecked." (p. 549) In the same chapter, Cynthia complains, "Even when John was around, he slept until one or two, then took off for London, rarely coming home until the early hours of the morning, often stoned or drunk." (p. 548) And referring to his life in 1965, John himself is quoted in *The Beatles: Ten Years that Shook the World* as saying: "It was my fat Elvis period. You can see it in the movie ["Help!"]. He — I — is very fat, very insecure, and he's completely lost himself." Things were beginning to unravel. Finally, Lewisohn and Howlett state in *In My Life: John Lennon Remembered*: "Restless and miserably putting on weight, John Lennon was drowning in a sea of excess."

Saturday, 9 January 1965
Kenwood
Weybridge, Surrey

Cynthia made cocoa on the attic nook hotplate and flicked on the telly in plenty of time to warm up the set.[72] John was to appear on Dudley Moore's new BBC2 programme, "Not Only...But Also."[73] In fact, before leaving for the Odeon, he'd reminded her several times: "Try 'n catch it, Cyn — that is, if y'er not up to yer ears in nappies." Then, he'd awkwardly pulled his Famous Eccles face.

Tonight, fortunately, Cynthia wasn't...covered in nappies, that is. Julian had enjoyed a nice, toy-laden bath and was tucked off to bed without a squabble. Though he'd been a rather colicky, discontented baby,[74] Jules had grown into an adorable, snuggly toddler: little fuss, little bother. Cynthia doted on him and vice versa.

But she doted on John as well, and watching his programme wasn't something he'd had to convince her to do. She wouldn't have missed it, especially since John was to read his own poetry tonight — a few choice selections from *In His Own Write*. For John, it was a refreshing break. Both George and he were miserably beleaguered — sullen over the never-diminishing screams that nightly suffocated their songs.[75]

This evening, however, John would actually be heard, "speaking with his own voice," as he was wont to say.[76] Cynthia smiled and dragged their worn, celery-green, high-backed chair closer to the TV. She grabbed her cup, tugged her long blonde hair from the collar of her thick, terrycloth robe, and tucked one leg beneath her. She snugged in.

John had recorded this programme weeks ago, back in late November.[77] And ever since, he'd been going on about it. His illustrious two days with Dudley Moore and Norm Rossington![78] It was a remembrance he prized.

"Especially that avvy on Wimbledon Common," John had raved on, "when Moore was shovin' me about in that swing...pushin' so hard that m' contact lenses flew out!"[79]

"I know," Cynthia had resisted throwing her eyes to the ceiling. It was a great story, but she'd heard the tale, ten times over. "I remember...you actually lost them!"

"Yeah, right, but fortunately for us all, I had a second pair with me, or else I wouldn't have been able to read, would I?"[80] John was set on telling the entire episode again. "I mean, the readin'...well, I was fairly nervous at first, y' know — recitin' m' own poetry in front of *the* Dudley Moore. *Beyond the Fringe* 'n all that!"[81]

Cynthia knew the end of the story and prompted him. "But he was so friendly..."

"Right, 'n Norm 'n he were makin' me laugh, makin' me forget about the fact that I was on the fuggin' telly[82]...so, I just read the stuff — straight out, y' know — 'n had fun with it...just as if we were all sittin' 'round havin' a bevvy, as it were, which is just what we did afterwards."[83]

"A wonderful day." Cynthia had smiled. She was always happy when John was happy.

**"Beyond the Fringe," Broadway's 1962-1964
satirical British comedy featuring Dudley Moore,
Alan Bennett, Peter Cook, and Jonathan Miller**
Photograph from Wikimedia Commons
Photographer Friedman-Abeles, New York

And now, she'd get to see the finished product, the "on air"
version of one of John's brightest memories. Cynthia bounced
from her chair to up the volume. Then, plopping down to wait, she
gnawed her cuticles and waggled her foot.

But when a conservatively-suited Dudley Moore (in white
shirt and tight, black tie) stood in front of a small classical quartet
and a sign reading "Borough of Margate, Blue Drive Lavatory,
LADIES, W.C. 1,"[84] Cynthia began to smile. The skit was already
funny. Moore, however, maintained a straight face.

"Poetry and music," the comedian said, thoughtfully. "This,
uhm, uneasy marriage of the arts has caused a lot of controversy
for a long time. Many opinions are for; many, against. We leave
you to judge for yourselves. What we're going to show you is a
visualization and a "musification" of a poem by a young poet

named John Lennon. And the poem is called, quite simply, 'Deaf Ted, Danoota, and Me.'"[85]

Moore stared meaningfully into the camera until the studio scene faded, revealing instead a raw, wintry Wimbledon Common: dark, barren limbs crisscrossing a frozen sky; an icy panorama lying empty — save one lone figure and one lone voice reading John's words.[86]

> "Thorg hilly grove and burly ive,
> Big daleys grass and tree..."[87]

The solitary figure motioned, it seemed, for someone else to follow, and presently, two comrades appeared — bedecked in winter coats, hats, and boots — walking side-by-side and staring boldly into the camera.[88]

> "We clobber ever gallup
> Deaf Ted, Danoota, and me."[89]

As the three characters came into focus, Cynthia giggled. There was John — dead centre. On his right stood Dudley Moore. To his left walked Norman Rossington who'd played The Beatles' manager, Norm, in "A Hard Day's Night."[90]

"Now *there's* an unlikely band of brothers!" Cynthia smirked, sipping her cocoa. She giggled as the three vagabonds strode purposefully down a dirt road, their eyes locked on the camera, their faces full of boyish challenge.[91]

> "Never shall we partly stray,
> Fast stirrup all we three
> Fight the battle mighty sword
> Deaf Ted, Danoota, and me."[92]

Against a crescendo of chamber music, the threesome was suddenly astride bicycles, riding out together — presumably, in pursuit of a grand quest. Inspired, the narrator's voice read gallantly on:[93]

"With faithful frog beside us,
Big mighty club are we
The battle scab and frisky dyke
Deaf Ted, Danoota, and me."[94]

Adventures, John had always told his wife, are not without complications. And suddenly, without explanation, there were plenty. Norman Rossington was mysteriously de-bicycled, and John (in what he called his "spazzle" mode)[95] was being pushed recklessly about in a swing. Moore was at the helm, and unsurprisingly, chaos reigned. The audience roared as the unperturbed narrator continued his spiel:[96]

"We fight the baddy baddies
For colour, race and cree"[97]

Rossington, with a glint of the "baddy baddie" in his eye, lurked behind a tree fork and peered surreptitiously into the camera.[98] Cynthia wondered if he just might be "the complication" in this quirky tale. But in almost the same breath, Norman was reunited with John and Dudley, and the three joined hands, larking about carelessly — holding fat, pale balloons and smoke bombs.[99]

For Negro, Jew and Bernie
Deaf Ted, Danoota, and me."[100]

Though John remained solemn throughout most of the episode, Norman and Dudley grinned widely. And dropping their smoke bombs, they performed a traditional "Ring Around the Rose-y." Balloons and hats bobbed everywhere.[101]

Then, without explanation, the balloons miraculously transformed into bouncing balls. One, tossed Norman's way, inspired him to dive into an imaginary pool of water. And when another orb was lobbed at John, he dodged it, releasing the first genuine Lennon grin of the evening.[102] In Kenwood, Cynthia smiled along with him.

"Thong Billy grows and Burnley ten,
And Aston Villa three
We clobber ever gallup
Deaf Ted, Danoota and me."[103]

Once more on their steeds (trusty bicycles), the three buccaneers now rode valiantly on. Bravely. Before them, a hefty, wooden gate loomed, blocking the path, but as in all good stories, it collapsed helplessly before the conquerors. Barely blinking, they plowed over it. [104]

"So if you hear a wonderous sight,
Am blutter or at sea..."[105]

Unscathed and back where they had started, the three dismounted on the vast, deserted common. Dudley and Norman — silhouetted against the grey afternoon — leapt and cavourted here and there. But earth-bound, John merely trudged between them.

Once, Norman nudged Lennon lightly, urging the lackluster "middleman" to try on a bit of frivolity. But John only eked out an awkward skip and lifted a tentative arm. He was far from playful.[106]

John, Cynthia thought, *is tethered these days. Truth told; he's becoming rather serious.*

Cynthia badly longed to blame Brian for giving John too little time for rest. She wanted to fault the manager for "signing on the dotted line" too quickly for The Beatles' next North American Tour.[107] She wanted to impugn producer George Martin for booking the next batch of demanding recording sessions in only three weeks. She wanted to lay fault at the feet of United Artists for pressing The Beatles straight into their next film.[108] She wanted John's unsmiling face to be someone else's oversight, not hers.

But in hushed moments, Cynthia knew she'd led John, by degrees, into a life he had never wanted. By begging John to leave London for the far reaches of the stockbroker belt, by bringing her mother into their home, and by wanting John to become a devoted husband and a father, Cyn was certain she'd made a tangle of his life. A muddle.

But John never said a thing. And his silent consent to live as she wanted hurt her more than any accusation he could have hurled in her direction. His refusal to spit retorts at her domineering mother crushed Cynthia. His solemn face on Boxing Day indicted her. John's resignation broke her heart.

And Cynthia blamed herself.

On screen — almost as if he'd read her mind — John halted his shenanigans and looked directly into the camera. He made eye contact. He smiled. As the narrator dramatically concluded the poem, John draped his arms loosely across his mates' shoulders and flashed two thumbs up.[109]

"Remember whom the mighty say
Deaf Ted, Danoota, and me."[110]

Then unexpectedly, finding their voice, the three closed the skit with a chuckling chorus of, "Sometimes we ask our friend, Malcolm!"[111] And an exuberant, middle-aged "Malcolm" appeared centre-screen. He twirled and swung his arms joyfully. He pointed to his name, childishly-scrawled across his forehead. He mouthed, "That's me! I'm Malcolm!"[112] He beamed.

Cynthia, applauding softly — so as not to wake Julian — stood and grinned. And laughing, the television audience joined her.[113]

But when John — in a bizarre postscript — hurled a rock in Malcolm's direction, the audience gasped.[114] For a moment, there was hesitant silence. Then...a roar! Applause and laughter rose, and with it, the decision became unanimous: John Lennon's off-beat poetry and music were only outdone by one thing — his unanticipated antics.

The crowd was won over.

Moments later, a suited Dudley Moore emerged, back in studio again. Standing primly in front of the now familiar Ladies' Lavatory sign, he clasped a copy of John's *In His Own Write* and said, "Now, before the film...that is, after it...or, to put it another way, during it, let us hear a few words 'about the awful.'"[115]

Cyn laughed softly. "About the Awful" was the clever catch-phrase John had devised for his "About the Author" segment on the book's back cover. His brief biography was ingenious — a smart volley of cunning phrases that seemed gibberish ("gobbledygook" was John's term for it)[116] but revealed far more than readers suspected of her husband's authentic history.

Now, John appeared on screen — close-up — his thick, long hair framing his face, his almond-shaped eyes down-turned and somber. John concentrated and read intently from cue cards:[117]

"I was bored on the 9th of October 1940 when, I believe, the Nasties were still boomin' us, led by Madalf Heathump (Who only had one)."[118]

The audience exploded in laughter, but John — impassive — read on, never pausing to relish the reaction.[119]

"Anyway, they didn't get me.
I attended varicous schools in Liddypol.
And still didn't pass-much to my
Aunties supplies. As a member of the most publified
Beatles my and
(P, G, and R's) records might seem
funnier to some of you than this book..."[120]

Here, for an instant, John betrayed emotion. He pulled his upper lip tightly across his teeth: an intimation of resentment, a show of disdain. But the glimpse swiftly vanished, and chortling, John went on, reciting the artfully calculated words that camouflaged his life's story.[121]

"...but as far as I'm conceived, this correction of short writty is the [best][122] larf I've ever ready. God help and breed you all."[123]

The final line was delivered not as a rehearsed reading but as gut-born sentiment. John's eyes simmered with rage. He glared into the camera.[124]

For a moment, Cynthia stopped breathing. For a moment, John surfaced — her John, the real John, the aggrieved artist, the man weary of being a Beatle, "a performin' flea."[125] Cynthia leaned forward. She hardly blinked. She bit her lip, wondering what Brian would say.

But almost as quickly as it had clouded, John's visage cleared. And without a bobble, the jolly proceedings rolled on.

The rest of the programme revealed nothing else untoward. John's peculiar brand of artistic nonsense rivaled Moore's own. He sparred and bandied with Rossington and Moore. He fit nondescriptly into the group.

It was becoming habitual these days: John participated without really taking part. He contributed and did what he was asked to do. John complied. But these days, he held himself in careful reserve. Aloof. Guarded.

Most people, Cynthia thought, not even those closest to him, ever knew. And the fans? They only wanted to squeal and scan the marvellous headlines that boasted:

4 January, U.K.: **Beatles Publisher, Dick James, Reveals Lennon and McCartney Gross Over £1 million in 1964**[126]

8 January, U.K.: **Beatles Given Private View of Boat Show at Earl's Court Exhibition Hall**[127]

9 January, U.S.: **Capitol's *Beatles '65* Reaches No. 1 on *Billboard* Charts**[128]

The fans cheered and clapped and clipped each article for their podgy scrapbooks. They wallowed in Beatlemania. They giggled and grinned, never guessing how "false and tinselly it was."[129] They thought John an unparalleled success. None of them saw a hint of correlation between John's life and the hauntingly dark poems and lyrics he penned.

As the programme's credits began to roll, Cynthia stood and turned off the set. The screen gradually darkened to a tiny white dot and after a time, even that disappeared.

Wandering to the high third floor window and peering into the darkness, Cyn hugged her robe about her. She squinted into the black void that was their estate, just beyond the icy glass. And she shuddered.

Logically, Cynthia knew that she and John should both be tremendously happy. They had a healthy son and a lovely showplace of a home that would soon be redesigned to their specifications. After months apart, they were finally getting to enjoy evenings alone together.[130] And soon, they'd be trekking off on a romantic winter holiday in Switzerland.[131]

But for the first time since they'd become a couple in May of 1958, Cyn felt that she and John were beginning to drift apart. More and more frequently, when they had a chance to motor into town and enjoy London's night spots, John had begun begging off. He'd even uncharacteristically suggested that their old Liverpool friend Terry Doran serve as Cynthia's escort. John had begun employing any tactic to avoid "goin' out again after workin' all day 'n tryin' to finish m' book as well."[132] John was not John.

Sitting around in his robe, staring vacantly at the telly,[133] and dreading the hectic days of filming ahead, John rarely talked; he rarely smiled. And nothing Cynthia could do would lift his spirits. In fact, quite often, when she chatted brightly with him, John wouldn't even glance up. He wouldn't respond.[134]

At the visionless window, Cynthia sighed. She drew the curtains and overlapped them — tugging them close and trying to shut out the night.

Then, curling on the tiny attic sofa, she fought to sleep so that when John trudged in, creased, around midnight, she could make tea and bacon butties and sit up with him, listening as he talked.[135] *Perhaps refreshed*, she thought, *I can find a way to resurrect our old "John-and-Cyn-times."*[136] *I can laugh, ask questions and...*

But a frightening voice cut across her, vowing that John's despair was no more her fault than it was Brian's or George's or the fans' or anyone's at all, really. The dismal shade over their lives was John's. Only he could will it away.

Notes!

How accurate is this account of John's increasing depression in the winter of 1965 and Cynthia's feeling that their relationship was beginning to flounder?

Here are Cynthia's words on the matter from A Twist of Lennon*:*

"A second film, recordings of singles and albums the avid fans craved, and John really had his work cut out for him…

The proprietors of the 'in' clubs…fell over themselves to welcome the boys and their entourage. Terry Doran, an old Liverpool pal of Brian, became a close friend to us all. Terry was willing to do anything, go anywhere. He adored The Beatles and was loved in return by us all…Due to the pressure of work on John and his natural bent towards the anti-social, I would frequently spend weeks of being virtually housebound by duties to child and staff. John being either too exhausted or bored by the whole idea would suggest that Terry be my escort.

"Difficulties began to arise due to the difference in life-styles between myself and John. I desperately fought for reality and a family unity in the home. I fought to keep the wolves and jackals from the door of our life…Yet I needed to experience was what was happening in the outside world however false and tinselly it was.

"John would sleep until two in the afternoon most days, eat a hurried brunch and be out to face the speed of decision-making…with the VIPs of show business. It was no wonder that the thought of socializing put him off especially when he had the chance to refuse. Holidays seemed to be the only times we really came together and had a chance to satisfy each other's needs without pressure or interruption." (pp. 133-134)

Similarly, in Cynthia's 2005 book, John, *she says:*

"When John wasn't working he lay on the sofa, apparently watching the TV — which he liked to keep permanently switched on — but often a million miles away, lost in a daydream. I'd talk to him but he wouldn't hear me. This was nothing new: he'd always been able to "tune out" of his surroundings and the busier his life became, the more often he was 'present but absent.'" (p. 150)

Finally, here is Paul McCartney's evaluation of John's predicament in 1964-1965: "…he was married to Cynthia and with a lot of energy bursting to get out. He'd tried to give Cynthia the traditional thing, but you kind of knew he couldn't. There were cracks appearing but he could only paste them over by staying at home and getting very wrecked." (Spitz, 549)

Sources:

Lewisohn, The Complete Beatles Chronicle, *177, 179-180, 181, and 183. There is a good photo of Dudley Moore, Norman Rossington, and John*

in the Wimbledon Common film sequence on p. 177.
Lewisohn, The Beatles: Day by Day, *55, 57, and 58.*
Lennon, John, A Spaniard in the Works, *68 and back cover.*
Lennon, Cynthia, A Twist of Lennon, *95, 126, and 134.*
Lennon, Cynthia, John, 95, 114, 150, 163, and 172.
Norman, John Lennon: The Life, *280, 386-388, and 456.*
Norman, Shout!, *272.*
Harry, The John Lennon Encyclopedia, *659-660.*
Harry, The Encyclopedia of Beatles People, *279.*
Miles, The Beatles' Diary, *Vol. 1, 178 and 187-188.*
Spitz, The Beatles, *549.*
Winn, John C., Way Beyond Compare: The Beatles' Recorded Legacy, *285 and 287.*
Connolly, Ray, Being John Lennon: A Restless Life, *77 and 192.*
Hill, John, Paul, George & Ringo, *176-177 and 185. There is a photo of John on the Wimbledon Common on p. 177.*
Thomas, Gareth, John Lennon: The Illustrated Biography, *90.*
Coleman, Lennon, *602.*
Schultheiss, 128-129.
Trynka, 166.
Buskin, 111.

During the writing of this chapter, much of the "Not Only...But Also" programme was available on YouTube. It has, sadly, been removed. In Way Beyond Compare, *Winn tells us that "the soundtrack of this programme, minus the closing segment, appeared on the bootleg,* The Beatles at the Beeb — TV."*

https://www.beatlesbible.com/1964/11/20/john-lennon-not-only-but-also/ There are excellent still shots of the filming on the Wimbledon Commons.

https://en.wikipedia.org/wiki/Not_Only..._But_Also This site includes a full listing of all episodes of "Not Only...But Also"

https://www.nytimes.com/2008/10/12/arts/television/12stew.html This is a New York Times article on "Not Only...But Also."

https://tinyurl.com/5ecfyf5t Although this website primarily supplies information about John's appearance on "Not Only But Also" in 1966, there is one excellent photo of John, Norm Rossington, and Dudley Moore on the 18 July 1965 episode.

https://www.youtube.com/watch?v=Udim8inlg9E This is a video of John reading "About the Awful" on the "Not Only...But Also" programme. Or use this QR code:

[72] Lennon, Cynthia, *A Twist of Lennon*, 126. Cynthia specifically mentions routinely spending many "simple evenings" in her attic "flat," watching TV. She says that she had everything she needed up there. "It was like living in a high rise flat."

[73] Miles, *The Beatles' Diary, Vol. 1*, 187, Schultheiss, Tom, *The Beatles, A Day in the Life*, 128, and Harry, *The John Lennon Encyclopedia*, 659.

[74] Lennon, Cynthia, *A Twist of Lennon*, 95, and Lennon, Cynthia, *John*, 114.

[75] Lewisohn, *The Beatles: Day by Day*, 57, and Buskin, *John Lennon: His Life and Legend*, 111. Lewisohn states, "The screaming wouldn't stop, the adulation was barely diminishing." Buskin says, "By 1965, matters were getting worse. John and George, in particular, were growing tired of performing live to hordes of girls who couldn't even hear their music."

[76] A direct quote from John on the 1963 *Beatles Fan Club Christmas Record*. To listen to the record, go to: https://www.bing.com/videos/search?q=The+Beatles+1964+Christmas+recod &&view=detail&mid=A28BD596D3AE5C7C52B9A28BD596D3AE5C7C52 B9&&FORM=VDRVSR

[77] Miles, *The Beatles' Diary, Vol. 1*, 178, Lewisohn, *The Complete Beatles Chronicle*, 179-180, Lewisohn, *The Beatles: Day by Day*, 55, and Harry, *The John Lennon Encyclopedia*, 659.

[78] Norman, *John Lennon: The Life*, 280, Connolly, 192, and Harry, *The John Lennon Encyclopedia*, 660. Bill Harry quotes "Not Only...But Also" director Joe McGrath as saying, "He [John Lennon] relished every minute of working with Peter [Cook] and Dudley [Moore]."

[79] Harry, *The John Lennon Encyclopedia*, 660.

[80] Harry, *The John Lennon Encyclopedia*, 660. Joe McGrath said they had to stop filming and try to help John find his lenses. "Luckily," McGrath states, "John had another pair on him, because we never found the first ones."

[81] Miles, *The Beatles' Diary, Vol. 1*, 178 and Norman, *John Lennon: The Life*, 280. As Norman explains, "In 1961, four Oxford graduates, Peter Cook, Dudley Moore, Jonathan Miller, and Alan Bennett, scored a massive West End [London] success with *Beyond the Fringe*, a satirical revue snapping at the sacred headquarters of parliament, the military, and the church..."

[82] Miles, *The Beatles' Diary, Vol. 1*, 178. Miles says, "[John] was apparently shy and self-conscious about reading aloud, but this was quickly dispelled by the antics of Moore and 'A Hard Day's Night' star Norman Rossington."

[83] Miles, *The Beatles' Diary, Vol. 1*, 178, Lewisohn, *The Beatles: Day by Day*, 55, and Harry, *The John Lennon Encyclopedia*, 660. Miles and Lewisohn say that George and John "had a few drinks afterwards and then went to The Crazy Elephant." However, Bill Harry quotes Joe McGrath saying, "At the end of the

show we all went for a Chinese meal at some restaurant round the corner." The reason for the discrpenacy is simple. There were **two** "Not Only...But Also" shows on which John appeared. One night they probably went to the Chinese restaurant for dinner and the other time, they went for drinks and then on to the Crazy Elephant.

[84] All details of the set for "Not Only...But Also," which aired on the evening of 9 January 1965 on BBC2, are taken directly from this video: https://www.youtube.com/watch?v=iC4D1phY3NE

[85] This is a direct quote from Dudley Moore on the 9 January 1965 episode of "Not Only...But Also," as seen in this video: https://www.youtube.com/watch?v=iC4D1phY3NE

[86] https://www.youtube.com/watch?v=iC4D1phY3NE

[87] Lennon, John, "Deaf Ted, Danoota, and Me," *In His Own Write, 68.*

[88] https://www.youtube.com/watch?v=iC4D1phY3NE

[89] Lennon, John, "Deaf Ted, Danoota, and Me," *In His Own Write*, 68.

[90] https://www.youtube.com/watch?v=iC4D1phY3NE

[91] https://www.youtube.com/watch?v=iC4D1phY3NE

[92] Lennon, John, "Deaf Ted, Danoota, and Me," *In His Own Write*, 68.

[93] https://www.youtube.com/watch?v=iC4D1phY3NE

[94] Lennon, John, "Deaf Ted, Danoota, and Me," *In His Own Write*, 68.

[95] Trynka, 166 and Connolly, 121. Trynka refers to John's "obsession with what he called 'spastics.'" Connolly says, "While...in Germany, John had taken to occasionally mimicking the mentally handicapped while on stage, sometimes seeming to claw with an inane smile on his face...what John would call his 'spazzle' act, which was short for 'spastic.'"

[96] https://www.youtube.com/watch?v=iC4D1phY3NE

[97] Lennon, John, "Deaf Ted, Danoota, and Me," *In His Own Write*, 68.

[98] https://www.youtube.com/watch?v=iC4D1phY3NE

[99] https://www.youtube.com/watch?v=iC4D1phY3NE

[100] Lennon, John, "Deaf Ted, Danoota, and Me," *In His Own Write*, 68.

[101] https://www.youtube.com/watch?v=iC4D1phY3NE

[102] https://www.youtube.com/watch?v=iC4D1phY3NE

[103] Lennon, John, "Deaf Ted, Danoota, and Me," *In His Own Write*, 68.

[104] https://www.youtube.com/watch?v=iC4D1phY3NE

[105] Lennon, John, "Deaf Ted, Danoota, and Me," *In His Own Write*, 68.

[106] https://www.youtube.com/watch?v=iC4D1phY3NE

[107] Lewisohn, *The Complete Beatles Chronicle*, 181 and Schultheiss, 129. Lewisohn states, "Brian Epstein had flown to the USA as early as 19 January to fix the dates for [The Beatles'] August American shows." So certainly by 9 January, the negotiations were in full swing.

[108] Lewisohn, *The Complete Beatles Chronicle*, 183. Lewisohn's entry for 15 February 1965 finds The Beatles in Studio Two of EMI recording "Ticket to Ride" in the afternoon and "Another Girl" in the evening. Lewisohn comments, "Another year, another film, another set of recording sessions, and yet more furious industry." That sums it up perfectly.

[109] https://www.youtube.com/watch?v=iC4D1phY3NE

[110] Lennon, John, "Deaf Ted, Danoota, and Me," *In His Own Write*, 68.

[111] Lennon, John, "Deaf Ted, Danoota, and Me," *In His Own Write*, 68.

[112] https://www.youtube.com/watch?v=iC4D1phY3NE
[113] https://www.youtube.com/watch?v=iC4D1phY3NE
[114] https://www.youtube.com/watch?v=iC4D1phY3NE
[115] https://www.youtube.com/watch?v=iC4D1phY3NE
[116] Connolly, 77.
[117] https://www.youtube.com/watch?v=iC4D1phY3NE
[118] Lennon, John, *In His Own Write*. This is John Lennon's self-penned author's biography from the back cover of the book.
[119] https://www.youtube.com/watch?v=iC4D1phY3NE
[120] Lennon, John, *In His Own Write*. This is John Lennon's self-penned author's biography from the back cover of the book.
[121] https://www.youtube.com/watch?v=iC4D1phY3NE
[122] This is not the original word in this piece on the cover of the book. This is what John says *when he reads it on the show*. Thanks to one of my wonderful editors, Janet Davis, who sleuthed this out!!! To hear it, go to: https://www.youtube.com/watch?v=Udim8inlg9E
[123] Lennon, John, *In His Own Write*. This is John Lennon's self-penned author's biography from the back cover of the book.
[124] https://www.youtube.com/watch?v=iC4D1phY3NE
[125] https://www.youtube.com/watch?v=iC4D1phY3NE
[126] Miles, *The Beatles' Diary, Vol. 1*, 187.
[127] Miles, *The Beatles' Diary, Vol. 1*, 187.
[128] Miles, *The Beatles' Diary, Vol. 1*, 187 and Schultheiss, 128.
[129] Lennon, Cynthia, *A Twist of Lennon*, 134. These are Cynthia's own words.
[130] Lennon, Cynthia, *John*, 172. Cynthia states, "After weeks apart, me running the household, John traveling and performing, it was wonderful to be close again and to shut out the world."
[131] Lennon, Cynthia, *A Twist of Lennon*, 134, Lewisohn, *The Beatles:Day by Day*, 58, Miles, *The Beatles' Diary, Vol. 1*, 188, and Norman, *John Lennon: The Life*, 388.
[132] Lennon, Cynthia, *A Twist of Lennon*, 134. Cynthia states, "John, being either too exhausted or bored by the whole idea [of going out at night], would suggest that Terry [Doran] be my escort."
[133] Lennon, Cynthia, *John*, 150. Cynthia writes, "When John wasn't working, he lay on the sofa, apparently watching the TV — which he liked to keep permanently switched on — but often, a million miles away, lost in a daydream. I'd talk to him, but he wouldn't hear me. This was nothing new; he had always been able to 'tune out' of his surroundings and the busier his life became, the more often he was 'present but absent.'"
[134] Lennon, Cynthia, *John*, 150 and Norman, *Shout!* 272.
[135] Lennon, Cynthia, *John,* 168.
[136] Lennon, Cynthia, *John*, 172. Cynthia says that she and John would "cuddle up together in front of the TV. We called these special John-and-Cyn times, and they were our oases of loving peace in the madness that was the world. I treasured them."

Sunday, 10 January 1965
Whaddon House, Flat 15
William Mews
London

Replacing the receiver, Brian gnawed his lip. Sidney Bernstein's proposal to book the boys in New York's Shea Stadium was indeed intriguing. Typically polished, self-assured, and persuasive, Sid had convinced him that the mammoth New York venue — a stadium that could house 55,600 people[137] — was the next logical progression for the lads.[138] But Brian was scrupulous. He poured himself a brandy and retraced the conversation, searching for anything amiss.

Sid: Brian…[139]
Brian: A treat to hear your voice, Sid! How are you?
Sid: I'm fine, Brian…how are you?
Brian: Hectic, everything's hectic. I'm fielding calls from all over the world — requests for the boys' endorsements and the like. By the way, Sid, thanks so much for sending those Book Review sections. My mum really enjoys them!
Sid: I'm so glad, Brian. Send her my regards…and how are the boys?
Brian: Working hard, as always…and I've also begun to sign some new acts, Sid, so we'll have to talk about bringing them to America. Actually, I was thinking of calling you; you beat me to it.
(Chuckling, they skipped a polite beat.)
Sid: Brian, when would you consider bringing the boys back to the States?
Brian: Well, not until the summer. That's the earliest.[140]

A pregnant pause. Brian had known, of course, that Sid hadn't rung him up for casual chat. This was a business proposal.

Sid: Brian, we made history a few months ago. Let's do it again. We have a ballpark in New York called Shea Stadium.[141] It's in Queens, on the grounds of the most recent World's Fair. It has 55,000 seats, and I'd like to present The Beatles there. [Pause.] It would be another history-making event![142]
Brian: Fifty-five *thousand*, Sid? Do you really think we could fill so many seats?[143]
Sid: Absolutely, Brian. If I didn't, I would never present this to you.[144]

Although he had questioned Sid, Shea was not entirely an alien concept to Brian. In fact, General Artists Corporation had proposed the baseball stadium the previous April, suggesting the "Home of the Mets" for the night of 13 September 1964.[145] Indeed, GAC's initial proposal for the 1964 North American Tour gave The Beatles' manager three choices for that particular evening:

1. One show at Baltimore's Civic Center
2. Two shows at Baltimore's Civic Center
3. Shea Stadium - 60,000 seats[146]

And beneath this succinct notation, Norman Weiss had typed in: "With ticket prices between $2-$4 apiece, gross for Shea Stadium expected to be $80,000."[147] The possibilities had been interesting six months ago. They were even more attractive now.

Over and over again throughout 1964, the boys had proven that they could draw record-breaking crowds. In Jacksonville's Gator Bowl, they'd sold tickets handily, although the actual attendance had been diminished by high winds — the fierce after-effects of Hurricane Dora.[148]

Furthermore, the 41,000 seat Kansas City Municipal Stadium hadn't frightened Kansas City Athletics' owner "Charlie" O. Finley one bit from booking The Beatles. Only Finley's decision to set ticket prices high — at $8.50, $6.50, and $4.50[149] — had stalled sales to conservative, Midwestern moms, dads, and teens. A last-minute decision to offer a more affordable $2.00 ticket had boosted the number of seats sold, but without a doubt, sales had been adversely affected by the earlier, costly admittance fee.[150] Nonetheless, 20,000 seats were filled in Kansas City: a town not even scheduled on the tour, a concert only advertised for a scant three weeks![151]

Still, although his boys had been warmly received in America, Brian fretted over something as large as Shea Stadium. In 1964, he'd definitely felt the New York baseball stadium a bit of "a reach." And when GAC's Ron Delsener had proposed a less demanding New York area alternative — the Forest Hills Tennis Stadium with a payoff of $50,000 plus 50% of the take — Brian had swiftly agreed to the more unadventurous venue.[152]

Now, however, with *Beatles for Sale* and *Beatles '65* doing extremely well, with "I Feel Fine"/"She's a Woman" lodged comfortably at the top of the U.K. and U.S. charts,[153] and with another United Artists full-length Beatles feature film in the offing, Shea seemed doable. For the 1965 Tour, it appeared an idea whose time had come.

Brian: (Clearing his throat) Tell me, Sid…what would you sell the tickets for?[154]
Sid: (Quietly, calmly) I was thinking of $4.50, $5.00, and $5.65.
Brian: (Recalling his chats with Finley, only six months ago) And you *really think* we can fill a fifty-five thousand seat stadium at those prices?
Sid: Yes, I do. I'm *so* sure that I'll pay you $10.00 for every unsold seat![155]

It was Brian's turn to hesitate. He felt his right eye twitching, as it had been doing for the past three weeks, ever since The Beatles had gone on "winter hiatus," performing only in the Odeon Christmas Show.

Brian: Are you *sure*, Sid? I don't want to be embarrassed or have the boys embarrassed.[156]
Sid: Brian, the box office people at Carnegie Hall told me we could have sold out *two hundred thousand seats*, leave alone the 2,870 for each show![157]
Brian: And even though the top ticket price would be $5.65, you would be willing to give us $10.00 for every unsold ticket?[158]
Sid: That's correct.

Brian: Why for heaven's sake?![159]

Sid: Because there will be *no unsold tickets*. We'll have a sellout, and the boys will gross three hundred thousand dollars and be able to clear one hundred and fifty thousand for one night's work! It's *never* been done![160]

Sid let the ponderous silence hover. He let Brian weigh matters out. Then...

Sid: What I'm saying, Brian, is that I'll *guarantee* The Beatles one hundred thousand dollars against 50 percent of the gross to play Shea Stadium in New York...on August 15, 1965.[161]

So, Brian thought, *if Sid already has a specific date, then he must've contacted the powers-that-be at Shea. He's that certain this venture will succeed.*

Yet, on the other hand, he's an incurable optimist. That much is a worry.

It was tempting. Very tempting. Filling an entire baseball stadium...a feat no other band had achieved! Ever. And yet...

Brian: But 55,000 fans, Sid — how could we provide security for the boys in a crowd such as that?[162]

Sid: Let me handle the security issues. I'll make certain the boys are *completely* protected. You know that.[163]

Another pause.

Sid: Brian, would you agree *in principle* to the concert?[164]

Brian: If you're *sure* about security...I...[165]

Brian pondered. He stalled. And then he knew exactly what to do.

Brian: Sid, this is quite astonishing really...fabulous! But let me talk to the boys, and I'll get back to you tomorrow.[166]

Sid: I'll look forward to it, Brian, and please remember me to Queenie.[167]

Brian: Of course. 'Til tomorrow then.

At the moment, however, Brian's mother was the very last thing on his mind. This unanticipated proposal was a king-maker. Sid's bright-shining Shea Stadium was nothing less than a pivot point.

If Brian cinched this prize for the lads and if things panned out, Brian knew he could restore their old, unwavering faith in him. *Shea would expiate a lot of sins, both real and imagined,* he thought, pacing. *It would soften the edges of the EMI agreement and the United Artists contract. It would mitigate the hardships of the Autumn Tour. It might even diminish the inflated aura of the much-discussed Andrew Loog Oldham "who's done so much for the Rollin' Stones."*

Above all, Brian rubbed his eyes wearily, it would make good on his long-ago pledge to Mimi Smith to take care of John.[168] In fact, her nephew would go down in the record books. In history.

And John? Brian hoped that this prize secured, John would begin to meet his eyes again…to look upon him once more as the hero he'd been to John, early on. Yet Robert Browning's poetic admonition that "a man's reach must exceed his grasp, or what's a heaven for,"[169] kept Brian chary. He would have to be absolutely certain about Shea, and more importantly, he would need cash money on the line.

****

Monday, 11 January 1965
Whaddon House, Flat 15
William Mews
London

Brian: Hello, Sid.
Sid: Hi, Brian. How are you?
Brian: Fine, and you?
Sid: Great — a bit nervous, though.
Brian: Well, the boys *are* keen on coming back to New York, Sid.[170]
Sid: (Smiling widely) *Wonderful!* I thought they might be! And

the concert?

Brian: Let's agree with the Shea Stadium.[171] (Pause) It will be very exciting! (Another pause) However, after a bit of thought, I'd like a guaranteed payment of $100,000 in advance, against 60% of gross receipts, whichever is larger, Sid.[172] I'll make it easy for you. You don't have to give me the other $50,000 right now. Send me $50,000 now and then give me the other $50,000 just before they play the date. But I *would* like the money before the concert."[173]

Sid Bernstein, 1969
Photograph from Wikimedia Commons

Sid: No problem, Brian. You've got it. But when would I be required to give you the $50,000?[174]

Brian: As soon as possible.

Sid: Well, my money is tied up at the moment. What would be the latest I could give it to you?

Brian: Investments and the like, Sid?

Sid: Yes. But I *will* be liquid in the not-too-distant future.[175]

And so, an arrangement was made. Sid would have approximately two months to secure the funds; in April, he would present the down payment to Brian at New York's Waldorf Towers.

After a series of questions and a litany of Brian's guidelines, the deal was done. But when Sid's fervour vanished into dial tone, Brian immediately began to second-guess the venture and himself. Was this foolhardy? Or was Shea simply the next common-sense step for a group destined to be "bigger than Elvis"?[176]

In only nine days, Brian would depart for America, to sit down with Weiss and the others at GAC, to put their heads together and finalize plans for the boys' August tour.[177] By then, he would have to be absolutely positive that Sid's funds were forthcoming and that Shea was not some hubris-filled pipe dream.

But I must risk it. Brian brushed the back of his hand lightly across his lips. *Because this one show could alter everything. Everything. If I can bring this to fruition, I can yet again be "The Man with the Midas Touch"[178]...or as some have said, "The King of Liverpool."[179] Everyone will be impressed.*

Even John.

Notes!

1. Why were Sid Bernstein's funds "tied up at the moment," compelling him to ask for several weeks in which to raise the Shea Stadium down payment for Brian Epstein?

At the conclusion of this phone conversation, Brian Epstein wasn't the only party equally thrilled and hesitant. Sid Bernstein had mixed emotions as well.

Sid was faced with the monumental hurdle of raising front money for the concert, and the down payment to Brian **wasn't the only expenditure** he had to provide. Chuck Gunderson, the definitive expert on The Beatles' North American Tours and the author of Some Fun Tonight!, The Backstage Story of the How The Beatles Rocked America: The Historic Tours of 1964-1966, Vols. 1 and 2, explained it to me this way:

"First, there was the rental of the venue by the promoter. For example, when The Beatles performed at the Hollywood Bowl in 1964, Bob Eubanks had to give the Bowl $500 plus 15% of net receipts. In 1965, the promoter for the San Diego show paid Balboa Stadium $7,713, which translated into 10% of the net receipts, and in 1966, the Memphis promoter paid the Mid-South Coliseum $12,000 flat for the rental. So, rentals...were all over the map." Sid would have to pay Shea Stadium long before the concert was performed.

Secondly, Bernstein would have to secure insurance for the boys' *performance. This would not be inexpensive. In* It's Sid Bernstein Calling..., *Sid tells us that, "It took five weeks before...Lloyd's of London...agreed to work out a deal at a cost of* **ten grand**.*" (p. 170) So, Bernstein had to come "out of pocket" for that amount as well.*

Bernstein faced a bevy of upcoming costs. That is why he informed Brian that his money was "tied up at the moment" and asked for a "grace period" to raise the funds.[180]

2. When did Bernstein propose the Shea Stadium venture to Brian, and how were the funds secured for the down payment?

In It's Sid Bernstein Calling..., *p. 166, Sid says that he rang Brian with the Shea proposal in late October and asked to pay the deposit to Brian during Epstein's 10 January visit to New York.*

*However, Beatles Guru Mark Lewisohn tells us that Brian didn't actually travel to New York until 19 January 1965. (*The Complete Beatles Chronicle, *181.) And of course, Lewisohn is correct. In Dave Schwensen's book,* The Beatles at Shea Stadium, *you can see an official letter on NEMS stationery from Brian Epstein to Bob Precht (Ed Sullivan's son-in-law) telling Bob that he will be in New York, staying at the Plaza Hotel, on 19 January 1965. (p. 39)*

Ray Coleman, in The Man Who Made The Beatles, *says that Sid* **rang Brian on 10 January** *and then agreed to pay the deposit to Brian at the Waldorf Towers on 10 April 1965. (p. 211-212) This rings true.*

Sid had limited time to raise Brian's deposit, and therefore, he requested permission to advertise the upcoming venture. Brian, however, flatly refused saying, "Oh no, Sid. Definitely not! It's not bona fide *until I get your deposit. No interviews, no advertisements, please." (Coleman, 212, and Bernstein, 169)*

So, grasping for the final straw, Sid asked, "May I **talk** *about it then?" (Coleman, 212, and Bernstein 169) To this plea, Brian acquiesced with: "How can I stop you from talking about it? That wouldn't be fair, now would it?" (Coleman, 212 and Bernstein, 169)*

In the interviews that I conducted with Sid in Stamford, CT, as well as in the interview that Steve Marinucci conducted with Sid for his Beatles Examiner *column, and in his own book,* It's Sid Bernstein Calling..., *Bernstein said that, armed with the knowledge that he had booked both Shea Stadium and The Beatles, he ventured over to New York's Washington Square Park. He says that he was pushing his son, Adam, in a pram "...when a group of kids [recognized me and] converged on me [and said], 'Mr. Bernstein, what's next? Who are you going to present next?' I waved them close and spoke in a whisper, 'The Beatles at Shea*

Stadium...August 15.'" (p. 170)
Bernstein goes on to say that "the word spread like wildfire, and in no time, there was pandemonium in the park. I was surrounded." (p. 171) Using word-of-mouth only and purchasing a P.O. box at the Old Chelsea Post Office, Bernstein began to leak the P.O. address (Box 21) where fans could send "checks or money orders only" to secure tickets for the August appearance of The Beatles at Shea. (p. 171)

"Three weeks to the day that I had gotten the okay from Brian Epstein," Bernstein reports, "I went to the post office to check out my P.O. box...I walked over to Box 21...and saw it was jammed." (p. 171) Bernstein discovered "three large duffel bags" all waiting for him, crammed with orders from eager, elated teens. (p. 171)

It took weeks for Sid and a group of volunteers to process these orders, but he tells us: "When all was said and done, our take came to $304,000. (Note: Mark Lewisohn validates this number in The Complete Beatles Chronicle, *p. 199.) I had kept my word to Brian. All I did was tell a couple of hundred kids where they could send money if they wanted to see The Beatles at Shea." (p. 174) And voila!*

What an incredible entrepreneurial accomplishment this was! For The Beatles, Shea Stadium would transform the face of a rather dull 1965 (which had seemed, in so many ways, merely a bland duplicate of 1964...until this). It would introduce the "super concert" to the world and alter music history forever.

***Final note:** Please read the important discussion of discrepancies in this early proposed fee and the actual, 26 April contractual fee in the footnotes. You can also view the contract below, thanks to Chuck Gunderson.*

Sources:

Interview with Sid Bernstein at Charles Rosenay's BEATexpo, Stamford, CT, 2009.
*Phone interview with Beatles North American Tour expert **Chuck Gunderson** (23 Feb. 2019) and numerous e-mail discussions. This chapter could not have been written without Chuck's constant help and advice. He also located the Shea contract and was very gracious to share it with me.*
Discussion with Bruce Spizer, New Orleans (27 Feb. 2019). Thank you, Bruce!
Taped interview with Steve Marinucci regarding his 2009 interview with Sid Bernstein. Thank you, Steve!

Lewisohn, The Complete Beatles Chronicle, *181 and 199-200.*

The Beatles, The Beatles Anthology, *185-186.*
Harry, The Ultimate Beatles Encyclopedia, *86, 319, and 600.*
Harry, The Encyclopedia of Beatles People, *45-46.*
Coleman, The Man Who Made The Beatles, *182 and 211-212.*
Bernstein, It's Sid Bernstein Calling…, *167-168 and 169-171.*
Gunderson, Chuck, Some Fun Tonight! The Backstage Story of How The Beatles Rocked America: The Historic Tours of 1964-1966, Vol. 1, *29, 72, 216, 219, 222, 225, and 272. (Henceforth referred to* as Some Fun Tonight!, Vol.1*)*
Gunderson, Chuck, Some Fun Tonight!, The Backstage Story of How The Beatles Rocked America: The Historic Tours of 1964-1966, Vol. 2, *26. (Henceforth referred to as* Some Fun Tonight!, Vol. 2*)*
Lennon, Cynthia, John, *130 and 156.*
Womack, Kenneth, The Beatles Encyclopedia, Vol. 1, *415.*
Womack, Kenneth, Maximum Volume: The Life of Beatles Producer, George Martin, *285.*
Norman, John Lennon: The Life, *353.*
Spizer, Bruce, The Beatles for Sale on Parlophone Records, *42.*
Turner, A Hard Day's Write, *61.*
Goldman, Albert, The Lives of John Lennon, *161.*
Riley, Lennon, *269.*
Schwensen, Dave, The Beatles at Shea Stadium, *39.*
Hill, John, Paul, George & Ringo, *187.*

Works Alluded to in this Chapter:

Browning, Robert, "Andrea del Sarto."

https://theclassicrocker.wordpress.com/2015/08/15/august-15-1965-the-beatles-at-shea-stadium/

https://www.deseretnews.com/article/765636310/Sid-Bernstein-who-brought-Beatles-to-Shea-dies.html Shea Stadium is discussed in this lovely tribute to the late Sid Bernstein.

https://en.wikipedia.org/wiki/I_Feel_Fine This contains chart dates for "I Feel Fine."

https://www.nytimes.com/2013/08/22/arts/music/sid-bernstein-who-helped-import-the-beatles-dies-at-95.html This is a good overview of Sid Bernstein's incredible accomplishments, including Shea Stadium, in his New York Times *obituary.*

https://tinyurl.com/yymzwpa5 Although there are a few historical errors in this film, you'll get a wonderful sense of the enthusiasm that was the late Sid Bernstein. This is a video of him talking (years after the fact) about persuading Brian Epstein to book Shea Stadium for The Beatles. Or use this QR code:

The contract for the 15 August Shea Stadium Show
Document used by kind permission of Chuck Gunderson

---

[137] Coleman, Ray, *The Man Who Made The Beatles*, 211, Gunderson, *Some Fun Tonight! The Backstage Story of How The Beatles Rocked America: The Historic Tours of 1964-1966, Vol. 2: 1965-1966*, 26, and Lewisohn, *The Complete Beatles Chronicle*, 199. Coleman says "Shea was a 55,600-seat baseball park…" Lewisohn echoes this number. Note: Gunderson's book will henceforth be referred to in the **Endnotes** as Gunderson, *Some Fun Tonight!, Vol. 2*.

[138] North American Tours guru Chuck Gunderson pointed out to me that on the 1964 tour, The Beatles had played Denver's Red Rocks Amphitheater (22,000 seats), Jacksonville's Gator Bowl (36,000 seats), and Kansas City Municipal

Coliseum (41,000 seats). So, the next logical step would have been a stadium the size of Shea with 55,600 seats. But for one reason or another — perhaps due to the inconvenient location of Red Rocks, or the weather at the Gator Bowl in the wake of Hurricane Dora, or the elevated ticket prices for the Kansas City concert — *none of these venues had sold out.* So, Brian must have harboured some real concerns about scaling up to a larger stadium in 1965,

[139] Bernstein, Sid. *It's Sid Bernstein Calling...*, 167. This segment is quoted directly from Sid Bernstein's book. According to Sid, this is word-for-word what he said during his phone call to Brian. I'm not going to footnote every line, but will footnote again at the end of the section. Sid places the call in late October. Ray Coleman places it in January.

[140] Bernstein, 167. This is the end of the quoted segment from Sid Bernstein's book in which he details his phone conversation with Brian Epstein.

[141] Coleman, *The Man Who Made The Beatles*, 211, Harry, *The Ultimate Beatles Encyclopedia*, 86, personal interview with Sid Bernstein at BEATexpo, 2009, and information given to Steve Marinucci of *Beatles Examiner*. This is a direct quote from Sid Bernstein, according to Ray Coleman.

[142] Bernstein, 167. Beginning with "We have a ballpark..." this is a direct quote from Sid Bernstein, as recorded in his book.

[143] Bernstein, 167. Direct quote from Brian Epstein, according to Bernstein.

[144] Bernstein, 167. Direct quote from Sid Bernstein.

[145] Gunderson, *Some Fun Tonight!, Vol. 2*, 26.

[146] Gunderson, *Some Fun Tonight!, Vol. 2*, 26.

[147] Gunderson, *Some Fun Tonight!, Vol. 2*, 26.

[148] Gunderson, *Some Fun Tonight!, Vol. 1*, 225. Gunderson states, "Dora had a significant impact on concert attendance. While 30,000 to 32,000 tickets had been sold, some 7,000 to 9,000 fans were no-shows due to the hurricane."

[149] Gunderson, *Some Fun Tonight!, Vol. 1*, 275.

[150] Gunderson, *Some Fun Tonight!, Vol. 1*, 275.

[151] Gunderson, *Some Fun Tonight!, Vol. 1*, 72 and 272. John agreed to the Kansas City show on 23 August 1964, the eve on the Hollywood Bowl concert in Los Angeles. The Kansas City concert took place on 17 September 1964. Thus, Charles O. Finley had *less than a month* to promote the Kansas City show, whereas the other concerts on the 1964 North American Tour had been promoted for months and months! Selling out 20,000 seats in three weeks for Kansas City's Municipal Stadium was no small feat.

[152] Gunderson, *Some Fun Tonight!, Vol. 2*, 26.

[153] https://en.wikipedia.org/wiki/I_Feel_Fine, Harry, *The Ultimate Beatles Encyclopedia*, 319, Womack, *The Beatles Encyclopedia, Vol. 1*, 415, Turner, *A Hard Day's Write*, 61, and Spizer, *Beatles for Sale on Parlophone Records*, 42. To quote Bruce Spizer: "'I Feel Fine' remained number one in *Melody Maker* for six straight weeks and charted for a total of 13...the single also debuted at number one in *NME* and topped the *BBC* and *Disc Weekly* charts."

[154] Bernstein, 167. This segment is quoted directly from Bernstein's book. I'm not going to footnote every line, but will footnote again at the end of the section.

[155] Bernstein, 167. This is the last line of this section quoted directly from Berstein's book, *It's Sid Bernstein Calling...* The same information, paraphrased, can be found in Coleman's *The Man Who Made The Beatles*, 211. And Sid repeated these words to me in an interview at BEATexpo, 2009.

[156] Coleman, *The Man Who Made The Beatles*, 211. Direct quote from Brian Esptein.

[157] Coleman, *The Man Who Made The Beatles*, 211 and personal interview with Sid Bernstein, BEATexpo, 2009. Direct quote from Sid Bernstein.

[158] Bernstein, 167. The next four quotes are directly from Bernstein's book. I will footnote again at the end of the section.

[159] Bernstein, 167. Direct quote from Brian Epstein.

[160] Bernstein, 167. This is the end of the section quoted directly from Sid Bernstein's book.

[161] Bernstein, 168. Direct quote from Sid Bernstein. Sid also repeated this in his interview with Steve Marinucci and with me. However, the **actual amount** finally agreed upon (see the Shea Stadium contract in this book) was **$85,000** plus 60% of gross. You can verify this in the contract at the end of this chapter. Thank you to Chuck Gunderson for sending me this copy of the contract.

[162] Coleman, *The Man Who Made The Beatles*, 211. Paraphrased quote from Coleman and from my personal interview with Sid Bernstein, BEATexpo, 2009.

[163] Coleman, *The Man Who Made The Beatles*, 211. Paraphrased quote from Coleman and from my personal interview with Sid Bernstein, BEATexpo, 2009.

[164] Coleman, *The Man Who Made The Beatles*, 211 and from my personal interview with Sid Bernstein, BEATexpo, 2009.

[165] Coleman, *The Man Who Made The Beatles*, 211 and from my personal interview with Sid Bernstein, BEATexpo, 2009.

[166] Bernstein, 128. The actual quote is "Fabulous! Quite astonishing, really!" But other than that one change, the wording is the same.

[167] Bernstein, 128. Direct quote from Sid Bernstein.

[168] Coleman, *Lennon*, 157, Lewisohn, *All These Years: Tune In (Expanded Edition)*, 1031-1032, and Davies, *The Beatles*, 129. Lewisohn, Coleman, and Davies point out that Brian visited Mimi Smith in Mendips to allay her fears about his management. He visited the parents of all of The Beatles.

[169] Browning, Robert, "Andrea Del Sarto," *Men and Women*.

[170] Bernstein, 168. Direct quote from Brian Epstein. Although Bernstein doesn't record the opening "Hellos" and "How are yous," I'm certain those took place. There is *not a single time* when The Beatles or Brian speak with someone (not even in an interview...see the many interviews with Brian Matthew on *Saturday Club*, for example) that they omit the courteous opening pleasantries. It simply isn't done.

[171] Coleman, *The Man Who Made The Beatles*, 211. All sentences following are direct quotes from Brian Epstein and Sid Bernstein. I'll footnote again at the end of this segment.

[172] Bernstein, 168. This was also the amount given to me by Sid Bernstein when I interviewed him at BEATexpo, 2009. So, this must have been the

initial agreement between Brian and Sid. However, looking at the actual Shea Stadium contract, one can see that Brian finally agreed upon **$85,000 with 60 percent of gross…not $100,000.**

[173] Coleman, *The Man Who Made The Beatles*, 211 and Bernstein, 168. Direct quote from Sid Bernstein, according to Coleman. Bernstein told me this story in our 2009 interview at BEATexpo but didn't use these exact words. He used similar words in his account with Steve Marinucci as well. In his book, Sid uses these words for Brian: "We require only two things. First the hundred thousand guarantee is fine, but we would like 60 percent of gross instead of 50 percent. And second we will need a fifty-thousand dollar deposit up front." All quotes essentially say the same thing.

[174] Bernstein, 168. Direct quote from Sid Bernstein. This segment is quoted exactly from Bernstein's account. I'm not going to footnote every line, but will footnote again at the end of the segment.

[175] Bernstein, 168. This is the last line of the segment quoted directly from Sid Bernstein's account.

[176] Lennon, Cynthia, *John*, 156 and The Beatles, *The Beatles Anthology*, 185. From the first time Brian traveled to London to promote The Beatles, he promised that the group was going to be "bigger than Elvis." In *The Beatles Anthology*, in 1965, referring to Shea Stadium, John says, "We wanted to be bigger than Elvis…the goal was always a few yards ahead…our goal was to be bigger than Elvis.…"

[177] Lewisohn, *The Complete Beatles Chronicle*, 181. Lewisohn states, "Brian Epstein had flown to the USA as early as 19 January to fix the dates for [The Beatles'] August American shows."

[178] Coleman, *The Man Who Made The Beatles*, 182. Coleman says that other names given to Brian were "Mister Beat" and, of course, "The Fifth Beatle."

[179] Coleman, *The Man Who Made The Beatles*, 182.

[180] Coleman, *The Man Who Made The Beatles*, 211 and Hill, *John, Paul, George & Ringo*, 187. Both Tim Hill and Ray Coleman say that Sid's funds were "tied up" because he had "just gone broke with a flop tour called Shindig at the New York Palladium. The weeklong show had featured several acts, including Gerry and the Pacemakers. He didn't want to tell Brian this bad news, which partly reflected on one of the acts in his stable." However, if one researches the "Shindig!" concert, you'll see that it did not take place until May of 1965, several months *after* this conversation took place (as shown in the poster below). Thus, the "Shindig!" show was not the reason that Sid's funds were "tight." Gunderson's explanation is the more accurate.

SHiNdiG!

FRI.   SAT.   SUNDAY
MAY 24, 8:30, MAY 15, 2:30, 8:30, MAY 16, 1:30, 5:30
GERRY AND THE PACEMAKERS
BOBBY SHERMAN • DONNA LOREN
SHIRLEY ELLIS • JOEY PAIGE
AND 3 OTHER BIG STARS
PLUS
"SHINDIG" GIRL DANCERS & "SHINDIG" BAND
YOUR HOSTS JIMMY O'NEILL AND COUSIN BRUCE MORROW
THE ACADEMY OF MUSIC $3, $4, $5 (INC. TAX)
126 E. 14th ST.   MAIL ORDERS ACCEPTED

THE ROLLING STONES
SAT.   MAY 29   1 P.M.
RETURN BY POPULAR DEMAND
AT THE ACADEMY OF MUSIC   3.50, 4.50, 5.50 (INC. TAX)
MAIL ORDERS ACCEPTED – ACADEMY OF MUSIC

THE DAVE CLARK 5
AT THE ACADEMY OF MUSIC   3.50, 4.50, 5.50 (INC. TAX)
FRI.   JUNE 18   7:30 P.M.

THE KINKS & THE MOODY BLUES
AT THE ACADEMY OF MUSIC   3.50, 4.50, 5.50 (INC. TAX)
SAT.   JUNE 19   1:00 P.M.

THE BEATLES
SUN.   AUG. 15   8:00 P.M.

SHEA STADIUM
4.50, 5.10, 5.65 (INC. TAX)
BY MAIL ONLY!
SID BERNSTEIN ENTERPRISES INC.
119 WEST 57TH STREET
NEW YORK, N.Y. 10019

AT CARNEGIE HALL
THE 1st NEW YORK FOLK FESTIVAL
WITH 40 OF THE NATION'S TOP FOLK ARTISTS
INCLUDING PHIL OCHS & CHUCK BERRY
4 DAYS JUNE 17 THRU JUNE 20
ALL TICKETS AT CARNEGIE HALL BOX OFFICE
FOR FURTHER INFORMATION PLEASE CALL 679-8281

Monday, 25 January 1965
London Airport
Heathrow, London

It was a relief to see Cyn so cheerful. For days, his wife had been out purchasing "lodge wear," "slope wear," and "naughty nighties." She'd been sorting and pre-packing.[181] Neat stacks of coordinated clothes had been carefully littered across their tiny attic bedroom, the nursery, and sitting room. On Saturday, John had even begged Alf Bicknell over, to assist with suitcases and last-minute details.[182] Cyn was a giddy vortex of activity.

This morning, when Alf had rolled up happily in the car,[183] Cyn hadn't dawdled over her customary teary goodbye. She'd left a wriggling Julian — after a quick kiss and a smile — in Lillian's unflinching grasp and Dot's loving guidance.[184] This "winter sports" holiday had become her happy distraction.[185] Cynthia thought John a hero for arranging it.

In reality, though, it had been George Martin's and Judy Lockhart-Smith's idea.[186] Or so John surmised.

"Well, you *are* slated to ski in the upcoming film, right?" Martin had supplied a practical motivation. "And you wouldn't want to appear inexpert, now would you? Certainly not clumsy...not in front of the fans."[187] The Beatles' lanky but elegant producer had lifted an eyebrow.

John had stuck his tongue in his cheek and pulled a face, though secretly, his ego had agreed. John needed experience on the slopes.

Martin's lady friend — soon to be his wife — Judy Lockhart-Smith, had suggested the perfect Swiss resort. She skied often (and well) and thought the opportunity to relax in the pristine Alps would do them all good.[188] And Cyn, who had thoroughly enjoyed her time with George and Judy during last February's American excursion,[189] couldn't wait to reconnoiter.[190] She'd raved on and on about what "a delightful couple" George and Judy were...how "beautifully matched" they always seemed.[191] Cynthia had been ready to fly off to Switzerland the very moment that the holiday had been proposed.

Now, shaking hands with their traveling companions in London Airport's private VIP lounge — the women exchanging hugs — Cynthia was flushed with anticipation. She'd teased her hair high, into a Pattie Boyd flip, and her expensive new sunglasses were tucked nicely into her blonde "do." Ever the proper Hoylake girl, she'd donned a modest, slightly flared wool skirt cinched with a narrow, leather belt just below the loosely-woven, navy blue jumper that topped a prim white under-blouse.[192] It was the height of propriety, if not fashion.

Judy was similarly attired. Both women, at heart, were helplessly conservative.

"Set for a bit of tobogganing, then?" Martin nudged the Beatle.

"Depends on what that's code for," John shot back, tossing his black wool overcoat[193] onto the lounge chair beside him.

Martin grinned. "Well, what I'm longing for is a long walk in absolutely silent snow. Truth told, I'm weary of being enclosed in one windowless studio after another. Claustrophobia, you understand. A sort of musical cabin fever."

"Yeah well, I'm just *weary*." John leaned over and extracted a packet of gum from his coat pocket. He unwrapped the minty stick and offered one to Martin. The producer shook his head, deferring in favour of a cigarette. "Ah, but we both know our fatigue holds little currency with Eppy," John went on. "If we'd stayed 'round, he would've discovered *somethin'* useful for us to do."

"He does want you successful," Martin agreed, "and to him, success arises in direct proportion to the amount of hard work one offers up."

John chewed his gum and nodded. His eyes narrowed.

"To be fair, however," Martin lifted his shoulders, "it was Brian who suggested we holiday together, actually. I suppose he thought Judy and I were decent, respectable people who could be trusted with Cynthia and you. He imagined, I suppose, we would behave ourselves."[194]

"Say it isn't so!" John groaned.

And smiling, the two men strolled towards the tea cart. There were still a few restful minutes before First Class would be called to board.

****

It's great to see John so happy! Cynthia's eyes followed him to the complimentary tea cart. Her husband sugared his tea and buttered a thick currant scone. Nodding, he chatted easily with George Martin. He even chuckled a bit, now and again.

All the way to the airport, he'd rabbited on to Alf about the "real hot chocolate" he planned to enjoy in Switzerland and the late-night rounds of Monopoly he was sure to win.[195] And just before leaving Kenwood, John had even dashed back to grab his guitar.[196]

When Cynthia had raised an eyebrow, her husband had shrugged, saying, "It's not work when *I* decide to do it! Not when it's for me, y' know."

And Cynthia had relaxed. It was wonderful to know that John still loved his music, no matter what — that fame hadn't destroyed his rock'n'roll, as it had ruined so many other things.

John had once craved the rarified air at the "toppermost of the poppermost."[197] But the blunt reality of non-stop performances and interviews, celebrity parties, and yellow journalists shadowed by pushy photographers — journalists who often, these days, besmirched The Beatles in newspapers and magazines — had now polluted that innocent longing. Even posh nights in London's swankest clubs were beginning to tire John and Cynthia.[198] They were growing jaded.

"I suppose it's the price we pay for being the toasts of Swinging London,"[199] Cynthia had smiled, trying to accept it all. "I mean, it's 1965, isn't it? We live in a mad era where people don't wait until Christmas to light their candles…they light them *every day*!"[200]

"Yeah," John had sighed, "'N some…at both ends!"[201]

It was true. John was due back in EMI Studios on 15 February, to begin work on the songs for the next film's soundtrack.[202] So, when he wasn't frantically completing his upcoming book,[203] John was scribbling lyrics on envelopes and ragged scraps of paper — stuffing them into his pockets and bedside table.[204]

Cynthia knew it was important for John to have as many (or more) hit songs as Paul did on The Beatles' LPs. John also needed to be the one who crafted the songs for George and Ringo. It was crucial to him to lead his band, to edge the others out. But Cynthia wished that for the next few days, her husband would find a way to put competition aside. She hoped he would strum his guitar, merely as diversion.

Last night when she'd "put on a private fashion show" for him — modeling the extravagant new lingerie that she'd purchased[205] — John had asked her to dance.[206] He'd held her close and vowed that he had nothing, save her, on his mind for the next fortnight. But *en route* to Heathrow, the guitar case had been propped between them on the car bench, and Cynthia realised that John was unable to shut out the world completely. As her favourite Romantic poet, William Wordsworth, had once penned: "The world [was] too much with [him], late and soon."[207] John found it impossible to live in the moment.

****

George Martin was glad that Brian had suggested this break with the Lennons. Already, before "wheels up," the four were having an outstanding time.

Recently, John and he had become quite companionable. Ringo was taken up with affairs in Liverpool — his fiancée, Maureen Cox, Martin supposed. And George Harrison had never warmed up to him as much as the others. Not really. Paul was busy traipsing[208] from gallery to gallery with John Dunbar, listening to Stockhausen and living in Jane Asher's glistening *avant garde* world. But John — being married and a father, writing his second book, and remodeling a Tudor home in the stockbroker belt — seemed approachable. In fact, Martin had begun to see him as a bit of a "pipe and slippers man."[209]

Judy had invited the Lennons to dinner a time or two,[210] and alternately, George and she had motored out to Kenwood for a glass of something wonderful and a stroll through the renovations. And every time, their rapport had been easy and delightful. John had seemed quite taken with Judy's upper-class manner,[211] and Judy was bowled over by John's irreverent Scouse humour.[212] Of course, they adored Cynthia, one and all. Sweet, agreeable, interesting. Judy had dubbed Cyn: "quite the lady."

Now, as George fastened his seatbelt and tried to find a way to fit his endless legs beneath the seat in front of him,[213] he felt more content than he'd been in a long time. This holiday was going to be remarkable — he predicted it would be one to remember.

****

Brian — or rather, NEMS — had organised it all beautifully. The holiday-makers were flown into Zurich, driven directly to the railway station, and promptly shown to their private car on the bright, candy-red train bound for St. Moritz.

For the next three hours,[214] as slanted, afternoon sunlight warmed silvery lakes and undulating, snow-swept valleys, the four Brits sat back, took tea, and absorbed the hushed magnificence of the Alps. Grander than they'd ever imagined — more imposing and more lovely — the alabaster mountains suspended ordinary conversation.[215] If the four spoke at all, it was just above a whisper.

Switzerland's snow-topped peaks were soft and welcoming in a way that America's Rockies had not been.

Here, John thought, *...well, it's a fuggin' snow globe, isn't it? Christmas...complete with sugar-frosted trees!*

And the farther the train wound from Zurich towards the secluded bliss of St. Moritz, the more tranquil the four travelers became — the more deeply they breathed, the more they smiled and jested with one another. They became their best selves. So much so that George Martin hated mentioning the inevitable.

"Once we arrive in the Palace Hotel, you know,"[216] he muttered, leaning over to John, "we'll get Brian's required photo shoot out of the way...dispense with it as soon as Cyn and you can conveniently change into ski gear.[217] The photographers'll want that dramatic light just before sunset, of course. And you'll want this publicity set aside, so that you can enjoy the rest of your time without interference."[218]

Brian had compromised with the European press, conceding a photo session just outside the hotel with John and Cynthia, George and Judy. Additionally, he'd promised them an exclusive shoot with the Lennons on the slopes.[219] But the placatory move wasn't completely unselfish; Brian would use the photos to promote The Beatles' new film and to dispel the ever-lurking rumours that John and Cynthia were divorcing.

It helped very little that John had vehemently denied the ugly scuttlebutt. (When asked by Brian Matthew of the BBC, "What does your wife think about the rumours that you're getting a divorce?", John had swiftly shot back, "No, she knows I'm not divorced because I keep seein' her every day!")[220]

But bored journalists — hungry for something dicey on the Fab Four — kept insisting that the Lennons were "on the ropes." Brian hoped that a bit of documentary film and some candid photos would quiet at least some of the unfounded accusations.

"Right, John and Cynthia Lennon, Take 1!" John rasped, with a sneer.

"I'm sure it won't be as awful as you think," Judy offered, her Queen's English making everything sound like a royal decree.[221]

But John's jaw had already set. "I've heard that before: 'This won't hurt a bit, lad!' That's how it goes."

Regardless, there was nothing for it. The photo shoot was a necessity. They had it to do.

****

Badrutt's Palace Hotel
Serlas 27
St. Moritz
Switzerland

As soon as the Palace Hotel's white-gloved chauffeur had transported them via Rolls Royce from the St. Moritz station along the snaking road to the enchanting Palace Hotel entrance,[222] the reporters were on them. They were panting and eager. They begged the celebrities to "hurry up and save the light."

Whisking rapidly through the hotel's Grand Hall laden with gilt mirrors, antique bowls, ginger jars heaving and lavish with fresh flowers — their petals falling onto exotic, inlaid marble floors — the Lennons hurried to the rambling suite that they would share with George and Judy.[223] They freshened up. They donned their new ski wear and clipped the tags. And in record time, "the Beatle and his wife" were back in the hotel's entrance, smiling pleasantly alongside their private ski instructor, the resort's polished manager, along with George and Judy.[224] It was the first of many holiday snaps; for the next hour-and-a-half, John and Cynthia belonged to the press.

First, there were the "action" shots: John gracelessly donning his skis; John prat-falling into drifted snow; John grinning astride a toboggan; John at the helm of a colourful snowmobile, and John and Cyn posed, skiing side-by-side.[225] It was all tightly-scripted. The press grinned when The Leader Beatle agreed to "play the fool." It made Lennon seem more approachable. It made him seem like them.

Then, as the first pale purples began to sift down over Badrutt's historic hotel, the photographers arranged more saccharine shots: John tying his wife's ski boot; Cynthia playfully shoving her husband into the snow; John pulling Cyn on a wooden toboggan, and Cynthia and John laughing together, their arms draped across each other's shoulders. These were glimpses that Cynthia's newly-formed "Cynthia Lennon Fan Club" would gush over, cherish.[226]

At last, as the sun began to lower — providing theatrical shadows for the scores of glinting lenses — Cynthia and John were asked to sit together, turning towards the press and peering over the back of a quaint wooden bench towards the Engadin mountains. At first, the shots were casual: Cynthia pointing out a lone skier racing back to the lodge, the last adventurer on the slopes for the day. Then, there were several posed "smile at nothings" for less-imaginative periodicals and newspapers. At last, came more intimate shots: the Lennons laughing together over some private joke; the couple staring into one another's eyes, and finally, John and Cyn trudging away across the snow, bound for what Cynthia termed some "much-needed time together."[227] Husband and wife, silent and holding hands. The portrait was lovely…poignant.

John and Cynthia in Switzerland, January 1965
Photograph purchased from Alamy.com

"Amazing that fame hasn't taken its toll on *that* relationship." A hollow-cheeked reporter peered over the top of lowered spectacles.

"Yeah, they still seem quite taken with one another," said a hawk-nosed photographer, winding the long length of film up inside his camera.

"I don't know," one of the rag writers predicted hungrily. "I sense a few crazes and cracks in that slick, shiny varnish."

But none of them could have known a thing, really…because

for the most part, John kept his dissatisfactions hidden away.

****

The following morning, there was one last chore to perform before the Lennons were left to it: John and Cyn were to star in a short documentary, showing off their newly-acquired skiing acumen. Fortunately, John had hired a private instructor for all four of them,[228] and after a late breakfast *en suite*, they'd learned the basics, practicing over and over.

Judy stayed alongside Cynthia, assisting her and giggling together over their "dishy" Swedish instructor.[229] But John, who'd never been particularly adept at any sport, was surprisingly — at first go — "a natural" on the slopes.[230] He was ready to film and dismiss the press long before Cyn felt confident enough to try it. In fact, it was mid-afternoon before she was really courageous enough to appear on camera.

Then, securing scarves and gear, the Lennons trudged into position. In his black, bulky-knit longshoreman's cap, John looked right into the camera and jammed his tongue into his lower lip, smirking.[231] He lowered his ski goggles slowly, mysteriously, and swiveled coyly away.

Cynthia, for her part, tediously tied her white fur bonnet and zipped the new white ski suit, replete with colourful, interlocking diamond patterns and matching gloves. She adjusted her sunglasses and for a time, skied dutifully alongside her husband.[232]

But on John's cue, Cynthia spurred into the lead. Darting past him, she giggled and upstaged the famous rhythm guitarist, whilst John complied by pretending to fall back. He even managed an authentic-looking tumble — his skis splaying awkwardly. John squinted, as though stunned. He mugged and lolled about in the snow.

And the press loved it. They snickered and filmed and thought the footage priceless. It was good enough, the press corps decided, to call it "a wrap." And so, they did.

John nodded. He shook hands and thanked them all. He signed a few autographs ("For my children, of course...") and waved his goodbyes.

Eppy, he thought, *would be proud. "The Beatle" has done his bit. Now, there're twelve whole days left with nothin' but sex 'n sleep 'n snow 'n silence. I'm left with m' wife, m' friends, and m' self. Oh, yeah... 'n m' guitar.*

"John and Cyn" time,
St, Moritz, Switzerland, 1965
Photograph purchased from Alamy.com,
#OY7154065
****

After it happened, it seemed so irresponsible, such a ludicrous mishap. George Martin loved to quote America's Ben Franklin who talked about people who "paid too much for the whistle" — who gave more than they should for something inconsequential.[233] And *this* was truly that. The peer approval Martin had endeavoured to snare had become "a last laugh" on him. Now he felt silly: a right buffoon. And really, it was all for nothing.

It had all started with a round of hot chocolate drinks liberally spiked with liqueur…and then another round or so.[234] Relaxed and silly, John had emerged from his shower with his hair wet, mussed, and strung down over his eyes. Wearing only black ski tights and jutting out his bottom teeth,[235] John had pranced about their shared suite in a nimble imitation of comedian Max Wall's famous stage walk.[236] Cynthia and Judy had fallen over in roaring fits of laughter.[237]

Secretly, George had been a tad jealous. He was used to being the centre of attention, the one in command. But John Lennon was well-known for stealing one's thunder.

So, not to be outdone, George had scurried off to his room and donned his own black tights, topping them with a pair of boxer shorts "fluffed out a bit to look like a tutu skirt."[238] He'd pulled Judy's wide "Bandar" around his head,[239] chuckling at himself in the mirror.

Then, opening the door to the sitting room, George had flung himself outward, attempting something light and aerial, something between a *pas-de-deux*[240] and "a leap with an *entrechat* in the middle."[241] Whatever he'd intended, the step was outlandish…and disastrous. Landing awkwardly on the side of his foot,[242] George had collapsed in "an agonized heap." And then, he'd lain extremely still.[243]

"George, you *do* look an idiot!"[244] Judy had sputtered, giggling furiously, unable to hear the brittle snap, the sound of a twig breaking.[245]

The others, too, continued cackling. There was a mad round of applause. And cheers. None of Martin's admirers suspected a thing. Only when George failed to move did they, one by one, fall silent.

"Are you quite all right, George?"[246] Judy had been the first to suspect.

"Martin?" John had taken a step in his producer's direction, his voice as stern as his face.

"Shall we ring the hotel medic?" Cynthia had suggested, as calmly as she could.

"You *fools!*" came the small, tight response from the man on the floor. "I've broken my foot!"[247]

And the rest of the evening had unfolded in a long and painful blur.

****

Tuesday, 26 January 1965
Badrutt's Palace Hotel
St. Moritz
Switzerland

6.30 p.m.

John was sitting on the bed and softly strumming his guitar, his head over the fretboard; his brow, furrowed.[248] It was the hundredth time Cyn had heard this latest creation, though she had tried not to. John kept rehearsing it over and over, honing the number for George Martin's ear.[249] And Cyn could hardly stand it.

"I-I-I once had a girl, or should I say, she once had me..." John sang it again, as if she were deaf...or dumb, in the popular vernacular. And Cynthia was neither. She'd been an exceptional student at Liverpool College of Art.[250] And not only was she smart — she was perceptive.

Every time John sang the words "Norwegian wood," she flinched. A memory sprang to mind — a vivid image of svelte, blonde, German Sonny Freeman who, in the post-war world, dubbed herself "Norwegian." Cynthia recalled the gorgeous model's chummy relationship with John,[251] and his clear attraction to the exotic neighbour downstairs, who lived in a lovely, wood-paneled flat.[252] Cynthia also recalled Bob Freeman's red-faced quarrel with John back in the Lennons' Emperor's Gate mansionette.[253] The ugly confrontation had left John scowling; Sonny, red-faced; and Bob, storming out of the mansionette with his weeping wife in tow.

Cynthia had never forgotten the scene — her intuition telling her that the fight must have erupted over an affair between John and Sonny. But when Cyn had gathered the courage to ask her husband what their friends had wanted, John had merely shrugged and run off to his music room upstairs.[254] He'd given Cynthia no answers at all.

Now, hearing John crow about a "one-night stand" with some "Norwegian" girl — it was difficult to bear. The very fact that he could sit right brazenly, in the midst of their romantic holiday, and rehearse a ballad about a real (or even vividly imagined!) infidelity whilst his wife pretended to curl her hair in the mirrored armoire[255]…it was an affront.

John's utter disrespect, Cynthia bit her lip, *is even worse than the lyrics.*

Cynthia was almost certain that John would unveil the song for the injured and restless George Martin this evening, offering it up to assuage the producer who, upon their return from the slopes that afternoon, had exclaimed, "If anyone else asks me where my accident happened and on which mountain, I'll scream! I've never felt such a fool in all my life!"[256]

And so, steeling herself for such a moment, Cynthia dressed carefully and slipped into kitten heels. She rehearsed a blank face — a visage devoid of comprehension or emotion.

But it was a hard-won ruse.

Cynthia had failed her June 1962 teacher's examination only because she'd sacrificed study to share precious time with John in Hamburg.[257] She'd always been a conscientious student, a clever girl.[258] In fact, she'd kept John afloat in college for years, happily completing his lettering homework for him whilst he larked about with his mad group of friends and the band.

So, one must wonder, Cyn mused, *what prompts John at this stage of the proceedings to think me naïve…unable to grasp the simplest of lyrics.*

She wondered if her husband was trying to force her hand and instigate a massive row…or if he just needed a way to confess.[259] Whatever the case, Cynthia refused to be complicit, to react. She wouldn't take the bait.

Cyn loved her life; she loved her son; and she loved her husband. No matter what John's motivation this evening, she wasn't about to toss it all away over a petty fling that had ended months ago.[260]

The bird who had flown wasn't returning, and that, Cynthia thought, was that.

****

8.00 p.m.

George Martin could hardly believe his ears. John was "owning up to having an affair," with Cynthia sitting just a few feet away.[261] He was singing the words to this haunting new song as if they were harmless lyrics to a ditty instead of a litany of infidelity — a destructive revelation.

Nor was Cynthia fazed. Instead, she sat composed and disengaged, staring into the cosy fire that crackled in the green-tiled corner fireplace.[262] When the song ended, she politely leaned towards Judy and began a quiet conversation.

"I thought that'd cheer you up."[263] John rested his hands on top of his guitar and swiveled towards his producer. "Y' know...make y' feel better, knowin' I'm still workin' away, even on holiday, as it were."

"Well..." George looked meaningfully from John to Cynthia and back again. He wasn't sure what to say. Paul was the songwriter who employed fictional scenarios for his lyrics. John, almost always, was strictly autobiographical. "It's rather, um...well, it's a very bitter, little story, isn't it?"[264]

"Yeah, right." John's eyes darted, unbidden, to Cyn as well. One could see he was trying to keep the conversation noncommittal. "A bit like havin' a broken foot on a winter sports holiday, I suppose."

"Yes," Martin nodded. They understood one another, even if the wives did not.[265] "Very intriguing, that song, but slightly sick, which is indeed apt to me nursing this sick foot of mine."[266]

"Right...the very same," John said.

"And it's called?"

"This Bird Has Flown."[267] John began strumming it again.

"Uhm...why don't you play another?" George was eager to move on. He liked the new song; it owned an evocative melody — a lingering, emotional echo — but he was afraid that the composition could wound. It held awful, terrible possibilities.

"Yeah, all right, well, I've got another, then…a bit of a rocker, as it were." And backing a second set of lyrics,[268] words that seemed to be fictional — as indeed, Martin hoped the first ones were — John began to strum enthusiastically.

"…the girl that's drivin' me mad is goin' awaaaay, yeah! She's got a ticket to ride! She's got a ticket to ri-i-ide!"[269] John grinned, busking to distract Martin from the throbbing ache that was sabotaging the producer's holiday.

This new song was terribly infectious. *A toe-tapper, if one had a functional toe to tap,* Martin thought. *It's a powerhouse — one of John's best yet!*

But even as he smiled and nodded, Martin found it difficult to shrug off the discomfort — a nasty feeling of unease for the prim and gracious Cynthia Lennon, who so obviously loved her husband and who had everything to lose if he tired of her and walked away.

George — undergoing his own marital woes — hoped that Lennon would use sound judgement in determining the course of his family's future…but discretion, clearly, was not John's long suit.

****

Sunday, 7 February 1965
London Airport
Heathrow

As Judy assisted the hobbling George — his leg in an unwieldy plaster cast — through Customs,[270] Cynthia padded alongside John[271] and said as little as possible. The holiday was over.

John was in a swivet of some sort. He'd said next to nothing on the flight home. He'd chain-smoked and scribbled away furiously on bits of paper, snarling curt answers to any conversation Cynthia had tried to initiate.[272]

At these times, Cynthia clung to the good days — to the fun they'd had over the last two weeks — to the laughs they'd shared with George and Judy, tobogganing or playing Monopoly[273] — to the evenings alone, cuddling with John on a moonlit, horse-drawn sleigh ride or talking on a blanket beside their bedroom fire, or sharing unhurried romantic nights

This morning's brusque and silent John made his appearance rather regularly before periods of pressure: before John's return to work, before moments of high expectation.[274] Cynthia just kept telling herself it had nothing to do with her — it had only to do with "Them," the suits and the arrogant press.[275]

As John clomped through the airport — his newspaper folded under one arm whilst he lit yet another cig — he scanned for the intrusive reporters.[276] Any moment now, they'd be on top of Cyn and him both, barking to know every detail of their time away. But increasingly jealous of the shred of privacy he still possessed, John was already close-lipped.

Cynthia knew, he was bracing for the rush at the end of the corridor. He was steeled against that instant when the door would swing open and he'd be thrust, once more, into "The World of The Beatles" — that frenetic kingdom where John, the lover; John, the husband; and John, the friend, would cease.[277] *That* John would retreat into the remote, protective place where he could hide. And Cynthia would follow him there, to give shelter.

The Palace Hotel where John and Cynthia, George Martin and Judy Lockhart-Smith vacationed, January 1965

Photograph from Wikimedia Commons
Photogrpaher Kecko from Switzerland (Rheintal SG) - St. Moritz - Badrutt's Palace
CC BY 2.0

Notes!

How accurate is this portrayal of John as struggling with depression and the tensions of Beatlemania in early 1965?

One need only note the differences between this date in 1965 and the same date in 1964 to see how much Beatlemania had affected John. On 7 February 1964, The Beatles were landing, for the first time, in New York City just prior to that first Ed Sullivan show! That afternoon, John was all smiles, beaming at his new-found fame. But only twelve months later, he had penned "I'm A Loser" and "Norwegian Wood." Truly, Beatlemania had taken its toll.

Those who knew John best concur. Paul McCartney states that John was "feeling a bit constricted by The Beatle thing." (Spitz, 555) And George Harrison said that John's worsening vision was also playing a significant role in his dark and gloomy moods. "He was paranoid about being short-sighted," George stated. "We'd have to take him into a club and lead him to his seat, so that he could go in without his glasses and look cool." (p. 554) After years of 'the Beatle façade," John was growing tired of the charade.

In The Beatles, *biographer Bob Spitz observes that "John plowed the tremendous emotional upheaval [of 1965] into his songs. He said 'Help!' grew out of one of the 'deep depressions' he went through, during which he fought the desire to 'jump out the window'...But dissatisfied with the direction The Beatles were taking, coupled with his appearance and dispiriting marriage, he was left feeling despondent and 'hopeless' during the writing of [the song 'Help!']. 'I was fat and depressed, and I was crying out for 'Help.'" (p. 555) Indeed, Spitz qualifies John in early 1965 as being "demoralized and depressed." (p. 554)*

Sources:

Lewisohn, The Complete Beatles Chronicle, *183.*
Lewisohn, The Beatles: Day by Day, *58.*
Harry, The John Lennon Encyclopedia, *658-659.*
Lennon, Cynthia, A Twist of Lennon, *13, 132, and 134-135.*
Lennon, Cynthia, John, *90, 137, 150, 156, 161-162, and 166.*
Norman, John Lennon: The Life, *326 and 388.*
Norman, Shout!, *329.*
Coleman, Lennon,*177 and 222. There are several photos of John and Cyn on the slopes on p. 221.*
Miles, The Beatles' Diary, Vol. 1, *188.*
Womack, Maximum Volume: The Life of Beatles Producer, George Martin, *245-246.*
Badman, Keith, The Beatles: Off the Record, *138-139 and 148.*

Bicknell, 27.
Winn, John C., Way Beyond Compare, *293.*
Spitz, 553-555.
Goldman, 184-185.
Connolly, 122.
Burns, Kathy, The Guitar's All Right for a Hobby, John, *6.*
Hill, John, Paul, George & Ringo, *184-185.*
Thomas, Gareth, John Lennon: The Illustrated Biography, *92.*
Sheff, David, The Playboy Interviews with John Lennon and Yoko Ono, *150-151.*
Riley, Lennon, *268.*

Works Alluded to in this Chapter:

Franklin, Benjamin, "The Whistle."
Wordsworth, William, "The World Is Too Much With Us."

https://www.badruttspalace.com/en This is the official website for Badrutt's Palace Hotel where John and Cynthia spent their holiday in January 1965.

http://www.thebeatlessongbysong.com/NorwegianScript.html This website furnishes information about the song, "Norwegian Wood."

https://commons.wikimedia.org/w/index.php?curid=37425059 This is the source of the photo of The Palace Hotel, used by permission.

https://www.youtube.com/watch?v=2gGpq3ceEbU This is British comedian Max Wall doing his famous comedy walk that John was imitating just before George Martin was injured.

https://www.beatlesbible.com/1965/02/07/john-cynthia-lennon-return-england-switzerland/ This is a brief account of 7 February 1965.

https://www.npr.org/2015/04/02/397057478/in-her-life-after-john-cynthia-lennon-didnt-stop-loving-him This is an incredible NPR interview with Cynthia Lennon about her married life and the pressures from other women, the demands of John's job, and the press.

https://www.youtube.com/watch?v=Yex7VJ9QkcQ This video shows all of the photos mentioned in this chapter as well as the footage of John and Cynthia skiing.
Or use this QR code:

[181] Lennon, Cynthia, *A Twist of Lennon*, 134-135, Hill, *John, Paul, George & Ringo*, 185, and Thomas, 92. In her early autobiography, Cynthia admits that prior to this holiday, she had never been skiing before. In Hill's and Thomas's pictoral chronicles, she is pictured wearing a lovely white ski outfit with diamond-patterned bodice and sleeves and ski boots. In many online photographs, she also sports a furry white hat that tied beneath the chin.

[182] Bicknell, 27. Alf says that John rang him on 23 January to ask if Alf could drive over and "help him and Cynthia pack some things for a trip they're planning next week."

[183] Bicknell, 27.

[184] Riley, Tim, *Lennon*, 268.

[185] Lennon, Cynthia, *A Twist of Lennon*, 134 and Norman, *John Lennon: The Life*, 388. Cynthia calls the holiday "a break from the pressure."

[186] https://heavy.com/entertainment/2016/03/george-martin-wife-judy-lockhart-smith-george-martin-wife-son-giles-age-pictures/ This website provides a brief biography of Judy Lockhart-Smith, who at this juncture was George Martin's lady friend. Later, she married Martin, and they were together 50 years.

[187] Riley, *Lennon*, 268.

[188] Badman, Keith, *The Beatles: Off the Record*, 138.

[189] Lennon, Cynthia, *John*, 137. During the American trip in February 1964, Cynthia refers to George Martin as "tall, debonair, polite, and charming." She calls Judy, "lovely, very old school — like a headgirl with a heart of gold."

[190] Womack, Kenneth, *Maximum Volume: The Life of Beatles Producer, George Martin*, 245.

[191] Lennon, Cynthia, *A Twist of Lennon*, 134.

[192] Thomas, Gareth, *John Lennon: The Illustrated Bibliography*, 94, Hill, *John, Paul, George & Ringo*, 186, and https://tinyurl.com/y5v6uatz. The photo in these sources is one of Cynthia dressed to return to London. But she had a habit of wearing the same traveling outfit to and from a destination. When she traveled to America in Feb. 1964, she wore the same outfit on the airplane, coming and going. Similarly, when she traveled to Tahiti in May 1964, she wore the same traveling outfit. Chances are very likely that the same thing took place here.

[193] https://tinyurl.com/y5v6uatz This photo shows John's coat.

[194] Norman, *John Lennon: The Life*, 388. This is a direct quotation from George Martin.

[195] Norman, *John Lennon: The Life*, 388.

[196] Norman, *John Lennon: The Life*, 388.

[197] Coleman, *Lennon*, 177. Coleman explains that in the early days of The Beatles, "John used to recite the short poem which he had concocted. It was a little rhyme that…became even truer than he ever dared to hope:
John: Where are we going fellas?
Chorus: To the top, Johnny, to the TOP!
John: And where is the the top, fellas?
Chorus: To the toppermost of the poppermost!"

[198] Lennon, Cynthia, *John,* 150. This is a close paraphrase of Cynthia's own words.

[199] Lennon, Cynthia, *John,* 150. This is a direct quote from Cynthia Lennon.

[200] Lennon, Cynthia, *John,* 156. This is a direct quote from Cynthia Lennon.

[201] Lennon, Cynthia, *John,* 156. This is a direct quote from Cynthia Lennon.

[202] Lewisohn, *The Complete Beatles Chronicle*, 183.

[203] Riley, *Lennon*, 268.

[204] Connolly, 108 and in my 2018 interview with Electra II head stewardess Bettie Westmoreland Birdsall, Bettie told me about John's habit of placing clean bits of paper in his right shirt pocket, scribbling on them during flights, and then placing them, completed, into his left pocket. Connolly tells us that John kept all of his childhood and teen creations in his bedside table at Mendips, so it's safe to assume that he did the same at Kenwood.

[205] Lennon, Cynthia, *John,* 166.

[206] Lennon, Cynthia, *John,* 166.

[207] Wordsworth, William, "The World is Too Much With Us," 1802.

[208] http://www.badruttspalace.com/en The train is depicted here.

[209] Womack, *Maximum Volume: The Life of Beatles Producer, George Martin,* 245.

[210] Womack, *Maximum Volume: The Life of Beatles Producer, George Martin,* 245.

[211] Connolly, 122.

[212] Womack, *Maximum Volume: The Life of Beatles Producer, George Martin,* 245.

[213] https://www.famousbirthsdeaths.com/george-martin-bio-net-worth-facts/ Although he looks much taller in the photographs from the St. Moritz holiday, George Martin was 6'2".

[214] Zurich is 124 miles from St. Moritz. By train, the trip was a bit over three hours. To see the landscape that John, Cyn, George, and Judy viewed, go here: https://www.bing.com/imhages/search?q=St.+Moritz+Winter&FORM=IDINTS

[215] http://www.badruttspalace.com All descriptions of the countryside surrounding St. Moritz come from wonderful photos on this website.

[216] Norman, *John Lennon: The Life*, 388, and Badman, 138. George Martin is quoted as saying "John and I went on a skiing holiday together to St. Moritz, very posh, and we stayed at the Palace Hotel, even more posh, and we had great fun!"

[217] Womack, *Maximum Volume: The Life of Beatles Producer, George Martin,* 246, Thomas, 92, and Norman, *John Lennon: The Life*, 388. Norman says that Brian tried to plan a "low-key" trip for John with "no press intrusion." And the easiest way to accomplish that was to have a photo session right at the start.

218 Womack, *Maximum Volume: The Life of Beatles Producer, George Martin,* 245.
219 Womack, *Maximum Volume: The Life of Beatles Producer, George Martin,* 245.
220 "Riding on a Bus," *Live at the BBC, Vol. 1, Side One.* Direct quotes from Brian Matthew and John Lennon.
221 Connolly, 122 and Womack, *Maximum Volume: The Life of Beatles Producer, George Martin,* 245. Connolly points out that John was always "attracted to sophistication" and Womack says that John loved to hear Judy read his poetry because she had a "cut glass accent."
222 http://www.badruttspalace.com/en This is the official website of Badrutt's Palace Hotel. All information about the hotel as well as the descriptions of the Grand Hall, the rooms, etc. will be taken directly from the facts provided on this site.
223 Womack, *Maximum Volume: The Life of Beatles Producer, George Martin,* 245 and Badman,138. George Martin says, "John and Cynthia and my wife and I had a suite, which was very, very comfortable and very expensive, and [John] paid for a private ski instructor."
224 https://www.youtube.com/watch?v=Yex7VJ9QkcQ This is one of many photos that can be seen in this touching video detailing John and Cynthia's trip to Switzerland with George and Judy in January 1965.
225
https://www.bing.com/images/search?q=john+and+cynthia+lennon+in+switze rland+1965&id=3466B67A41C584B1CB7BA35F1FEAE09E837E7FFC&FO RM=IQFRBA The photos detailed in this paragraph and in the next few paragraphs can all be seen at this website.
226 Lennon, Cynthia, *A Twist of Lennon,* 132, Thomas, 94, and Burns, Kathy, *The Guitar's All Right as a Hobby, John,* p. 6. Jane, who became a pen-pal of Mimi's in the process, was one of the founders of "The Cyn Lennon Beatle Club." In fact, she wrote to Cynthia to ask her permission to organise the group, and Cynthia responded, sending Kathy a black-and-white photo of The Beatles with this written on the back side: "Best of luck with your Cyn Lennon Club! Love Cynthia & Julian"
227 Thomas, 92.
228 Badman, 138.
229 Lennon, Cynthia, *A Twist of Lennon,* 134. Cynthia refers to their ski instructor as "a very dishy Swiss and obviously fond of the ladies."
230 Hill, *John, Paul, George & Ringo,* 184 and Thomas, 93.
231 https://www.youtube.com/watch?v=xf76s5NSjAk This is the video being described. I'm not going to footnote every sentence, but will footnote again at the end of this section.
232 Winn, John C., *Way Beyond Compare,* 293. This is part of the short clip filmed by ITV on the slopes at St. Moritz.
233 https://www.thoughtco.com/the-whistle-by-benjamin-franklin-1688774 This is the short essay by Benjamin Franklin to which Martin is referring. It is entitled "The Whistle."
234 Lennon, Cynthia, *A Twist of Lennon,* 134 and Womack, *Maximum Volume: The Life of Beatles Producer, George Martin,* 245-246.

[235] Badman, 139. Direct quote from Sir George Martin.

[236] https://www.youtube.com/watch?v=2gGpq3ceEbU This is British comedian Max Wall doing his famous comedy act and walk that John was imitating.

[237] Womack, *Maximum Volume: The Life of Beatles Producer, George Martin*, 246.

[238] Womack, *Maximum Volume: The Life of Beatles Producer, George Martin*, 246. Direct quote from George Martin.

[239] Badman, 139, Womack, *Maximum Volume: The Life of Beatles Producer, George Martin*, 246. Badman quotes Martin saying, "Not to be outdone…I wore a pair of boxer shorts on top of my tights, which stuck out a bit like a tutu skirt on a ballet dancer. I put on my wife's Bandar round my head and entered the room in a beautiful Nureyev type entrance, and I sped across the room, did a huge leap and landed on the side of my foot."

[240] Lennon, Cynthia, *A Twist of Lennon*, 135.

[241] Womack, *Maximum Volume: The Life of Beatles Producer, George Martin*, 246.

[242] Badman, 139. Many sources say that George Martin broke his toe. Martin clearly says that he landed on the side of his foot and goes on to say that he broke the foot, not the toe.

[243] Lennon, Cynthia, *A Twist of Lennon*, 135. Direct quote from Cynthia Lennon.

[244] Lennon, Cynthia, *A Twist of Lennon*, 135. Direct quote from Cynthia Lennon, repeating the words she remembers Judy Lockhart-Smith saying.

[245] Womack, *Maximum Volume: The Life of Beatles Producer, George Martin*, 246. Direct quote from Sir George Martin.

[246] Lennon, Cynthia, *A Twist of Lennon*, 135.

[247] Badman, 139. "You fools! I've broken my foot!" is a direct quote from Sir George Martin.

[248] Badman, 138. Sir George Martin is quoted as saying that John composed "Norwegian Wood" on the skiing holiday in Switzerland "in the hotel bedroom."

[249] Harry, *The John Lennon Encyclopedia*, 658. Harry states that "This Bird Has Flown" (later "Norwegian Wood") was written in the hotel room John shared with Cynthia whilst they were on holiday in St. Moritz.

[250] Lennon, Cynthia, *A Twist of Lennon*, 13.

[251] Lennon, Cynthia, *John*, 161-162 and Norman, *John Lennon: The Life*, 24. Norman explains Sonny Freeman's heritage by saying, "Sonny had been born in Berlin but, growing up in Britain in the postwar years, preferred to say she was Norwegian." Norman goes on to point out that "The Freemans' apartment [at Emperor's Gate] was mostly paneled in wood."

[252] Norman, *John Lennon: The Life*, 326. Norman says, "Often, after a night's clubbing, [John] still wouldn't be tired, but happily sat up until dawn in the Freemans' wood-paneled apartment, talking to his beautiful faux-Norwegian neighbor 'about things life life and death, the way you always do when you're young.'"

[253] Lennon, Cynthia, *John,* 161.

[254] Lennon, Cynthia, *John*, 162. Cynthia writes of the argument beween John and Bob Freeman, "When John came back into the kitchen I asked him what had been going on, but he shrugged and disappeared upstairs to his music room. It was never mentioned between us again, but not long afterward I heard that Bob and Sonny were divorcing. I couldn't escape the conclusion that she'd had an affair with John, although I never had any proof."

[255] https://www.badruttspalace.com/en

[256] Lennon, *A Twist of Lennon*, 135.

[257] Lennon, Cynthia, *John*, 90.

[258] Lennon, Cynthia, *A Twist of Lennon*, 13. Cynthia states, "[Phyllis McKenzie and I] were both very conscientious; we were at [Liverpool College of Art] to work, and we were not amused by [John's] rowdy lot."

[259] Harry, *The John Lennon Encyclopedia*, 659. These are the very reasons John gives for writing "This Bird Has Flown." Harry quotes John as saying, "I wanted to get the affair out of my head and on to paper, but not in a way that Cyn would suspect what I was really on about. Yes, I was hiding this love away, but I was also getting it off my chest right in front of everyone's nose, which I find exciting."

[260] Lennon, Cynthia, *John*, 162. Cynthia states, "…I began to wonder if John had had affairs with Alma [Cogan], Sonny [Freeman] and a couple of other women who were around us at the time. **I decided to let it go.** I believed that John and I were strong enough together to come through anything, and that unless an infidelity was staring me in the face I wouldn't ask him or look for evidence. I knew that if I tried to confront him he would walk away and I'd end up tormenting myself. In any case, I wasn't the sort of of woman to be controlling and possessive. I knew I was the bedrock of John's stability and that he loved me, and **I let that be enough.**" The highlights are mine.

[261] Norman, *John Lennon: The Life*, 388. Sir George Martin says, "I remember hearing the words and not believing my ears…[John] was owning up to having an affair, and obviously not very long previously. And Cyn was a few feet away, not understanding any of it."

[262] https://www.badruttspalace.com/en This is an exact description of the hotel bedroom fireplace.

[263] Riley, *Lennon*, 268.

[264] Womack, *Maximum Volume: The Life of Beatles Producer, George Martin*, 246. The term "very bitter little story" is a direct quote from Sir George Martin.

[265] Norman, *John Lennon: The Life*, 388 and Harry, *The John Lennon Encyclopedia*, 658.

[266] Badman, 139. George Martin says of "Norwegian Wood," "It had a slightly sick lyric, which was apt to me nursing my injured toe."

[267] Womack, *Maximum Volume: The Life of Beatles Producer, George Martin*, 246.

[268] Badman, 148.

[269] Womack, *Maximum Volume: The Life of Beatles Producer, George Martin*, 246. Womack states, "Then, according to Martin, John 'debuted another new composition, 'Ticket to Ride.' I liked it straight away. John said he would get together with Paul as soon as he got back to London and finish it off.'"

[270] Womack, *Maximum Volume: The Life of Beatles Producer, George Martin,* 246.

[271] https://tinyurl.com/y6fpwyld

[272] https://tinyurl.com/y6fpwyld This is the 7 Feb. 1965 photo of the incident I'm describing. Look at John's face, Cynthia's face, the newspaper, cigs, etc. A photo is, indeed, worth a thousand words.

[273] Coleman, *Lennon,* 222.

[274] Norman, *Shout!,* 329. Norman says that Cynthia knew John was struggling with depression in 1965. In fact, she referred to that year as a "trough" in their marriage "at the height of Beatlemania, when no one thought to ask why the idol of millions would write a song entitled 'Help!'"

[275] Coleman, *Lennon,* 222. Cynthia says "I could see [John] felt under pressure, but I didn't know how much. But had had enjoyed the holidays…"

[276] https://www.beatlesbible.com/1965/02/07/john-cynthia-lennon-return-england-switzerland/ and https://tinyurl.com/y6fpwyld

[277] https://www.npr.org/2015/04/02/397057478/in-her-life-after-john-cynthia-lennon-didnt-stop-loving-him In this candid 2 April 2015 interview with *NPR*, Cynthia admitted that "the whole fabric of our life changed because of the work that [John] was doing, and because of the pressures from outside." She also states that her presence in "The Beatles World" was always a problem for the press: "I was the fly in the ointment, because I was the wife of one of The Beatles. So it was embarrassing for them, and embarrassing for me…I realized [sic] then what it was going to be like, you know, in the future. I mean, obviously that was what it was going to be like, just women throwing themselves at them the whole time."

February 1965

Chart Toppers

"You've Lost That Lovin' Feeling" — The Righteous Brothers
"This Diamond Ring" — Gary Lewis and the Playboys
"My Girl" — The Temptations[278]

In the News

7 February: George Harrison's tonsils are removed.

10 February: The first "one-injection" measles vaccine (with 99% effectiveness) is made available to U.S. doctors to administer.

10-13 February: Another U.S Figure Skating Championship is won by Peggy Fleming.

21 February: Civil Rights activist Malcolm X is shot dead by Nation of Islam followers at Audubon Ballroom, New York City, New York.

22 February: The USSR launches Kosmos 57 into earth orbit.

22 February: Both the U.S. and France perform nuclear tests.[279]

Tuesday, 2 February 1965
Playboy Magazine
919 N. Michigan Avenue[280]
Chicago

On 28 October 1964, in a Torquay hotel room, *Playboy* reporter Jean Shepard had recorded a rather frank, risqué, and unusual interview with The Beatles. Now, as February 1965 began its icy stroll across the calendar, the magazine — with pert, blonde Teddi Smith on the cover and the exotic Jessica St. George as Playmate[281] — was ready for release.

As anticipated, the moment the slick publication hit the stands, the uncensored conversation with the Fab Four was "all the buzz":

Our interviewer this month is the inimitable Jean Shepard, whose nostalgically comic boyhood reminiscences and acerbic social commentary have earned him not only the applause of **PLAYBOY's** *readers, but also a loyal audience of three-million for the free-form one-man radio talkathon, which he wings weekly over New York's WOR from the stage of The Limelight in Greenwich Village. A nimble-witted and resourceful broadcast reporter who's tilted verbal lances with such formidable subjects as Malcolm X and Harry S. Truman, he débuts herein as an interviewer for the printed page. Shepard writes of his subjects:*

**Jean Shepard, who interviewed The Beatles
for *Playboy* magazine, 1965**
Photograph from Wikimedia Commons

"I joined The Beatles in Edinburgh in the midst of a wild, swinging personal-appearance tour they were making throughout the British Isles. The first glimpse I had of them was in a tiny, overheated, totally disorganized dressing room backstage between their first and second shows. I had taken the night flight up from London and suddenly found myself face to face with one, or rather four, of the 20th Century's major living legends. All of them looked up suspiciously as I walked in, then went back to eating, drinking, and tuning guitars, as though I didn't exist. Legends have a way of ignoring mere mortals. I looked hard at them through the cigarette smoke, and they began to come into focus, sprawling half-dressed and self-involved amid the continuous uproar that surrounds their lives.

"They had been playing one-night stands in Glasgow and Dundee, and I went along with them from Edinburgh to Plymouth, Bournemouth, and half a dozen other towns. They were all the same: wild, ravening multitudes, hundreds of policemen, mad rushes through the night in a black Austin Princess to a carefully guarded inn or chalet for a few fitful hours of sleep. And then the cycle started all over again.

"It became impossible to tell one town from another, since to us they were just a succession of dressing rooms and hotel suites. The screams were the same. The music was the same. It all assumed the ritual quality of a fertility rite. Latter-day Druids, The Beatles sat in their dressing room – a plywood Stonehenge – surrounded by sweaty T-shirts, trays of French fries, steak, pots of tea, and the inevitable TV set; while from somewhere off beyond the walls of the theatre came the faint, eerie wailing of their worshipers, like the sea or the wind. But The Beatles no more heard it than a New York cop hears traffic. Totally oblivious to the mob – and to the honks and plunks of other Liverpudlian rock'n'rollers warming up down the hall – they sat sipping Scotch from paper cups and watching 'Dr. Kildare' on the telly.

"I, meanwhile, sat and watched them – and wondered why. In two years they had become a phenomenon that had somehow transcended stardom – or even showbiz. They were mythical beings, inspiring a fanaticism bordering on religious ecstasy among millions all over the world. I began to have the uncomfortable feeling that all this fervor had nothing whatever to do with entertainment, or with talent, or even with The Beatles themselves. I began to feel that they were the catalyst of a sudden world madness that would have burst upon us whether they had come on the scene or not. If The Beatles had never existed, we would have had to invent them. They are not prodigious talents by any yardstick, but like hula hoops and yo-yos, they are at the right place at the right time, and whatever it is that triggers the mass hysteria of fads has made them walking myths.

"Everywhere we went, people stared in openmouthed astonishment that there were actually flesh-and-blood human beings who looked just like the Beatle dolls they had at home. It was as though Santa Claus had suddenly shown up at a Christmas party. Night after night, phalanxes of journalists would stand grinning, groveling, obsequious, jotting down The Beatles' every word. In city after city, the local mayor, countess, duke, earl, and prelate would be led in, bowing and scraping, to bask for a few fleeting moments in their ineffable aura. They don't give interviews; they grant audiences, which is the way the world wants its legends to behave.

"All around them, wherever they go, shimmers a strange, filmy, translucent pall of palpable unreality, so thick that you can almost taste it. And at the very center of this vast cloud of fantasy are the four young men themselves, by far the most real and least enchanted of them all. They have managed somehow to remain remarkably human, totally unlike the kewpies created by fandom and the press. In real life, The Beatles don't make Beatle noises. Nor are they precocious teenagers. They are grown-up, Scotch-drinking men who know what the world expects of them — which is to be Beatles and to wear long hair, funny clothes and be cute. But all that stops when the curtain falls and the high-heeled shoes come off and the drums are put away.

"Their unimaginable success — which has made them world figures important enough for the Prime Minister and the Queen's consort to discuss in news conferences, and has made them without a doubt the most successful money machine in recent times — has left them faintly bemused, but also extremely guarded in their day-by-day life, almost as though they're afraid that an extraloud sneeze will burst the bubble, and they'll be back in reality like the rest of us.

"Of the four, **George Harrison** seems to be the one most amused and least unsettled by it all. The truest swinger among them, he is also the most sarcastic, and unquestionably the most egotistical; he fingers his hair a lot, and has a marked tendency to pause meaningfully and frequently before mirrors. Even so, he's a very likeable chap - if he happens to like you. **John Lennon**, on the other hand, is a rather cool customer and far less hip than he's made out to be. He does radiate a kind of on-the-top-of-it confidence, however, and is the unacknowledged leader of the group. Equally poised, but far more articulate and outgoing, **Paul McCartney** (sometimes known as 'the cute Beatle') reminded me of Ned, the fun-loving Rover Boy: He's bright, open-faced and friendly - the friendliest of the lot; but unlike Ned, he also has a keen eye for a well-turned figure, and he worries a lot about the future. **Ringo Starr**, the smallest Beatle - even smaller in person than he appears to be on the screen - is a curious contrast with the others. Taciturn, even a bit sullen, he spends a good deal of his time sitting in corners staring moodily at the Venetian blinds. Perhaps because he wasn't their original drummer, he seems slightly apart from the rest, a loner. Still, he has a way of growing on you - if he doesn't grow away from you.

"But they all find it difficult to make any real contact with anybody outside of their immediate circle. And vice versa. As they appear unreal to their maniacal fans, so their fans appear to them. And an incessant infestation of interviewers has erected a wall of hackneyed wisecracks and ghostwritten ripostes between them and the press. So getting to know The Beatles, and to draw them out, was a discouraging task at first. I traveled and lived with them for three days before the first crack appeared in the invisible shield that surrounds them. Paul suddenly asked me about my cold – which I had been nursing since my arrival – and I knew that real life had reared its unexpected head.

"We began to become friends. And a week or so and what felt like 10,000 miles and 10,000,000 screams later, we found ourselves ensconced in a hotel room in Torquay in southwest England, on the gray shores of the English Channel. They had just played two shows before a raging throng of subteen girls in nearby Exeter. Within seconds after the final curtain, like a gang of convicts executing a well-rehearsed and perfectly synchronized prison break, they had eluded a gimlet-eyed army of idolaters outside the stage door and careened off in anonymous vehicles, with coat collars up and hats pulled low – four hunted fugitives and one terrified hostage (me) – into the wintry night. Pseudonymously registered and safely padlocked in their suite at the hotel – the identity and whereabouts of which were a more closely guarded secret than SAC's fail-safe recall code – they slipped out of their Beatle suits and into the comfort of sportswear, ordered up a goodly supply of Coke, tea, and booze, and began to unwind. We found ourselves talking quietly – and all of a sudden, almost communicating. Somewhere along the line, I turned on my tape machine. Here's what it recorded:[282]

Playboy: (Checking the tape recorder) Okay, we're on. Why don't we begin by...
John: Doin' Hamlet.
(Laughter)
Ringo: Yeah, yeah, let's do that.
Playboy: That sounds like fun, but just for laughs, why don't we do an *interview* instead?
George: Say, that's a fine idea. I wish I'd thought of that.
Paul: What shall we ask you for a first question?
Ringo: (Lifting an eyebrow) About those Bunny girls...

The February 1965 issue of *Playboy*
that featured this interview
Photograph used by kind permission of Rande Kessler

Playboy: No comment. Let's start over. Ringo, you're the last Beatle to join the group, aren't you?

Ringo: (Hangs his head, feigning sadness) Yes.

Playboy: How long were you fellows working together as a team before Ringo joined up?

John: A few years probably, sort of off 'n on, really, for three years or so.

Paul: Yeah, but really amateur.

George: The local pub, y' know. And in each other's uncles' houses.

John: 'N at George's brother's weddin'. Things like that. Ringo used to fill in sometimes if our drummer was ill. With his periodic illness.

Ringo: He took little pills to make him ill.

Playboy: When you joined the others, Ringo, they weren't quite as big as they are now, were they?

Ringo: (Jumping to The Beatles' defense) They were the biggest thing in Liverpool! In them days that was big enough!

Paul: This is a point we've made before. Some people say a man is made of muscle 'n blood...

No, they don't! They say, "How come you've suddenly been able to adjust to fame, y' know, to nationwide fame 'n things?" It all started quite nicely with us, y' see, in our own sphere, where we used to play — in Liverpool. We never used to play outside it, except when we went to Hamburg. Just those two circles. 'N in each of them, I think we were 'round the highest paid, 'n probably at the time the most popular. So, in actual fact, we had the same feeling of bein' famous *then* as we do now.

George: We were recognized then, too, only people didn't chase us about.

Paul: But it just grew. The quantity grew; not the *quality* of the feeling.

Playboy: When did you know that you had really hit it big? There must have been one night when you knew it had really begun.

John: Well, we'd been playing 'round in Liverpool for a bit without gettin' anywhere, tryin' to get work, 'n the other groups kept tellin' us, "You'll do all right! You'll get work someday." 'N then we went back to Hamburg, 'n when we came back, suddenly we were a wow. Mind you, 70 percent of the audience thought we were a *German* wow, but we didn't care about that.

Paul: We were billed in the paper: "From Hamburg —The Beatles."

John: In Liverpool, people didn't even know we were from Liverpool. They thought we were from Hamburg! They said, "Christ, they speak good English!" Which we did, of course, bein' English. But that's when we first, y' know, stood there bein' cheered for the first time.

Paul: That was when we felt we were...

John: ...on the way up.

Paul: ...gonna make it in Liverpool.

Playboy: How much were you earning then?

John: (Crossing his leg) For that particular night, twenty dollars.

Playboy: Apiece?

John: For the *group*! Hell, we used to work for a lot less than that.

Paul: We used to work for about three or four dollars a night.

Ringo: (Chuckling) Plus all the Coke we could drink. 'N we drank a lot!

Playboy: Do you remember the first journalist who came to see you and said, "I want to write about you"?

Ringo: We went 'round to *them* at first, didn't we?

John: We went 'n said, "We're a group, 'n we've got this record out. Will you..."

George: (Grinning) ...'n the door would slam!

Playboy: We've heard it said that when you first went to America you were doubtful that you'd make it over there.

John: That's true. We didn't think we were going to make it at all. It was only Brian tellin' us we were gonna make it. 'N George. Brian Epstein, our manager...'n George Harrison.

George: (Nods) I knew we had a good chance — because of the record sales over there.

John: The thing is, in America it just seemed ridiculous — I mean, the idea of havin' a hit record over there. It was just, y' know, somethin' you could never do. That's what I thought, anyhow. But then I realized [sic] that it's just the same as here, that kids everywhere all go for the same stuff. 'N seein' we'd done it in England 'n all, there's no reason why we couldn't do it in America, too. But the American disc jockeys didn't know about British records; they didn't play them; nobody promoted them, 'n so you didn't have hits.

George: Well, there were one or two doin' it as a novelty.

John: But it wasn't until *Time* 'n *Life* 'n *Newsweek* came over 'n wrote articles 'n created an interest in us the disc jockeys started playin' our records. 'N Capitol said, "Well, can *we* have their records?" Y' know, they had been offered our records years ago, 'n they didn't want 'em. But when they heard we were big over here, they said, "Can we have 'em now?" So we said, "As long as you promote them." So Capitol promoted, 'n with them 'n all these articles on us, the records just took off.

Playboy: There's been some dispute, among your fans and critics, about whether you're primarily entertainers or musicians — or perhaps neither. What's your own opinion?

John: We're money-makers first; then, we're entertainers.

Ringo: No, we're not.

John: (Turning to the drummer) What are we, then?

Ringo: Dunno. (Shrugging) Entertainers first.

John: O.K.

Ringo: 'Cause we were entertainers *before* we were money-makers.

John: That's right, of course. It's just that the press drivels it into you, so you say it 'cause they like to hear it, y' know?

Paul: Still, we'd be idiots to say that it isn't a constant inspiration to be makin' a lot of money. It always is, to anyone. I mean, why do big business tycoons *stay* big business tycoons? It's not because they're inspired at the greatness of big business; they're in it because they're makin' money at it. We'd be idiots if we pretended we were in it solely for kicks. In the beginnin' we were, but at the same time we were hopin' to make a bit of cash. It's a switch around now, though, from what it used to be. We used to be doin' it mainly for kicks 'n not makin' a lot of money, 'n now we're makin' a lot of money without too many kicks — except that we happen to like the money we're makin'. But we still enjoy makin' records, goin' on stage, makin' films, 'n all that business.

John: (Leaning towards the mic) We *love* every minute of it, Beatle people!

Playboy: As hard-bitten refugees from the Liverpool slums —
according to heart-rending fan magazine biographies — do you
feel prepared to cope with all this sudden wealth?
Paul: (Smiling wryly) We've managed to make the adjustment.
(He takes a drag on his cig and thinks a moment. Then...)
Contrary to rumour, y' see, none of us was brought up in any
slums or in great degrees of poverty. We've always had enough;
we've never been starvin'.
John: Yeah, we saw these articles in the American fan mags that
"Those boys struggled up from the slums..."
George: We never starved. Even Ringo hasn't!
Ringo: (Shaking his head and pulling a glum face) Even I.
Playboy: What kind of families *do* you come from?
George: Well, y' know, not rich. Just workin' class. They've got
jobs. Just work.
Playboy: What does your father do?
George: (Chuckles) Well, he doesn't do anythin' now. He used
to be a bus driver...
John: In the Merchant Navy.
Playboy: Do you have any sisters or brothers, George?
George: I've got two brothers.
John: 'N no sisters to speak of.
Playboy: How about you, Paul?
Paul: I've got one brother 'n a father who used to be a cotton
salesman down in New Orleans, y' know. That's probably why I
look a bit tanned. But seriously, folks, he occasionally had
trouble payin' bills — but it was never, y' know, never, "Go out
'n pick blackberries, son; we're a bit short this week."
Playboy: How about you, John?
John: Oh, just the same. I used to have an auntie. 'N I had a dad
whom I couldn't quite find.
Ringo: John lived with the Mounties.
John: Yeah, the Mounties. They fed me well. No starvation.
Playboy: How about *your* family, Ringo, old man?
Ringo: Just workin' class. I was brought up with my mother 'n
me grandparents. 'N then she married me stepfather, when I was
thirteen. All the time she was workin'. I never starved. I used to
get most things.
George: Never starved?

Ringo: No, I never starved. She always fed me. I was an only child, (he shrugged) so it wasn't amazin'.

Playboy: It's quite fashionable in some circles in America to hate your parents. But none of you seem to.

Ringo: We're probably just as against the things our parents liked or stood for as they are in America. But we don't hate our parents for it.

Playboy: It's often exactly the opposite in America.

Paul: Well, y' know, a lot of Americans are unbalanced. (He chuckles.) I don't care what you say. No, really. A lot of them are quite normal, of course, but we've met many unbalanced ones. You know the type of person, like the political Whig.

Playboy: How do you mean?

Paul: Y' know — the professional politician type; in authority sort of thing. Some of them are just mad! And I've met some really *maniac* American girls! Like this one girl who walked up to me in a press conference and said, "I'm Lily." I said, "Hello, how do you do?" and she said, "Doesn't my name *mean* anything to you?" I said, "Ah, no..." 'n I thought, "Oh God, it's one of these people that you've met 'n you should know." And so, Derek, our press agent, who happened to be there at the time, hangin' over my shoulder, givin' me quotes, which happens at every press conference...

George: (Out of the side of his mouth) You better not say that.

Paul: (Giggling) Oh yes, that's not true, Beatle people! But he was sort of hangin' about, 'n he said, "Well did you ring, or did you write, or something?" 'N she said, "No." 'N he said, "Well, how *did* you get in touch with Paul? How do you know him?" 'N she said, "Through God." Well, there was sort of a ghastly silence. I mean, we both sort of gulped 'n blushed. I said, "Well, that's very nice, Lily. Thanks very much. I must be off now."

Playboy: (Smiling) There wasn't a big lightning bolt from the sky?

Paul: No, there wasn't. But I talked to her afterward, 'n she said she'd got a vision from God, 'n God had said to her...

John: (Using air quotations) "It's been a hard day's night!" (Laughter, all around)

Paul: No, God had said, "Listen Lil, Paul is waitin' for you; he's in love with you, 'n he wants to marry you, so go down 'n meet him, 'n he'll know you right away." It's very funny, y' know. I was tryin' to persuade her that she didn't in actual fact have a vision from God, that it was...

George: It was probably somebody *disguised* as God.

Paul: You wouldn't hardly ever meet somebody like that in England, but there seemed to me to be a lot like her in America!

John: (Lighting a cig) Well, there are a lot more *people* in America, so you've got a much bigger group to get nutters from.

Playboy: Speaking of nutters, do you ever wake up in the morning, look in the mirror and say, "My God, I'm a Beatle"?

Paul: No, not quite.

(Laughter)

John: Actually, we only do it in each other's company. I know I never do it alone.

Ringo: We used to do it more. We'd get in the car. I'd look over at John 'n say, "Christ, look at you; you're a *bloody phenomenon!*" 'n just laugh — 'cause it was only him, y' know. 'N a few old friends of ours done it, from Liverpool. I'd catch 'em lookin' at me, 'n I'd say, "What's the matter with *yew?*" It's just daft, them just screamin' 'n laughin', thinking I'm one of them people.

Playboy: A Beatle?

Ringo: (Nods) Yes.

Paul: The thing [sic] makes *me* know we've made it is like tonight, when we slipped into a sweetshop. In the old days, we coulda just walked into a sweetshop 'n nobody woulda noticed us. We would have just got our sweets 'n gone out. But tonight, we just walked in — it took a coupla seconds — 'n the people just dropped their sweets! Before, y' see, there would have been no reaction at all! Except possibly, "Look at that fella with the long hair. Doesn't he look daft?" But nowadays, they're just amazed; they can't believe it. (Shrugging and looking at the others) But actually, we're no different.

Playboy: The problem is that you don't seem to be like real people. You're Beatles.

Paul: (Snickering) I know. It's very funny, that.

George: It's all the publicity.

Paul: We're taken in by it, too! Because *we* react exactly the same way to the stars *we* meet. When we meet people we've seen on the telly or in films, we still think, "Wow!"

John: It's a good thing, because we still get just as tickled.

Paul: The thing is that people, when they see you on TV 'n in magazines 'n up in a film, 'n hear you on the radio, they never expect to meet you, y' know, even our fans. Their wish is to meet you, but in the back of their mind they never think they're actually gonna meet us. And so, when they *do* meet us, they just don't believe it.

Playboy: Where do they find you — hiding in your hotel rooms?

John: No, on the street, usually.

Playboy: You mean you're brave enough to venture out in the streets without a bodyguard?

Ringo: Sure.

George: (Grinning wryly) We're always on the street. Staggerin' about.

Ringo: Floggin' our bodies.

George: You catch John sleepin' in the gutter occasionally.

Playboy: When people see you in the street, do you ever have any action?

George: Well, not really, because when you're walkin' about, you don't bump into groups of people, as a rule. People don't walk 'round in gangs, as a rule.

Playboy: Can you even go out shopping without getting mobbed by them, individually or collectively?

John: We avoid that.

Paul: (Holding up his index finger) The mountain comes to Mohammed!

George: (Nodding) The shop comes to us, as he says. But sometimes we just roll into a store 'n buy the stuff 'n leg out again.

Playboy: Isn't that like looking for trouble?

Paul: (Smiling widely) No, we walk four times faster than the average person.

Playboy: Can you eat safely in restaurants?

George: Sure, we can. I was there the other night.

John: (Snapping his head around) Where?

George: (Smirking) Restaurants.

Paul: Of course, we're *known* in the restaurants we go in.

George: And usually, it's only Americans that'll bother you.

Playboy: (An eyebrow lifted) Really?

George: (Nodding) Really. If we go into a restaurant in London, there's always goin' to be a couple of 'em eatin' there; you just tell the waiter to hold 'em off if they try to come over. If they come over anyway, you just sign.

Ringo: But y' know, the restaurants I go to, probably if I wasn't famous, I wouldn't go to them. Even if I had the same money 'n wasn't famous, I wouldn't go to them, because the people that go to them are drags. The good thing when you go to a place where the people are such drags, such snobs, y' see, is that they won't bother to come over to your table. They pretend they don't even know who you are, 'n you get away with an easy night! (He smiles.)

George: 'N they think they are laughin' at us, but really we're laughin' at them...'cause we know they know who we are!

Ringo: (Feigning confusion) How's that?

George: They're not goin' to be like the rest 'n ask for autographs.

Ringo: 'N if they do, we just swear at 'em!

George: (Leaning into the microphone) *I* don't, Beatle people. I sign the autograph 'n thank 'em profusely for comin' over, 'n offer them a piece of my chop.

John: If we're in the middle of a meal, I usually say, "Do y' mind waitin' till I'm finished?"

George: 'N then we keep eating until they give up 'n leave.

John: (Leaning into the mic, as George did, but using a deep announcer's voice) That's not true, Beatle people!

Playboy: Apart from these occupational hazards, are you happy in your work? Do you really *enjoy* getting pelted by jellybeans and being drowned out by thousands of screaming subteenagers?

Ringo: Yes!

George: (Nodding) We still find it excitin'.

John: Well, y' know...

Paul: After a while, actually, you begin to get used to it, y' know.

Playboy: Can you really get *used* to this?

Paul: Well, you still get excited when you go onto a stage 'n the audience is great, y' know. But obviously you're not as excited as you were when you first heard that one of your records had reached Number One! I mean, you really do go *wild* with excitement then; you go out drinkin' 'n celebratin' 'n things!

Ringo: Now we just go out drinkin' anyway.

Playboy: Do you stick pretty much together offstage?

John: Well, yes 'n no. Groups like this are normally not friends, y' know; they're just four people out there thrown together to make an act. There may be two of them who sort of go off 'n are friends, y' know, but...

George: (Feigning indignation) Just what d' y' mean by *that*?

John: (Biting off a grin) Strictly platonic, of course. But we're *all* rather good friends, as it happens.

Playboy: Then you do see a good deal of one another when you're not working?

Paul: Well, y' know, it depends. We needn't always go to the same places together. In earlier days, of course, when we didn't know London, 'n we didn't know anybody *in* London, then we really did stick together, 'n it would really be just like four fellows down from the North for a coach trip. But nowadays, y' know, we've got our own girlfriends —they're in London — so that we each normally go out with our girlfriends on our days off. Except for John, of course, who's married.

Playboy: Do any of the rest of you have plans to settle down?

Paul: (Answering rapidly) I haven't got any.

George: Ringo 'n I are gettin' married.

Playboy: Oh? To whom?

George: To each other. But that's a thing you better keep a secret.

Ringo: You better not tell anybody.

George: I mean, if we said somethin' like that, people'd probably think we're queers. After all, that's not the sort of thing you can put in a reputable magazine like PLAYBOY. 'N anyway, we don't want to start the rumor goin'.

Playboy: We'd better change the subject, then. Do you remember the other night when this girl came backstage...

George: Naked...

Playboy: Unfortunately, not. And she said...

George: "It's been a hard day's night."

Playboy: No. She pointed at you, George, and said, "There's a Beatle!" And you others said, "That's George." And she said, "No, it's a Beatle!"

John: 'N you said, "This way to the bedroom."

Playboy: No, it was, "Would you like us to introduce you to him?"

John: I like my line better.

Playboy: Well, the point is that she didn't believe that there was such a thing as an actual Beatle *person*.

John: She's right, y' know.

Playboy: Do you run across many like her?

George: (Sighing) Is there any other kind?

Playboy: In America, too?

Ringo: (Nodding) Everywhere.

Playboy: With no exceptions?

John: In America, y' mean?

Playboy: Yes.

John: (He shrugs.) A few.

Paul: Yeah, some of those American girls have been great.

John: Like Joan Baez.

Paul: (Nodding) Joan Baez is good, yeah, very good.

John: She's the only one I like.

George: 'N Jayne Mansfield. PLAYBOY made her.

Paul: She's a bit different, isn't she? *Different.*

Ringo: She's soft.

George: (Snickers) Soft 'n warm.

Paul: Actually, she's a clod!

Ringo: ...says Paul, the god of The Beatles.

Paul: (Leaning into the mic) I didn't mean it, Beatle people! Actually, I haven't even met her. But you won't print that anyway, of course, because PLAYBOY is very *pro*-Mansfield. They think she's a rave. But she really is an old bag.

Playboy: By the way, what *are* Beatle people?

John: It's somethin' they use in the fan mags in America. They all start out, "Hi there, Beatle people, 'spect you're wondering what the Fab Foursome are doing these days!" Now, we use it all the time, too.

Paul: It's low-level journalese.

John: But I mean, y' know, there's nothin' wrong with that. It's harmless.

Playboy: Speaking of low-level journalese, there was a comment in one of the London papers the other day that paralleled you guys with Hitler. Seriously! It said that you have the same technique of drawing cheers from the crowd...

Paul: That power isn't so much us bein' like Hitler; it's that the audiences 'n the show have got sort of, y' know, a "Hitler *feel*" about them, because the audience will shout when they're told to.

That's what the critic was talkin' about. Actually, that article was one which I really got annoyed about, 'cause she's never even *met us*.

Playboy: She?

Paul: The woman who wrote it. She's never met us, but she was dead against us. Like that Hitler bit! 'N she said we were very borin' people. "The Boresome Foursome," she called us. Y' know, really, this woman was really just shoutin' her mouth off about us — as people, I mean.

Ringo: (Waving off Paul's criticism) Oh, come on!

Paul: No, *you* come on! I rang up the newspaper, y' know, but they wouldn't let me speak to her. In actual fact, they said, "Well, I'll tell you, the reason we don't give her phone number out is because she never likes to speak to people on the phone because she's got a terrible stutter."

So I never did actually follow it up. Felt sorry for her. But I mean, the cheek of her, writin' this damn article about us. 'N tellin' everybody how we're startin' riots, 'n how we're such bores — 'n she's *never even* met us, mind you! I mean, we could turn around 'n say the same about her! I could go 'n thump her!

George: Bastard fascist!

Playboy: (Moving on quickly) Ringo...

Ringo: Yes, PLAYBOY, sir?

Playboy: How do *you* feel about the press? Has your attitude changed in the last year or so?

Ringo: Yes.

Playboy: In what way?

Ringo: I hate 'em more now than I did before!

Playboy: Did you hear about the riot in Glasgow on the night of your last show there?

John: (Nods) We heard about it after.

Playboy: Did you know that the next day there was a letter in one of the Glasgow papers that accused you of directly *inciting* the violence?

Ringo: (Furious) How can they say that about us? We don't even wiggle. It's not bloody fair.

George: Bastards!

Paul: Glasgow is like Belfast. There'll probably be a bit of a skirmish there, too. But it's not because of us. It's because people in certain cities just hate the cops more than in other cities.

George: (Nodding) Right.

Paul: There were ridiculous riots last time we were there — but it wasn't riots for us. The crowd was there for us, but the riots after the show...

Ringo: All the drunks come out...out of the pubs.

Paul: ...it was just beatin' up coppers.

Playboy: They just used the occasion as a pretext to get at the cops?

George: (Nodding) Yeah.

Paul: In Dublin this trip, did you see where the crowd sort of stopped all the traffic? They even pulled a driver out of a bus.

John: They also called out the fire brigade. We had four fire engines this time.

Playboy: People were also overturning cars and breaking shop windows. But all this had nothing to do with your show?

Paul: Well, it's vaguely related, I suppose. It's got *somethin'* to do with it, inasmuch as the crowds happen to *be there* because of our show.

John: But nobody who's got a bit of common sense would seriously think that 15-year-old girls are goin' 'round smashin' shop windows on account of us!

George: Certainly not. Those girls are *eight* years old. (Everyone laughs.)

Playboy: This talk of violence leads to a related question. Do you guys think there'll be another war soon?

George: (With mock seriousness) Yeah. Friday.

Ringo: I hope not. Not just after we've got our money through the taxes.

John: The trouble is, if they do start another war, then everybody goes with you.

Playboy: Do you think the Rolling Stones will be the first to go?

Paul: It won't matter, 'cause we'll probably be in London or Liverpool at the time, 'n when they drop the bomb, it'll be in the middle of the city. So we probably won't even know it when it happens.

Playboy: We brought this up for a reason, fellows. There **was** an essay not long ago in a very serious commentary magazine, saying that before every major war in this century, there had been a major wave of public hysteria over certain specific entertainers. There was the Irene Castle craze before World War One...

Paul: Oh, yes.

George: (Throwing his eyes to the ceiling) I remember that well.

Playboy: And then, before World War Two, there was the swing craze, with Benny Goodman and Artie Shaw, and all the dancing in the aisles. And now *you* — before...

John: (His eyes full of fire) Hold on! It's not our fault!

Playboy: We're not saying you may have anything to do with inciting a war...

Paul: (Sardonically) Thanks.

Playboy: But don't you think you may be a symptom of the times, part of an undercurrent that's building up?

Paul: That sort of comparison just falls down when you look at it, really. It's just like sayin' that this morning a fly landed on my bed 'n that I looked at my watch 'n it was eight o'clock, 'n that therefore every mornin' at eight o'clock, flies land on the bed. It doesn't prove anything just 'cause it happens a few times!

Playboy: Let's move on to another observation about you. Did you know that the Duke of Edinburgh was recently quoted as saying that he thought you were on the way out?

John: (Edgily) Good luck, Duke.

George: No comment. See my manager.

Paul: He didn't say it, though. There was a retraction, wasn't there?

John: Yeah, we got a telegram. (Sarcastically) Wonderful news.

Paul: We sent one back. Addressed to "Liz and Phil."

Playboy: Have you ever met the Queen?

John: No, she's the only one we haven't met. We've met all the others.

Paul: (Winks) All the mainstays.

Playboy: Winston Churchill?

Ringo: (Shaking his head) No, not him.

John: (Sniffs comically) He's a good lad, though.

Playboy: Would you like to meet him?

George: Not really. Not any more 'n anybody else.

Paul: I dunno. Somebody like that you wish you could have met when he was at his peak, y' know, 'n sort of doin' things 'n bein' great. But there wouldn't be a lot of point now, because he's sort of gone into retirement 'n doesn't do a lot of things anymore.

Playboy: Is there any celebrity you *would* like to meet?

Paul: (With a wry grin) I wouldn't mind meetin' Adolf Hitler.

George: (To Paul) You could have every room in your house papered.

Playboy: Would you like to meet Princess Margaret?

Paul: We have.

Playboy: How do you like her?

Ringo: O.K. 'N Philip's O.K., too.

Playboy: Even after what he supposedly said about you?

Ringo: I don't care what he said; I still think he's O.K. He didn't say nothin' about me personally.

Paul: Even if he *had* said things about us, it doesn't make him worse, y' know.

Playboy: Speaking of royalty...

Paul: (Still on the former topic) Royalty never condemns anythin' unless it's somethin' that they know everybody else condemns.

Ringo: If I was royal...

Paul: If I was royal, I would crack long jokes 'n get a mighty laugh...if I was royal.

George: (Shaking his head) What would *we* do with Buckingham Palace? Royalty's stupid.

Playboy: You guys seem to be pretty irreverent characters. Are any of you churchgoers?

John: No.

George: No.

Paul: Not particularly. But we're not antireligious. We probably seem to be antireligious because of the fact that none of us believe in God.

John: If you say you don't believe in God, everybody assumes you're antireligious, 'n you probably think that's what we mean by that. We're not quite sure *what* we are, but I know that we're more agnostic than atheistic.

Playboy: Are you speaking for the group or just for yourself?

John: For the group.

George: (Smirking) John's our official religious spokesman.

Paul: We all feel roughly the same. We're all agnostics.

John: Most people are, anyway.

Ringo: It's better to admit it than to be a hypocrite.

John: The only thing we've got against religion is the hypocritical side of it, which I can't stand. Like the clergy is always moanin' about people bein' poor, while they themselves are all goin' around with millions of quid worth of robes on. That's the stuff I can't stand!

Paul: A new bronze door stuck on the Vatican.

Ringo: Must have cost a mighty penny.

Paul: But believe it or not, we're not anti-Christ.

Ringo: Just anti-Pope 'n anti-Christian.

Paul: But y' know, in America...

George: They were more shocked by us saying we were agnostics.

John: They went potty; they couldn't take it. Same as in Australia, where they couldn't stand us not likin' sports.

Paul: In America, they're fanatical about God. I know somebody over there who said he was an atheist. The papers nearly refused to print it because it was such shockin' news that somebody could actually be an atheist. Yeah,'n admit it.

Ringo: He speaks for all of us.

Playboy: To bring up another topic that's shocking to some, how do you feel about the homosexual problem?

George: Oh yeah, well, we're all homosexuals, too.

Ringo: Yeah, we're all queer.

Paul: (One finger in front of his lips) But don't tell anyone.

Playboy: Seriously, is there more homosexuality in England than elsewhere?

John: (His nostrils flaring) Are you sayin' there's more over here than in America?

Playboy: (Hesitantly) We're just asking.

George: It's just that they've got crewcuts in America. You can't spot 'em.

Paul: There's probably a million more queers in America than in England. England may have its scandals —like Profumo 'n all — but at least, they're heterosexual.

John: Still, we do have more than our share of queers, don't you think?

Paul: It just seems that way because there's more printed about them over here.

Ringo: If they find out somebody is a bit bent, the press'll always splash it about!

Paul: Right. Take Profumo, for example. He's just an ordinary...

Ringo: Sex maniac.

Paul: ...just an ordinary fellow who sleeps with women. Yet it's adultery in the eyes of the law, 'n it's an international incident. But in actual fact, if you check up on the statistics, you find that there are hardly *any* married men who've been completely faithful to their wives.

John: (Touching his chest) *I* have! Listen, Beatle people...

Paul: All right, we all know John's spotless. But when a thing like that gets into the newspapers, everybody goes very, very Puritan, 'n they pretend that they don't know what sex is about.

George: They get so bloody virtuous, all of a sudden.

Paul: Yes, 'n some poor heel has got to take the brunt of the whole thing. But in actual fact, if you ask the average Briton what they really think of the Profumo case, they'd probably say, "He was knockin' off some bird. So what?"

Playboy: Incidentally, you've met Mandy Rice-Davies, haven't you?

George: (Pointing to himself...eyes wide) What are you lookin' at *me* for?

Playboy: Because we hear *she* was looking at you!

John: We did meet Christine Keeler.

Ringo: I'll tell you who *I* met. I met what's-her-name — April Ashley.

John: I met her, too, the other night.

Playboy: Isn't she the one who used to be a man, changed her sex, and married into the nobility?

John: (Nodding) That's the one.

Ringo: She swears at me, y' know. But when she sobers up, she apologises.

John: Actually, I quite like her. Him. It. That.

Paul: The problem with sayin' something like, "Profumo was just a victim of circumstances" or "April Ashley isn't so bad, even though she's changed sex" — sayin' things like that in print to most people seems so shockin'; whereas in actual fact, if you really think about it, it isn't. Just sayin' a thing like that sounds much more shockin' than it is.

Ringo: I got up in the Ad Lib the other night, 'n a big handbag hit me in the gut. I thought it was somebody I knew; I didn't have any glasses on. I said, "Hello," 'n a bloody big worker went, "Arrgghhh." So, I just ran into the bog. Because I'd heard about things like that.

Playboy: What are you talking about?

George: (Shaking his head) He doesn't know.

Playboy: Do *you*?

George: (Shrugging and trying not to grin) Haven't the slightest!

Playboy: Can you give us a hint, Ringo? What's the Ad Lib, for example?

Ringo: It's a club.

George: Like your Peppermint Lounge 'n the Whisky à Go Go. It's the same thing.

Paul: No, the English version is a little different.

John: The Whiskey à Go Go is exactly the same, isn't it? Only they have someone dancin' on the ceiling, don't they?

George: Don't be ridiculous. They have *two* girls dancin' on the roof. In the Ad Lib, they have a coloured chap. That's the difference.

Playboy: We heard a rumour that one of you was thinking of opening a club.

John: (Cutting his eyes) I wonder who that was, *Ringo...*

Ringo: I don't know, John. There was a rumour, yes, I heard that one, too.

Playboy: (Smiling) Is there any truth to it?

Ringo: Well, yes. We was goin' to open one in Hollywood, but it fell through.

John: Dean-o wouldn't let you take the place over.

Ringo: (Sighs) No.

Paul: 'N we decided it's not worth it. So we decided to sit tight for six months, 'n then buy...

George: America!

Playboy: Have you heard about the PLAYBOY Club that's opening in London?

Ringo: (Nodding) Yes, I've heard about it.

Playboy: What do you think of our clubs?

Ringo: They're for dirty old men, not for the likes of us — dirty *young* men. They're for businessmen that sneak out without their wives knowin', or if their wives sneak out first, for those who go out openly.

George: There's no real fun in a bunny's fluffy tail.

Playboy: Then, you don't think a club will make it here?

George: (Smiling) Oh yes, 'course it will.

Ringo: There's enough dirty old men here.

(They all laugh.)
Playboy: Have you ever read the magazine?
John: Yes.
George: Yes.
Ringo: (Chuckling) I get my copy every month. Tits!
Playboy: Do you read the *philosophy*, any of you?
Paul: Some of it…when the journey's really long, 'n you can't last out the pictures, you start readin' it. (Shrugging) It's O.K.
Playboy: How about *PLAYBOY's* "Jazz Poll"? Do you read it, too?
John: (Nodding) Occasionally.
Playboy: Do you enjoy jazz, any of you?
George: What kind?
Playboy: American jazz.
John: Who, for example?
Playboy: You tell us.
Paul: We only dig those who dig us.
Playboy: Seriously, who? Anyone?
John: Getz. But only because somebody gave me an album of his. With him 'n somebody called Iguana, or somethin' like that.
Playboy: You mean João Gilberto?
John: I don't know. Some Mexican.
Playboy: He's Brazilian.
John: (Lifting one shoulder) Oh.
Playboy: Are you guys getting tired of talking?
John: No.
Paul: No. Let's order some drinks. Scotch or Coke?
John: I'll have chocolate.
George: Scotch for me 'n Paul 'n chocolate for the Beatle teenager.
John: Scotch is bad for your kidneys.
Paul: How 'bout you, Ringo? Don't you want somethin' to keep you awake while you're listenin' to all this rubbish?
Ringo: (Nods) I'll have a Coke.
John: How about you, *PLAYBOY*? (He scratches his right sideburn and then says) Are you man or woman?
Paul: It's a "Beatle people!"
George: (to *Playboy*) Who's your fave rave?
Paul: (Shouts playfully) I love you!
George: (Chuckling) How gear!

Playboy: Speaking of fave raves, why do you think the rock-'n'-roll phenomenon is bigger in England than in America?
John: (Lifting an eyebrow) Is it?
Paul: Yes. Y' see, in England, after us, you have thousands of groups comin' out everywhere, but in America they've just sort of had the same groups goin' for ages. Some have made it, 'n some haven't, but there aren't really any *new* ones. If we'd been over there instead of over here, there probably would've been the same upsurge over there. Our road manager made an interestin' point the other day about this difference in America. In America, the people who are the big stars are not our age. There's nobody who's a really big star around our age. Possibly it may seem like a small point, but there's no conscription — no draft — here. In America, we used to hear about somebody like Elvis, who was a very big star 'n then suddenly he was off to the army.
John: (Nods and reaches for a cig) 'N the Everly Brothers...
Paul: (Nodding) Yes, the Everly Brothers as well went into the army at the height of their fame. 'N the army seems to do somethin' to singers. It may make them think that what they're playing is stupid 'n childish. Or it may make them want to change their style, 'n consequently they may not be as popular when they come out of the army. It may also make people forget them, 'n consequently they may have a harder job gettin' back on top when they get out. But here, of course, we don't have that problem.
John: Except those who go to prison.
Paul: It's become so easy to form a group nowadays 'n to make a record, that hundreds are doin' it — 'n makin' a good livin' at it. Whereas when we started, it took us a couple of years before record companies would even *listen* to us, never mind give us a contract. But now, you just walk in 'n if they think you're okay, you're on.
Playboy: Do you think you had anything to do with bringing all this about?
John: It's a damn fact.
Paul: Not only us. Us 'n people who followed us. But we were the first really to get national coverage because of some big shows that we did, 'n because of a lot of public interest in us.
Playboy: What do you think is the most important element of your success — the personal appearances or the records?

John: (Decisively) Records. Records have always been the main thing. P.A.s follow records. Our first records were made, 'n then we appeared.

Playboy: Followed closely by Beatle dolls. Have you seen them?

George: They're actually life-size, y' know.

Playboy: The ones we've seen are only about five inches high.

Paul: (Blinking his eyelashes, innocently.) Well, we're midgets, y' see.

Playboy: How does it make you feel to have millions of effigies of yourselves decorating bedsides all over the world? Don't you feel honored to have been immortalized in plastic? After all, there's no such thing as a Frank Sinatra doll or an Elvis Presley doll.

George: Who'd want an ugly old crap doll like that?

Playboy: Would you prefer a George doll, George?

George: (Laughing) No, but I've got a Ringo doll at home!

Playboy: Did you know that you're probably the first public figures to have dolls made of them — except maybe Yogi Berra?

John: (Smirking) In Jellystone Park? D' ya mean the cartoon?

Playboy: No. Didn't *you* know that the cartoon character is based on a real person —Yogi Berra, the baseball player?

George: (Shrugging and snickering a bit) Oh.

Playboy: Didn't you know that?

John: I didn't know that.

Paul: Well, they're making *us* into a cartoon, too, in the States. It's a series.

John: (Mock serious face) The highest achievement you could ever get!

Paul: (Ducking his head) We feel proud 'n humble.

Playboy: Did you know, George, that at the corner of 47th Street and Broadway in New York, there is a giant cutout of you on display?

George: (Points to himself) Of me?

Playboy: Life size.

Ringo: (Leaning confidentially towards George) Nude!

Playboy: No — but the reason we mention it is that this is really a signal honor. For years on that corner, there's been a big store with life-size cutouts of Marilyn Monroe, Anita Ekberg, or Jayne Mansfield in the window.

John: (Smirking) 'N now, it's George.

Paul: The only difference is that they've got bigger tits.
Ringo: I suppose that's *one* way of puttin' it.
George: The party's getting rough. I'm goin' to go to bed. You carry on, though; I'll just stop my ears with cotton — so as not to hear the insults 'n the smutty language.
Playboy: We've just about run out of steam, anyway.
John: D' ya have all y' need?
Playboy: Enough. Many thanks, fellows.
John: 'Course a lot of it you won't be able to use — "crap" 'n "bloody" 'n "tit" 'n "bastard" 'n all.
Playboy: (Smiling smugly) Wait and see.
Ringo: Finish your Scotch before you go.
John: (To Jean) You don't mind if I climb into bed, do you? I'm frazzled.
Playboy: Not at all. Good night.
Ringo: Good night, *PLAYBOY*!
George: (Standing and stretching) It's been a hard day's night.

Sources:

Playboy *magazine, Vol. 12, No. 2, February, 1965.*
Evans, Mike, ed. The Beatles, Paperback Writer: 40 Years of Classic Writing, 99-102. This is an excerpt from the interview found in this chapter.

https://www.vintageplayboymags.co.uk/60s/Feb/05.htm   This website shows the cover photo for the February 1965 Playboy *and gives concise details of the articles, features, interviews, and Playmate of the Month.*

https://www.beatlesbible.com/1964/10/28/interview-playboy/ Journalist Jean Shepard's preface to his interview with The Beatles for Playboy *may be found here.*

http://beatlesinterviews.org/db1965.02pl.beatles.html   This   is   the interview between Jean Shepard and The Beatles for the 2 February. 1965.

https://chicago.cbslocal.com/2011/12/13/playboy-moving-from-chicago-to-l-a/ This website furnished information about the move of the Playboy *corporate headquarters to Chicago in early 1965.*

---

[278] https://www.billboard.com/archive/charts/1965/hot-100 The top *Billboard* hits of 1965 are listed here, week by week.

[279] https://www.onthisday.com/date/1965/february/27

[280] https://chicago.cbslocal.com/2011/12/13/playboy-moving-from-chicago-to-l-a/ The relocation of the Playboy corporate headquarters to Chicago in 1965 is documented here.

[281] https://www.vintageplayboymags.co.uk/60s/Feb/05.htm This website gives a concise summary of each *Playboy* magazine, including Playmates, articles, literary excerpts, features, and interviews.

[282] https://www.beatlesbible.com/1964/10/28/interview-playboy/ This is the introduction to Jean Shepard's 28 October 1964 interview with The Beatles, published in *Playboy* on 2 Feb. 1965.

Thursday, 11 February 1965
Kenwood
Weybridge, Surrey

For days, Cynthia had known that Maureen was pregnant.[283] John as well.[284] And George. And naturally, Brian, who'd made all the wedding arrangements.[285] But none of them had discussed it,[286] especially since Ringo and Maureen had been "a couple" for years — always "ascloseasthis," in the current vernacular.[287]

Despite rabid press rumours that Ringo had lately been seeing exotic model Vicki Hodge, he loved Maureen.[288] In fact, Ritchie[289] went out of his way, on any free day, to return to Liverpool and spend time with "his girl."[290] From the first time they'd met outside the Cavern Club, Ritchie had tumbled for the sultry, charcoal-eyed brunette, a Junior Hair Dresser from Liverpool's Ashley du Pre Beauty Salon.[291]

He'd first spotted her, standing hopefully in the Cavern's long lunchtime queue, in early September 1962.[292] The Beatles' brand-new drummer — his hair barely long enough for the Beatle coif — had approached boldly, asking Miss Cox to "come out with him" after the Cavern gig the following night.[293]

But 16-year-old Maureen[294] had shyly declined, explaining that her parents expected her home no later than 11:50 p.m.[295] So, Ritchie had impatiently counted the days, waiting until he could escort the girl on "a full day out" — to the park and pictures, to drinks at the Pink Parrot and finally, to Allan Williams's Blue Angel Club for the show.[296] He'd done everything he possibly could to "fill the whole time."[297]

Happily, the Starkey charm had worked. Ritchie and Maureen had become an item, and "Mo" had, happily, turned out to be Cynthia's friend and confidante. A comrade through the long absences of touring and the strains of Beatlemania. And now,

Ringo's "Liverpool Lou" was about to become the second Beatle wife, Mrs. Ringo Starr. Cynthia sighed for her.

**The heart of Liverpool, near the Ashley du Pre Salon,
where Maureen Cox worked in the early 1960s**
Original 1960s photographer unknown

"How's this?" John stood, bleary-eyed, his shirt sleeves rumpling inside his jacket. Cynthia smiled and arranged his cuffs evenly, turning the cufflinks out. Then carefully, she folded her husband's collar down and smoothed it over his tie.

"Perfectly handsome," Cynthia smiled.

"Yeah, well, I'm nearly comatose, Powell," John growled, running a finger inside the cinching collar. "I mean, it's the middle of the fuggin' night, y' know! What the fuggin'ell 'm I doin' in a fuggin' suit at this hour?"

John was right. It was inordinately early, as far as The Beatles were concerned.

To minimize press interference, Brian had scheduled the Starkey wedding for 8.00 a.m. in London's Caxton Hall Registry Office,[298] conveniently close to Ringo and George's Montagu Square flat.[299] But for the Lennons, the London locale meant at least an hour's commute during rush hour, and John was ragged, unaccustomed to functioning before noon.

Cynthia tried changing the subject.

"Is our Ringo nervous, do you think?" She slipped her fingers through John's hair, the way she'd once seen Helen Anderson do so many years ago in Liverpool College of Art.[300] Her husband's hair needed a trim. But she'd let Brian deal with that. She just enjoyed it.

"Nervous? Starkey? Nah, he's the marryin' kind…a sort of family man, isn't he?"[301]

Cynthia heard the vague implication and wanted to say, "Meaning you're not, then?" But she didn't. She wanted no parsing with John this morning. She'd determined to make it a joyous day.

Cyn had even purchased a new burgundy suit with black trim and a matching beret, of sorts, for the ceremony. As she'd pointed out to John, she'd frugally worn her Foyles Literary Luncheon green two-piece "to almost every grand occasion over the last year," but for Rich and Mo, Cyn had splurged on something bright and new. With her hair sleeked straight over her shoulders, Mrs. Lennon looked quite mod — very London chic.[302]

"Where's Alf?!" John barked, slugging back strong Irish tea as if it were Scotch.

"He'll be here, John. He hasn't forgotten. Ritchie had him out running errands all day yesterday.[303] He's probably dotting the last of the i's and crossing the final t's."

"Yeah, well, let's hope he's not after drivin' Elsie 'n Harry, 'n inadvertently leavin' us in the lurch!"

"Of course not…Alf's always here. And…there he is now. I'll run and tell Dot we're off."

In minutes, the Lennons were rolling away to yet another Beatle nuptial. As George Harrison would quip to the press hours later, "Two down; two to go."[304] The field of bachelors was narrowing.

****

Caxton Hall Register Office
Westminster

8.00 a.m.

They stood yawning and shifting, foot to foot — a drowsy, well-dressed assembly of family and friends. George, in his best suit, had pedaled over on bicycle.[305] Brian had plastered down his hair, and he sported the pink carnation Maureen had ordered for Ritchie's Best Man. Her mother wore two lilies at the neckline, and Elsie had pinned a single orchid on her cornflower blue suit.[306]

"Right well, where's George's 'n *my* boutonnières, eh son?"[307] John nudged a very muted Ringo.

"You're not really part of the wedding party. That's what Maureen says." Ringo eyes wandered restlessly. He was unsure about flowers and such trappings.

"Then why am I up 'n dressed at such an unhealthy hour?" John glanced around, seeking answers. "Y' coulda doled out a coupla *radishes*, at the very least!"[308]

"Yeah, well, talk to the bride." Ringo shrugged.

"I'm not sure as I'd do that," George advised out of the corner of his mouth.

"Wise man," Cynthia said in passing.

But John continued to grouse until Registrar Mr. D. A. Boreham[309] moved briskly through the door and up to the front of the room. Then, all chatter ceased.

"Good morning, everyone," Boreham called, as warmly as an early morning registrar could call. "If all are present and accounted for then, shall we get started, then?"

"We shall!" John answered, taking command as usual. And murmuring happily, Elsie and Harry, John and Cynthia, George, Alf, and Maureen's parents turned to face the happy couple. Brian hovered solicitously beside Ringo. And biting her lip, Cynthia moved beside Maureen, ready to assist, if need be.[310]

Both sets of parents here, Cynthia sniffed, trying not to resent it. *No drilling from the street. No giggling at the ridiculousness of it all. No gig tonight for the boys, and a true honeymoon in the offing.[311] So* this *is what a* real *wedding is like! Lovely.*

And it was.

****

8.30 a.m.

But, inevitably, as they emerged from the Registry, the clearly prescient journalists had somehow located them. John stepped in front of the assemblage. Fielding the rapid-fire questions, he stalled the press as the Starkeys sped away to Brian's Belgravia flat for a special wedding breakfast.

Q: John Lennon, how was the wedding? Were there tears?
John: There were no tears. We'd threatened Mrs. Starkey that if she cried, she wouldn't be one of the gang![312]

(He Cheshire grinned. Chuckles rippled through the crowd as rapidly as the sound of snaps.)

Q: Do you think Ringo's marriage will hit your group's success?
John: I don't think his marriage will affect The Beatles' popularity really, but there might be some shufflin' of fans from one of The Beatles to another…at least that's what happened when news that I was married was revealed, as *you* said.

(More photos and shouted questions)

Q: What was *your* first reaction to Ringo and Maureen's decision to wed? Did you consider the fans' reaction?
John: No, no! The first thing *I* thought was what a sneaky thing to do, arrangin' it before I flew back from holiday! But still, he's good. He's joined the club!

(John flashed a thumbs-up to a downpour of inqueries. This time, George stepped up to answers several questions in one collective response.)

George: The ceremony was over in ten minutes. There was no music, although I *did* think about hummin' the weddin' march. Maureen is great, 'n we like her a lot. This means that there are now *two* married Beatles and two unmarried Beatles. Two down, two to go![313]
And as the crowd laughed and surged forward, the boys quickly waved. In seconds, they departed for Brian's flat.

****

Noon

As they rumbled back towards Kenwood, John was grateful for Bicknell's radio. He melted into the deep leather seats and listened to Petula Clark belting out "Downtown." Cyn's faint humming — slightly off tune — was the only thing between John and sleep.

Eyes closed, jaw tight, he kept going back to something Ringo had said to Maureen's parents, something he knew Rich meant and had, in fact, recently repeated in some magazine: "I was told, y' know, as a Beatle, to pretend I didn't know Maureen, and it wasn't love. But...well..." And beaming, Rich had proudly hugged his new bride. [314]It was obvious that Ring was happily married.

John wished for the recipe. *The "Love Potion #9" that The Searchers are always goin' on about.* He wished he knew how to be...content.

He'd tried his best, over the holidays, to be a good husband. Despite the muddle of dusty renovations all over Kenwood, John had offered to clear a spot for a Christmas tree, and he'd helped Cyn decorate it. He'd invited in George, Pattie, Ringo and Mo for festivities.[315]

On Christmas Eve, they'd nibbled *hors d' oeuvres*, drank, talked, and listened to records right up 'til midnight. Then, riotously, the six of them — and Julian, who'd been allowed to "stay up late-late!" — had torn into the beautifully wrapped "prezzies." They'd laughed and squealed and hugged each other.[316]

"Happy Christmas!"

"Cheers!"

"Whoopee!"

They'd shouted and danced about with Julian, his eyes bright with exhilaration. And everyone seemed to be genuinely having fun.

"Seemed" was the turn-word. John was only going through the motions. Smiling. Saying the cleverest things. Trying to gin up happy.

And all through January, he'd followed suit. Nightly, he'd imitated "a good husband."

After the Odeon shows, he had lounged about in front of the telly — smoking, doodling, and reading. He'd played Bob Dylan on the record player. He'd sat up late with Cyn and tried to think of things to discuss.[317] But there was nothing for it. Peter Pan was only halfheartedly "playing house," when what he really wanted to do was murder pirates and hurtle recklessly through an icy, uncharted night sky.

Sadly, John guessed that Cynthia saw through the sham. She knew. "Miss Powell" was a clever girl. She'd never been easily hoodwinked. Nor was she now…not even by him.

****

Cynthia had learned to mitigate her life's unfortunate circumstances. When John crept about under a cloud, she busied herself in another room or tended to Julian. She pretended not to notice.

This morning, the wedding — and Ringo's enthusiastic embrace of it all — had left John withdrawn and monosyllabic. So, humming along with Alf's radio, Cyn stared out the side window. She persisted, unwaveringly cheery.

It's a matter of survival,[318] she reminded herself. *As the world throws us into a chaotic future, I have to stand apart from Beatlemania and be the bedrock of John's stability.*[319] *I have to be the constant.*

But lately, she'd become frightened.

The nearer John travels to the centre of the whirlpool, the more distant we're becoming in our understanding of each other.[320]She tried to blink the tears away. *He wants to dive in headlong, but I'm fighting to stay on the periphery.*[321] *And the nearer he travels towards the centre, the farther away I pull.*

The situation was quite complicated, and the drugs that Bob Dylan had introduced to The Beatles in America were right at the heart of it all. John found them a release, a way of escaping into a world less severe and demanding. Cynthia found them untenable, terrifying.[322] Whilst John wanted to shed reality — to encounter something finer than what life was offering him[323] — Cyn fought to remain steady, clear-headed, and calm.[324]

And so, whilst days ago Ringo had told the press, "No matter what the consequences, *I don't want to remain single* all my life! I want to get married someday, and I don't plan to wait too long about it!",[325] the Lennons were finding marriage a trial — at best, a challenge.

Ringo besieged by reporters, 1965
Photograph from Wikimedia Commons

As the car left London and the Starrs' wedding festivities behind, John yawned, folded his arms behind his head, and tried his best to "catch a spot of kip." And lifting her chin, Cynthia hummed along with The Righteous Brothers as they flooded the car with the disturbing strains of "You've Lost That Loving

Feeling."[326]

****

Friday, 12 February 1965
Kenwood
Weybridge, Surrey

"Well, they've certainly made the newspapers!" Cynthia had John's tea, milk, and bowl for cornflakes ready when he stumbled into fuzzy wakefulness around 2.00 p.m.[327]

"Who's that?" He tightened his striped terrycloth robe and collapsed into the ladder-back chair at their battered, attic dining table.[328]

"Ringo and Mo, of course…they've been rumbled. The trusty press…at it again!"[329]

"All the way out in fuggin' Hove?!"[330]

"Ummhmm. Seems the newlyweds were compelled to host an impromptu press conference — in David Jacobs' rather, uhm, untended rear garden."[331] Cynthia shook her head. "It's to be on the evening news, I've been informed." At John's raised eyebrow, she added, "George rang."

"Brian'll go into a fuggin' rigour!" John snorted, adjusting his glasses. "I mean, he told Barrow 'heads'll roll' if the slightest detail of the weddin' *or* the honeymoon was leaked!"[332]

"Well, it's not a *leak*." Cynthia slid into the chair across from her husband. "George says it's more of a torrent — a slew of journalists and photographers! Poor Maureen," Cynthia sighed. "She was hoping for one brief, quiet weekend away."

"Well," John hooked his bare feet on the lowest chair rung and hunched over his breakfast. "If anyone can deal with newspaper men, Ritchie Starkey can. He's great with a 'quitty wip' 'n a camera!"

"I suppose we'll find out…"

"Says here," John read from the newspaper in front of him, "Pictured above, Ringo Starr, The Beatles' drummer, stands with his bride, Maureen Cox, following their wedding at Caxton Hall registry office in London. Ringo is 24, and the bride, whose name when christened was Mary, but who is known to all as Maureen, is 18."[333]

"And there you have it!" Cynthia threw her eyes to the ceiling. "They find a way to make even straightforward details seem somehow suspect. As if she's changed her name for some…clandestine cause!"

"It'll be okay in the end, Powell." John slurped his Corn Flakes as if he hadn't eaten for days. "If it's not okay, y' know…" another slurp, "it's not the end."[334]

"Ah yes, the world according to John Winston Lennon," Cynthia smiled. And cutting his eyes, her husband pulled his "Famous Eccles" face.

****

And as usual, John was right. Everything was okay.

Ringo and Maureen did all the right things on film. They were dressed to the nines: Maureen in a dark shell and two-piece grey suit, and Ringo in a black-and-white polka dot shirt beneath a pale jacket. The newlyweds were smiling, waving, and posing — holding hands in Jacobs's tatty winter garden.[335]

ITV featured a short chat with The Beatles' drummer at the top of the Sunday night news. Whilst Julian rolled a fire truck back and forth, back and forth across the fraying sisal rug, Cynthia and John turned up the volume and listened:

Q: Congratulations, Ringo![336]
Ringo: (Beaming) Thanks a lot. If I may shake your hand as you congratulate me.
Q: Congratulations, too, Mrs. Starkey!
Ringo: (Looking around, as if searching for someone) Ha! I'm still not used to that yet, y' know.
Q: Are you really going to get a honeymoon?
Ringo: (Shrugging) No, I don't think so. Not with the likes of you chaps around!
(The crowd chuckles, though a bit uneasily.)
Q: No. Are you thinking of a honeymoon?

Ringo: Well, this was supposed to be it, but it didn't work.

Q: Well, for how long was it supposed to be?

Ringo: Well, I have to start work on Monday — so I was goin' back Sunday or Monday, y' know.

Q: What do the other Beatles think of your marriage?

Ringo: John 'n George were at the weddin', 'n they were made up, y' know. They're happy. But we don't know about Paul yet, 'cause he's away on holiday.

Q: He hasn't been in contact? Did he know you were getting married?

Ringo: (Shakes his head) No. No.

Q: Where is he?

Ringo: He's away.

Q: Do you know where?

Ringo: (Smiles) Umm, yes. But I'm not tellin' you. (Laughter) Well, he might as well have a bit of peace; *I'm* not gettin' it![337]

John was cheering Ringo on. "Fanfuggin'tastic! Someone has to keep the press on their toes! Might as well be you, son!"

"Oh, but wait! There's more!" Cynthia jumped up and quickly changed channels just moments before the BBC began broadcasting their conversation with the new Mr. and Mrs. Starkey.

"And there they be!" John teased. "Quite the charmin' twosome, aren't they?"

"*Shhhh, John*! Listen!"

Q: Maureen, you presumably met Ringo before the group were very successful. Did you?[338]

Maureen: (Nodding) Yes, yes.

Q: Did you expect he was going to become a public monument like this?

Maureen: Well, in Liverpool I did. I didn't think sort of, more or less, all over *the world*, y' know.

Q: Does that worry you — the fact that you can't go anywhere with him?

Maureen: Umm, no, not really. (She shrugs.) I just sort of enjoy myself.

Q: Do you intend to keep out of the limelight, like Mrs. Lennon for example...John Lennon's wife?

"They're 'talkin' 'bout you,' Powell!" John ribbed her lightly, his eyes glinting at the reference to one of her old favourite Cavern Club numbers.

"'Out of the limelight!'" she sputtered. *"Out of the limelight*?!! Did you know they're *daft*, those people?!"

"Yeah, because they report everythin' we do, even before we do it! Even when we never do it!"

Maureen: Well, (Shyly cutting her eyes at Ringo) I, um, don't like reporters 'n things.
Ringo: (Grinning widely) She's on OUR side!
(Laughter from all sides)
Q: How long have you known each other?
Ringo: About two-and-a-half years now.
Q: So, this means, Maureen, that you knew Ringo *before* he was right at the top of the tree?
Maureen: (Demurely) Yes.
Q: How does it feel to be married to a very famous man?
Maureen: (Glancing coyly at her husband) Very nice!
Q: Well, I'm sure you wanted a rather different honeymoon from this. What do you think about all this?
Ringo: Well, y' know, we took a chance. We tried to keep it quiet, 'n we tried to arrive here quiet, but we must've been spotted, 'n that's the end of it, y' know. (He shrugs, hopelessly.) So, from now on, it's not really a honeymoon, it's just...we're just stayin' here.
Q: How do you think the other Beatles reacted?
Ringo: Well, John 'n George were great, y' know. They were happy 'n congratulated us 'n everythin'. 'N they, in fact, went to the weddin'.

"Even without our boutonnières, son!" John shouted at the telly.

Q: When are the rest of you going to get married?
Ringo: When are the rest of *them*? I don't know. I've no idea. As I said before, I don't think 'cause I'm married, next week they'll all pop up 'n say, "We're gettin' married 'cause Ringo is!", y' know.

Q: What sort of an effect, really, do you think the marriage is going to have on The Beatles' future?

Ringo: On The Beatles as a whole, I don't think any great effect...as much as that everyone will sorta say, "Well, we can't sorta *like* them anymore 'cause Ringo's married," y' know. I don't think I've got *that* image. I don't think it'll bother 'em too much. It may help, in fact, y' know. We don't know yet. It's too early to say.

Q: Have you decided where you're going to live?

Ringo: Only in the flat I've already got in London, up to now. Then we have to move 'n get a house or something, but it'll be a while yet.

Q: Maureen, what do you think of the flat and the furnishings? Are there any changes you'd like to make?

Maureen: No, it's great!

Ringo: It's a *big flat*, y' know!

(A round of laughter and flashbulbs)

Q: Ringo, where did you propose?

Ringo: In a club.

Q: Can you tell me which club?

Ringo: Yes, if you don't mind a plug. The Ad Lib club.

Q: You mean, you made it up as you went along?

Ringo: *Oh, ho!!* Bad joke!! (Ringo shakes his head.) No, y' know...I was sort of thinkin' about it, 'n I just sort of said, "Will you marry me?" 'n she said, "Yeah...have another drink!" (Laughter) 'N we did, 'n that was it.

Q: Congratulations! Thank you both very much.

Ringo: (Wagging his finger at the press) Thank you. *All right? Goodbye!* Hope *not* to see you out my window again![339]

"Good on yer, Ring!" John was smiling widely. "That's tellin' 'em!"

"You know," Cynthia yawned. She'd been up since 6.00 a.m. "It might be nice if Ringo and Mo moved out here, close to us. We'd have friends nearby who understood...friends to share evenings and holidays and weekends..."[340]

It was a brilliant suggestion, John thought. *Ringo's easy-goin', and Cynthia adores trekkin' about with Maureen.* The Starkeys would be the perfect buffer for the odd malaise that had somehow settled on John's marriage.

"Right, yeah, great! Why don't you ring 'em straightaway 'n sorta suggest it, y' know?" John was instantly on board.

"Oh, I think it can wait until Sunday evening when they're home, don't you?" Cynthia giggled. "Or Monday even!"

But secretly, she, too, was delighted. The Starkeys were happy and good-natured. True friends. And tonight, they seemed a welcoming port in what felt like a large and looming storm.

Notes!

What titbits of information were not covered in this chapter that are of interest?

1.) Paul, who was on holiday with Jane Asher in Tunisia, North Africa, received an early telephone call from the telegraph service reading him Brian Epstein's terse message: "Rich wed early this morning." When Paul returned to London, he told Tony Barrow that he hadn't understood the message and thought the caller was "on about early morning tea." He went on to say, "It was a drag I wasn't there because I would have enjoyed it." (Barrow, 143) Paul did return with a lovely silver apple as a gift for the Starkeys. (Clayson, 141)

2) There is a bit of discussion about how Ringo and Maureen met. I've used Bill Harry's version found in The Ultimate Beatles Encyclopedia, *p. 621, since quite often The Beatles offer less reliable accounts of their own lives than do their close friends or careful biographers. (Who really remembers the intricate details of one's own past without doing the research necessary to dig up the facts?)*

In The Beatles Anthology, *Ringo offers a slightly different version of how he met Maureen. Although Bill Harry places the event at a lunchtime Cavern queue and has Ringo, of necessity, wait several days to escort the lovely Mary (Maureen) Cox on a first date, Ringo states, "We had met in the Cavern. She was in the audience, and I had taken her home (and her friend). There was always that Liverpool thing, "I'll take you home, love." — "Sure, can you take my friend, too?" — "Er, all right." Then, one day you'd ask, "Can we go out alone?" (p. 163) Both stories are charming, and either way, it's clear that Ringo was smitten with Maureen from the very first.*

3) Finally, Brian not only gave the happy couple, their friends, and family a lovely post-wedding breakfast in his Belgravia home, but he also paid for their honeymoon. (Harry, The Encyclopedia of Beatles People, *315 and Clayson, 141) That night, Alf Bicknell says that he drove Maureen's parents and Ringo's parents to London's West End "to have a night out."*

He says "We went to an old pub down the East India Dock Road, and we all got legless." (Bicknell, 29)

Sources:

Lewisohn, The Beatles: Day by Day, *59.*
Harry, The Ultimate Beatles Encyclopedia, *621.*
Harry, The Encyclopedia of Beatles People, *315.*
The Beatles, The Beatles Anthology, *163.*
Barrow, *143.*
Lennon, Cynthia, A Twist of Lennon, *139.*
Lennon, Cynthia, John, *98, 150, 152, 158, 161, and 170.*
Coleman, Lennon, *176-177 (An account of the Lennons' wedding for comparison) and 222.*
Miles, The Beatles' Diary, Vol. 1, *188.*
Spitz, The Beatles, *551-552.*
Norman, Shout!, *161.*
Clayson, Ringo Starr: A Life, *141-142.*
Starr, Ringo: With a Little Help From My Friends, *58-59.*
Brown, *168.*
Winn, *294.*
Wells, Simon, 365 Days, *Feb. 12, 1965.*
Hill, John, Paul, George & Ringo, *188-189.*
Kenny, The Making of John Lennon, *172.*
Riley, Lennon, *270.*
Bicknell, *29.*
Connolly, *138.*
Badman, *139-140.*
Freeman, Robert, The Beatles: A Private View, *122-125. Excellent photos of the day tell the happy story of this wedding.*
Davis, Andy, The Beatles Files, *84. Photos of the Starkey press conference can be found here.*
Solt, Andrew and Egan, Sam, Imagine, *82.*
Schultheiss, *129.*

https://www.beatlesinterviews.net *This is the source of the ITV and BBC television interviews in this chapter. Thanks to Jay Spangler for such careful transcription!*

https://flashbak.com/ringo-and-maureens-glamorous-honeymoon-in-hove-in-1965-17874/ *This article covers the press conference that Ringo and Maureen gave the press on Friday, 12 April. It includes several photos.*

http://www.meetthebeatlesforreal.com/search?q=Ringo%27s+wedding+1965 *This is a very detailed account of the wedding written by a fan named Cheryl Hillman.*

https://en.wikipedia.org/wiki/List_of_Billboard_Hot_100_number-one_singles_of_1965 This website lists the top Billboard hits of 1965, month-by-month.

https://www.goodreads.com/author/quotes/19968.John_Lennon   This website has a compilation of quotes by John Lennon.

https://inanyeventblog.files.wordpress.com/2014/02/650211-ringo-starr-maureen-starkey-wedding_01.jpg Another photo of the Starkey wedding.

https://www.youtube.com/watch?v=Sqy3JG68bvk This is a four-minute video of photos from Ringo's wedding. You can see George and John in one photo, without their boutonnières! Or use this QR code:

---

[283] Bicknell, 29. Alf says that Cynthia went to visit Maureen on the day after she returned from Switzerland, and "John [was] excited about the wedding" as well.

[284] Bicknell, 29.

[285] Lennon, Cynthia, *John*, 158.

[286] Barrow, 143. Barrow says that although all of The Beatles and retinue knew that Maureen was pregnant, they also knew that the couple "acted like a couple of lovebirds." It clearly wasn't an unwanted pregnancy or wedding.

[287] Barrow, 143.

[288] Harry, *The Encyclopedia of Beatles People*, 315, Harry, *The Ultimate Beatles Encyclopedia*, 621, Norman, *Shout!*, 161, and Brown, Peter, 168. Bill Harry says, "…[Ringo's] name was linked in the press with model, Vicki Hodge…but it was common knowledge in Liverpool that [Maureen Cox] was Ringo's girlfriend." Peter Brown says that Ringo did go out with Vicki Hodge a few times "for the kick of it," but says he was sincerely in love with Maureen.

[289] The spellings of Ringo's nickname are many and varied. In the first official band biography, *The Beatles*, Hunter Davies uses "Ritchie," and Philip Norman in *John Lennon: The Life* uses "Ritchie." Bill Harry, in *The Ultimate Beatles Encyclopedia*, uses "Richie" as does Alan Clayson in *Ringo Starr: A Life*. Michael Seth Starr in *Ringo: With a Little Help* employs "Richy" as does

Beatles Guru Mark Lewisohn in *Tune In*. When I began **The John Lennon Series** 34 years ago, I followed Hunter Davies's lead and used "Ritchie," so I will remain consistent with that spelling, but that preference does NOT indicate a misspelling of the fond moniker by any other researcher.

[290] The Beatles, *The Beatles Anthology*, 163. Ringo says that when The Beatles started out, few people booked gigs on Mondays, and so, he'd "dash up to Liverpool and we'd go to a pub, to the movies, or see a show, and then go to a restaurant." He says that "any time we *did* have off, I spent with [Maureen]."

[291] Harry, *The Encyclopedia of Beatles People*, 315, Harry, *The Ultimate Beatles Encyclopedia*, 621, Miles, *The Beatles' Diary, Vol. 1*, 188-189, Starr, 58, and Norman, *Shout!*, 161.

[292] Harry, *The Beatles Ultimate Encyclopedia*, 621.

[293] Harry, *The Beatles Ultimate Encyclopedia*, 621. Harry points out that Ringo had only been a Beatle for three weeks when he spotted Maureen.

[294] Maureen had turned 16 years old on 4 August 1962.

[295] Harry, *The Ultimate Beatles Encyclopedia*, 621.

[296] Harry, *The Ultimate Beatles Encyclopedia*, 621.

[297] The Beatles, *The Beatles Anthology*, 163. Direct quote from Ringo Starr.

[298] Lewisohn, *The Beatles: Day by Day,* 59, Harry, *The Encyclopedia of Beatles People*, 315, Harry, *The Ultimate Beatles Encyclopedia*, 621, Spitz, 551, Riley, *Lennon,* 270, Bicknell, 29, Hill, *John, Paul, George & Ringo*, 188, Barrow, 143, and Lennon, Cynthia, *John*, 158.

[299] Spitz, 551.

[300] Harry, *The Encyclopedia of Beatles People*, 27, Coleman, *Lennon*, 7, Lennon, Cynthia, *John*, 20, and Lennon, Cynthia, *A Twist of Lennon*, 15. And read about this event in Vol. 1 of **The John Lennon Series**, *Shoulda Been There*, pp. 255-258.

[301] Spitz, 552. This is a direct quote from John Lennon. In fact, he repeats it to the press later that day.

[302] https://inanyeventblog.files.wordpress.com/2014/02/650211-ringo-starr-maureen-starkey-wedding_01.jpg You may see the photo of the wedding party, including Cynthia and John, here.

[303] Bicknell, 29.

[304] Barrow, 143. Direct quote to the press from George Harrison.

[305] Spitz, 551, Harry, *The Ultimate Beatles Encyclopedia*, 621, and Harry, *The Encyclopedia of Beatles People,* 316.

[306] https://inanyeventblog.files.wordpress.com/2014/02/650211-ringo-starr-maureen-starkey-wedding_01.jpg

[307] Starr, 142. Starr states, "Brian Epstein was best man, and Lennon noted that Ringo hadn't even bought his male guests boutonnieres, joking to a reporter that 'they were goin' to wear radishes, actually.'"

[308] Badman, 139-140 and Starr, 142,

[309] Miles, *The Beatles' Diary, Vol. 1*, 188.

[310] Harry, *The Encyclopedia of Beatles People*, 316, Lennon, Cynthia, *John*, 158, Miles, *The Beatles' Diary, Vol. 1*, 188, Schultheiss, 129, Hill, *John, Paul, George & Ringo*, 188, Bicknell, 29, and Harry, *The Ultimate Beatles Encyclopedia*, 621

[311] Lennon, Cynthia, *A Twist of Lennon*, 81-82 and Lennon, Cynthia, *John*, 95-96. The story of John and Cynthia's rather "eventful" wedding may be found on these pages. All of the details Cynthia is recalling really took place. And read about this event in Vol. 2 of **The John Lennon Series**, *Shivering Inside*, pp. 244-245.

[312] Badman, 139. This is the first line of an interview with John and George after Ringo's wedding. I'm not going to footnote every line but will footnote again at the end of the interview.

[313] Badman, 139. This is the last line of the interview with John and George after Ringo's wedding.

[314] Harry, *The Encyclopedia of Beatles People*, 315. Harry says that Ringo gave this direct quote to *Woman's Own* magazine.

[315] Lennon, Cynthia, *A Twist of Lennon,* 139 and Harry, *The Encyclopedia of Beatles People*, 316.

[316] Lennon, Cynthia, *A Twist of Lennon*, 139 and Harry, *The Encyclopedia of Beatles People*, 316. All of the details in this paragraph are from Cynthia's own description of Christmas 1964.

[317] Norman, *Shout!*, 161. Norman quotes Cynthia as saying that John sat up with her at night, "smoking, reading, doodling, and endlessly playing the same Bob Dylan LP."

[318] Lennon, Cynthia, *A Twist of Lennon*, 139. This is a direct quote from Cynthia Lennon.

[319] Lennon, Cynthia, *A Twist of Lennon*, 139 and Lennon, Cynthia, *John*, 163. Direct quote from Cynthia Lennon.

[320] Lennon, Cynthia, *A Twist of Lennon*, 139. This is a direct quote from Cynthia Lennon.

[321] Lennon, Cynthia, *A Twist of Lennon*, 139. This is a paraphrase of a comment by Cynthia Lennon.

[322] Lennon, Cynthia, *John,* 195.

[323] Lennon, Cynthia, *A Twist of Lennon*, 139. This is a direct quote from Cynthia Lennon.

[324] Lennon, Cynthia, *A Twist of Lennon*, 139. Cynthia says that as the drug scene accelerated for The Beatles, she stood apart. "I couldn't go along with [John]," she states.

[325] Spitz, 552. This is a direct quote from Ringo Starr.

[326] https://en.wikipedia.org/wiki/List_of_Billboard_Hot_100_number-one_singles_of_1965 "You've Lost That Lovin' Feelin'" was #1 on the U.S. *Billboard* charts on 6 February and was topping the charts in the U.K. as well. Ironically, this is the song that The Righteous Brothers recorded not long after leaving The Beatles' 1964 North American Tour, due to fan apathy in the wake of the Fab Four!

[327] Lennon, Cynthia, *John*, 170 and Solt, Andrew and Sam Egan*, Imagine*, 82. In John, Cyn says that when he was home, "at two p.m., John received a wake-up call and a cup of tea." She is quoted in *Imagine* as saying, "He would sleep until late and be up late."

[328] Lennon, Cynthia, *John*, 150.

[329] Wells, 12 February 1965 and Starr, 143. Wells states, "The newlyweds had hoped to spend a week at the house owned by their lawyer, David Jacobs, but word quickly spread, with fans camped outside the home…"

[330] Lewisohn, *The Beatles: Day by Day*, 59, Miles, *The Beatles' Diary, Vol. 1*, 188, Bicknell, 29, Brown, 188, Winn, 294, and Barrow, 143. Tony Barrow says that David Jacobs (one of The Beatles' financial advisors) graciously offered his place near Brighton because he felt it would be quiet and secluded…difficult for the press to locate. But almost immediately they were discovered, and Ringo was advised by Brian to give a press conference in the "unglamorous back garden" of Jacobs's home. That was done on the afternoon of Friday, 12 February. Lewisohn lists the address as 2 Princes Crescent, Hove, Sussex.

[331] Clayson, *Ringo Starr: A Life*, 141-142,

[332] Barrow, 143. This is a direct quote from Brian Epstein, according to Tony Barrow.

[333] http://www.scienceagogo.com/store/1965-Press-Photo-Ringo-Starr-And-Maureen-Cox-At-Wedding-Caxton-Hall-London_352619340732.html The original newspaper wedding announcement for the Starkeys can be viewed at this website.

[334] https://www.goodreads.com/author/quotes/19968.John_Lennon

[335] http://tinyurl.com/y44vmhr8 You can see images of the Starkeys at the Hove press conference here.

[336] http://www.beatlesinterviews.org/db1965.0212.beatles.html This is the first line of the ITV honeymoon interview with Ringo and Maureen Starkey from David Jacobs' home in 2 Princes Crescent, Hove, Sussex. I'm not going to footnote every line, but will footnote again at the end of this interview.

[337] http://www.beatlesinterviews.org/db1965.0212.beatles.html This is the last line of the ITV honeymoon interview with Ringo and Maureen Starkey from David Jacobs' home in 2 Princes Crescent, Hove, Sussex.

[338] Winn, *Way Beyond Compare*, 294. Wynn tells us this interview was filmed by ITV on 12 Feb. 1965 at 1:00 p.m. and lasted two minutes, 42 seconds. The transcript was found at: http://www.beatlesinterviews.org/db1965.0212.beatles.html This is the first line of this ITV honeymoon interview with Ringo and Maureen Starkey from David Jacobs' home in 2 Princes Crescent, Hove, Sussex. I'm not going to footnote every line, but will footnote again at the end of this interview.

[339] Winn, *Way Beyond Compare*, 294 and http://www.beatlesinterviews.org/db1965.0212.beatles.html This is the last line of the ITV honeymoon interview with Ringo and Maureen Starkey.

[340] Lennon, Cynthia, *John*, 98. Cynthia says that although, at first, Ringo thought she was "stuck up," after a few months, they "became very good friends, and I discovered he was one of the most kind-hearted, easy-going and good-natured men alive." Cynthia was also very close with Maureen and was quite influential in convincing the Starkeys to move to Weybridge.

Monday, 15 February 1965
Studio Two, EMI Studios
3 Abbey Road
London

2.30 p.m.

They had only five days in studio to record the tracks for the upcoming film. Five days. But everything about returning to work felt right: the slightly dank, nicotined smell of Studio Two and the "cushy" give of the faded floral carpet beneath John's feet. The clang of dinted, littered ashtrays; rickety, metal stools; and reedy music stands. The bedlam of equipment everywhere; cords looping recklessly, up and around.[341] In a world crumbling beneath John's feet and falling away in chunks, the studio remained solid and unchanging.

In this den of imaginative chaos, harmony lingered. In EMI, John was instantly at home. Here, he was a piece of the puzzle that neatly fit. He was one of a group. And grateful to be back again, John stood, drawing a deep breath. He very nearly smiled.

Two years ago, almost on this date, they'd all arrived in EMI early...before 10.00 a.m.[342] Wearing similar coats and ties, they'd mumbled quietly to one another and begun industriously setting up gear to record their first LP. Regarded as "berks down from Liverpool,"[343] The Beatles had said little and concentrated on their work.

But that day, despite a bout of flu that had them all tossing back lozenges[344] and draining waxy cartons of cold milk,[345] they had accomplished more than the powers-that-be had ever imagined. They'd changed their futures, dramatically. And they had changed the state of EMI.

Today, in dark, tieless shirts — unbuttoned at the collar — and casual sport jackets of every variety, the boys confidently ambled in after noon. A cig dangled from George's lips. And John's hair — carelessly coifed — was just above the collar.[346] But John was even more excited this afternoon than he'd been at that first session, back in '63. He'd found that he craved work, required work. John needed music to make himself whole again.

Recently, he'd told a reporter, "Work is life, 'n without it, y' know, there's nothin' but fear 'n insecurity."[347] It was as honest as John had ever been.

Now, John carried his German-made, 12-string Framus Hootenanny with him, but recently, George and he had sent Mal on a shopping spree for two Fender Stratocasters, and he was itching to assay the new instrument. George, who'd lately decided that his Gretsch Tennessean "sounded like crap,"[348] was even more elated to experiment with the new Strat sound.[349] Happily, the guitars were already waiting in studio, in the stands.[350] The "Sonic Blues" sat proudly beside John's Rickenbacker 325, Paul's '63 Höfner, and Ringo's sturdy North American Tour Ludwigs.[351]

John, too, was ready. He'd completed the new rocker he'd performed on holiday for Martin. "Ticket to Ride," he called it. And he'd worked up a ballad, somewhat in the vein of their old "She Loves You," dubbed "You're Going to Lose That Girl." Encouraged by Dylan's praise of his early autobiographical ventures, John had penned yet another revealing track about his life: "You've Got to Hide Your Love Away."[352] And then, there was his song for the ever-present Julia. "Yes It Is"[353] made John catch his breath. Although it probed the wound that never healed, it allowed him to sing his heart.

"Well," Paul was already tuning up, "I assume y' passed the audition, then?"

"I'm legal now, son, or so they say." John grinned, toothily, waving his new driver's permit.[354]

"God help 'n save us all." Paul carelessly made the sign of the cross. "You know exactly two speeds, John: fast and stop."[355]

"Well, I passed, now didn't I? Bugger off!"

"What're *you* worried about, Paul?" George chimed in from the corner where he'd been chatting with Neil. "You live in the city. It's Ring 'n me who're considerin' movin' out *closer* to him...into the danger zone, as it were."

"Anyone fancy a lift tonight?" John looked around with raised eyebrows. "I brought m' permit with, y' know."[356] And he flashed it again, like a lad with a new toy.

"Um, thanks, but no thanks," George sniggered. "I prefer to walk. Marvellous exercise!"

John gave him the backhanded V, just as Ringo made a smiling entrance. "Ah, the clergy's all here, I see!"[357] The drummer was full of Scouse vigour.

"Well, it's the very groom himself!" Paul tossed back. "The one who, quite sadly," he sniffed, "left me out!"[358] He pretended to pout.

"Yeah, well, you had better things to do, I'm sure," Ringo chuckled. "It was all very early mornin' 'n very bare bones, y' know."

"Hmph!" John strolled to his new guitar and bent down to pick it up. "Compared to mine 'n Cyn's, it was a matrimonial *production*!"[359] He slipped the Strat's strap over his head and adjusted the instrument higher on his chest.

"Welcome back, everyone," George Martin called over the 1MC. "I'd plod down and greet you all in person, as you well deserve, but as John can attest, my mobility is, uhm, rather limited at present. Let's just call it a skiing accident, shall we?"

"We shall!" John raised an invisible toast.

"So, I hate to break with tradition, as it were, but things being as they are, I'd like to invite you all up for a short discussion, if you don't mind. I have an idea that I think might save us a lot of time and energy. Mind traipsing up?"

"No, Ringo's been up all weekend," George muttered. "'H' orta be well-practiced."

Laughing and slapping Ringo on the back, they headed for the stairs and the sound booth.

When they were settled, George Martin took a deep breath and began outlining a new and rather economical concept he'd devised for recording their upcoming LP. He suggested that, beginning this afternoon, they record their rehearsals — for self-critique — and then, once ready to record in earnest, they could spool back over the tape, re-recording on top of the used portion.[360] Having focused carefully on the song's key elements during trial runs, they could then record a basic, foundation track upon which they could superimpose element after element as needed.[361]

"For example," Martin elucidated, "the rhythm track could be recorded first. Then, we'd liberally overdub on top of that, dropping in additional sounds — as many as we deem necessary — after the fact."[362]

"So," Paul made certain they all understood, "we could later add in lead, any number of instruments, our vocal effects, 'n so forth."[363]

Martin smiled. "Whatever your heart desires, Paul."

"What about what *my* heart desires?" Ringo was chipper, atypically vocal.

"You've had enough of *that*, son!" John cut his eyes at the drummer. "It's down to work now."

And in minutes, they were at it. The boys recorded a backing track for John's "Ticket to Ride," consisting of Paul's bass and Ringo's drums. Then, immediately after, they captured John's rhythm and George's lead on a second track[364] — including a signature riff that echoed throughout the song on Harrison's 12-string Rickenbacker.[365]

The booth was well-satisfied.

"When these sessions begin," George Martin confessed to engineer Norman Smith, "my heart's usually in my mouth. I wonder, sometimes, whether they can keep it up time after time..."[366]

"And?" Smith lifted a palm to the room below.

"And they do!" Martin grinned. "They're very workmanlike in studio, aren't they? I-I don't mean they're serious and somber...I mean, look at them, they're always full of fun. But, inevitably, *they get the job done!*"[367]

"Ready with the vocal!" John called up, neck craned forward, eyes serious. And as the red light blinked on, a third track rolled, capturing an almost flawless rendition of John's edgy lyrics and his gravelly rock voice.[368]

Moments later, on a fourth track, John sang a second vocal — this one to be used in the choruses. Ringo added a bit of tambourine. There were handclaps for the middle eight and coda.[369] And meticulously, Paul overdubbed guitar fills.[370] Inch by inch, the lads added bits — bits that transformed the ordinary into the excellent.

Then, the boys captured something rather unique. On Track 4, using his hollow-bodied, 1962 Epiphone ES-230TD, Paul played the self-same repeating lead riff that George Harrison had performed on Track 1, superimposing the Epiphone tone onto the resonance of the Rick.[371] It was a bright, full sound. Strong and demanding.[372]

"Wonderful!" Martin pronounced over the mic. He nodded at Norman. The Beatles were acquiring a finesse that permitted him to take a step back. No longer was he the "schoolmaster" teaching his boys. These days, he was a co-creator. Martin worked his magic at the mixing board[373] and chimed in during sessions when requested, but no longer did he instruct a group of ingenues.[374]

"Ringo," Martin pushed the speaker button once again, "that drum pattern's magnificent! The song's coming together rather nicely...don't you agree, John?"[375]

John nodded, pleased with the translation from his imagination to tape. Back in January, he'd heard The Who's release, "I Can't Explain." He'd also noted the Kinks' "You Really Got Me," as well as Them's "Baby, Please Don't Go," and the Stones' unflinching "It's All Over Now." And a bit jealous, John had been challenged to take his music in a heavier direction.[376] "Ticket to Ride" did just that.

Still true to his rock'n'roll roots, John felt he'd instilled a bolder, harder sound here, gritty rock with a unique overwash of blues. Undeniably different from anything he'd ever done.[377] Even the bridge lyrics — hissing the veiled threat, "She oughta think twice!" — were gutsier than traditional Beatles fare. "Ticket to Ride" was a bitter song of love betrayed.[378] The words and music were fired with fury.[379] Every element drew a sharp, unbending line.[380]

John was taking his music where *he* wanted to go. He was weary of compromise and vapid "smiles at nothing." He was beginning to say "no." He was beginning to be less "The Leader Beatle" and more John.

"All right, everyone," George Martin intoned, "it's nearing 5.45,[381] and as such, we're coming upon the dinner hour. Why don't we take a break before moving on? You've made outstanding progress."

And for the odd once, The Beatles agreed to a breather. It had been an intense afternoon, and everyone was ready for a drink, a plate of hot food, and a smoke.[382]

****

8.43 p.m.[383]

John wasn't oblivious to the subtle encroachment, and he was sure George wasn't either. That afternoon, Paul had stepped in to "perfect" the repeating lead lick on "Ticket to Ride," and now, Macca was unhappy with George's lead work on Paul's "Another Girl."[384] As he'd done with Ringo earlier in the day, Paul kept suggesting this and recommending that, trying to "make it a bit better."[385] At this point, the only "carrot" keeping Harrison from grim resentment was the knowledge that his own song, "I Need You," was next on the docket.[386] George shrugged Paul off and kept his own counsel.

John had known, since that first afternoon at the Woolton Garden Fête, that once in the group, McCartney wouldn't fail to assert his prowess. He realised that Paul would always be a leader, "a coup waiting to happen."[387] But longing desperately for the "toppermost of the poppermost," John had acquiesced to The Quarry Men's pleas for the talented Allerton boy — and John conceded that Paul was the one who could help get him there: into the spotlight, onto the marquee, into the Top Ten...bigger than Elvis. And Paul *had* done.

Tonight, after more than a dozen rehearsal takes, John stood eyeing McCartney. Front and centre, in control, Paul was "conducting" the work on "Another Girl" — a vamping ditty written on his holiday in Tunisia.[388] Stepping up, taking charge, Paul directed each detail. Just as he'd schooled Ringo on the technique needed for his "Ticket to Ride" drum part, now he was leaning over George's Jumbo Gibson and offering very specific instructions.[389]

It was a trend to be watched, John noted — something to keep an eye on, whilst remembering that Paul produced results.

The group moved swiftly through Track 1 — the backing track with bass and drums — straight into Track 2 featuring John's new Fender Strat and George's acoustic. "Another Girl" was piecing together nicely.

On Track 3, Paul sang his lead vocal whilst George and John supplied the backing bits. And then, Track 4 was filled with overdubs: additional vocals from Paul and John with George performing on his Gretsch and perfecting a guitar flourish as Ringo added in tom-toms.[390] Martin's new system was proving a rapid and effectual way to work. Already, there was a second song well in the works, with ample time left over to focus on George's composition.

"Ready with your song, George?" George Martin was heartening, good-humoured. He, too, had been able to observe the dynamics playing out in studio. He was the silent, "all-seeing eye." But rarely did Martin intrude in studio politics.[391]

"Yeah, right, whenever you are." George offered his cock-eyed smile. "Or everyone else is." The words held thinly-veiled significance.

"Well, let's have a few run-throughs first, shall we?" Martin smiled warmly through the overhead glass. And the boys complied — stopping to confer with Harrison, listening to his plans and making suggestions.

Ringo decided to deliver the muted, bongo-esque drums George desired by pounding out beats on the back of Harrison's Gibson Jumbo,[392] whilst John agreed to mount Ringo's podium and steer the tempo, striking the snare on the two and four.[393] With Paul this time only on bass and George gently strumming his Spanish guitar, the melancholy love song, "I Need You," began to emerge.[394] George's minor key vocal was the star of Track 2.[395] And on Track 3, harmony and overdubs came into play. Finally, close to 10.30 p.m., Track 4 was completed, including additional vocal doubling and the lonesome sound of Ringo's cowbell.[396]

"I think we've toiled enough for one day," Martin called down, as Track 4 concluded. "Shall we call it a night?" He rarely added "boys" any longer, as he had in the old days, when Brian was in studio. The Beatles weren't boys any longer. They were men — highly-regarded musicians.

"Yerrokay," George nodded.

"Right...2.30 tomorrow, then?" Paul slipped out of his guitar.

"Yes, 2.30 p.m.," Martin confirmed.

"We'll be here." John made it official.

And whilst the others untethered from this instrument or that, John made a point to stroll over to George and cadge a cig. It had been a productive session, but the sort that called for one of Uncle "Ge'rge's" bawdy limericks — a laugh, a nod, and a wink.

"Not bad, that song, y' know." John gave his "little brother" a fond nudge.

"Says you." George threw his eyes to the ceiling. "Others might care to disagree."

"Well, we all know *I'm* the only one who really fuggin' matters!" John made George sputter. But they both knew that one vote from any Beatle could nullify a song altogether.[397] According to group rules, no one claimed command.

Until very recently, however — perhaps even until tonight, John *had* enjoyed a certain amount of clout over the others. His band, his leadership, his word. He had held unspoken sway. Now, he felt the balance of power finely shifting, and John was certain George did as well.[398]

So, they packed their gear and dealt in small talk. They chatted and ignored the obvious. And as they ambled towards the door, John suggested George and Pattie "drop 'round Kenwood, come Sunday, for a Monopoly marathon 'n this single-malt Scotch someone 'r other gifted me, birthday last." It wasn't much, but it was the kind of comfort John could offer.

"Yeah," George nodded, pledging the old loyalty right back, "will do."

And as he tossed John another loosie, George reached down deep and found his smile.

Notes!

1. Did George Harrison really feel slighted during the 15 February taping in Studio Two, EMI?

One can only imagine how George Harrison reacted to having his lead flourish in "Ticket to Ride" overlapped by Paul's rendition of that line. Then, when Paul began to find fault with George's lead in "Another Girl" — and ultimately decided to tackle the lead himself, things must have been a bit tense.

In fact, in Dr. Kenneth Womack's Maximum Volume: The Life of Beatles Producer, George Martin, *Martin is quoted as saying, "George got a bit discouraged...when none of us liked something he had written." (p. 249) And in* The Beatles' Diary, Vol. 1, *Barry Miles's entry for 15 February 1965 says that thankfully, "George Harrison's misgivings about his diminished role in these tracks ["Ticket to Ride" and "Another Girl"] were presumably dampened by the fact that the third song taped that day was one of his own." (p. 204)*

Indeed, the fortunate recording of "I Need You" on 15 February 1965 did assuage Harrison's injured ego. George Martin commented: "'I Need You' worked out very well...[Harrison] has got something to say as a songwriter, and I hope he keeps it up." (Womack, p. 249) *Furthermore, Womack notes that, "Harrison, who had long toiled in the shadows of Lennon and McCartney," hurdled a "significant milestone" with the recording of "I Need You." (*Maximum Volume, the Life of Beatles Producer, George Martin, *p.* 249) *It helped elevate his credibility with the band at a juncture where this boost was most required.*

2. Why isn't the use of the sound volume pedal on "I Need You" mentioned in this chapter?

It was added on the following day, 16 February, and will be covered in the following chapter.

Sources:

Lewisohn, The Complete Beatles Chronicle, *99 and 183.*
Lewisohn, The Beatles Recording Sessions, *24 and 54-56.*
Lewisohn, The Beatles: Day by Day, *59.*
Harry, The Ultimate Beatles Encyclopedia, *22, 292, and 651.*
Lennon, Cynthia, John, *166-167.*
The Beatles, The Beatles Anthology, *173.*
Womack, Maximum Volume: The Life of Beatles Producer, George Martin, *247-249.*
Womack, The Beatles Encyclopedia, *909.*
Hammack, 14-15, 16-17, and 18-19.
Winn, 31-34 and 295.
Everett, Walter, The Beatles As Musicians: The Quarry Men Through Rubber Soul, *282-283 and 288.*
Margotin and Guesdon, 230, 232, and 236-237.
MacDonald, 112-116.
Russell, Jeff, The Beatles Complete Discography, *72.*
Babiuk, Beatles Gear, *157-159.*
Miles, The Beatles' Diary, Vol. 1, *85, 189, and 204.*
Spizer, The Beatles for Sale on Parlophone Records, *46 and 188-189.*
Spignesi and Lewis, 99-100, 152-153, and 283.
Turner, 78 and 80.
Riley, Tell Me Why, *142-145.*
Cain and McCusker, 168-169.
Badman, 140.
Barrow, 143.
Pawlowski, Gareth, How They Became The Beatles, *120.*
Spitz, 555.
Trynka, 42-46 and 169.
Norman, John Lennon: The Life, *394.*
Hill, John, Paul, George & Ringo, *187.*
Solt and Egan, Imagine, *75.*
Sheff, 165.

Schultheiss, 129.
Coleman, Lennon, *176-177.*

A more detailed account of John's wedding (in contrast to Ringo's) may be found in **The John Lennon Series,** *Vol. 2,* Shivering Inside, *pp. 244-253.*

In Hill's book, The Beatles: A Life in Pictures, *p. 54, there is a photo of John just after receiving his license. He's posing in George Martin's car in the EMI Studios car park. There is another similar photo in Buskin's* John Lennon: His Life and Legend, *p. 133.*

https://www.beatlesbible.com/songs/ticket-to-ride/
This website provides additional information about "Ticket to Ride," including many direct quotes from John and Paul.

https://en.wikipedia.org/wiki/I_Can%27t_Explain
This website gives information about The Who's song "I Can't Explain," a forerunner to "Ticket to Ride."

https://www.last.fm/music/The+Beatles/_/Ticket+to+Ride
Months later, The Beatles "mimed" this performance of "Ticket to Ride." Thought you might enjoy it.

https://www.youtube.com/watch?v=h3h--K5928M
You can listen to "I Can't Explain" by The Who at this site.

https://www.beatlesbible.com/1969/07/01/john-lennon-crashes-his-car-in-scotland/
Information on John Lennon's acquisition of his driver's license can be found here.

https://www.thedailybeast.com/what-made-the-beatles-so-big-diagnosing-beatlemania In this article, John Lennon addresses the conflict he felt when inviting a strong leader such as Paul McCartney into the band.

---

[341] Solt and Egan, *Imagine*, 72, Lewisohn, Mark, *The Beatles Recording Sessions*, 55-56, and Babiuk, Andy, *Beatles Gear*, 159. The descriptions of Studio Two (or Two Studio, as Paul refers to it on the 1964 Christmas Record) come from photos found in these three sources. Although the Solt and Egan photo was taken in 1964, you can see the carpet, music stands, and stools, which would have been the same in 1965.

[342] Lewisohn, *The Complete Beatles Chronicle*, 99, Lewisohn, *The Beatles Recording Sessions*, 26-29, Miles, *The Beatles' Diary, Vol. 1,* 85, and Winn, *Way Beyond Compare*, 31-34.

[343] Trynka, 42-46.

[344] Lewisohn, *The Beatles Recording Sessions*, 24 and Pawlowski, Gareth, *How They Became The Beatles*, 120.

[345] Lewisohn, *The Complete Beatles Chronicle*, 99 and Lewisohn, *The Beatles Recording Sessions,* 24. For more on the 11 Feb. 1963 EMI recording session for *Please Please Me*, go to *Shivering Inside*, Vol. 2 in **The John Lennon Series**, pp. 436-481. Utilizing the EMI tapes from that day, carefully transcribed by John C. Winn, this chapter is almost a minute-by-minute account. (Available in all e-book formats.)

[346] Lewisohn, *The Complete Beatles Chronicle*, 55-56 and Hill, *John, Paul, George & Ringo,* 187. This description taken from the photos Lewisohn and Hill provide.

[347] Solt and Egan, *Imagine*, 75. Direct quote from John Lennon.

[348] Babiuk, *Beatles Gear,* 157-158. Direct quote from George Harrison.

[349] Babiuk, 158. A photo of the sonic blue Fender Stratocasters that John and George acquired can been seen on pp. 159-160. Babiuk says that in the week-long "recording sessions at Abbey Road Studio [beginning] on 15 February…Lennon's repaired '64 Rickenbacker made its way back into the guitar line-up…" But he goes on to say that "Lennon was playing a Fender Stratocaster during these sessions" as well.

[350] Hammack, Jerry, *The Beatles Recording Reference Manual, Vol. 2*, 35, Guesdon and Margotin, *All the Songs: The Story Behind Every Beatles Release*, 239, and Babiuk, 157 and 159. Although John uses the new Strat sparingly during these sessions, Babiuk says the new guitar is in the studio. Futhermore, Jerry Hammack says that during both the 20 February recording of "That Means a Lot" and the recording of "Ticket to Ride," John did use his "1961 Fender Stratocaster." On p. 159, Babiuk says that John's new Sonic Blue Strat had "December 1961" on the neck. So, although Lennon and Harrison's new guitars played a larger role in *Rubber Soul* than in *Help!*, the new instruments were in Studio Two and were used. In *Beatles Gear*, p. 159, you can actually see a photo of John in EMI with his new Strat, February 1965.

[351] Babiuk, 157.

[352] Everett, *The Beatles and Musicians, Vol. 1*, 288.

[353] Lewisohn, *The Beatles Recording Sessions*, 54-56, Lewisohn, *The Complete Beatles Chronicle*, 183-184, and Miles, *The Beatles' Diary, Vol. 1*, 189.

[354] Miles, *The Beatles' Diary, Vol. 1*, 189, Lewisohn, *The Beatles: Day by Day*, 59, Hill, *John, Paul, George & Ringo*, 187, Badman, 140, and Schultheiss, 129. At the age of 24, John finally passed his driving test out in Weybridge. There is a photo of the happy motorist on p. 187 of Hill's book with the other Beatles around, giving him thumbs up. Although John had a wide reputation as a bad driver, his driving instructor Paul Wilson said, "He was one of the most apt pupils I have had to teach in my thirty years of driving instruction. He has done very well in such a short time. He was very quick."

[355] https://www.beatlesbible.com/1969/07/01/john-lennon-crashes-his-car-in-scotland/ Author Joe Goodden points out in his BeatlesBible website that John was "a notoriously bad driver" and rarely got behind the wheel.

[356] Lennon, Cynthia, *John,* 166-167. Cynthia says that although "one of John's biggest indulgences…was cars," he didn't want to drive them himself. They were purchased "for the chauffeur to drive us around in." Partly because of his vision and partly due to lack of practice, Cynthia indicates that John was never comfortable behind the wheel, and all of The Beatles knew it.

[357] Scouse phrase meaning, "all the important people are present."

[358] Barrow, 143. This is in keeping with Paul's comment to Tony Barrow that he was sad that he hadn't been included in the wedding because he would have enjoyed it.

[359] Coleman, *Lennon,* 176-177. A full account of John's rushed and rather "bare bones" wedding is found on these pages. It is also told in detail in Vol. 2 of **The John Lennon Series,** *Shivering Inside,* pp. 244-253.

[360] Lewisohn, *The Beatles Recording Sessions,* 54 and Womack, *Maximum Volume: The Life of Beatles Producer, George Martin,* 247. As Womack points out, this new practice "established a shift in the band's recording practices that would leave an indelible mark on their sound. As the tape ran unabated, The Beatles would focus their attention on perfecting the bedrock of the song — often concentrating purely on the backing or rhythm track."

[361] Lewisohn, *The Beatles Recording Sessions,* 54 and Womack, *Maximum Volume: The Life of Beatles Producer, George Martin,* 247. Womack says that using this process they "literally [built] 'Ticket to Ride' from the ground up."

[362] Lewisohn, *The Beatles Recording Sessions,* 54 and Womack, *Maximum Volume: The Life of Beatles Producer, George Martin,* 247.

[363] Womack, *Maximum Volume: The Life of Beatles Producer, George Martin,* 247.

[364] Winn, *Way Beyond Compare,* 295, Lewisohn, *The Beatles Recording Sessions,* 54, Lewisohn, *The Complete Beatles Chronicle,* 183, Hammack, 14-15, Womack, *Maximum Volume: The Life Of Beatles Producer, George Martin,* 247, Everett, Walter, *The Beatles As Musicians: The Quarry Men through Rubber Soul,* 282, and Babiuk, 159. Dr. Kenneth Womack in *Maximum Volume: The Life of Beatles Producer, George Martin,* states, "Harrison execut[ed] the twelve-string Rickenbacker riff." Winn says that George "play[ed] the repeating riff of his twelve-string Rickenbacker." And respected Beatles musicologist Dr. Walter Everett states, "The song's main guitar riff was played by Harrison on his Rickenbacker 12-string." For those of you who are saying, "Wait, I thought the riff was played by Paul!", please wait. We'll get to that in a minute.

[365] Womack, *Maximum Volume: The Life of Beatles Producer, George Martin,* 247, Winn, *Way Beyond Compare,* 295, Babiuk, 159, and Everett, 85.

[366] Badman, 140. Direct quote from George Martin on the *Help!* recording sessions.

[367] Badman, 140. Direct quote from George Martin except for the words "look at them," which were added for stage direction.

[368] Lewisohn, *The Beatles Recording Sessions,* 54, Winn, 295, Womack, *Maximum Volume: The Life of Beatles Producer, George Martin,* 247, and Hammack, 15.

[369] Lewisohn, *The Beatles Recording Sessions*, 54, Winn, 295, Womack, *Maximum Volume: The Life of Beatles Producer, George Martin*, 247, and Hammack, 15.

[370] Womack, *Maximum Volume: The Life of Beatles Producer, George Martin*, 247.

[371] Lewisohn, *The Beatles Recording Sessions*, 54, Womack, *Maximum Volume: The Life of Beatles Producer, George Martin*, 247, Harry, *The Ultimate Beatles Encyclopedia*, 651, and Hammack, 14. Mark Lewisohn clearly states that "Paul played both bass guitar and lead guitar on the song, including the characteristic opening." Hammack agrees, stating, "Superimpositions onto Take 2 followed, including McCartney on lead guitar, playing his 1962 Ephiphone Casino ES-230TD." This superimposition of McCartney's Epiphone over Harrison's Rickenbacker is the sound you hear on the signature riff of "Ticket to Ride." This is what Womack is talking about when he refers to Paul as overdubbing the solo.

[372] Womack, *Maximum Volume: The Life of Beatles Producer, George Martin*, 247. Womack states, "…the production teems with a clear sense of energy and immediacy…a live, crisp sound that finds the band barreling ahead of their most recent work on *Beatles for Sale*."

[373] Womack, *Maximum Volume: The Life of Beatles Producer, George Martin*, 248. Womack points out that "George [Martin] was devoting more of his energies to post-production efforts — particularly in terms of enhancing the finished product."

[374] Womack, *Maximum Volume: The Life of Beatles Producer, George Martin*, 248. Womack says that as The Beatles proved how "truly fearless they could be in the studio…Martin made a conscious effort…to provide the bandmates a wide berth in which to exercise their evolving imaginations."

[375] Lewisohn, *The Beatles Recording Sessions*, 54 and MacDonald, Ian, *Revolution in the Head: The Beatles Recordings and the Sixties,* 113. Lewisohn says that the drum pattern is "said to have been suggested by Paul." Indeed, in Sheff's *The Playboy Interviews with John Lennnon & Yoko Ono*, John says, "Paul's contribution [to 'Ticket to Ride'] was the way Ringo played the drums." Ian MacDonald classifies the sound as "rumbling floor tomtoms." John was reaching for a weighty, harder rock sound, and he achieved his vision.

[376] MacDonald, 113, Turner, 80, Margotin and Guesdon, 236, Trynka, 169, and Spignesi and Lewis, 100. MacDonald makes a point of saying that John "may have been going for the sound effect he'd heard The Who produce seven months earlier." He then (p. 45) refers to that sound as being The Who's "Anyway Anyhow Anywhere," but "Anyway Anyhow Anywhere" wasn't recorded and released until April 1965, **after** "A Ticket to Ride." The song that *might* have had an effect on John could have been The Who's "I Can't Explain," which was released in January 1965. Pete Townsend says that song was based on the Kinks' "All Day and All of the Night," so it had that edgier sound. You can read more about "I Can't Explain" here: https://en.wikipedia.org/wiki/I_Can%27t_Explain And to listen to "I Can't Explain," go to: https://www.youtube.com/watch?v=h3h--K5928M

[377] Spizer, *The Beatles for Sale on Parlophone Records*, 46, Norman, *John Lennon: The Life*, 394, and Trynka, 169. Spizer points out that when "Ticket to Ride" was reviewed by *Record Mirror*, they called it a "mid-tempo rocker with a bluesy feel." Norman calls it "embryonic heavy rock, even heavy metal."

[378] MacDonald, 112.

[379] Riley, *Tell Me Why*, 145. Riley states, "Lennon's solo vocal is so cool it verges on anger..."

[380] Spignesi, Stephen and Lewis, Michael, *100 Best Beatles Songs: An Informed Fans' Guide,* 99. They quote John as saying, "'Ticket to Ride' was slightly a new sound at the time. It was pretty fuckin' heavy for then, if you go and look at the charts for what other music people were making...It's a heavy record and the drums are heavy, too. That's why I like it."

[381] Lewisohn, *The Beatles Recording Sessions*, 54. Lewisohn tells us that the first session was 2.30-5.45 p.m.. The second session was 7.00-10.30 p.m.

[382] Winn, *Way Beyond Compare*, 295. The Beatles often eschewed the evening dinner break, but Winn makes it clear that there was an afternoon session from 2.30-5.45 and then a distinct and separate evening recording session. This indicates a break between the two sessions rather than non-stop work.

[383] Lewisohn, *The Beatles Recording Sessions*, 54. The evening session on Monday, 15 February 1965 began at 7.00 p.m. We are joining the group an hour and 43 minutes into their work.

[384] Martin and Guesdon, 232.

[385] Cain, Alex and McCusker, Terry, *Ringo Starr and The Beatles Beat,* 168 and Spignesi and Lewis, 101. In discussing Ringo's drumming on "Ticket to Ride," Cain and McCusker state: "At the heart of the song is Ringo's magnificent drum pattern, with a refreshing variety of tom fills and no-nonsense tambourine." The authors then note that "the drum pattern [was] apparently suggested by McCartney." (p. 168) To that bit of information, Lewis comments, "If Paul did, in fact, suggest this drum styling, he done good."

[386] Miles, *The Beatles' Diary, Vol. 1,* 204.

[387] Spitz, 555, and https://www.thedailybeast.com/what-made-the-beatles-so-big-diagnosing-beatlemania John Lennon is quoted in this article as saying: "I had a group [the Quarry Men]...I was the singer and the leader; then I met Paul, and I had to make a decision: Was it better to have a guy who was better than the guy I had in? To let the group be stronger, or to let me be stronger?" By the recording sessions in February 1965, Spitz observes that "Paul still deferred to John, but skillfully. He knew how to play the angles..."

[388] Winn, 295, Spizer, *The Beatles for Sale on Parlophone Records*, 189, Margotin and Guesdon, 232, Womack, *Maximum Volume: The Life of Beatles Producer, George Martin, 248,* and Spignesi and Lewis, 284.

[389] Winn, 295.

[390] Winn, 295, Lewisohn, *The Beatles Recording Sessions*, 55, and Margotin and Guesdon, 232. George Martin, in *Playback*, is quoted in Margotin and Guesdon as noting that George was playing his Gibson Jumbo and John was "on the Fender Stratocaster Sonic Blue." (p. 232)

[391] Womack, *Maximum Volume: The Life of Beatles Producer, George Martin,* 248-249.

[392] Winn, 295, Spizer, *The Beatles For Sale on Parlophone Records,* 189, Hammack, 18, and Lewisohn, *The Beatles Recording Sessions,* 54. Hammack says that Ringo used "one of the Gibson acoustic guitars." Winn and Spizer both specify that it was "Ringo thumping the back of a Jumbo Gibson."

[393] Margotin and Guesdon, 230, and Winn, 295.

[394] Winn, 295, Spizer, *The Beatles for Sale on Parlophone Records,* 189, Hammack, 18, and Lewisohn, *The Beatles Recording Sessions,* 54. Hammack tells us that Harrison was either playing his Jose Ramirez Guitarra de Estudio or his Jose Ramirez A1 Segovia nylon string acoustic. Spizer identifies the guitar George is using as "his nylon-stringed acoustic."

[395] Winn, 295.

[396] Winn, 295, Lewisohn, *The Beatles Recording Sessions,* 294, Spizer, *Beatles for Sale on Parlophone Records,* 189, Margotin and Guesdon, 230, Hammack, 18-19, and Spignesi and Lewis, 153. For everyone who is wondering why the use of the tone-volume pedal (or "wah-wah" pedal, as some have termed it) is not mentioned here, that is because it is added **the next day, 16 Feb.** (Hammack, 18-19)

[397] Margotin and Guesdon, 232.

[398] Davies, Hunter, "John Lennon, My Friend," found at: <u>Absolute Elsewhere: The Spirit of John Lennon | Articles: My Friend John</u> In this article by Davies on the relationship between John and Pete Shotton, Pete states: "John never forgot that The Beatles started out as his band. Sometimes it irritated him when Paul appeared to imagine otherwise."

Wednesday, 17 February 1965
Studio Two, EMI Studios
3 Abbey Road
St. John's Wood
London

Yesterday, they'd made tremendous progress on the film soundtrack. Martin had been especially intrigued by the new foot-controlled volume pedal George Harrison had introduced and incorporated into "I Need You."[399] The innovation was brilliant, giving Harrison the ability to lower or raise the sound level quickly.[400] Fascinated with the "handy gadget," but still a novice on the device, George had only employed it on the song's opening, however.[401] For additional volume swells, he'd relied on John to turn his 12-string Rickenbacker's volume knob manually, whilst George played.[402]

"More to come when I've mastered the pedal," George promised the others, "once I've got it up 'n down, so to speak…" A quick grin had brightened his face.

The 16th had been full of changes. In the afternoon, they'd wiped George's lead from Monday's session with a re-recording.[403] Then, the backing vocals — and even Ringo's cowbell — had been re-worked.[404]

Devoting careful attention to detail, The Beatles had honed their sound. But working diligently, they'd put "I Need You" to bed in just over an hour and without a pause, they'd moved right on to Paul's "Another Girl."

Having completed most of the work on the jaunty, new McCartney offering on the 15th, Tuesday's touches to "Another Girl" had been the finale. Using his Epiphone Casino, Paul had overdubbed the lead guitar part, giving special attention to his dramatic solo at the end of the number. Then, wiping Track 2, John and George had re-recorded their backing guitars as well.[405] In just a portion of the afternoon's session, they'd tweaked and tightened the song to perfection; The Beatles were working quite effectively via Martin's new method, coupled with their customarily undiluted focus. They were making strides.

Thus, when the booth — around 5.00 p.m. — suggested a dinner break, the boys had batted it about for a few moments, but decided to press on instead. They were making heavy headway, and the last thing they needed was an hour's distraction.[406] So, the second session of the 16th had begun right where the first left off. No intermission.

February's early evening had been swiftly falling on London when John had presented those gathered with a song that held more emotion than he was willing to admit.

Really, only Jacqui and Ju'll understand the lyrics, anyway,[407] he'd thought, *although, of course, Cyn knows.* And out of respect, his wife had never worn true red. Tomato, orange, maroon, peach, and pink: yes. But red, never. It was precious to John.

"Yes It Is" was a tender, painful lament…a song of memory for the rare and remarkable woman John had loved — still loved — and had lost. It was an aching tribute to Julia Stanley Lennon.[408]

"I would remember all the things we planned… understand… it's true." John's lyrics were confessional. After all this time, he still remembered…still ached for her. And although Julia was with him in shade only, she was the larger part of him still.[409] She would always be.

The song's guitar work, John had entrusted to George, knowing that his "kid brother" would wrap the melancholy lyrics in a doleful cry.[410] And indeed (although John had written the perfect intro and close for the ballad),[411] George had, on his own, created a haunting but lovely lead line for the song — enhanced by the violining volume pedal.[412] The result — a heartbroken line — was bearable only through the tender, three-part harmony of friends, cupping around it.[413] Standing shoulder-to-shoulder with those who knew him best, John had sung his burdened heart.

The bridge had been punishing and raw — hard to hear, harder to sing: "I could be happy with you by my side, if I could forget her…but that's my pride, yes, it is!"

John's longing for the girl he'd never be able to hold close had been laid bare.[414] Revealed.

John had wailed his fevered heart in Studio Two, knowing that in years to come, he'd deny the song altogether. Embarrassed, he would shove it away. He'd rebuke this composition as "a failed copy of 'This Boy.'"[415] Or something worse.

John was always ashamed, in retrospect, by his uninhibited lyrical admissions of emotion. He always reviled them later as "meaningless" or "rubbish" or "shite."

But yesterday, he'd been honest. Over and over again through the years, John had tried to transmute his life's aching regret into some lonely track. He had struggled to find exactly the right words, the right sound. "Yes It Is" had accomplished that.

At night's end, John had recounted the session for Cynthia, down to the finest detail. And Cyn — being Cyn — had stopped to listen.

"I started out on the Gibson Jumbo…my 'go to,' as it were. A steel-stringed guitar. But about a minute or so into the second take, somehow a fuggin' string broke. 'N that was that."[416] He'd stopped for a moment to take the cup of hot Ovaltine Cyn had handed him, a favourite late-night indulgence, left over from childhood. He blew on the surface and ventured a sip. "Anyroad, as George would say…"

"Harrison or Martin?" Cynthia lifted an eyebrow, trying — as weary as she was — to keep track of the story.

"George the Younger," John had smirked, taking another slurp.

"Just making sure."

"Anyroad, as George 'n me were sayin', I had no other choice than to resort to m' Jose Ramirez acoustic…but the thing about it is, Powell, *that* guitar's got these nylon strings, y' know. So, the sound was…I dunno…muted. More reverential, if y' want to get elaborate about it."[417]

"Softer?" Cyn had asked over a stretching yawn.

"Yeah, that."

"And?"

"'N it was…" John had yawned as well, "…just right. I mean, despite havin' to work the song over 'n over for hours on end — I think we did 14 takes or thereabouts[418] — it turned out just the way I wanted it. In fact, George says it's one of m' best thus far. He's even after endorsin' it for the single!"[419]

"Harrison or Martin?" Cyn smiled.

"The one with the 'valuable Veatle vote,' girl. The one who actually *has a say* in what goes onto the single 'n what doesn't."

"Ah, Harrison! The very one!" Cynthia had chuckled.

And fatigued from false starts and double tracks and the search for four perfect ending notes to his new song, John had lifted his steaming beaker and guided his wife to their tatty sofa, where he'd collapsed, groaning when his bare feet touched the cold, brass coffee table that Mimi had reluctantly given them as a very belated wedding gift.

****

2.00 p.m.

Now, this afternoon, they filtered into Studio Two without babble. For John, it was "morning" — his customary rising hour.[420] He'd slept in the car, *en route* to EMI, and upon arrival, he'd sent Mal in search of "murderously strong tea." John still yawned and muttered his hellos.

Without preamble, The Beatles began quietly tuning up. Ringo was making adjustments on the podium. George sat apart, enjoying his new Sonic Blue. Up above, Norman Smith readied the sound board whilst Second Engineer Ken Scott cued tape.[421] And soundlessly, George Martin lingered at the overlook window, waiting for someone to give the official nod.

The afternoon ahead belonged to Paul. Last night, in fact, they'd all been given "assignments," parts to perfect for his number, "The Night Before."[422] John had been tasked with working out a piano backing on the group's new 1964 Hohner Pianet C electric,[423] and he'd come prepared with a syncopated piano rhythm, reminiscent of his traditional guitar strum. It added an innovative dimension — never having been employed in their catalogue before.[424] The pianet was unique; it was both percussive and tonal.

Reluctant, at first, to surrender his guitar, John found the instrument intriguing, and as the day went on, he offered to supply another bit for George's evening recording of "You Like Me Too Much."[425] Weaving the pianet artfully (with an added tremolo effect)[426] onto the fourth track of Harrison's song, John found the new sound as fascinating as rhythm guitar had always been.[427] He was instantly hooked.

Growing up, John had always craved a piano of some sort and, during his pre-teen years, had badgered Mimi and George for one. But his pragmatic aunt had firmly insisted there was "no room for such things" in the tight Mendips parlour, filled to capacity with a fireplace and twin built-in bookshelves — and in later years, of course, a modest television set on a stand. She'd reminded John that if they did invest in a piano, he would be expected to take lessons and practice the instrument daily. That sort of regimentation had swiftly halted John's campaign for a piano altogether.[428] He wanted no part of musical homework; he'd had enough of that in Dovedale.

The front parlour at Mendips, 251 Menlove Avenue, Woolton, the home where John Lennon grew up with his aunt and uncle, George and Mimi Smith
Photograph from Wikimedia Commons

So instead, John had latched onto a tatty, old mouth organ he'd found somewhere — or "cadged" from an unsuspecting school mate.[429] And for months, that seemed to be enough. John was fascinated with the bluesy sounds he could make, and he carried the harmonica everywhere.

In the summer of 1955, a kindly bus driver who'd shuttled John from Liverpool to his Auntie Mater's home in Edinburgh had been impressed with the boy's performances on the long ride north, and he'd offered John "a really good harmonica." It was, indeed, an excellent instrument, and John had been wildly elated.[430] But still, the boy needed something more.

Two weeks later, in the crushing wake of his Uncle Ge'rge's untimely death, John had found that "something." Julia (clumsily trying to fill the void that George's passing had created in her son's life) had offered John the use of her banjo. She'd patiently taught him to play.[431] And then, whispering that John had "music in his bones," she'd suggested that her son join the skiffle rage sweeping England and learn to play the guitar.

By 1957, John's mad obsession with the guitar (despite the fact that he possessed only a cheap, mail-order Gallo Champion)[432] completely superseded everything else. He'd all but forgotten about the piano until Autumn of 1960, when he'd frequented The Seaman's Mission in Hamburg. There, in an icy side room adjoining the dining hall, John had clumsily plunked out the tune to "There's A Place" on the ramshackle, mahogany upright. The tinny piano — despite its chipped, browned ivory keys and useless pedals — had afforded a nameless peace that the "chanka-chanka" of his guitar couldn't supply.

Now today, the feeling was back again — this curious fondness for the keyboards. It gave John back his grin.

"Y' know, in the last coupla sessions," John sauntered over to Ringo, flashing a toothy grin. "I've been on snare, tambourine, and pianet as well. [433] It appears I'm breathin' down yer neck, Sonny Jim. Word has it, I'm the next Ringo."

"Ah, shirrup, Lennon!" Ringo waved him off, chuckling deeply and heading towards the door. "Y'er not werth a light! Yew *and* yer ilk!"

And jamming his tongue behind his lower lip, John followed his "fellow percussionist" out towards the car park.[434]

"Ad Lib?"[435] George joined them, offering John a smoke. "We're headed to the clubs, y' know.[436] You're great to come with."

John turned his head, slowed his walk. "Yeah, right." He huffed a disgusted sigh. "If only there was someone else to complete m' manuscript 'n rush right home to the Missus."

"Ah, Cyn wouldn't mind!" Ringo knew her well.

"No, but Jonathan Cape, Incorporated would. I have to have

the new book done 'yesterday,' or so they aver."[437]

"Well," George shrugged, "the invitation's still out there, anyroad."

"Right, we'd never ignore 'the new Ringo,'" Starkey deadpanned.

"*What*?!" George snapped his head around. He was ever-protective of Ritchie's place in the band.

"It's an inside joke, lad," Ringo chortled, patting George on the back.

"Yeah," John added, "y'er far too young to understand, Georgie Porgie."

"Right," George said, "I'll just go drown m' self in bitters then."

"That's the way!" Ringo laughed.

And bantering, the boys piled into the limo. As Alf made plans to drop them at the club, drive John out to Kenwood, and then return for the festivities,[438] they took the mickey out of one another. They smoked and waited for Paul. They laughed. It was the only way to close the day if you were under 25, rich, famous, and full of mischief. Indeed, for all of them — except John — this promised to be a perfect evening.

Notes!

There was a good bit of discussion about which of the two songs on The Beatles' single should be the A-side and which should be the B-side. And, as always, each of The Beatles got a vote.

George Harrison was very much in favour of "Yes It Is" being the single's A-side. He said, "I prefer this one ["Yes It Is"]. It should have been on the major side."[439]

However, Paul, who really liked the song as well, stated, "I know what you mean. I probably prefer it, too. But you mustn't confuse what you prefer with what's the best A-side. They're two totally different things."[440]

Incidentally, Cynthia Lennon said that "Yes It Is" was her "favourite Beatles track so far."[441] Although John told Ray Coleman in 1965 that he had "lost his art," Cynthia thought it was "his finest songwriting year."[442]

Sources:

E-mail discussion with Scott Freiman of Deconstructing The Beatles *about the "violining" technique used in Harrison's "I Need You" and about the differences between the Hohner Pianet C and the Hohner Pianet N. Thank you, Scott, for being so willing to explain these important details to a non-musician!*

E-mails exchanged with Jerry Hammack on songs recorded on 17 Feb. Many thanks to Jerry for his expertise!

Lewisohn, The Complete Beatles Chronicle, *183.*
Lewisohn, The Beatles Recording Sessions, *54.*
Winn, 298.
MacDonald, 117-118.
Womack, Maximum Volume: The Life of Beatles Producer, George Martin, *250.*
Womack, The Beatles Encyclopedia, *1033-1034 and 1047.*
Hammack, 24-25.
Everett, The Beatles as Musicians: The Quarry Men Through *Rubber Soul, 286-287.*
Spizer, The Beatles for Sale on Parlophone Records, *189.*
Margotin and Guesdon, 226 and 244.
Babiuk, 160.
Trynka, 169.
Norman, John Lennon: The Life, *394 and 410.*
Davies, The Beatles, *20.*
Schaffner, 47.
Spitz, 554-555.
Badman, 149.
Riley, Tell Me Why, *141 and 147.*
Turner, 76 and 82.
Coleman, Lennon, *37, 223, and 245-246.*
Bicknell, 33.

Freiman, Scott, "Deconstructing HELP!", Deconstructing The Beatles *dvd.*

https://www.beatlesbible.com/songs/you-like-me-too-much/ This is a discussion of "You Like Me Too Much."

https://www.beatlesbible.com/songs/the-night-before/ A similar discussion of "The Night Before."

---

[399] Lewisohn, *The Beatles Recording Sessions*, 54, Winn, 296-297, Margotin and Guesdon, 230, Spizer, *Beatles For Sale on Parlophone Records*, 189, Hammack, 18-19, and Womack, *Maximum Volume: The Life of Beatles*

Producer, George Martin, 249. Although every source identifies the new device as a foot pedal, Jerry Hammack states, "…and Harrison on a tone-pedal style part using his 1963 Rickenbacker360-12 (12-string) electric guitar…To create the volume swells on Harrison's part, **Lennon manipulated the volume knob on the guitar as Harrison played."**

[400] Margotin and Guesdon, 230. Margotin and Guesdon refer to "violoning" as the technique employed through the use of the volume foot pedal. Unable to find a definition for that effect, I wrote to noted Beatles music expert Scott Freiman, of *Deconstructing The Beatles,* for an explanation of what "violoning" entailed. He responded that it is correctly spelled "violining" and further stated: "Violining is defined as the manipulation of the volume control of an electric guitar (or in George's case, a volume pedal connected to the guitar) to suppress note attacks so as to produce sounds suggesting those of bowed string instruments. You don't hear the string being plucked since the volume is turned down. But you hear the sound of the note when the volume pedal is turned up." Many, many thanks to Scott Freiman for his expertise and the gift of his time!

[401] Spizer, *Beatles for Sale on Parlophone Records*, 189, and Hammack, 18-19.

[402] Spizer, *Beatles for Sale on Parlophone Records*, 189.

[403] Spizer, *Beatles for Sale on Parlophone Records*, 189.

[404] Spizer, *Beatles for Sale on Parlophone Records*, 189. Spizer states that on 16 February 1965, "George's original vocal on Track 2 was wiped with the recording of more backing vocals from John and Paul. Ringo's cowbell…needed to be re-recorded after being wiped from Track 4."

[405] Spizer, *Beatles for Sale on Parlophone Records*, 189-190, Winn, 296, Lewisohn, *Beatles Recording Sessions*, 54, and Hammack, 17. Hammack says, "On February 16th, in Studio 2, another superimposition was added to take 1, which included Lennon and Harrison duplicating their backing track guitar parts, while McCartney added a new lead guitar part on his 1962 Epiphone ES-230TD, Casino electric guitar with Selmer Bigsby B7 vibrato."

[406] Lewisohn, *The Beatles Recording Sessions*, 54 and Winn, 296-297. Both sources show the afternoon session ending at 5.00 p.m. and the evening session beginning at 5 p.m.

[407] John is referring to his half-sisters, Jacqui and Julia Dykins.

[408] MacDonald, 116 and Trynka, 169. Trynka calls this song "a lyrical mourning" for the past and says that "the mysterious figure in red" is either "his mother, Julia, or Stuart Sutcliffe."

[409] MacDonald, 116. MacDonald says that the heroine of this song is "a transmutation of Lennon's dead mother, Julia." And he goes on to say that "in folk tradition, these love/death figures traditionally dwell in a twilight borderland of the male psyche where masculine identity dissolves."

[410] Womack, *Maximum Volume: The Life of Beatles Producer, George Martin,* 249. Womack observes: "Harrison's plaintive guitar work imbued Lennon's wistful ballad with even greater depths of meaning."

[411] Winn, 297. Winn points out that at the end of Take 1, you can hear John say, "We'll have to have an ending…" And Winn also observes that at the

beginning of Take 2, George "searches for the right notes to play over the intro…"

[412] Margotin and Guesdon, 230, Lewisohn, *The Beatles Recording Sessions*, 54, and Spizer, *Beatles for Sale on Parlophone Records,* 46. In *All The Songs,* Margotin and Guesdon (with the guidance of Scott Freiman) state that the volume pedal George Harrison is using is completely different from a wah-wah pedal. They state, "George used a volume foot pedal allowing him to quickly increase or lower the sound level of an instrument according to the desired effect. This gives a characteristic effect called "violoning" [sic], **not to be confused with the wah-wah pedal,** immortalized by Jimi Hendrix, **which in no way mediates the sound level of the instrument,** but only varies its frequency." (p. 230)

[413] Lewisohn, *The Complete Beatles Chronicle*, 183, Lewisohn, *The Beatles Recording Sessions,* 54, Margotin and Guesdon, 262, Winn, 297, Hammack, 21, and Spizer, *Beatles for Sale on Parlophone Records*, 46. We are reminded by Margotin and Guesdon that "with respect to the group's work, it was John's songs that featured superb three-part backing vocals — "This Boy," "Yes It Is," and "Because." (p. 262)

[414] MacDonald, 116. MacDonald says, "In YES IT IS, the essential masochism of this fixation [on the goddess, the Bell Dame archetype] appears in the song's Gothic overtones and the self-flagellatory outburst of its ten-bar middle section. The 'pride' Lennon curses stems from his attachment to this feminine ideal, Herself…a reflection of the personal uniqueness he had felt since childhood."

[415] Sheff, David, *The Playboy Interviews*, 165, Margotin and Guesdon, 262, and Turner, 11.

[416] Margotin and Guesdon, 262, Winn, 297, and Hammack, 21.

[417] Hammack, 21. This observation is all the genius of Jerry Hammack. He astutely says, "It's wondrous how serendipity sometimes factors into what we…believe to be so deliberate.…Take 1 [of 'Yes It Is'] was a complete pass at the new song with Lennon playing his 1964 Gibson J-160E — a steel-stringed guitar. But just after a minute into Take 2, he broke a string on the Gibson. The soft, muted sound of the [Jose Ramirez] nylon string acoustic guitar is one of the reasons 'Yes It Is' comes across as such a delicate ballad…"

[418] Spizer, *The Beatles For Sale on Parlophone Records*, 46, Winn, 297, and Hammack, 20-21.

[419] Margotin and Guesdon, 262.

[420] Coleman, *Lennon*, 223. Cynthia says, "[John] would collapse in a dead sleep and be unmovable until afternoons unless there was an appointment to be kept earlier."

[421] Lewisohn, *The Beatles Recording Sessions*, 54 and Winn, 298.

[422] Norman, *John Lennon: The Life*, 410. Norman quotes George Martin as saying, "If we were doing a song of Paul's, he'd get hold of his guitar and tell George what he wanted him to play in the middle; he'd get on the drums and show Ringo what he wanted." The Beatles were given specific assignments for their parts on a McCartney number.

[423] Winn, 298, Hammack, 22, Womack, *Maximum Volume: The Life of Beatles Producer, George Martin*, 250, Margotin and Guesdon, 226, Babiuk, 160, and Lewisohn, *The Beatles Recording Sessions*, 54. Hammack observes that Lennon's use of the Hohner Pianet C added "an urgency to the song and demonstrated the difference the right arrangement could make." Some noted sources say that John was using the "Hohner Pianet N" model. Babiuk clearly states, "The model the group [The Beatles] used was the Pianet C, with its classic wooden case, 'coffee table' legs and a folding lid that doubled as a music stand when opened." To make certain that I was using the correct model in this chapter, I wrote to Scott Freiman of *Deconstructing The Beatles* and asked him which instrument John was actually using. He responded immediately with this answer: "The Hohner Pianet 'C' had cylindrical legs, and the Pianet 'N' had rectangular cross section legs. In photos from 'Help!', you can see both John and Paul playing their pianet, and the legs are clearly cylindrical. That is the Pianet 'C.'" Many thanks to Scott for helping me make this distinction.

[424] Margotin and Guesdon, 226.

[425] Womack, *Maximum Volume: The Life of Beatles Producer, George Martin*, 250, Lewisohn, *The Beatles Recording Sessions*, 54, Everett, 287, Hammack, 24, MacDonald, 398, and Margotin and Guesdon, 244. MacDonald points out that "As on the previous track, Lennon plays the Hohner electric, this time with reverb." Margotin and Guesdon refer to this reverb as "a tremolo effect." Everett explains more in detail, saying, "Lennon's Pianet [features] heavy knob-controlled tremolo in the intro, as if to balance Martin's hand tremolo, if not to compete with Harrison's pedal device."

[426] Margotin and Guesdon, 244 and MacDonald, 398.

[427] Winn, 298, Hammack, 24, and Womack, *Maximum Volume: The Life of Beatles Producer, George Martin*, 250.

[428] Davies, *The Beatles*, 18. Davies quotes Mimi Smith as saying, "I would have sent [John] to music lessons, the piano or violin, when he was very young. He couldn't be bothered with anything which involved lessons. He wanted to do everything immediately, not take time learning."

[429] Davies, 20. Mimi Smith says, "He'd got a battered old mouth organ from somewhere..."

[430] Davies, 20.

[431] Davies, 20.

[432] Davies, 20 and Babiuk, 7. There is a photo of the guitar in Babiuk's *Beatles Gear*, p. 8. Davies says the guitar cost only £10 and was "guaranteed not to split."

[433] Lewisohn, *The Complete Beatles Chronicle*, 183, Lewisohn, *The Beatles Recording Sessions*, 54, and Winn, 298. Lewisohn and Winn tell us that the evening session lasted from 7.00 p.m. to 11.00 p.m.

[434] Norman, *John Lennon: The Life*, 410. This friendly banter between John and Ringo is fun, but it also has a significant side to it. Norman quotes George Martin as saying, "I didn't sufficiently recognize at the time but Ringo's opinion was always important to John, just because he knew that with him there'd never be any bullshit. He'd often turn to Ringo and ask what he thought, and if Ringo said, 'That's crap, John,' he'd do something else."

[435] Bicknell, 33. Bicknell's diary says that he drove The Beatles, minus John presumably, to the clubs on this night.

[436] Bicknell, 33.

[437] Trynka, 170, Miles, *The Beatles' Diary, Vol. 1*, 199, Womack, *Maximum Volume: The Life of Beatles Producer, George Martin*, 265, and Norman, *John Lennon: The Life*, 401.

[438] Bicknell, 33.

[439] Badman, 149.

[440] Badman, 149.

[441] Badman, 149.

[442] Coleman, *Lennon*, 256.

Thursday, 18 February 1965
Kenwood
Weybridge, Surrey

Just after midnight

"I've sold m' self to the devil!"[443] John flung his copy book across the room. Viciously downing the last of his Johnnie Walker and Coke, he slammed the glass on the table.[444]

"Oh, John." Rescuing the illustration, Cyn carefully smoothed the folds out. John had been labouring over the sketch for the better part of the last hour, and it was worth saving.[445] "You're just spent."

John sighed. "Everyone else goes home to watch telly or read a book...or they're off to the clubs![446] But here I am...homebound, like a good little boy, 'n still, there's all this *work*!"

He thumped the disheveled manuscript for *A Spaniard in the Works* — his next volume, due out in June[447] — and stood to mix himself another drink. Jonathan Cape Publishers was unrelenting in their deadline. "No later than mid-April!" they insisted. Only six weeks to go.

"Every day, m' eyesight's worse 'n worse from all this late-night work!" John growled, pouring more whisky than he should. "'N all I do is sit here in this mucky attic,[448] gettin' fatter 'n softer 'n fatter 'n fuggin' softer!!"[449]

"John, if you looked any better..." Cynthia shook her head and moved to the cupboard. She drew out a letter she'd received from the States, several days ago. "Here, read *this*! It's from a Sandi Stewart, somewhere in New Hampshire, America. She apologises most sincerely, but wants me to know she's in love with you."[450]

"Yeah well," John ignored the compliment and pinched a definite roll of flab around his middle, "Sandi hasn't seen me lately, has she?"

"I *hope* she hasn't seen you *at all!*" Cynthia squiggled a smile.

"Before," John went on, ignoring her, "when we were in Emperor's Gate, we used to be able to go *out* of an evenin', y' know…to the Ad Lib or what have you![451] But here — on the virtual Edge of Fuggin' Nowhere — all I ever do is fuggin' work!"[452]

"John," Cyn tried reason, "if memory serves, weren't *you* the one who contracted with Tom Maschler to do this sequel?[453] Aren't *you* the one who told me that writing kept you sane?"

"Yeah well," John ran a hand through his greasy mop, "that was before it all started feelin' exactly like fuggin' *homework!*"[454] Nevertheless, he took the paper from his wife's hands and smoothed it again.

"I know, but…" Cynthia let the unsaid linger.

Sighing again, John returned to the table and threw himself down. He hunched his shoulders, huddling over the poem he'd been tediously illustrating. Leaning closer, he squinted at the erratic scrawl. He hitched his feet on the bottom chair rung and picked up his pen.

"All right, all right!" John gave in. "I'm back at it!" And after a scant handful of silent minutes, he barked, "Listen Powell…how's this sound?"

The National Health Cow

I strolled into a farmyard
When no-one was about
Treading past the troubles
I raised my head to shout,

"Come out the Cow with glasses"
I called and rolled my eye.
It ambled up toward me,

I milked it with a sigh.

"You're just in time" the cow said,
Its eyes were all aglaze,
"I'm feeling like an elephant,
I aren't been milked for days."

'Why is this?' I asked it,
Tugging at its throttles.
'I don't know why,
perhaps it's 'cause
MY milk comes out in bottles.'

'That's handy for the government,'
I thought, and in a tick
The cow fell dead all sudden.
(I'd smashed it with a brick.)"[455]

When he paused and Cyn said nothing, John pushed the thick Buddy Holly glasses higher on his nose and lifted his head — a frosty stare.

"Well," Cynthia cleared her throat, stalling for time, "I mean, it's as clever as I'd expect it to be…though…" she hesitated again, "you must admit, John, it ends rather…abruptly."

"Right gerl, for us all," John shoved the stack of papers aside, "once we're fat as cows 'n a queer oddity. Then, we're no longer of fuggin' use to anyone, are we?!"

"Well, thank goodness that's not us!" Cynthia flared. "I mean, I'm a mother and a homemaker. And you? Amongst other things, you're a gifted artist and a Foyles Literary Award-winning author! And if the newspapers are correct, as in this case I believe they are, you're also the *world's most famous* musician — *very much* needed, I believe, in a top-notch London studio...precisely tomorrow afternoon!"

"Forever on the bright side, aren't you, Powell?" John rubbed his eyes. He stood slowly.

"Guilty as charged, I suppose," Cynthia sighed. "*Someone* has to be."[456]

"Yeah, right. Might as well be you, eh?"

And abandoning his papers, quills, pens, inkwells, erasers, glasses, fingerprinted tumbler, and well-depleted bottle of Johnnie Walker Red, John grabbed Cynthia's hand.

"Enough," he said, begrudgingly, "is efuggin'nough."

And without another word, the weary couple trudged off to bed.[457]

****

<h2 style="text-align:center">EMI Studios
3 Abbey Road
London</h2>

3.30 p.m.[458]

They'd been after him for months to write something more authentic, "something similar to your work in *In His Own Write*." Kenneth Allsop, Maureen Cleave, and Bob Dylan[459] — they'd all badgered John to pen something autobiographical. And a bit peeved that they hadn't noticed that he'd been doing that all along, John tried even harder.

What could be more fuggin' autobiographical than "I'll Cry Instead"? John smoked, waiting for the others, whilst upstairs in the control booth, George Martin, Norman Smith, and Ken Scott were busy doing whatever it was they did before the "real work" began.[460] *I mean, "I've got every reason on earth to be mad, 'cause I've just lost the only girl I had. If I could get my way, I'd get myself locked up today...but I can't..."*

Immediately, it was September 1958 again: Liverpool College of Art. John stood alone in the vast and chilly Registration Room, grief clinging to him as intimately as Uncle George's tweed jacket.[461]

"Hey John!" the girl called to him across the Registration Room.[462] It was the first day back, and there were hopefuls everywhere — meeting with advisors, grabbing up the best classes, inquiring about professors' reputations. John was disinterested. He was merely going through the motions and doing so without his glasses. He had no earthly idea who had hailed him.

"Hey John! John Lennon!" The voice came again, this time closer, but John could make out a female form without having to deal with details.

"Yeah," he mumbled back, unenthusiastically.

"Hey, I believe your mother was killed, wasn't she?" The girl's voice was too loud, too shrill. "Wasn't it an off-duty policeman, then? At least that's what we all heard."

John felt all motion cease. The hum of the Registration Room suspended; the crowd held its collective breath, waiting for his reply. John could hear the blood singing in his ears, a piercing, high-pitched squeal.

"Yeah, right," he shrugged, nonchalantly. "It was her."

Then the room began to buzz again, and the world moved on to someone else.[463]

Immediately, he'd stomped out into Hope Street, lifting his chin and hurtling towards the tiny passageway called Rice. He'd struggled to appear unruffled. But once in the alley, he had collapsed. And secretly, he'd cried instead.

"I have a chip on my shoulder that's bigger than my feet." John had written, months ago. "I can't talk to people that I meet." *Not like Paul,* he thought, begrudgingly, hating himself but hating the universe even more, for making him this way. *And who can't see that every fuggin' word of those lyrics is absofuggin'lutely* **real***?!*[464] *It's m' fuggin' life story...'n I wrote it months ago! Months!*

For so long, John had wanted to punish his mother for leaving him. He'd ached to accomplish miraculous things that she'd never be able to see, to achieve things that she'd never be able to adore. John had yearned to make her...*I dunno, sad somehow.* And fame — he'd reasoned in a fog of anger-infused grief — had seemed the best revenge.

But "the toppermost of the poppermost" hadn't abated his pain, not as he'd imagined it would. Fame had only fashioned a window for prying eyes — a drawbridge against the Keep.

"I get shy when they start to stare," John whispered now,[465] crushing the butt of his cig in the studio's black, plastic ashtray.

George strolled in, and the song drifted away.

"So, it's yew today, eh Johnny?" George smiled.

"Yeah," John stretched, "I thought I'd try recordin' somethin' about m' life, fer a change."[466]

George waved John off. "Have y' ever done anythin' else?"

"Well, no one seems to think so! They keep tellin' me to *try it*!"

"What about Cyn's songs, eh — 'When I Get Home,' 'n 'Do You Want to Know a Secret?' I mean, I know *I sang* the last one, but everyone knows you *wrote* it — over in Falkner, right after you 'n Cyn were married…back when it was all hush-hush, you 'n her! This "big Beatles secret" 'n all."

"Yeah, I remember. I was there."

"'N what about 'There's a Place'?" George removed his top coat and hung it on the spindly, unbalanced rack.

John snorted. "I'm tellin' ya, old son, the fans, the critics, what have you…they haven't a *clue* what I'm on about."

"I s 'pose," George said, wistfully, "it's because they didn't know her, not like we did. They didn't know the lovely Julia."

John bit his lip; even the mention of her name was a corkscrew in his heart. "They didn't know her at all," he finally managed.

George prised at a rip in the carpet with the toe of his boot. He kept his head down and his memories private.

Moments in, John almost offered, "'N furthermore, what about 'Not a Second Time'?!" but he censored himself. Not even George would understand the bitterness he'd felt as a boy, those early days in Mendips — seething in resentment at being abandoned without a hint of explanation, without a word his dad or mum.[467] John had never shared that dangerous loneliness[468] with anyone, except Cyn. And he didn't intend to start today.

"So," George half-grinned, "I'll be able to say I was here for yer very first exposé song, right? Johnny Lennon with the real deal…at very long last!" He threw his eyes to the heavens.

"As real as it fuggin' gets," John spat.

And sputtering, George patted John's shoulder...two quick, reassuring raps, the way he'd always done. Then together, they strolled to their instruments, ready to record one of the most heartbreaking songs of John's career.

Notes!

1. Was John's unhappy opinion of himself in this early part of 1965 affecting The Beatles as a whole?

John's close friend, reporter Ray Coleman, states in his work, Lennon, *that in 1965, "something from deep within [John] gave vent to his insecurity..." He says that John could never shake the "feeling that all was not well, despite the millions of record sales, [and] the adoration...[John] could not stand the inflated descriptions of what The Beatles were...He did not see himself as a profound performer." (pp. 256-257)*

In The Beatles, *Spitz tells us that "[John] was getting tired of hearing Paul described as 'the handsome Beatle' or 'the cute Beatle,' tired of seeing Paul charm the media, posing as the band's spokesperson, and voicing opinions [John] didn't share." (p. 554)*

John and Paul had always been very competitive, but in early 1965, the media's attraction to the easy-going McCartney was beginning to aggravate John. In fact, in a very bitter and sarcastic tone, John told one interviewer, "He's a good P.R. man, Paul. He's about the best in the world, probably, he really does a job." (Spitz, 555) It wasn't a compliment.

Ray Coleman in Lennon *agrees saying "...while [John] admired Paul McCartney's musical strengths, the two men were not reacting in the same way to fame. Paul loved it." (p. 257) But John, on the other hand, told Coleman that he "felt old." (p. 258)*

As John continued to gain weight and grow round-faced, his jealousy of Paul mounted. But McCartney, Spitz says, artfully side-stepped John's ire. "[Paul] knew how to play the angles, which is what it took to humour a cranky hothead like John." (p. 555) Paul was learning to "dance" around John's moods. The relationship was becoming rather tricky.[469]

However, the final insult to John during this period of self-doubt was the fact that the fans and critics completely overlooked the cries for "Help!" he was sending out to the world at large. As Norman observes, "It was a strange and wholly new kind of frustration [John] was discovering: to have his every new song awaited so hungrily yet listened to so inattentively, his least predictable themes greeted with the same shrieks of undiscerning rapture, his bleakest thoughts submerged and transfigured by The Beatles' joie de vivre…Would you believe…ecstasy could be generated by a song called 'I'm a Loser'?" (p. 393-394) John was pouring out his heart, and no one even listened. No one seemed to care.

2. Is "You've Got to Hide Your Love Away" really the first Beatles song since "Love Me Do" in which a studio musician was used?

"You've Got to Hide Your Love Away" was recorded throughout the shortened afternoon session[470] of 18 February, with Take 9 being considered "best." (What a coincidence, Take 9!) John performed on his Framus Hootenanny 12-string. Paul was on the Höfner.[471] George played one of his Spanish guitars, either the Jose Ramirez Guitarra de Estudio or the Jose Rameriz A1 Segovia.[472] Ringo was on drums, using brushes.[473]

After Take 9 was selected, these overdubs were added, according to John C. Winn in Way Beyond Compare: *"John re-taped his lead vocal [on the second track]…[then] Paul's maracas, Ringo's tambourines, and George's 12-string acoustic guitar occupied the third track." (p. 299)*

Many Beatles biographies state that "You've Got to Hide Your Love Away" is the first song since "Love Me Do," (featuring Andy White's drum work) on which a session musician was invited in to add contributions to a Beatles recording session.

However…

In The Complete Beatles Chronicle, *Mark Lewisohn tells us that on 10 March 1964, "a 'drummer' participated in [the] 10.00 a.m. — 1 p.m. session with regard to "Can't Buy Me Love' — which can only mean that he did some overdubbing. He was paid a Musician's Union session fee of £5 15s (£5.75)…but his name was not detailed in the document." (p. 150)*

Lewisohn goes on to explain that "This answers one question that has long puzzled Beatles students: why the drumming on this song's stereo mix differs slightly from the mono. But it also raises questions about the drummer's identity. Ringo's 'A Hard Day's Night' shooting schedule would seem to suggest that he had little, if any, opportunity to visit Abbey Road on this day." (p. 150)

If the undesignated drummer used in EMI on 10 March was **not** *Ringo, then "Can't Buy Me Love" was the first song since "Love Me Do" on which a session drummer was used.*

If Ringo was, indeed, that unnamed drummer brought in on 10 May 1964, then the assertion that "You've Got to Hide Your Love Away" is the first song with that distinction still holds true.

The studio musician used on "You've Got to Hide Your Love Away" is flautist Johnnie (John) Scott.[474]

Sources:

Lewisohn and Howlett, John Lennon: In My Life, 44-46.
Lewisohn, The Complete Beatles Chronicle, 150 and 183-184.
Lewisohn, The Beatles Recording Sessions, 54-55.
Norman, John Lennon: The Life, 393-394, 400-401, and 417.
Norman, Shout!, 241.
Spitz, 546-548 and 554.
Davies, The Beatles, 49-50 and 189.
Coleman, Lennon, 91, 151, and 240-246.
Goldman, 79 and 185.
Lennon, John, A Spaniard in the Works, 61-63.
Lennon, Cynthia, John, 142.
Harry, The Encyclopedia of Beatles People, 26.
Harry, The John Lennon Encyclopedia, 830-834.
Harry, The Ultimate Beatles Encyclopedia, 378 and 718.
Hammack, 26-27.
Winn, 299.
Spizer, The Beatles for Sale on Parlophone Records, 189
Womack, The Beatles Encyclopedia, Vol. 2, 858 and 1055-1056.
Womack, Maximum Volume: The Life of Beatles Producer, George Martin, 265.
Womack, Long and Winding Roads, The Evolving Artistry of The Beatles, 108-109.
Miles, The Beatles' Diary, Vol. 1, 189.
Margotin and Guesdon, 228-229.
Hertsgaard, A Day in the Life: The Artistry of The Beatles, 127-128.
Turner, 77.
Riley, Tell Me Why, 141-142.
Robertson, The Art and Music of John Lennon, 40-41.
Trynka, 170.
Hill, John, Paul, George & Ringo, 207.
Carlin, McCartney: A Life, 117.
Egan, The Mammoth Book of The Beatles, 376.
Bicknell, 33.
DeWitt, Howard A., The Beatles: Untold Tales, 136-137.
Sheff, The Playboy Interviews, 149.

https://www.youtube.com/watch?v=V8nLraecPRY This link will allow you to listen to "You've Got to Hide Your Love Away."
https://reverb.com/brand/jose-ramirez?category=classical&product_type=acoustic-guitars

This website provides information and pictures of a wide variety of Jose Ramirez guitars.

---

[443] Spitz, 547. Direct quote from John Lennon.

[444] Norman, *John Lennon: The Life*, 401 and Robertson, *The Art and Music of John Lennon*, 40-41. John is quoted as saying that in order to write *A Spaniard in the Works*: "I could only loosen up to it with a bottle of Johnnie Walker."

[445] Harry, *The Ultimate Beatles Encyclopedia*, 830.

[446] Bicknell, 33. Bicknell says he drove The Beatles to the London clubs and that they were so hung over the next day that he had trouble getting them to the afternoon session.

[447] Trynka, 170, Miles, *The Beatles' Diary, Vol. 1*, 199, Womack, *Maximum Volume: The Life of Beatles Producer, George Martin*, 265, and Norman, *John Lennon: The Life*, 401. The British release date for *A Spaniard in the Works* was 24 June 1965.

[448] Spitz, 548.

[449] Norman, *Shout!*, 241 and Spitz, 554. Spitz says, "Weight, too, had become a nagging problem...and he was demoralized and depressed by his worsening vision."

[450] Davies, 189. Stewart's letter was, she says, written in 1963, but it was typical of the many letters Cynthia received, pledging undying love for John.

[451] Spitz, 548. Spitz points out that John and Cyn were "cooped up...annoyingly in the attic apartment...miles from nowhere."

[452] Spitz, 548.

[453] Norman, *John Lennon: The Life*, 400.

[454] Howlett and Lewisohn, *In My Life: John Lennon Remembered*, 44, Coleman, *Lennon*, 240, and Norman, *John Lennon: The Life*, 400. Coleman quotes John as saying that *A Spaniard in the Works* "was more disciplined than the first [book]." John states, "It was 'starting from scratch.' The publisher said you've got so many months to write a book in. With the first book, I'd written a lot of it at odd times during my life." But this book had to be created in the end of 1964 and the early months of 1965, while John was busy writing songs for the next United Artists Film, shoooting the film, etc.

[455] Lennon, John, "The National Health Cow," *A Spaniard in the Works*, Simon and Schuster, New York, 1965, 61-63.

[456] Spitz, 548. Spitz says that Cynthia "dedicate[ed] all her personal energy to intensifying her husband's star power."

[457] Egan, *The Mammoth Book of The Beatles*, 376. Egan points out that the songs for the film "Help!" were written during a very difficult period in John's life. He says, "Lennon was bored by it and in the middle of what he would call his 'Fat Elvis' period, overweight and unhappy at what he had found upon his ascent to the mountaintop of success."

[458] Lewisohn, The Complete Beatles Chronicle, 183. Lewisohn tells us that mix work was done that morning, and that the session in which The Beatles recorded "You've Got to Hide Your Love Away" went from 3.30 p.m. to 5.15 p.m.

[459] Harry, *The Encyclopedia of Beatles People*, 26, Coleman, *Lennon*, 246-247, Norman, *John Lennon: The Life*, 417, and Sheff, 49. As Norman points

out, Allsop asked John in a 1964 interview why John's "song lyrics did not have the same highly individualized stamp as his prose." And in the *Playboy Interviews* with David Sheff, John states, "I remember Maureen Cleave, a writer...asked me, 'Why don't you ever write songs with more than one syllable?' So, in 'Help!' there are two and three syllable words, and I very proudly showed them to her. I was insecure then..." (p. 149)

[460] Lewisohn, *The Beatles Recording Sessions*, 55.

[461] Coleman, *Lennon*, 91, Goldman, 79, and Davies, *The Beatles*, 49-50.

[462] Coleman, *Lennon*, 91, Goldman, 79, and Davies, *The Beatles*, 49-50.

[463] This incident, which occurred in Sept. 1958, is taken verbatim from *Shoulda Been There*, Vol. 1 in **The John Lennon Series**. The sources for this event are Goldman, 79, Coleman, *Lennon*, 91, and Davies, *The Beatles*, 49-50.

[464] Riley, *Tell Me Why*, 142. Riley calls "You've Got to Hide Your Love Away," "personally revealing" and reminds us that "Lennon is singing more to himself than to the 'clowns' he sees around him...Although Lennon is speaking to the world at large, what comes across is...sober introspection."

[465] Womack, *The Beatles Encyclopedia, Vol. 2*, 1055 and Harry, *The Ultimate Beatles Encyclopedia*, 718.

[466] Carlin, *Paul McCartney: A Life*, 117, Hertsgaard, *A Day in the Life*, 127-128, and The Beatles, *The Beatles Anthology*, 173. "You've Got to Hide Your Love Away" is so intensely personal that Carlin refers to the song as "an acoustic confessional." Hertsgaard says that the song showcases John's ability "to reach inside himself and articulate truths" and reveals a "Lennon racked by self-doubt." And John has done this purposely. In *The Beatles Anthology*, John talks about the fact that Maureen Cleave and others constantly urged him to write songs with deeper meaning, similar to his poetry and prose. Cleave challenged him to use "words with more than one syllable." This song filled that bill.

[467] Womack, *The Beatles Encyclopedia, Vol. 2*, 1055, and Harry, *The Ultimate Beatles Encyclopedia*, 718. Both Harry and Womack quote John, in reference to the lyrics of "You've Got to Hide Your Love Away," as admitting, "It's one of those you sing a bit sadly to yourself, 'Here I stand, head in hand.' I started thinking about my own emotions...I just tr[ied] to express what I felt about myself..."

[468] Womack, *The Beatles Encyclopedia, Vol. 2*, 1055. Womack, in talking about Lennon's abiding loneliness in biographical songs such as "You've Got to Hide Your Love Away," comments on loneliness's "too-real capacity for engendering self-effacement." John's childhood abandonment, especially in light of the fact that Julia had two other children, whom she kept, certainly led John to hate himself and think of himself as "a loser."

[469] Spitz, 554-555. Spitz concludes his observations with, "Gone was the extraordinary bond that had distinguished the first years of their partnership. In its place was a creative tension, an emotional game of chess, of sorts."

[470] Spizer, *The Beatles for Sale on Parlophone Records*, 189 and Lewisohn, *The Complete Beatles Chronicle*, 183. Spizer tells us the session was "less than two hours." Mark Lewisohn gives us the exact time frame: 3.30 p.m. to 5.15 p.m.

[471] Winn, 299.

[472] Hammack, 26, Spizer, *The Beatles for Sale on Parlophone Records*, 189, and Womack, *The Beatles Encyclopedia, Vol. 2*, 1056. Spizer identifies the guitar George is using as a "nylon-stringed acoustic guitar." That would make the guitar the Jose Ramirez A1 Segovia.

[473] Winn, 299.

[474] Lewisohn, *The Complete Beatles Chronicle*, 184, Hammack, 27, Winn, 299, Womack, *The Beatles Encyclopedia, Vol. 2*, 1056, Lewisohn, *The Beatles Recording Sessions*, 55, and Spizer, *The Beatles for Sale on Parlophone Records*, 189.

Friday, 19 February 1965
Studio Two, EMI Studios
En Route to
3 Abbey Road
London

2.30 p.m.

Already, John was dreading the evening ahead — an upmarket, private dinner party at the Connaught Hotel, given in their honour.[475] EMI's long-time chairman, Sir Joseph Lockwood, was hosting the fête,[476] and it would be, as the Americans loved to say, "soup to nuts." Lockwood, John thought, was the height of Mimi-esque propriety.

Nothin' but the best, John wagered. *Brian, of course, 'll be in his element. Paul, as well.*

But for John, the starched gathering was everything he wanted to dodge: neckties, formality, pleasantries, and idle conversation. John would have given anything to come down with *a raging case of Bombay crud, or for God's sake, even typhus!!*[477] Unfortunately, feigning something catastrophic would also cancel John's studio time, and today, he had another song to record.

"Y' missed one for the books last night, Lennon!" Bicknell grinned, adjusting the car's rear-view mirror. "I mean, it's a good thing, we're after startin' late today, y' know. Even *I've* got a head on…and I was the bloody driver!"[478]

"Well, that brightens things right up." John's face was full of regret. "Missin' out on yet another grand PAFO event! There's fantastic news."[479]

Seeing John's resentment, Alf quickly backtracked. "Well, would I call it *grand*, actually? Not entirely. I mean…well…"

"It's all right, Alf." John held up a hand. "I made my bed. I'll lie in it. I had choices."

But lately, John had begun to wonder if he *did* actually have any options…if he'd *any* say at all in his life, in the year that loomed ahead. Not only was Brian already planning The Beatles' second World Tour and North American Tour, but he was also meeting with United Artists about a third feature film, to be shot in autumn.[480] No one had bothered asking John — or any of them, really — what *they* wanted to do. Appointments were being made. Deals, done. The Beatles were expected to show up and perform. Simple as that.

At first, having someone else resolve everything had been freeing — the boys had gleefully sidestepped the entangling details of contracts and scheduling. None of them had time for it, anyway. Or the bent.

But now — discovering that one's life was booked solid, filled with perpetual events over which one hadn't a bit of control — John chafed.

It's a lot like bein' in the fuggin' army! he snarled. *Private John W. Lennon, reportin' for duty, Sir! Who'd've believed it?*

And throwing himself down on the rear leather seat, John folded his arms beneath his head and pitched off his shoes.

Despite John's closed eyes, Alf could see the boy fidgeting restlessly — shifting about, clenching his jaw, fluttering his eyelids, sighing, even working the electric windows with his toes.[481] And respecting the boy's dour mood, Alf drove on, volunteering nothing else, all the way to EMI.[482] It was a token of friendship.

∗∗∗∗∗∗∗∗

Studio Two, EMI Studios
3 Abbey Road
London

3.30 p.m.

It was the fourth song John had recorded for the new film,[483] and for him, the count was crucial. It mattered that he owned the large margin of songs on each LP. It mattered that his voice dominated the albums.[484] It mattered that The Beatles — no matter what anyone else said — were still his band. To John, it was important.

"You're Going to Lose That Girl," he explained, was merely "a commercially viable call-and-answer composition[485] with the ever-popular sound of The Shirelles."[486] After yesterday's humiliating, "walkin' round with odd socks on"[487] soul-baring in "You've Got to Hide Your Love Away," John wanted today's recording to mean nothing, to convey nothing. He'd already revealed too much to too many people. And John despised being vulnerable.

Today, he wanted the focus off him and on his recording. Without a shred of emotion or nostalgia,[488] John wanted the session to proceed, all business.

Take 1 was somehow announced as "Take 2," but The Beatles forged ahead, ignoring the numerical glitch. Within seconds, however, there was a problem, a false start, and the mis-numbered take ground to a halt.[489]

But "Take 3" (actually, the second take)[490] was note-perfect. John manned lead vocal, backed expertly by George and Paul. Ringo managed the famous Ludwigs; Paul played his Höfner 500/1; and John strummed away on George's Chet Atkins Tennessean[491] — the deserted Gretsch that George had lately abandoned in a remote corner.[492]

"Excellent work," Martin pronounced, following the end of Take 3.

And without hesitation, the string of superimpositions began, including John's doubled vocal lead, Paul's work on Hohner keyboard, Ringo's bongos, and a splendid lead solo from George.[493] The hours of Kenwood "prep work" that John and Paul had executed paid off;[494] in just under three hours, the new rock-ballad was complete.

"One more day's work, in the can!" Having limped his anguished way downstairs to accompany the boys to the EMI gala, Martin rested for a moment on his high, three-legged stool. "Only one track to go, and then, you're off to sunshine!" The boys were headed to New Providence, Bahamas, for the first day of work on the upcoming film.[495] "One last afternoon of London's chill and then…"

"Well, two, actually," Paul corrected. "We're to pack and have our luggage ready for collection on Sunday. Then Monday, we travel."[496]

"All right, two then." Martin shook his head, watching John struggle into the "fuggin' straitjacket," the dinner jacket he'd reluctantly brought along for the evening. "So, with that in mind, let's plan to wind things up tomorrow with 'That Means a Lot.'"[497]

"'N it will, y' know," Ringo winked, "...mean a lot, that is...*if* we can get all this over 'n done with."

"We're overdue for a birrova break," George added, wryly.

"I empathize," Martin smiled, "but I must congratulate you four. You've done amazingly well: 11 songs completed in only six days![498] That's quite a record, if you'll pardon the pun."

" Um," George dead-panned, "sorry, but I'm afraid we can't."

"And we won't," John completed his tie, knotting it loosely.

"Sorry." Ringo turned palms up. "Make that three."

"And you?" Martin swiveled towards Paul.

"Me?" McCartney clicked his cheek twice. "I rather liked it."

Standing slowly, carefully shifting his weight from his wounded foot, Martin forced a smile. "Well, let them say what they will then, Paul. You're now riding to the gala with me."

And heckling the affable McCartney all the way down the hall, the unruly crew exited, just as the lights in Studio Two began to fade.

Notes!

1. Was John Lennon playing George Harrison's Gretsch Chet Atkins Tennessean on "You're Going to Lose That Girl"?

Here are the varying opinions about what instrument John used on this song:

Both John C. Winn in Way Beyond Compare *(p. 300) and Jerry Hammack in* The Beatles Recording Reference Manual, Vol. 2 *(p. 32) say that John was playing George's guitar, the Gretsch Chet Atkins Tennessean. This is a hollow-body electric guitar. (See the guitar in Terry Burrows'* Guitar Family Trees *foldout chart on p. 146.)*

Bruce Spizer, in The Beatles for Sale on Parlophone Records, *says John was playing "his Rickenbacker Capri." (p. 190) This is a semi-hollow electric guitar. (See this guitar in Burrows, p. 222.)*

Ken Womack in The Beatles Encyclopedia, *Vol. 2 (p. 1053) and Walter Everett in* The Beatles as Musicians, *Vol. 1 (p. 291) say John was playing his Epiphone Casino. This is a semi-hollow body double cutaway. (See this guitar in Burrows, p. 67.)*

Margotin and Guesdon in All the Songs *(p. 234), state that John was playing an "acoustic guitar." Similarly, Ian MacDonald in* Revolution in the Head *(p. 119) says John was playing an "acoustic rhythm guitar." Presumably, these two sources are referring to John's Gibson J160e, his acoustic electric guitar. This is, indeed, the guitar used in the studio scene of "You're Going to Lose That Girl" in the film "Help!", but it is not necessarily the guitar used in EMI on 19 February.*

No comment about John's guitar selection is made in Alan Pollock's "Notes on You're Going to Lose That Girl" nor in Riley's Tell Me Why *(pp. 143-144) or Mark Lewisohn's highly-respected work,* The Beatles Recording Sessions *(p. 56).*

After several weeks of research and help from Beatles music experts, I decided to use Winn and Hammack's selection of the Gretsch Chet Atkins Tennessean for this chapter because Winn in Lifting Latches *(p. 54) states:*

"The mystery behind this song was finally cleared up thanks to George Martin's production notes [from his limited release book Playback, *ISBN-10: 0904351823, ISBN-13: 9780904351828, Publisher: Genesis Publications, 2002]. The backing (there was no Take 1) was taped February 19th, with Paul's bass, Ringo's drums,* **and John playing Gretsch,** *all going on track 1 of the tape. Track 3 had John, Paul and George's vocals, while track 2 was filled with electric piano and George playing a guitar solo. Finally, John doubled his lead vocal on track 4."*

2. Is John's attitude towards attending functions such as the EMI dinner for The Beatles, Brian Epstein, and George Martin accurate?

In Hunter Davies's "official biography of The Beatles," John is quoted as saying, "I always hated the social things. All the horrible events and presentations we had to go to. All false. You could see right through them all and all the people there. I despised them. Perhaps it was partly from class. No, it wasn't. It was because they really were *all false." (*The Beatles, *p. 208)*

Sources:

Lewisohn, The Complete Beatles Chronicles, *184-185.*
Lewisohn, The Beatles Recording Sessions, *55-56.*
Harry, The Ultimate Beatles Encyclopedia, *717.*

Lennon, Cynthia, John, *227-228.*
Winn, Way Beyond Compare, *299-301.*
Winn, John C., Lifting Latches, *54.*
Hammack, 27, 32-33, and 35.
Womack, The Beatles Encyclopedia, Vol. 2, *1053 and 1056.*
Womack, Maximum Volume: The Life of Beatles Producer, George Martin, *252-253.*
Spizer, The Beatles for Sale on Parlophone Records, *189-190.*
Spizer, "Turning Beatles Throwaways into an Album," Beatlefan, *Vol. 40, No. 2, Jan. - Feb. 2019, 19-22.*
Everett, The Beatles as Musicians: The Quarrymen through Rubber Soul, *291.*
MacDonald, 119-120.
Stark, Steven J., Meet The Beatles, *120.*
Babiuk, Beatles Gear, *160-161.*
Riley, Tell Me Why, *143-144.*
Miles, The Beatles' Diary, Vol. 1, *189-190.*
Coleman, Lennon, *245-246.*
Davies, The Beatles, *208.*
Goldman, 248.
Spignesi and Lewis, 210.
Margotin and Guesdon, 234.
Bicknell, 33.

Bob Mytkowicz's "Fab Gear! The Guitars of The Beatles," Guitar Player *(#11) Nov.1987 is found here:*
http://www.beatles.ru/books/paper.asp?id=2413

Alan Pollock's "Notes on 'You're Going to Lose That Girl,'" is found here:
http://www.icce.rug.nl/~soundscapes/DATABASES/AWP/ygtltg.shtml

https://www.youtube.com/watch?v=H5wVWBTi23I This article provides information on and the opportunity to listen to "You're Going to Lose That Girl."

https://www.beatlesbible.com/songs/youre-going-to-lose-that-girl/
Additional information about "You're Going to Lose That Girl" is provided on this web page.

Finally, this chapter could not have been completed without Help! and guidance from Al Sussman, Beatlefan *Executive Editor and Beatles author; Jerry Hammack, author of* The Beatles Recording Reference Manual; *and Scott Freiman, author of* Deconstructing The Beatles. *Many thanks to these noted music experts for their wisdom and time!*

---

[475] Winn, 300 and Miles, *The Beatles' Diary, Vol. 1*, 189.
[476] Winn, 300 and Miles, *The Beatles' Diary, Vol. 1*, 189.

[477] Davies, *The Beatles*, 208.

[478] Bicknell, 33. Alf writes, "19 February 1965: A very late start indeed today. I had difficulty getting the boys to the studio after last night's binge."

[479] P.A.F.O. is a Scouse abbreviation for "Pissed and Fell Over" Drunk.

[480] Spizer, "Turning Beatles Throwaways Into an Album," *Beatlefan*, Vol. 40, No. 2, Jan.-Feb. 2019, 19-22.

[481] Coleman, Lennon, 245-246. Coleman tells us that "John never just sat in his Rolls. He lay down in it. He operated the electrically controlled windows with his feet, playing ups and downs with them all the time. He smoked a lot, often passing the cigarette to his chauffeur."

[482] Coleman, *Lennon*, 245-246.

[483] Lewisohn, *The Beatles Recording Sessions*, 54-55. To date, John had written and recorded "Ticket to Ride" on Monday, 15 February; "Yes It Is" on Tuesday, 16 February; "You've Got to Hide Your Love Away" on Thursday, 18 February; and now "You're Gonna Lose That Girl" on 19 February.

[484] Goldman, 248.

[485] Womack, *The Beatles Encyclopedia, Vol. 2,* 1053.

[486] Harry, *The Ultimate Beatles Encyclopedia*, 717 and Spignesi and Turner, 210.

[487] Stark, Steven, *Meet The Beatles*, 120. John Lennon is quoted as saying, "Marriage is like walking around with odd socks on or your fly open."

[488] Coleman, *Lennon*, 293.

[489] Lewisohn, *The Beatles Recording Sessions*, 56 and Hammack, 33.

[490] Womack, *Maximum Volume: The Life of Beatles Producer, George Martin*, 252, Lewisohn, *The Beatles Recording Sessions*, 56, and Hammack, 33.

[491] Hammack, 32 and Winn, 300. There is considerable controversy about which guitar John is playing on "You're Gonna Lose That Girl." This will be addressed in the end *Notes!* of the chapter.

[492] Babiuk, 157. George had decided the Gretsch "sound[ed] like crap" and had set it aside for his new Sonic Blue Strat.

[493] Winn, 300, Spizer, *The Beatles for Sale on Parlophone Records*, 190, and Hammack, 32.

[494] Spizer, *The Beatles for Sale on Parlophone Records*, 190.

[495] Lewisohn, *The Complete Beatles Chronicle*, 184.

[496] Miles, *The Beatles' Diary, Vol. 1*, 190.

[497] Lewisohn, *The Complete Beatles Chronicle*, 185, Lewisohn, *The Beatles Recording Sessions,* 56, Winn, 301, Womack, *Maximum Volume: The Life of Beatles Producer, George Martin*, 253, and Hammack, 35.

[498] Lewisohn, *The Complete Beatles Chronicle*, 184.

Monday, 22 February 1965
London Airport
Heathrow, London

John hated flying.[499] Despised it. Nevertheless, here he was again, bound for an all-day trek from London Airport to New York City to the Northwest Indies[500] — or as the Americans said, the Bahamas.[501] Hours of fear and dread. Hours of waiting for the worst to transpire. But this time, the boys had been gifted a bit of marijuana to enjoy aboard their chartered Boeing 707,[502] and John hoped it would mitigate at least some of the trepidation.

Now, debarking from the limo and waving Alf Bicknell goodbye,[503] John and the others were alert — bright-eyed, and smiling.[504] Pivoting artfully towards the 1,400 young British fans who'd turned out to see them off, they posed for photographs.[505] They clowned and grinned. They offered "thumbs up."[506]

This part, John loved. He wasn't trying to sing through a smokescreen of screams; he wasn't fighting to shout introductions over squeals. He wasn't being questioned or prodded or tricked into saying the wrong thing. He wasn't in peril. He was simply being adored.

The Beatles' long-devoted fans filled all three upper, outdoor levels in London Airport. Despite a slicing February chill, the devotees were there, hoisting homemade signs that proclaimed, "Tara Boys!" and "Beatles Forever!" and "P.S. We Love You!"[507] The red-cheeked young punters — in bright scarves, jumpers, gloves, and hats — were as exuberant as ever.

The Beatles, however, had changed. Although Paul, George, and Ringo wore the traditional suits and ties, John — tired of "the image" — had insisted on a dark polo beneath his jacket.[508] The boys' hair was considerably longer as well, less coifed, less photo-ready.[509] And their innocent enthusiasm had mellowed to a pleased acceptance of this thing called Beatlemania. No longer were the lads giddy at the turnout; no longer were they thrilled and amazed.

Instead, all of them were eager to leave London behind. The warmest point of the day would top five degrees Celsius in London, but at Nassau's Balmoral Club on Cable Beach — where their private cabana awaited — it was already 90 degrees.[510]

"Shall we trade this cruel British winter for money in the bank?" John continued to smile and wave.[511]

"Ready when you are, Johnny!" George said through his teeth.

And giving the crowds one last McCartney wink and one last Ringo grin, they turned towards the plane and headed into summer.

****

There were 78 of them on the Boeing 707 flight[512]: The Beatles; Brian and his assistant, Wendy Hanson; Mal and Neil; select members of the media, including the *Daily Mirror*'s caustic Donald Zec; and the United Artists extensive cast and crew.[513]

Elegant, 31-year-old, brunette actress Eleanor Bron was getting her first glimpse of Beatlemania after a quiet but highly successful career in television, starring in "Not So Much a Programme…More a Way of Life."[514] In a chic, tailored, cream-coloured dress, gloves, heels, and carrying a travel bag, she politely posed with The Beatles, her dark eyes warily scanning the flailing crowds all around her.[515]

And thick-necked, Australian-born actor Leo McKern, who had received rave reviews for his role in Dick Lester's "The Running Jumping & Standing Still Film" and Walter Shenson's "The Mouse that Roared,"[516] boarded the plane with vigilant glances over his shoulder. He narrowed his eyes at the frenetic crowds that were doing anything but standing still. Furrowing his brow, he shook his head.

Long-limbed Patrick Cargill, who was to portray a rather snobbish Scotland Yard Superintendent, and John Bluthal, chosen to play the half-hearted villain Bhuta,[517] cautiously climbed the airline stairs together. Startled, they glanced circumspectly at the fans and then at one another. "Quickly, I'd say," Cargill directed, and they hurried into the cabin's safety.

Only director Dick Lester, producer Walter Shenson, and veteran actor Victor Spinetti — who'd become inured to the mania during the filming of "A Hard Day's Night" — took the scene in stride.[518]

"If you work with The Beatles..." Victor shouted over the fray.

"...you come to expect all of this!" Lester chuckled. The crowd was his film's best omen.

The Beatles were thrilled to reunite with Spinetti, who had filled the role of the fussy, anxious television director in "A Hard Day's Night." John, especially, had formed a close bond with him. Spinetti had become a mentor, of sorts — a father figure to John.

But the man most heralded on the departing aircraft this morning wasn't part of The Beatles' entourage, cast, or crew. He was barely an acquaintance.

Good-looking, 23-year-old, American actor Brandon deWilde, who had already enjoyed a remarkably successful film career as the young boy in the movie "Shane," as co-star with Patricia Neal and Paul Newman in "Hud," and as a versatile star on popular TV programs such as "Wagon Train" and "Alfred Hitchcock Presents,"[519] was "the man of the hour." An ardent Beatles fan, deWilde had presented the boys with a rather impressive token of his admiration: a large bag of very high-grade marijuana for the long and frightening excursion to the Caribbean.[520]

"'N the very moment of wheels-up," George buckled into his seat, his face ashen with fear, "that bag lands right here!"

It was one idea on which the boys could all agree. This time, they would soar, oblivious to the bumps and dips and rattles of the cabin.[521] And although John had dutifully carried along his *Spaniard in the Works* manuscript for revision,[522] he now shoved it aside. Minutes after take-off, John was in the clouds.[523]

****

It was almost 10.00 p.m. by the time the group reached its exotic location. But the long-suffering masses, who'd waited all day in the heat, were insensible to the lateness of the evening.

Hundreds and hundreds of ecstatic Bahamian fans engulfed the airport.[524] Flooding the warm, floral air — heavy with the scent of yellow elder, trailing bougainvillea, and bright hibiscus — with sweat and screams, the fans pushed and tumbled over one another. They wedged, tighter and tighter, against the guard rails in the sultry starlight.

Watching it all, Brian sighed and shook his head. "We'll be compelled to call a news conference,"[525] he whispered. There were journalists overflowing the roped-off tarmac, photographers elbowing for vantage points. This was the boys' first visit to the island, and the press was demanding its due. Even at this ungodly hour, a conference was inevitable.

"Brian," Neil Aspinall came forward, hesitantly.

"Yes, yes, I know…an obligatory news conference," Brian spat. "Inescapable."

"Well, we'll make it a brief one."

"See that you do."

And the nailing down of logistics was left to Neil. All John, Paul, George, and Ringo needed to do was find a way to clear their foggy heads. Brian expected them to be "interesting and articulate." Quite soon.

****

Even at midnight, the Bahamas were awake: lush vines and frangipanis crawling across every stuccoed surface;[526] brick walkways meandering through shadowed parks, and just beyond view, indigo waves slushing and sighing.

A bit 'o rhythm 'n blues, John sputtered. He leaned happily into the car's leather seats.

John knew — they all knew — that The Beatles had come here primarily for monetary purposes, to put foundations under the tax shelter that their shrewd accountant, Dr. Walter Strach, had created for them in the British crown colony.[527]

"We need to prove to the Bahamian authorities that you're an asset to their business community, as it were,"[528] Walter Shenson had explained to the boys, on Brian's behalf. "The film's a goodwill exercise, if you will, a way to bolster the image of

Strach's newly-formed Cavalcade Productions….to give validity to a company which, after a year's residence, will prove exceedingly advantageous to you all, if you get my drift."[529]

And John did. He understood the shell company and Strach's need to establish legitimate residency on the island. He grasped the *quid pro quo* — knew what the financial experts were about.

But tonight, the lucrative tax benefits weren't nearly as attractive as the scented air and the time away from his controlling mother-in-law. Nassau's salt-laced night was a new, easy, and irresistible drug. John drew a deep breath; he exhaled. *Free!*

"Hey, let's have a swim, once we're there!"[530] George was still soaring.

"Nah, not me." Ringo waved him off. "I'm dead creased, son. Why aren't you?"

"I'm much younger than you, I suppose."

"Y'er right," Paul shrugged, "but only for a coupla more days, y' know."

"Yeah, but everyone knows," George cocked an eyebrow, "that even past m' birthday, I'll still be *decades* younger than you lot!"

George laughed, already in party mode. His sister, Louise, was expected on location at any moment, to commemorate George's twenty-second.[531] And Paul was waiting for family as well — his father, Jim, and Jim's new bride, Angie, were flying into Nassau with Angie's daughter, Ruth. The senior McCartneys were enjoying a belated honeymoon,[532] and Ruth was to celebrate her fifth birthday.[533]

"Well, with or without you geriatrics, *I'm* up for a swim!" George crowed.

"Y'er on, Lloyd Bridges!"[534] John piped up. "Count me in."

"Well, if *he's in*…" Paul lifted a shoulder.

"…I suppose I'm in as well!" Ringo shook his head, relenting.

And within the half hour, the boys had carelessly dropped their luggage just inside the private lodging Brian had reserved for them, and they were up to their ears in the balmy water of the Balmoral's Olympic-sized swimming pool.[535]

****

Dashing American reporter Larry Kane had arrived earlier and stowed his luggage at a rather vanilla, two-storey house on Bay Street — Nassau's lively, commercial thoroughfare, bordering the old docks.[536]

And without unpacking or even pausing for a meal, he'd hired a taxi to the Balmoral Club, the prestigious hotel where Kane thought almost everyone else was registered.[537] The Beatles, for sure, were there. The United Artists cast and crew as well, he surmised.

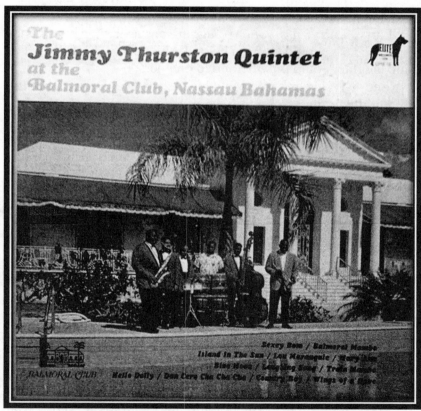

**The Balmoral Club, where The Beatles lodged
in the Bahamas, whilst filming "Help!"
The Beatles did not stay in the hotel
but had a private house on the grounds.**
Photograph from Wikimedia Commons

But probably not Brian, Larry mused. *He almost always reserves a separate place, in hopes of sanity and a few nights' rest.*

But surprisingly, when the taxi dropped Kane on the secluded dirt road leading up to The Beatles' cabin, all was strangely serene.[538] Larry looked around, shrugged, and shouldered his cumbersome tape recorder and camera bag. Rapidly devising a suitable introduction for himself, the svelte young journalist strolled deliberately towards two stern guards positioned in front of The Beatles' manicured, colourful, tropical residence.[539]

"Larry Kane, American," he began, flashing his press I.D. and smiling charismatically. "I traveled with the boys on last year's North American Tour...Brian's expecting me."

"Larry, Larry, it's *you*, y' fuggin' bastard!"[540] Huge hands gripped Kane's shoulders from behind. "I love you, Larry!"[541] The titanic laughter could only belong to one person.

Kane swiveled around to find his ole pal, Mal Evans, beaming with childlike glee. Hugging as if they were brothers, they chuckled and slapped one another on the back.[542]

"Mal!" Larry was thrilled...and relieved. He hadn't a formal letter of introduction or any documents to convince wary guards.

"Good to see you, Larry, my boy! Just great!"[543] Evans towered over the slender Kane. And without realizing his own strength, he pulled Kane closer, the height difference causing Mal's arm to loop uncomfortably around Larry's neck.[544] Kane sputtered and coughed as he grinned.

"Come on, come in!" Mal let go, leading the way inside to a spacious main room open to the warm Bahamian night via screened windows boasting Bermuda shutters.[545] The bright gathering place was littered with The Beatles' gear: suitcases thrown open hurriedly on cushioned wicker chairs, discarded hanging bags tossed across floral sofas, newly-delivered stacks of fan mail spilling onto the sisal rug, and crumpled travel suits that had evidently been cast off rapidly.

"The boys 're out takin' a midnight swim, as it were," Mal explained, offering Larry a nightcap. "But they'll be 'round soon enough, I'll wager...I just strolled over 'n told 'em there were 'pool sharks' trollin' this time o' night!" He offered another belly laugh. "That'll sort 'em out, won't it?"

But before Larry could respond, George Harrison shuffled in. He paused, dripping on the doormat.[546]

"Good to see y' Larry!"[547] George toweled off. His eyes were wide and his face, unusually pale.[548]

"Hey, George," Larry returned, his reporter's eyes zeroing in. "Great to see *you*!" Larry studied the boy, who appeared either ill or "on some substance."[549] As a journalist, Kane missed little, and one glance told him this wasn't the same George Harrison he'd known last September.[550]

Larry automatically connected the dots between tonight and his last evening with The Beatles in September 1964 — back in New York's Riviera Idlewild Hotel, where Bob Dylan (a rucksack on his shoulders) had visited the boys' suite.[551] Larry recalled smirking with journalists Art Schreiber and Ivor Davis that night, when late in the evening, The Beatles had emerged with Dylan from a side room, their eyes glazed and their steps unsure.[552] The boys had tried to acknowledge the room full of reporters with equanimity, but it had been a chore; in spite of themselves, The Beatles had snickered and giggled like schoolboys.[553]

Larry had thought then, and he thought now, that drugs were involved. And the *Daily Express*'s Cockney foreign correspondent, Ivor Davis, had informed his comrades the sickly-sweet smell seeping in from the Riviera side-room was marijuana.[554] He'd been certain of it.

Now, the front door creaked open again, and the others tumbled in: Paul McCartney, Neil Aspinall, and John Lennon.[555] John was carrying two pairs of slippers (presumably, Paul's and his own), and Paul was holding wet swimming fins.[556] Neil balanced a bundle of damp towels, which he quickly dispersed to the chatty, dripping duo.

"Larry Kane!" Paul saw him first. "You're back, aren't you!"

"Larry!" John was delighted to see one of the few reporters who would chat honestly with him about "things that really matter," including politics. "We have to stop meetin' like this, son!"

But despite John's customary wit, Larry could see that Lennon, too, wasn't entirely himself. His eyes were red-rimmed, and he was far less reserved than John normally tended to be.

"Hi Paul, Neil," Larry walked over to shake wet hands. "And you, Lennon!" He pivoted towards the Beatle. "Why are you dressed like *that,* man? What's with *that*? How old are you?" They were the very words John had hurled at Larry the first time the two of them had met. It was a fond joke between them now, their club pass-phrase.

Widening his eyes in mock innocence and repeating the retort he used to hurl at his Aunt Mimi when she rebuked him — demanding to know "who in the world he thought he was" — John grinned. "Don't you knooooooow me, Larry? Aii'm Johnnnnnn Lennon!!!!!!"[557] And jamming his tongue behind his lower lip, John pulled his favourite face.

Larry sputtered. He shook John's hand and gave his friend a quick hug whilst the others burst into "talk-at-once" chatter.

For the next quarter hour, the room brimmed with unsteady fun. Only Aspinall, anxious about Larry's seeing the boys "out of sorts," remained remote.[558] But the more Larry ignored the obvious, the more Neil eased back. At last, mixing himself a drink and settling into a thickly cushioned loveseat, Aspinall put his feet up on the ottoman.

"Well, where's our newlywed...Ringo?" Larry asked, ambling back towards the white, hand-rubbed coffee table and his tape recorder. He'd plugged the machine in and cued the tape, ready for business.

"Oh, sharks, y' know," Paul responded, tersely.

"Yeah, pool sharks." John threw a loppy grin in Mal's direction.[559]

"Well," Larry chuckled, "if you don't think he'd mind, I'd like to go ahead and do a fairly brief interview."

"Sure, right." Paul wrapped a towel around his waist and found his slippers, right where John had dropped them.

"Yeah. Brief us!" John snickered, toweling off as well.

And giggling at each other, John and Paul ambled over to Kane's bulky recorder, ready for their first 1965 WFUN interview, whilst George sniggered and pulled faces at them from the buffet.[560]

Kane: Hey Paul?[561]
McCartney: Yeah?
Kane: How ya doin'?
McCartney: (Smiling) Hello Larry...lovely to see you.
Kane: John?
Lennon: (Leaning in) What's that, Larry?
Kane: How are *you* doing?

Lennon: Well, look, all I can say, Larry, is, "This thing's wide open! *Anythin' can happen*, man!"

Kane: Well...

Lennon: (Explaining) It's a new phrase. Have you got it?

Kane: What is this "everything can happen" business?

McCartney: Listen — "Everythin' is wide open; anythin' can happen, man!" It's a new phrase, which sums up everythin'!

Lennon: Now look, Larry, all I can say is, this thing is wide open! *Anythin'* can happen, man!

McCartney: (Enthusiastically) *That's it!*

Lennon: *Anythin'!*

McCartney: (Gesturing towards John) See the way he said it?

Kane: (Smiling and shaking his head) What was the highlight of the '64 tour?

McCartney: Ummm, meetin' Larry Ellis.

Kane: (Helpfully) That's Larry *Kane*.

McCartney: No, I didn't like him! Larry Ellis was the one!

Kane: (Chuckling) Thanks a lot.

McCartney: Mr. Kane, for you, okay![562]

Grinning, Larry snapped off the recorder. This wasn't, he concluded, quite the right time for a news-worthy conversation. Instead, he and the others joined George over a large bamboo tray of breads, cheeses, fruits, and pastries. They filled their plates. John had two of everything. None of them were shy.

And 45 minutes later, when the boys seemed more grounded, Larry invited George and the newly-arrived Ringo back to the tape recorder for "a quick chat." The wait was worth it:

Kane: George, welcome to Nassau.[563]

Harrison: Hello, Larry. And welcome you to Nassau, too.

Kane: Looking forward to another tour?

Harrison: First the film, Larry! That's what *we're* thinkin' of.

Kane: Ringo, welcome to the Bahamas.

Starr: Thank you, Larry. It's good to see you again, and give my regards to everyone in Miami and all over America. And (the drummer leaned towards the recorder) I haven't changed 'cause I'm married! I'm still nice.[564]

Larry chuckled and ended the quick set before anyone could

start shouting, "This thing's wide open! Anything can happen!" again.

This last conversation, he thought, *will be ideal for tomorrow's press feed.* Ringo had been practical and down-to-earth; George, genuine and unaffected. It would constitute the perfect first American interview with The Beatles on the set of their new film.

"Well, look," Larry stood and gathered his things, "I hear you four are shooting in a pool tomorrow."[565]

"Yeah, though they're after lettin' us sleep in a bit, I hear." John stood, too, now yawning audibly. "We're on set 'round noon, or so they say."

"They actually want us to jump in that pool with our clothes 'n shoes on!"[566] Ringo was still appalled. "*Our shoes,* Larry! They're rather dear — our shoes!"

Larry chuckled. *The Beatles! Worried about the cost of footwear!* "Well," he shook his head, "I'll wager you can afford another pair or two!"

"Don't let my mother hear you say that!" George chimed in.

"Waste not, want not!" John waggled in Kane's direction.

"He's always quotin' Shakespeare," Ringo sighed.

"Poor Richard, son," John corrected. "Poor Richard!"

"Cummoffit John, Little Richard never said anythin' like that!" George dead-panned. "He never once mentioned it when I was with him!"

And laughing at the usual Scouse mickey-talk, Larry hoisted his gear and headed towards the front door. He couldn't believe he was actually paid to do this job. It was, day-to-day, incomparable.

****

Tuesday, 23 February 1965
Balmoral Club
Nassau, Bahamas

The Balmoral Club was the ideal place to host The Beatles. Situated well out of Nassau, on the far end of New Providence island near Cable Beach,[567] it was a spacious Greek Revival resort encased in tall, swaying palms, spreading yuccas, and lush vegetation. Built on a private cul-de-sac drive that curtailed curious onlookers and journalists from motoring past,[568] the elegant hotel was the perfect lodging for international celebrities. In fact, Ted Kennedy was expected in just days.[569] But most of all, the Balmoral was peaceful and quiet.

This morning, the boys were allowed to sleep in,[570] and then, as they unpacked, a lavish breakfast was delivered to their quarters.[571] Whilst stumbling about, jamming jeans, T-shirts, and socks into dresser drawers, Brian tried to give them some sense of the film. They'd all known since October 1963 that, just after the Christmas holidays, they were slated to make a second United Artists full-length motion picture.[572] And they'd been told, time and again, that it would be "a thriller," but up to now, that was the full extent of their understanding.[573]

"Now, above all else," Epstein began a bit dramatically, "our hope is that this production will be completely and utterly different from 'A Hard Day's Night.'"[574] He paused, wondering if any of this was sinking in. "Unique, you understand."

None of them even looked his way, but he went on. "Since 'A Hard Day's Night' was shot in black and white, this one, of course, will be full colour, filmed on the silvery slopes of Austria and the sparkling beaches here in Nassau. We'll replace drab, this time, with rich and exotic."[575]

The boys, carelessly emptying their suitcases, barely nodded. John stopped to pour a second cup of Earl Grey. No one, except Brian, spoke.

"Even when we return to London, we'll seek out…well, striking settings for you — such as Cliveden House and Asprey's — elegant locales in which to film.[576] We're endeavouring, you understand, to craft a bit of a spoof on the popular James Bond series[577] in which the heroes (you, of course) — backed by a Bond-esque sound track[578] — are being pursued by hordes of evildoers and are always just one step ahead of the villains, whilst you jet off to sensational corners of the world!"

"'N what's this film known as?" George droned.

Brian smiled, pleased that Harrison had actually been listening. "Well, initially, Dick Lester suggested 'Beatles 2,' but almost immediately, he was overruled."[579]

"Ole Dick lacked a tad of ingenuity, as it were." John slurped his tea loudly.

"Yes, so everyone said." Brian nodded. "And therefore, the current moniker is Ringo's own."

"'Eight Arms to Hold You'!"[580] Ringo grinned, speaking up for the first time all morning.

Paul and John exchanged glances.

"Great, that," Paul gave a wink and quick sideways nod, "but...uhm..."

"Look," John was less tactful, "me 'n Paul can't write a song about eight arms holdin' someone, y' know![581] I mean, as a rule, we don't *do* lyrics about orgies...or octopi!"

"Yes, of course," Brian tried to circumvent any sort of conflict before the first day's filming, "quite true. But still, as Paul pointed out, extremely clever, Ringo."

"Ta." The drummer was rolling a towel to use after the afternoon's pool scene. His smile had vanished.

"However," Brian tried to navigate off rocky shoals to a more neutral topic, "all nomenclature aside, United Artists was so exhilarated with the results of the last film that they've more than *doubled* the budget on this one.[582] And not to be obvious, but I'm sure you realise that means we'll be shooting this film with some of Britain's finest stars..."

"Look here, Eppy," George strode over and perched on the sofa arm, "what's the film *about*, really? I mean, no one's said a word to us, have they?"[583] He looked to the others. "I mean, yeah, we know it's got a bit of 'zany,' as they say, comedy but..."[584]

"I mean, they told us to watch the Marx Brothers' 'Duck Soup' to get the gist o' the humour,"[585] Paul added.

"But no one's told us a fuggin' thing about the script, y' know!" John's voice elevated a bit. "'N we've had *zero* creative input in this film...not like the last one."[586]

Brian quickly drew the back of his hand across his lips, his nervous tic.[587] "Well, from what I've gathered," Brian made a mental note to interrogate Lester this very afternoon, "it's rather a spy spoof, you see. Some international fan sends Ringo an exotic red ring..."

"Well, isn't that apropos!" John spat, unimpressed.

"...which is linked to a religious cult of some sort who desperately want the ring back and threaten Ringo's life in the process. You, as I understand it, are trying to protect him, as it were."

"All right," Paul shrugged, "though I'm not certain how that pertains to The Beatles 'n who we are 'n what we are. But at least now we know somethin' rather than nothin', y' know."

"Look," George pointed out, "this filmin' in a pool wearin' street clothes![588] How's *that* fit in?"

"Well," Brian lifted his palms, "I would imagine you're making a great escape of some sort, though no one's informed me, either. But rest assured, I'll make certain to sort this all out, straight away."

"You do that," John said.

And nodding glum faces, the boys gathered their long-sleeved shirts, hats, and suntan lotions. Since the film's early Austrian snow scenes wouldn't be recorded for days yet, and suntans would be "highly implausible on lads from Liverpool," they'd been cautioned over and over to mitigate the effects of the scorching Bahamian sun.[589]

"They want us all pasty!" Ringo had grumbled to Mal and Neil.

"Who craves a pasty rocker?" George had seconded.

But as usual, The Beatles did as they were told. They fell in line. They "got along to get along" and even agreed to wear "perfectly good clothes, y' know, in a chlorine pool." Being obedient was expected of them. But John was finding dictum harder and harder to follow.

****

A tight ring of belligerently-hungry news photographers and shouting reporters surrounded the lads the moment they debarked the limo. Pushing and bellowing "Look over here, John!" or "Wave for us, Paul!" or "Show us that new wedding ring, Ringo!", the boys were inundated with sharp commands. "Try to smile more, George!" the *paparazzi* cawed. "Give us a grin, now!"

No requests, only orders. The Beatles blinked and backed protectively against their car.

Within seconds, Neil and Mal wedged between the aggressive

journalists and The Beatles. At first, they cajoled, explaining that the boys needed a few private moments to learn their lines for the afternoon's shoot.[590] But instead of retreating, the crowd surged constantly closer.

As Neil began to elbow, shove, and lose ground (as well as his temper), he hardened his tone, demanding that the throng move back. Hotel security guards arrived, joining forces in wrestling with the mob. But when nosy tourists and Bahamian fans gathered alongside the press — shoving their way towards The Beatles[591] — the situation became treacherous.

"If y' don't mind," Paul McCartney tried diplomacy on the fans closest to him, "we, uhm...we need just a few minutes to study our lines, y' know."

But the sound of his voice ignited the giddy girls. They surged. One arrogant photographer jammed a lens in John's face and exploded the flashbulb in his eyes.

"Get the fuck out of here!"[592] John bellowed, "browned off" before the day had even really started. "*Get out!*"

But another flash fired away, blinding the snarling Lennon.

"Boys, in the car!" Neil barked. "All o' you, now!"

And needing no other warning, The Beatles vanished. The car doors clicked, and the motor started, threatening retreat. Roaring in frustration, the horde of photographers clicked away at the frightened British musicians, sitting behind their thin shield of glass. And just as determinedly, The Beatles turned their backs, ignoring the public.

Larry Kane stood, flabbergasted. On last year's North American Tour, he had seen crazed fans encroaching rather relentlessly, but rarely had the press intruded. They had almost always maintained a respectable level of professionalism.

"Who *are* these people?" he asked Mal, once the crowd had been somewhat subdued.

"No idea." Mal shook his head. "Origins unknown."[593]

"Yes well, manners unknown as well," Larry hissed. "And of course, they'll probably all write stories painting John as 'the bad guy' here. Not for nothing, but I thought he was relatively patient with them. Knowing John, I thought he had every incentive to come out swinging."

"Yeah well, thank God he didn't!" Neil was still daubing perspiration from his face. "*That* wouldn't have endeared The

Beatles or Strach or his Cavalcade Productions with the powers-that-be. Not one iota."

"But it wasn't John's..." Mal began.

"I never said it was." Aggravated, Neil cut across him. "It's just...look, the way things are...we have to be massively careful these days. Everythin' the boys do is madly exaggerated. Every word they say is weighed 'n measured...'n almost always, nowadays, they're found wantin'. Every fuggin' thought they think becomes what Brian calls 'public domain.' What I call 'drama.'"

"Unfortunately," Larry nodded, "Brian's a hundred percent right. From that first Number One on, your boys fell under microscopic scrutiny, and with every additional hit record or project, it'll only get worse. The world, you know, despises winners and goes out of its way to find chinks in their armour."

"Well, not if we get to the world first!" Mal robustly declared.

But although the three friends nodded agreement, they realised the vast impossibility of that task. Sooner or later, the boys would slip up. Sooner or later, one of them would give journalists the fodder they craved. Sooner or later, a tragic flaw would be revealed. Realistically, it was only a matter of time.

****

Pert Louise Harrison had arrived from America just a tad after the boys had landed, and the airport security team that George had waiting for his blonde "big sister" had whisked Lou off to the boys' impromptu press conference — "already in progress," as television was fond of saying. As she'd entered the jam-packed room, she had seen John (in his new, more comfortable contacts) recognize her instantly. He had nudged George, pointing in Lou's direction.[594] And beaming, George had given his sister a rippled-fingers wave.[595]

To protect "his Lou" from potential bedlam, George had requested that Louise be lodged far from The Balmoral. She was registered, instead, in the lovely downtown Nassau hotel where Mal and Neil were housed.[596] Mal had promised "round-the-clock security" at Lou's door.[597] And George knew that pledge included Mal himself, cautiously overseeing every detail. Lou was guaranteed a carefree, mid-winter island holiday that she'd never forget.[598]

This afternoon, George had arranged to have Lou stationed around the Nassau Beach Hotel's enchanting pool[599] where John, Paul, Ringo, and he would "emerge topside," swimming for their lives from some fictitious subterranean tunnel, in a daring escape from the film's blood-thirsty villains.[600] Louise was ecstatic at being included in the action. In her new beachwear and cat-eye sunglasses, she lingered in the umbrellaed shade, chatting cheerfully with the boys whilst they waited to film.

There had been, she'd heard, a bit of an ugly roolya-broolya with the press earlier, when the lads had arrived. But now, all intruders had been cordoned back. Without too much ado, the boys had been returned to the set.

"I'd be happy to run lines with you lot," Louise offered brightly — eager to assist.

"Um, I don't know as we've got any in this scene," John muttered, distractedly.

"Yeah, not quite sure," George mumbled.

"No one's told us a bloody thing!" Ringo fanned himself with a locally-woven straw hat.

The boys were hazy and relaxed. As Louise nattered on about this and that, the boys simply nodded and smiled dreamily.

When, at last, The Beatles were called to jump — fully dressed — into the pool, they complied, without discussion, without debate, even without the customary Beatles banter. John (who despised photos of himself with wet, plastered-back hair that exposed his receding hairline) walked hesitantly, via the concrete steps, into the pool.[601] He was compelled to have his shirt-front doused by the crew, but even then, John was quiet and utterly acquiescent.[602]

Louise watched him with curious eyes. She watched them all.

Something, she thought, was very different thisavvy (as she used to say back in Liddypool), but exactly *what*, she wasn't sure yet. Her curiosity, however, was aroused, and Big Sister was determined to sleuth out the mystery.

Notes!

Did The Beatles get "bad press" from the pool incident?

Just as Larry Kane had predicted, the newspapers the following day were filled with strident criticism of The Beatles. In Ticket to Ride, *Kane says, "What followed that battle was an international media attack on The Beatles, with strong suggestions that The Beatles were rude and nasty to ordinary people and members of the press. Since I was there...I took great pains in my own reports and dispatches to the wire services to explain what was really happening." (p. 198)*

*Additionally, Kane did several interviews with The Beatles to give the boys the opportunity to tell their side of the incident. When Paul was asked by Larry what had occurred that day, he spelled it out: "We were doin' a film 'n we were tryin' to learn the script. A couple of pressmen kept takin' pictures 'n things, so we asked them if they would sort of go away...I think a couple of them got ratty 'n started writin' things about us being rude to everyone. I don't think it was true, you know. But what can we do about it?" (*Ticket to Ride, *198)*

In the days to come, the scenario would only get worse.

Of note: *Few biographers mention the fact that Paul's brother Michael McCartney was along on this trek as well. He was, and in his book,* Remember: Recollections and Photographs of The Beatles, *he shares several extremely rare shots of the boys on the Bahamian set of "Help!" He also divulged some interesting titbits about what the lads and he did to pass the time in between filming! (pp. 122-128)*

Sources:

Interview with Louise Harrison, Beatlefest, Kansas City, 1993.
Interview with Larry Kane, Philadelphia, PA, 2010.
Interview with Angie and Ruth McCartney, "She Said She Said" podcast with co-host, author Lanea Stagg of **The Recipe Records Series,** *found here: https://shesaidshesaid.podbean.com/*

Lewisohn, The Complete Beatles Chronicle, *185.*
Lewisohn, The Beatles: Day by Day, *59.*
Harry, The Ultimate Beatles Encyclopedia, *299-301.*
Harry, The Encyclopedia of Beatles People, *72-73, 214, and 295.*
The Beatles, The Beatles Anthology, *167.*
Harry, The Beatles, Vol. 4, The History of The Beatles on Film, *29.*
Lennon, Cynthia, A Twist of Lennon, *143.*
Womack, Maximum Volume: The Life of Beatles Producer, George Martin, *253-254.*
Miles, The Beatles' Diary, Vol. 1, *190.*
Norman, John Lennon: The Life, *394.*
Norman, Shout!, *318.*
Goodden, Joe, Riding So High: The Beatles and Drugs, *56.*
Badman, 141.

Davis, Ivor, The Beatles and Me on Tour, *211-212.*
Harrison, Louise, My Kid Brother's Band, *216.*
McCartney, Angie, The Long and Winding Road, *82-83.*
Coleman, Lennon, *39.*
Coleman, The Man Who Made The Beatles, *170.*
Kane, Ticket to Ride, *196-197.*
Kane, When They Were Boys, *316-318.*
Yule, 98-99.
Carr, Roy, Beatles At the Movies, *59.*
Margotin and Guesdon, 216.
Schaffner, 42.
Spitz, 170.
Buskin, Richard, The Complete Idiot's Guide to The Beatles, *198-199.*
Hill, John, Paul, George & Ringo, *190-191.*
Trynka, 158 and 162-164.
Egan, The Mammoth Book of The Beatles, *376.*
Brown, 170.
Robertson, John, "Help! The End of the Beginning," Trynka, The
Beatles: Ten Years that Shook the World, *164.*
Riley, Lennon, *275.*
Bicknell, 34.

*http://london-weather.eu/article.104.html This helpful website furnished
information about the weather at the London airport on 22 Feb 1965.*

*https://www.dailymail.co.uk/news/article-2514041/Beatle-George-
Harrisons-sister-Louise-82-lives-broke-rural-Missouri.html This website
has biographical information on Louise Harrison.*

*https://beatlesarama.com/beatles-sister-louise-harrison-departs-
midwest/ Many excellent true stories about Louise Harrison and her
work on behalf of The Beatles have been collected here by Pat Matthews
of BeatlesARama.*

*The Beatles' Help! at 50: rare behind-the-scenes photos | BFI This
website supplies candid photos of The Beatles on location, making
"Help!"*

*https://www.bing.com/videos/search?q=louise+harrison+george%27s+
sister&view=detail&mid=2A7537ADBDD2E15F838F2A7537ADBDD2E
15F838F&FORM=VIRE This is an interesting interview with Louise
Harrison from her post-Beatles days, looking back.*

*https://www.antiquestradegazette.com/news/2018/menu-signed-by-all-
four-beatles-from-a-flight-when-getting-high-was-the-refreshment/ This
article shows a menu signed on board the flight by all four Beatles and
talks about their "activities" during the long flight.*

https://www.youtube.com/watch?v=qmjfDlkXKC0
At the beginning of this video, you can see The Beatles being escorted onto the pool set, fully dressed to film the scene in this chapter. You'll see Paul, George, and Ringo go down the deeper end, presumably to jump in. John walks down the pool steps and is given a bicycle to ride in the water. The bike doesn't make it into the film, obviously, but it was a part of the original script. Also included in the film are scenes on the beach and later in Austria.
Or use this QR code:

---

[499] Coleman, *Lennon*, 263.

[500] Lewisohn, *The Complete Beatles Chronicle*, 185. Lewisohn uses the British term "Northwest Indies" in *lieu* of the more American term, the Bahamas.

[501] Miles, *The Beatles' Diary, Vol. 1*, 190.

[502] Norman, *Shout!*, 244, Miles, The *Beatles' Diary, Vol. 1*, 190, Harry, *The Ultimate Beatles Encyclopedia*, 299, and Goodden, Joe, *Riding So High: The Beatles and Drugs*, 56.

[503] Bicknell, 34.

[504] The Beatles, *The Beatles Anthology*, 167. Here, Brian describes the scene as they rolled up to London Airport. He says "The group posed for the mass of photographers, continuing to wave to the fans as long as the airlines would allow them."

[505] Miles, *The Beatles' Diary, Vol. 1*, 190.

[506] Hill, *John, Paul, George & Ringo*, 190-191. There are several photographs of the boys departing from London Airport on these pages. You can see them giving "thumbs up," along with Eleanor Bron, who was traveling with them.

[507] Hill, *John, Paul, George & Ringo*, 190-191. These are the actual posters in the photos.

[508] Hill, *John, Paul, George & Ringo*, 191. Look at John in the photo with Eleanor Bron. He is the only one not wearing a dress shirt and tie under his jacket.

[509] Hill, *John, Paul, George & Ringo*, 191.

[510] Harry, *The Ultimate Beatles Encyclopedia*, 299-300, Harry, *The Beatles, Vol. 4: The History of The Beatles on Film*, 29, Miles, *The Beatles' Diary, Vol. 1*, 190, and Lewisohn, *The Complete Beatles Chronicle*, 185. For weather in London, I consulted: http://london-weather.eu/article.104.html

[511] Goodden, 55. Goodden states, "Eager to escape the cold and damp British climate, [The Beatles] lobbied the producers to set parts of the film in foreign locations…it was decided to go on location in the Bahamas."

[512] Yule, 98.

[513] Harry, *The Ultimate Beatles Encyclopedia*, 299-300.

[514] Harry, *The Encyclopedia of Beatles People*, 72-73 and Norman, *John Lennon: The Life*, 396.

[515] Hill, *John, Paul, George & Ringo*, 191 and Davis, *The Beatles Files*, 89. Photos of Eleanor Bron with the boys can be found in both sources.

[516] Harry, *The Encyclopedia of Beatles People*, 214.

[517] Harry, *The Ultimate Beatles Encyclopedia*, 301 and *The Encyclopedia of Beatles People*, 295.

[518] The Beatles, *The Beatles Anthology*, 167. Brian lists the cast and crew members on board the plane, including all of those mentioned in this paragraph.

[519] https://en.wikipedia.org/wiki/Brandon_deWilde

[520] The Beatles, *The Beatles Anthology*, 167 and Goodden, Joe, *Riding So High*, 56. In *The Beatles Anthology*, George Harrison says of Brandon deWilde: "Brandon deWilde was an actor, a James Dean type. (He died in a car crash in 1972.) He liked The Beatles' music, and he heard we were going to film in the Bahamas, so he came over from the States with a big bag of reefer. We smoked on the plane, all the way to the Bahamas."

[521] Robertson, John, "Help! The End of the Beginning," Trynka, *The Beatles, 10 Years that Shook the World*, 164. Robertson says, "The joints were first lit on the long flight from Heathrow to Nassau and were only extinguished when the cameras were rolling."

[522] Trynka, 163.

[523] Yule, 98 and Goodden, 56. Goodden quotes George Harrison as saying, "We smoked on the plane, all the way to the Bahamas. It was a charter flight with all the film people — the actors and the crew — and we thought, 'No one will notice.' We had Mal smoking cigars to drown out the smell." Goodden goes on to say that when the plane landed in New York City, The Beatles were so stoned that "they flatly refused to disembark" and go through Customs. Fortunately, at long last, Customs gave up trying, and the plane took off again.

[524] Trynka, 164.

[525] Miles, The *Beatles' Diary, Vol. 1*, 190.

[526] This detail was supplied by Angie McCartney in the "She Said She Said" interview that Lanea Stagg, author of **The Recipe Records Series**, and I did with Ruth and Angie McCartney, July 2020, found here: https://shesaidshesaid.podbean.com/

[527] Lewisohn, *The Complete Beatles Chronicle*, 185, Norman, *John Lennon: The Life*, 394, Brown, 170, Egan, *The Mammoth Book of The Beatles*, 376, Norman, *Shout!*, 318, Womack, *Maximum Volume: The Life of Beatles Producer, George Martin*, 253, and Trynka, 162.

[528] Norman, *Shout!*, 318, Womack, *Maximum Volume: The Life of Beatles Producer, George Martin*, 253, Egan, 376, Trynka, 162, and Spitz, 170. Direct quote from Walter Shenson. Norman tells us that The Beatles filmed in the Bahamas "not because the plot demanded it, but simply as a *quid pro quo* to that celebrated tax haven for sheltering some of The Beatles' earnings."

[529] Norman, *Shout!*, 318. Direct quote from Walter Shenson.

[530] Miles, *The Beatles' Diary, Vol. 1*, 190.

[531] Harrison, Louise, *My Kid Brother's Band*, 216.

[532] McCartney, Angie, *My Long and Winding Road*, 82. Angie says that Jim had asked Alistair Taylor to "book us a trip for a honeymoon," early in 1965. (She and Jim had wed in late 1964.) So Taylor arranged for Jim, Angie, and Angie's daughter Ruth to visit the Bahamas whilst The Beatles were filming "Help!" They flew separately from The Beatles, leaving London on BOAC and then transferring to an international flight.

[533] McCartney, Angie, 82.

[534] Lloyd Bridges is an American actor who starred in the extremely popular TV show "Sea Hunt," about a S.C.U.B.A. diver, Mike Nelson, who rescues people and encouters various adventures. It ran from 1958 to1961 and then was constantly in re-runs on many American stations throughout the 1960s. The Beatles had seen many episodes of this show during the North American Tour. For more information on the syndicated TV show, go to: https://en.wikipedia.org/wiki/Sea_Hunt

[535] Miles, *The Beatles' Diary, Vol. 1*, 190.

[536] Kane, Larry, *When They Were Boys*, 318.

[537] Kane, Larry, *Ticket to Ride*, 196.

[538] Kane, *Ticket to Ride*, 196.

[539] Kane, *Ticket to Ride*, 196.

[540] Kane, *When They Were Boys*, 318. Direct quote from Mal Evans.

[541] Kane, *When They Were Boys*, 318. Direct quote from Mal Evans.

[542] Kane, *When They Were Boys*, 318 and *Ticket to Ride*, 196.

[543] Kane, *Ticket to Ride*, 196.

[544] Kane, *When They Were Boys*, 318. Kane says, "He hugged me hard when I walked through the doors of the boys' rented cottage on the Nassau beachfront…the differential between our height caused him to grab my neck…causing a troubling nosebleed."

[545] Kane, *Ticket to Ride*, 196.

[546] Kane, *Ticket to Ride*, 196. In the version of this story in *When They Were Boys*, p. 318, both George and John were already in the room when Larry arrived.

[547] Kane, *Ticket to Ride*, 196.

[548] Kane, *Ticket to Ride*, 196. Direct quote from George Harrison. And the description of George's appearance is Kane's. He says that George's "eyeballs looked as if they were going to pop from the sockets" and that the boy was very pale.

[549] Kane, *Ticket to Ride*, 196. Larry says that George Harrison was "not in a good state of mind," that George appeared "either sick or on a substance." He notes that George was "very different" from the George he'd said goodbye to in New York the previous fall.

[550] Kane, *Ticket to Ride*, 196.

[551] Davis, Ivor, *The Beatles and Me on Tour*, 211.

[552] Davis, 212. Davis says of that late night appearance by The Beatles in the Riviera Idlewild: "Ringo looked the worse for wear. He could barely stand up straight. He was bleary-eyed and, with great effort, tried to string a few words together. He would start, then stop, in mid-sentence, grappling for the right words, as if he had lost his way completely. But try as he might, he could never quite finish what he had started out to say. And he giggled a lot."

[553] Davis, 212. Davis describes the boys, re-entering the room with the reporter, as "lethargic lads." He says, "We [the reporters] tried to start a conversation with them. Their answers were…somewhat vague."

[554] Davis, 211. Davis says, in *The Beatles and Me on Tour*, that he recognized "that certain pungent aroma" coming from the side room where Dylan and the boys were gathered despite the fact that "a wet towel had been stuffed under the door…to prevent fumes from one room entering another." In a 2018 interview with Davis, he told me in no uncertain terms that the smell was marijuana.

[555] Kane, *Ticket to Ride*, 196 and *When They Were Boys*, 318. In *When They Were Boys*, John and George are in the room when Larry arrives, but Paul and Neil Aspinall enter a bit later. Here, I combined the two stories to have Paul, John, and Neil enter together, after George.

[556] Kane, *When They Were Boys*, 318. In this version of the story, Paul carries "swimming fins." In *Ticket to Ride*, 196, he carries slippers.

[557] Coleman, *Lennon*, 39.

[558] Kane, *When They Were Boys*, 318. In this account, Larry says that "[Mal] and Aspinall asked me to avoid reporting on what the guys were smoking. I agreed."

[559] Kane, *When They Were Boys*, 316.

[560] Kane, *Ticket to Ride*, 196. Larry worked for radio station WFUN in Miami, and the "Boss Jocks" had asked him to fly to the Bahamas and interview his friends, The Beatles. After getting permission from NEMS to do so, Larry flew there and landed on the same day that The Beatles did.

[561] Kane, *Ticket to Ride*, 196-197. This is the first line of an interview between reporter Larry Kane and Beatles John Lennon and Paul McCartney from The Beatles' house in The Balmoral Club, Nassau, Bahamas on the late night of 22 Feb. 1965. I am not going to endnote every line but will endnote again on the last line.

[562] Kane, *Ticket to Ride*, 196-197. This is the last line of an interview between reporter Larry Kane and Beatles John Lennon and Paul McCartney from The Beatles' house in The Balmoral Club, Nassau, Bahamas on the late night of 22 Feb. 1965.

[563] Kane, *Ticket to Ride*, 197. This is the first line of an interview between reporter Larry Kane and Beatles George Harrison and Ringo Starr from The Beatles' house in The Balmoral Club, Nassau, Bahamas on the late night of 22 Feb. 1965. I am not going to endnote every line but will endnote again on the last line.

[564] Kane, *Ticket to Ride*, 197. This is the last line of an interview between reporter Larry Kane and Beatles George Harrison and Ringo Starr from The Beatles' house in The Balmoral Club, Nassau, Bahamas on the late night of 22 Feb. 1965.

[565] Kane, *Ticket to Ride*, 197.

[566] Kane, *Ticket to Ride*, 197 and Lewisohn, *The Complete Beatles Chronicle*, 185.

[567] Lewisohn, *The Complete Beatles Chronicle*, 185. Lewisohn tells us, "All of the shooting took place on the 21-mile-long island of New Providence, amid great numbers of sightseers."

[568] For information about the location of the Balmoral Club, Nassau, Bahamas: https://www.bahamaslocal.com/showlisting/14833/The_Balmoral_club.html

[569] McCartney, Angie, 83.

[570] Lewisohn, *The Complete Beatles Chronicle*, 185 and Miles, *The Beatles' Diary, Vol. 1*, 190.

[571] Lewisohn, *The Complete Beatles Chronicle*, 185 and Miles, *The Beatles' Diary, Vol. 1*, 190.

[572] Carr, Roy, *Beatles At The Movies*, 59.

[573] Carr, 59.

[574] Lewisohn, *The Complete Beatles Chronicle*, 185.

[575] Badman, 141. Keith Badman quotes Walter Shenson as saying, "The film will have a spectacular look about it. We aim to make it even more exciting visually than 'A Hard Day's Night'…The colour of the Bahamas and the snow of the Alps will provide a wonderful background for The Beatles and the action of the film."

[576] Lewisohn, *The Complete Beatles Chronicle*, 185.

[577] Womack, *Maximum Volume: The Life of Beatles Producer, George Martin*, 254, Riley, *Lennon*, 275, and Harry, *The Ultimate Beatles Encyclopedia*, 301.

[578] Schaffner, 42.

[579] Lewisohn, *The Complete Beatles Chronicle*, 189, Womack, *Maximum Volume: The Life of Beatles Producer, George Martin*, and Harry, *The Ultimate Beatles Encyclopedia*, 299. Harry has the title as "Beatles II."

[580] Lewisohn, *The Complete Beatles Chronicle*, 189, Margotin and Guesdon, 216, and Harry, *The Ultimate Beatles Encyclopedia*, 299.

[581] Lewisohn, *The Complete Beatles Chronicle*, 189. Lewisohn tells us: "After a few days, Ringo…suggested 'Eight Arms to Hold You' but after a couple of days, nobody seemed to care for this very much either, especially John and Paul who didn't fancy the prospect of writing a song with such a laboured title…"

[582] Coleman, *The Man Who Made The Beatles*, 215, Riley, *Lennon,* 270, Womack, *Maximum Volume: The Life of Beatles Producer, George Martin*, 254, Harry, *The Ultimate Beatles Encyclopedia*, 299, Greenwald, *The Beatles Companion,* 104, and Trynka, 162.

[583] Sheff, *The Playboy Interviews*, 149 and Trynka, 165. Years later, when John was interviewed by David Sheff, he had this to say about 'Help!': "Dick [Lester] didn't tell us what it was about, though I realize, [sic] lookin' back, how advanced it was." John goes on to say that none of them understood the Bond premise at the time. And because they filmed the scenes completely out of sequence, the plot made no sense at all to them. And in Trynka's work, John states, "The movie was out of our control! With 'A Hard Day's Night,' we had a lot of input. But with 'Help!' Dick didn't tell us what it was about. Maybe it was because we hadn't spent a lot of time together since we made 'A Hard Day's Night.'"

[584] Egan, 376.

[585] Norman, *Shout!*, 248.

[586] Trynka, 163-164. Even Dick Lester admitted, "[The Beatles] found themselves increasingly alienated from the creative process."

[587] Coleman, *The Man Who Made The Beatles*, 270.

[588] Lewisohn, *The Complete Beatles Chronicle*, 185.

[589] Trynka, 164, Harry, *The Ultimate Beatles Encyclopedia*, 299, Harry, *The Beatles, Vol. 4, The History of The Beatles on Film*, 29, and Harrison, Louise, 313-314. In his article, "Help! The End of The Beginning" in Trynka's book, author John Robertson says that the boys "spent the day, when not filming, under the shelter of umbrellas" to avoid getting a tan. Louise Harrison, George's sister, says the four had to sit in their "air-conditioned limo" on many occasions to avoid sun exposure and heat.

[590] Kane, *Ticket to Ride*, 198.

[591] Kane, *Ticket to Ride*, 198.

[592] Kane, Ticket to Ride, 198. Direct quote from John Lennon.

[593] Kane, *Ticket to Ride*, 198.

[594] Harrison, Louise, 311.

[595] Harrison, Louise, 311.

[596] Harrison, Louise, 313.

[597] Harrison, Louise, 313.

[598] Harrison, Louise, 313. Louise says that Mal treated her "as a younger sister."

[599] Lewisohn, *The Complete Beatles Chronicle*, 185 and Harrison, Louise, 314. Many sources claim this filming took place at the Balmoral Club. According to Louise herself, Lewisohn is quite correct in naming a West Bay area hotel, The Nassau Beach Hotel, as the actual location.

[600] Harrison, Louise, 314.

[601] https://www.youtube.com/watch?v=qmjfDlkXKC0 The beginning of this video shows the boys entering the pool deck and doing the things mentioned here.

[602] Harrison, Louise, 314.

Thursday, 25 February 1965
Nassau
The Bahamas

John told himself he'd call Cyn "down the road," when he'd collected a few stories she might be interested in. Never mind that he'd rung her every night of last year's North American Tour. This go-round, he just didn't have the "oomph" — "the fuggin' dynamism," he said. Nothing seemed important enough to share.

And frankly, John didn't understand enough about what they were doing to chat about it. *Everythin' about the film's virtually inexplicable,* he groused to himself.

"It's a drag," he'd tell Cyn eventually, when he finally gathered the energy to ring her up. "We don't know *what's* happenin'!"[603]

But what he *didn't* confide to his wife was that his hazy puzzlement was due, in part, to an inordinate intake of marijuana.[604] At the boys' request, Neil and Mal had emptied a regular carton of cigs and had carefully refilled the commercial box with 200 pre-rolled joints.[605] Then, meticulously resealing the cellophane wrapper, the two roadies had artfully smuggled the contraband past Customs and straight onto the film set.[606]

The Beatles thought they were cunningly "puttin' one over" on Lester and the others. But it wasn't difficult to see what was happening to the boys as they rapidly inhaled their "special cigs" from the closely-guarded carton.[607]

"They're having joints for every meal,"[608] Lester cautioned the film crew. "Whatever shots we want of them must needs be captured well before noon."[609]

The director was a practical man, and he had worked with stars for years. Lester knew when to set limits and when to smile and look away. "It's a happy high,"[610] he consoled the crew when they attempted the same take for the tenth or eleventh time. "No harm in it, is there?"[611]

And so, they all pressed on.

But for John, this second film was vexing. Everything annoyed him: the gawping crowds, the unseasonable heat, the hideous palms, the tilting Tiki huts, and gaudy umbrellas. The penurious, suntanned souls hopelessly weaving baskets to sell for pennies along rutted roadways. The dilapidated fishing boats irksomely clacking in syncopated rhythm, in the dock.

It's a mawkish set 'n a silly script 'n a swarm of insincere smiles. John narrowed his eyes. *A fuggin' pseudo-spy, James Bond world of makey-up*[612]*—— that's what it is!*

But most of all, John despised himself. He hated the squishy pot belly that had begun to chafe against his carefully-cut stage suit. He hated his alcohol-bloated face and puffy eyes. He loathed being "a fat clown" instead of a sensual rocker.[613] And unable to "play the fool"[614] a moment longer, John nudged Mal for another "magic fag," and he wandered away to await the merciful oblivion that would help him survive.[615]

****

Brian was constantly guilty. If he was on set with The Beatles, he felt remiss in his duties to Cilla Black,[616] Billy J. Kramer, Gerry and The Pacemakers, the Fourmost, and the others. If he was apart from "the boys," tending to the NEMS stable, Brian felt negligent in leaving The Beatles unsupervised. Unable to delegate more than minor duties to others, Brian still tried to do it all — to be everything to everyone.[617]

And it was ruining him.

He was restless — constantly frustrated. Already quite bored with standing on the film set sidelines and watching the boys go through their paces,[618] he fidgeted for something more important to do.

According to one of his London employees, Brian was "increasingly bad-tempered" these days and too often, uncensored.[619] He was sharp-tongued and mercurial.

And though he thought no one knew it, Brian was significantly escalating his drug intake.[620] It was the only way he could make ends meet — ends that seemed to be unraveling everywhere. His life demanded more than Brian could summon alone, and fraught, he had turned to drugs for support.

Brian had always wanted things "to go right." From childhood, he'd wanted things to follow along, according to plan. To play out nicely and end well. And despite myriad complications, he still did. But life rarely behaved that way.

Tonight, for example, Brian had approved Dr. Strach's suggestion of a birthday *soirée* for George, and he'd even made arrangements for George's sister to fly in for the occasion. But unbeknownst to Brian, Strach had stealthily set about inviting the global press to the private gala.[621] And late in the muggy, torpid afternoon, when Brian had discovered the accountant's betrayal, he knew George would be enraged. All of the boys would feel duped…and they wouldn't hide it.

Trying to dismiss the premonition of an impending public incident with a chirpy, "Never mind…we're going to have a lovely party!"[622] Brian had bloomed with hives. As the catered food arrived, Brian gnawed the inside of his cheek and paced with worry.

To begin with, the boys were already in a funk. All morning, they'd worked hours in an exacting sun,[623] out in Interfield Road — circling one another on bicycles[624] and shouting helps such as, "Let's go back 'n get 'em!" or "A man's got to do what he's got to do!" whilst Ringo had moped and feebly protested.

Sadly, although the boys assumed that the odd sketch had something to do with the assorted villains who were relentlessly attacking them, no one was quite sure.[625] Their work was largely unexplained and thus, lacked purpose.

Just after lunch, the four had stood awkwardly about in their makeup and "costumes," pacing uncomfortably in the humid shadows.[626] And though none of it was Brian's fault, they had scowled and grumbled at him.

"Put the boys back in the car," Brian had sighed softly to Mal. "Run the air."[627]

But when Dick Lester had spied the wilting lads exiting the set, he'd scurried over and politely protested. The Beatles, Lester had explained, were required in mere minutes. He'd begged Brian for just a bit more patience.

And so, whilst the four Scousers had lurked and groused as only Scousers can, a thin but muscular, olive-skinned man[628] in orange Indian robes[629] had pedaled up on a rickety bicycle.[630] Eyes downcast, demeanor meek but purposeful, the young stranger had made his way directly to Lester and The Beatles,[631] speaking a handful of words to them and handing each a small booklet. Paul had nodded, muttering something in return. Ringo and John had merely tucked their books away. But leaning in, George had engaged the visitor in conversation.[632]

"Hey, look," George had proudly explained to Brian, ten minutes later, "it's like a birthday gift![633] And it's from that man over there. He said it's a book about how everyone — even people who're constantly busy, as we are — can find a means of spiritualizin' their lives, through yoga 'n meditation."[634]

"Yes, I see." Brian had dispiritedly fingered the thin paperback.

"He said he was meditatin' thisavvy when he got this strong feelin' that we should make contact..."[635]

"No doubt." Brian had pursed his lips. It was a given that the author of this obscure work could reap lucrative benefits by befriending "the Fab Four."

"No, no, it's not like that! *Really!*" George had flared, instantly on the defensive. "He said it was unthinkable not to help with someone's pain.[636] He said he just felt that..."

"It's a little book about yoga,"[637] John had peeked over George's shoulder, "from a little yogi."[638]

"He said," George had babbled on, sliding John a warning look, "that peace isn't just a state of warlessness...it's an inner experience of oneness 'n self-knowledge."[639]

"Beatles! On set!" someone had cried.

"Well," John had leaned close to George's ear and stage-whispered, "*I* have the inner knowledge that we're wanted on set. *I* have the inner knowledge that we're bein' summoned, as it were."

And roughly recovering his fragile book from Brian's grasp, George had snarled and wheeled away.

Within minutes, The Beatles were hoisting their bicycles and obediently rolling them towards the scorching tarmac once again. Cameras had clicked. And from the sidelines, the perspiring, rumour-crazed press had pummeled the boys with questions.[640] A highly-perfumed local fan club had resumed their litany of love whilst a few determined girls broke ranks, hurling themselves heedlessly towards the group. Then, under the cover of this pandemonium, a handful of journalists had plowed audaciously forward — their determined cameramen in tow.[641]

Paul, recalling the events of yesterday, had attempted to be friendly, but Ringo had drawn nervously away — terrified after his knock-downs in Australia and Texas.

Inadvertently, George had brushed back against a reporter who'd stumbled into him, and John had pivoted immediately, ready to shatter. A tense moment. No one breathed. Then rapidly stepping in, Mal and Neil had quelled the fray with hard glances. Peace had been restored.

The ordeal, however, had left the boys shaking and browned off — George and John especially. And now, as the press came trailing into what had been promised to be George's "small, private birthday party," The Beatles were aghast. Affronted.

Brian fought back tears. The gathering was ruined; already, the side-winding journalists were edging forward and whispering behind cupped hands.[642]

"Brian," Larry Kane approached Epstein carefully, "if you don't mind, I'd like to do an interview with the boys later, for the wire services.[643] I'd like to make sure everyone understands that John was provoked at the pool yesterday. And that George's minor irritation this afternoon was only natural. The boys are constantly 'set upon,' as you British say. I think people forget that they're surrounded. Always inundated."

"Yes, wonderful, Larry. Thank you," Brian nodded. "That would be most appreciated."[644]

Regardless, Brian was certain that the evening papers would boast yet another unsavoury "Bad Beatles in Bahamas" incident. Already, he could sense this afternoon's three-minute brush-up becoming "an ordeal." And with Strach's party *cum* press conference at hand, another set-to seemed inevitable.

At times, Brian thought he should just resign. "This job," he whispered to no one there, "is too monstrous to bear."

****

Brian's misgivings were not unfounded. The Beatles, especially George, were incensed that their revelry had been invaded — transformed into a press conference, as it were. Their faces were grim.

After several minutes, George, silently and calmly removed a large, decorative sword from the wall and sliced the enormous birthday cake, topped with fresh, tropical flowers and colourfully-striped candles[645] into hundreds of slashed ribbons.[646] Then whispering, "Thanks for the lovely party," he walked out.[647]

Brian blanched. He blinked back tears and dispatched John to see to the party's honouree.

But most of the guests, laughing and chatting in the house where the boys were "billeted" (as Louise phrased it),[648] were unaware of the dark undercurrent. The crowd was having a grand time. Striding in just as John strode out, Leo McKern — the film's villain, Clang — was fondly "booed."[649] And keeping character, McKern closed one eye and growled at the revelers. Everyone laughed.

Within the half hour, a game had been called for. The guests, even young Ruth — Angie McCartney's five-year-old daughter — was required to perform some sort of entertainment: a song, a short skit, a recitation, or a poem. And as one might expect, those bravely "taking the stage" were lampooned more than applauded. The room held an exacting audience.

By the time that a stack of American LPs was placed on the Victrola and the sound turned up, John and George had returned and were loitering in a snug, away from the press. They drank and watched as Victor Spinetti invited Louise to dance,[650] as Paul sauntered over to Eleanor Bron suggesting a friendly twirl.

Good spirits prevailed. By 9.00 p.m. even John and George were jovial. They rushed outside to re-enact their "carry Ringo past the windows" scene from "A Hard Day's Night."[651] And then giggling, John, Paul, and Ringo led the traditional "Happy Birthday" chorus over and over and over again, taking liberties with the words.

It wasn't until most of the guests wandered away that Larry Kane suggested a quick interview with Paul and Ringo, a chat to clear up misconceptions about what had occurred between The Beatles and the press. The boys had already seen the early accounts, calling The Beatles "disrespectful to reporters," so they were eager to have their say in the matter.

Kane: Describe exactly what happened in Nassau.[652]
Paul: Well, yesterday, we were doin' a film, 'n we were tryin' to learn the script. A couple of pressmen kept takin' pictures 'n things, so we asked them to go away while we were learnin' it because we hadn't really learned it well enough. I think a couple of them got ratty 'n started writin' things 'n bein' rude to everyone...[653]
Kane: (Swiveling towards Ringo) All those reports...[654]
Ringo: Well, the thing is, this was in an English newspaper that we sort of "insulted everybody." This thing is, today in Nassau, there were a lot of tourists havin' a good time. They didn't seem to realize [sic] that we were in a middle of a shot, 'n sometimes someone would leap across with a piece of paper, sayin', "Sign this!" 'N we didn't mind signin' things, as a rule, but if it ruins a shot, 'n we have to start over again (Ringo shrugged as if the situation was self-explanatory), well then, I think it's a bit much! So, I think maybe we were to blame, 'n maybe the people were partly to blame.[655]
Kane: A lot of people approaching you at times do not use proper manners. Do they treat you as human beings?[656]
Ringo: (Sighing and shaking his head) A lot of people don't. We go in restaurants sometimes, 'n you can have your fork full of food, halfways to your mouth, 'n someone will smash you on the hand 'n say, "Sign this!" without a please, thank you, or anythin', 'n this annoys you, naturally. I don't want anyone to think of me as a piece of furniture; I'm a *human being*. I have feelings, same as anyone else.[657]

"Ah, we all know y'er a *real boy*, Pinocchio!!!" John barked irreverently from the sidelines. Larry chuckled.

"Get stuck, Lennon!" Ringo tossed back, unabashed. "Nobody gives a ruby red slipper what *you* think!"

Cheshire grinning, John flipped Ringo a high-handed backwards "V," and Larry had, thankfully, snapped off the recorder, before damage was done.

"I think we should toast to that, don't you, Larry?" Ringo stood and ambled towards the two-tiered bamboo cart. But as the others poured nightcaps, Larry packed his gear away.

It was late, and the warm cadence of conversation and laughter covered them all. Even John — who'd been morose most of the afternoon — was tossing out Lennon barbs. Cackling. Victor Spinetti, fondly surrounded by a group of younger crew members, was spinning tales of his West End theatre days.

But out on the cottage deck, Brian sipped Hennessy and wondered if George...or John — or any of them, really — even realised he wasn't in the room. He wondered if they ever thought of *him* as "a human being, with feelings, same as anyone else." He wondered if The Beatles ever gave a moment's notice of how hard he worked to make them successful. How hard he worked to make them happy.

They aren't the only ones under a microscope, Brian fussed, running his finger around the snifter's crystal rim. *In fact, there're quite a few of us out here, staggering under scrutiny...tottering under it.*

Wandering down the Balmoral's white-washed wooden steps into the damp, midnight lawn, Brian sighed and promised himself a few days off — well, with a modicum of business incorporated, of course. He resolved to ask Wendy Hanson to book him a long weekend in America. And, this time, he pledged to follow through. Brian craved a bit of anonymity. He needed New York.

Fame, as it turns out, Brian thought, *is a punitive servant turned taskmaster. A veritable Rasputin.*[658]

Notes!

1. Was The Beatles' marijuana usage on the set of "Help!" as prevalent as portrayed?

Let's let The Beatles and their inner circle answer this question.

Tony Barrow, who was still running publicity at NEMS, wrote in John, Paul, George, Ringo & Me: *"There were several reasons for choosing the Bahamas as one of the two main places where 'Help!' would be filmed. The gloriously warm and sunny climate clearly appealed to the boys and they believed they could indulge in their pastime of smoking 'unbranded cigarettes' more freely and without hassle from the authorities..." (p. 144) He goes on to say, "It became common knowledge on the film set that the boys were smoking pot to relieve their stress and alleviate their irritation with the slow filming process. Lennon put the situation in a nutshell: 'We were smoking pot for breakfast.'" (p. 144)*

Years later, Ringo talked openly about drug usage on the set of the film, "Help!" He said: "A hell of a lot of pot was being smoked while we were making the film…That helped make it a lot of fun. Dick Lester knew that very little would get done after lunch. In the afternoon, we very seldom got past the first line of the script. We had such hysterics that no one could do anything." (Womack, Maximum Volume: The Life of Beatles Producer, George Martin, *254, Goodden,* Riding So High, *56, and The Beatles,* The Beatles Anthology, *167)*

Similarly, John Lennon stated: "The Beatles thing had just gone beyond comprehension. We were smoking marijuana for breakfast. We were well into marijuana and nobody could communicate with us, because we were just all glazed eyes, giggling all the time. In our own world." (Womack, Maximum Volume: The Life of Beatles Producer, George Martin, *254) And John also said, "'Help!' is where we turned onto pot and dropped drink, simple as that. I've always needed a drug to survive. The others, too, but I always had more, more pills, more of everything." (Badman, 141)*

Cynthia Lennon also candidly admitted, "Marijuana was a giggle to the boys and it enabled them to relax. The trouble was that they smoked it whenever they could — on the film sets of their second film, "Help!", in the recording studios, at home. It enabled them all to escape from the pressures and responsibilities of their position instead of seeing life in the raw…It slowed them down and caused them to laugh at each other and the world." (A Twist of Lennon, *143 and Badman, 141)*

In this short video, both Richard Lester and Eleanor Bron talk candidly about The Beatles' use of marijuana during the making of "Help!": https://www.youtube.com/watch?v=Fkedw92qOUs

*Finally, journalist Ray Coleman, who was a close friend of The Beatles and Brian Epstein, states that Brian, too, was becoming heavily involved with drug usage in early 1965. He states: "Privately, [Brian] was using drugs too much — either experimentally, as with LSD, or as medication with stimulants and downers…although he continued to function well, when he was in the right frame of mind." (*The Man Who Made The Beatles, *221)*

2. Is the Interfield Road sketch all that The Beatles did on this day?

No, after the bicycling sequence, Ringo and John were filmed in the field of the Bahamas Softball Association. Paul was filmed at some lime quarry caves. (Lewisohn, The Complete Beatles Chronicle, *185)*

3. Were The Beatles having a difficult time with the press this early in 1965?

In Beatles at the Movies, *author Roy Carr — in his chapter on the making of "Help!" — states, "Aside from a handful of journalists that they had befriended earlier, The Beatles had now become highly suspicious of the Press at large. Not without reason. Stories were constantly fabricated: Ringo seriously ill, The Beatles on the slide, a bad example to young people. Their collective response was: 'We never said we were symbols of British youth. Other people said that. We are just a rock'n'roll group playing music we like. Getting well paid for it. And so, what?'" (p. 60)*

Sources:

Interview with Ruth McCartney, Kansas City Beatlefest, 1993.

July 2020 Interview with Angie and Ruth McCartney on "She Said She Said" podcast with co-host, author Lanea Stagg, found here: https://shesaidshesaid.podbean.com/

Interview with Larry Kane, 2010.

Lewisohn, The Beatles Complete Chronicle, *185.*
Harry, The Ultimate Beatles Encyclopedia, *303.*
The Beatles, The Beatles Anthology, *166-167.*
Norman, John Lennon: The Life, *396.*
Norman, Shout!, *244 and 250.*
Harrison, Louise, *313.*
McCartney, Angie, My Long and Winding Roads, *84-85.*
McCartney, Angie, Your Mother Should Know, *66-70.*
Barrow, *144.*
Coleman, The Man Who Made The Beatles, *268, 270.*
Womack, Maximum Volume: The Life of Beatles Producer, George Martin, *255.*
Carr, *59-60.*
Kane, Ticket to Ride, *197-198.*
Margotin and Guesdon, *216.*
Carlin, *116.*
Egan, The Mammoth Book of The Beatles, *376-377.*
Brown, *170.*
Badman, *141-142.*
Yule, Andrew. The Man Who Framed The Beatles: A Biography of Richard Lester, *100-101.*
Trynka, *166.*
Goldman, *179.*
Schultheiss, *130.*
Hill, John, Paul, George & Ringo, *193.*
Riley, Lennon, *272.*
The Beatles, "Live at the BBC," Vol. 1, Side 1, Track 1.

https://en.wikipedia.org/wiki/Grigori_Rasputin *This article gives a concise biography of Grigori Rasputin.*

https://www.youtube.com/watch?v=X82R1yE-3k0
This is a video about Swami Vishnu-Devananda, the man who gave books on yoga to The Beatles on George Harrison's birthday. There is a discussion of his philosophies and photos of him at the age that this event occurred.

https://www.cillablack.com/biography *This website provides insight into the immense popularity of NEMS' own Cilla Black in 1964-1965.*

This is a video of The Beatles filming "Help!" in the Bahamas: https://www.youtube.com/watch?v=ziKc5J6keQl

This is a video about The Beatles' drug usage during the making of the film "Help!": https://www.youtube.com/watch?v=Fkedw92qOUs. The video includes appearances from Dick Lester and Eleanor Bron. Or use this QR code:

---

[603] Harry, *The Ultimate Beatles Encyclopedia*, 303. John later said "['Help!'] was a drag, because we didn't know what was happening."
[604] Carlin, 116, Margotin and Guesdon, 216, and Norman, *John Lennon: The Life*, 396.
[605] Norman, *John Lennon: The Life*, 396 and Norman, *Shout!*, 244.
[606] Norman, *John Lennon: The Life*, 396.
[607] Carlin, *McCartney*, 116, Egan, *The Mammoth Book of The Beatles*, 376-377, and Brown, 170.
[608] Carlin, *McCartney*, 116, Egan, *The Mammoth Book of The Beatles*, 376-377, Buskin, *The Complete Idiot's Guide to The Beatles*, 199, Barrow, 144, Hill and Clayton, *The Beatles Unseen Archives*, 129, and Brown, 170. Egan says "the band were, by all accounts, having joints for breakfast, dinner, and tea." Tony Barrow says: "There were several reasons for choosing the Bahamas as one of two main places where "Help!" would be made. The gloriously warm and sunny climate appealed to the boys, and they belived they could indulge their pastime of smoking 'unbranded cigarettes' more freely and with less hassle from the authorities…"
[609] McCartney, Angie, 84. Angie states that the boys "were pretty laced on something most afternoons" and said that Dick Lester would have to film afternoon scenes over and over.

[610] Norman, *Shout!*, 244.

[611] Norman, *Shout!*, 244. The full quote from Dick Lester is: "They were high all the time we were shooting ['Help!'] But there was no harm in it then. It was a happy high."

[612] Brown, 169.

[613] Goldman, 179.

[614] On the LP *Beatles Live at the BBC, Vol. 1,* Side 1, Track 1, as The Beatles introduce themselves, John admits, "I play the guitar. Sometimes, I play the fool."

[615] Badman, 141. Keith Badman quotes Cynthia Lennon as saying that John was smoking marijuana on set because "it enabled him to relax" and "when [he] smoked, the merry-go-round stopped for a while. The world looked brighter."

[616] Norman, *Shout!*, 250. Norman reminds us that Cilla had had a Number One U.K. hit with "Anyone Who Had a Heart" in 1964, followed by a second 1964 Number One with "You're My World." So clearly, this early in 1965, Brian felt an obligation to be working closely with her in guiding her career.

[617] Coleman, *The Man Who Made The Beatles*, 270. Coleman, who knew Brian quite well, tells us that he was juggling too many interests at once. He states, "His inability to delegate well, plus the juggling act he had now assumed with his multitude of interests, meant severe pressure on his time and patience." And Coleman goes on to say that Brian was alienating people, left and right.

[618] Coleman, *The Man Who Made The Beatles*, 268. This is an observation from Brian's assistant, Wendy Hanson.

[619] Coleman, *The Man Who Made The Beatles*, 271. This is a direct quote from NEMS employee Joanne Newfield.

[620] Coleman, *The Man Who Made The Beatles*, 270.

[621] Yule, 100. Yule says: "...the ever-so-slightly sinister Strach organised a party in [George's] honor without letting him know that in his kindly, highly manipulative way, he had summoned press representatives from around the globe."

[622] Coleman, *The Man Who Made The Beatles*, 270. This was a direct quote from Brian Epstein, though Coleman does not indicate when he said it. Coleman indicates that he used it quite often as he planned elegant galas to soothe the irritation of life in general.

[623] McCartney, Angie, 84 and Harrison, Louise, 313. Angie says the day was blazing hot and The Beatles were miserable.

[624] Lewisohn, *The Complete Beatles Chronicle*, 185, Womack, *Maximum Volume: The Life of Beatles Producer, George Martin*, 255, and Harrison, Louise, 313. Louise explains that Lester filmed them riding in circles because that was the easiest way to capture their dialogue.

[625] Harry, *The Ultimate Beatles Encyclopedia*, 303.

[626] McCartney, Angie, 84.

[627] Harrison, Louise, 313. She says the boys often sat in the air-conditioned car, learning their lines.

[628] The description of Swami Vishnu-Devananda in 1965 comes from this video on his life: https://www.youtube.com/watch?v=X82R1yE-3k0

[629] The Beatles, *The Beatles Anthology*, 171.

[630] Badman, 142, Riley, *Lennon*, 272, Norman, *Shout!*, 596, Trynka, 166, and Schultheiss, 130.

[631] Yule, 101. Yule says the man "handed a book to Lester and one to each of the four Beatles."

[632] Badman, 142, Riley, *Lennon,* 272, Norman, *Shout!*, 596, Trynka, 166, Yule, 100, and Schultheiss, 130.

[633] The Beatles, *The Beatles Anthology*, 171 and Yule, 100.

[634] The Beatles, *The Beatles Anthology*, 171, Badman, 142, Riley, *Lennon*, 272, Norman, *Shout!*, 596, Schultheiss, 130, and Missick, "Beatlemania Comes to the Bahamas," *The Tribune*, Nassau, Bahamas, 12 July 2013, found in http://www.tribune242.com/news/2013/jul/12/when-beatlemania-came-to-the-bahamas/
Also, https://www.youtube.com/watch?v=X82R1yE-3k0 This video explains the philosophy of the man on the bicycle, who turned out to be Swami Vishnu-Devananda, a young swami teaching yoga and meditation and writing in the Bahamas. Riley quotes George as saying, "This was the first swami I had ever met." And both Riley and *Tribune* reporter Missick agree with the other sources that the unusual event took place on George's 22nd birthday. Finally, in *The Beatles Anthology*, George states, "I suppose that was the start of it all for me. It was a chance meeting — the guy had a place on Paradise Island and somebody must have whispered in his inner ear to give us his book, *The Illustrated Book of Yoga*. We were on our bikes on the road, waiting to do a shoot, when he walked up in orange robes. Swami Vishnu-Devananda, the foremost hatha yoga exponent. It was on my birthday."

[635] Hill, *John, Paul, George & Ringo: The Definitive Illustrated Chronicle of The Beatles, 1960-1970*, 193 and Riley, *Lennon*, 272.

[636] https://www.youtube.com/watch?v=X82R1yE-3k0

[637] Badman, 142. John is quoted as saying, "…this little guy comes leggin' over 'n gives us a little book each, signed to us, and it was on Yoga. We didn't look at it, just stuck it along with the other stuff people gave us."

[638] Trynka, 166. Direct quote from John Lennon.

[639] https://www.youtube.com/watch?v=X82R1yE-3k0

[640] Carr, 60.

[641] Kane, *Ticket to Ride*, 197.

[642] Carr, 60. Carr tells us that the press had begun to fabricate stories about The Beatles and criticize them for not being "good examples" for young people. Every move they made was scrutinized.

[643] Kane, *Ticket to Ride*, 198.

[644] Kane, *Ticket to Ride*, 198.

[645] Harrison, Louise, 313.

[646] Yule, 100 and Harrison, Louise, 313. Yule, telling the story from Lester's perspective, describes, the incident thus: "After cutting the first slice with icy calm [George] hacked a second slice, stabbed through the cake for the third, then slowly demolished what was left. Laying down the knife quietly on the plate, he looked across the table at the startled Strach. 'Thanks for the lovely party,' he whispered, turned and walked out." Louise Harrison describes the incident as a light-hearted joke.

[647] Yule, 100 and Harrison, Louise, 313.

[648] Harrison, Louise, 313.

[649] McCartney, Angie, 85. Angie reports that in the evenings, when The Beatles and the other cast members were gathered in the bar, they would always greet McKern's entrance in this fashion. He, in turn, would snarl menacingly at them, one eye narraowed.

[650] Harrison, Louise, 313.

[651] Harrison, Louise, 313.

[652] Kane, *Ticket to Ride*, 198. This is the beginning of a short interview that Larry Kane did with Paul McCartney just after the incident when John shouted at the intrusive reporters in Nassau. Larry was giving "the boys a chance to tell people in their own words" what occurred. I will endnote again at the end of the interview.

[653] Kane, *Ticket to Ride*, 198. This is the end of the short interview that Larry Kane did with Paul McCartney just after the incident when John shouted at the instrusive reporters in Nassau.

[654] Kane, *Ticket to Ride*, 198-199. This is the beginning of a short interview that Larry Kane did with Ringo Starr, just after the incident when John shouted at the intrusive reporters in Nassau. I will endnote again at the end of the interview.

[655] Kane, *Ticket to Ride*, 198-199. This is the end of the short interview that Larry Kane did with Ringo Starr just after the incident when John shouted at the intrusive reporters in Nassau.

[656] Kane, *Ticket to Ride*, 199. This is the beginning of another short interview that Larry Kane did with Ringo Starr about the way that the press were treating The Beatles in Nassau (and in general). I will endnote again at the end of the interview.

[657] Kane, *Ticket to Ride*, 199. This is the end of another short interview that Larry Kane did with Ringo Starr in Nassau.

[658] Grigori Rasputin (1869-1916) was a self-proclaimed mystic and healer who gained power over the Russian royal family of Czar Nicholas II, after supposedly healing their son from hemophilia. He wielded great power, not always for good, in the Russian government until the time of his assassination in 1916. For more information, go to:
https://en.wikipedia.org/wiki/Grigori_Rasputin

Friday, 26 February 1965
Deauville Cottage[659]
Balmoral Beach Club
Nassau, Bahamas

10.30 a.m.[660]

"Y' must've passed Brian, mid-air." John lit a cig, offering one to Gloria Stavers, the chic and respected editor of America's popular *16 Magazine*.[661] "He after a bice o' The Big Apple, as we speak."

"You don't say," Stavers smiled cooly. "My loss."

Stavers was no giddy Beatlemaniac, no head-over-heels fan. Indeed, *16* — a slick fanzine primarily geared to "Bobbysoxers" (teenage girls) — was surprisingly headed by a hard-charging woman whose reputation was well-regarded, even across the pond.[662] When, over a year ago, Tony Barrow had summoned the courage to ring the attractive brunette about publicity for the boys, he had been rather intimidated.[663]

Stavers, who had relinquished a lucrative career as a model to rise from subscription clerk to Editor-in-Chief at *16*, was widely known as a "star maker." She uncannily identified rising stars with unique potential and then marketed them in her teen publication, employing what Barrow called "editorial exposure that money can't buy." Stavers had been "the doing" of Bobby Vee, Bobby Rydell, and more recently, Paul Revere and the Raiders.[664] And in the autumn of 1963, Barrow had craved her valuable endorsement of The Beatles.[665]

But Tony needn't have been anxious about the call; Stavers had been well aware of the Liverpool boys. In fact, she'd read numerous articles about the rise of Beatlemania in the U.K. and was intrigued.

"I hear some good things about your boys, Mr. Barrow!"[666]

She'd taken his phone call and been surprisingly receptive.

"Well," Tony had sprung at the opportunity, "let me tell you a bit more."[667] And the two had talked for over a half-hour, covering the various accomplishments of John, Paul, George, and Ringo, their management by Epstein, and the essence of the so-called "Mersey Sound."[668]

Since then, Stavers had been the group's chief champion in the States. Boasting a distribution of over one million copies a month,[669] *16* had given its impressionable fans a healthy dose of The Beatles.[670]

Now, taking the opportunity to get to know the boys better, Stavers had flown into Nassau. She had featured each band member in *16*'s February issue, and she wanted to thank them for their input — despite the fact that Tony Barrow had supplied the lion's share of their "original" scribblings.

Stavers slowly drew a cig from John's packet and chuckled at Lennon's Cheshire grin. "Is Mr. Epstein on business in New York?" She arched an artfully-plucked eyebrow.

"I dunno, now do I?" John leaned back in his chair and smirked at her. "All we were told is that he was *en route* there whilst you were *en route* here. Star-crossed rovers, as it were."

Gloria smiled, wondering if this witty John Lennon was a mere veneer. She'd heard tales of his charged unpredictability, and Gloria intended to suss him out.

"John," she plunged in, "what I really want to discuss are the letters you wrote for our magazine."

"Do you?" John folded his arms across his chest. He took a slow draw on his fag. Gloria self-consciously touched the tendrils of her loose upsweep, a style that gave her an air of sophistication.

"Yes," she leaned even closer. "I knew, of course, that you were...*are*...a writer — so I was delighted when you agreed to answer some of our fan mail. I'm, quite honestly, a genuine fan of your work."

John eyed her up and down. "Y' haven't read m' work, have you, Stavers? If y' had, you'd know it's all jibberish 'n jargon.. Gobbledygook."

"Oh, but you're wrong," Gloria shot back. "I *have* read your work."

"And lived to tell of it!" John bit off a smile.

"Yes, imagine that!" Stavers gave as good as she got. The two were worthy opponents, and they levelled unvarnished glances at one another. "So...back to what I was saying...I wanted to tell you how much I appreciate your answering our readers' fan mail...and to thank you for, as they tritely say, going 'above and beyond' what *16* asked you to do. Your opening letter was hilarious...and the answers you gave those girls...well, they were as kind as they were candid."

When Gloria saw John fidgeting beneath her praise, she quickly turned to the others. "Listen guys," she smiled, "I hope all of you were happy with the answers that *16* provided in knocking down those 'evil Beatle rumors' in the last issue!"[671]

"Right yeah," George grinned, going along. He had no idea what the good-looking American was "on about."

"Dead good," Ringo said, pleasantly.

"Right yeah, brilliant!" Paul winked. "And um...what *were* those answers once again?"

"Well," Gloria snickered, "there was an ugly rumour that *you*, Paul, are bitterly jealous because Ringo's so popular in America."[672]

"*Is he?*" Paul frowned.

"He is!" Ringo lifted a finger and beamed.

"*Hmpf!*" Paul turned to Gloria. "And what did *16* have to say about that?

"*16* said," her hand traced an imaginary headline, "'Now, I ask you — does Paul McCartney need to be jealous of *anyone* or *anything*? Quite untrue!'"[673]

"De gear answer, *16!*" Paul, who ordinarily strove to be cosmopolitan, gave Stavers a slathering of Scouse charm.

"Well, it leaves a bit to be desired, if anyone's askin' me," Ringo muttered.

"Yeahbut, no one is," John said.

"'N what were the very famous evil rumours about *me?*" George leaned down from his perch on Stavers' cushioned chair back.

"Well," Gloria glanced at him over her shoulder, "there was a rather rampant myth that *you* want to own a house in every country in the world!"[674]

George squeezed out a smile. "I'm just tryin' to gin up the courage to buy *one* house out near John, in Surrey...one with a pool."[675]

"And that's precisely what we responded, George. Almost word for word."

"What about the drummer, eh?" Ringo tapped his chest. "What were *my* evil Beatle rumours?"

"Well, you know, health concerns keep popping up, Ringo — fans writing in that they've heard you've been advised to take a 'complete rest,' which of course, you're stubbornly refusing."[676]

"*What!?*" Ringo exploded, forgetting that the rumours had already been quelled in February's publication. "All I did was have me tonsils out! I just didn't want 'em to keep flarin', over 'n over again, y' know! That's all it was!"[677]

"And that's exactly what we said," Stavers reassured him. "Rumour completely put to bed!"

"Uhm, speakin' of which," Paul cleared his throat, "I uhm…suppose there were the unavoidable questions about me 'n Jane."

"Well, actually, we headed those off at the pass as well," Gloria laughed. "We did a nice cover story on Jane and how you've changed her life — for the better, of course. Several weeks ago, I approached Alan Freeman about conducting an interview with Jane and her brother, Peter, and the article was absolutely fantastic! Here. Take a look."[678] She handed Paul *16*'s February issue, and folded the pages back. He dived in.

"For you two," Stavers handed Ringo and John copies as well, "we included data sheets on your gorgeous Beatle wives."[679]

Ringo scanned the brief list of facts and shrugged, "Ta."

But as John's eyes skimmed the half-page article, he chewed his bottom lip.

Cyn 'll fuggin' despise this! She fuggin' hates bein' pawed over. She'll fly into a swivet over it. And once again, John felt the nudge to ring his wife. It had been too long; he knew it. But honestly, he felt as if he had nothing to say to her. To anyone, really. Nothing that mattered, anyway.

Maybe this can be the talkin' point we could use to keep from gettin' at one another, he mulled. *I could even make a point of tellin' her how* 16 *said, right here in print, that I love her looks. That ought to stand me in good.*

"Yeah, great, ta," he said, aloud.

"So really," George frowned, "there's a feature article here on everyone but me, yeah?"

"No," Stavers had saved the surprise for last, "actually, we made *you* the focal point of the entire magazine, George — since you're February's birthday boy, of course! We wrote a big feature story entitled 'George's Hates and Loves.' And I think it's all fairly factual, but I'd be thrilled if you'd give it the once-over."

George accepted the magazine and grinned to see himself — cartooned and banging on bongo drums beneath a palm tree whilst John strummed a tiny ukulele — on *16*'s lampoonish cover. Chuckling, he thumbed to the article and read aloud: "I hate tea or coffee without sugar. True. I hate bein' closed in a theatre dressin' room for too long. *Very* true! I hate gettin' up in the mornings. True as well. I love fairly small parties with good music 'n good company. True! I love listening to all the Tamla-Motown artists."[680] George glanced up at Gloria. "All completely true! How'd you find this out?"

"Well, a little bird named Tony Barrow..." Stavers raised an open palm.

"A little bird, eh?" George smiled at the American idiom. "Just wait 'til I try *that one* on him!"

"Baby Birdie Barrow!" Ringo chanted.

"So, it appears," John leaned over to pour another cup of tea and sweeten it, "I'm the only one 'round here who actually wrote his own work, eh?"

"Well," Gloria chuckled, "you *are* the only author in the bunch!"

"Oh, sorry there, Gloria," Paul sniffed. "I can see you're a bit confused. He's not Arthur, actually. He's John Winston, y' see."

"Boooo! Hisss!" George cupped a hand and shouted.

"Ugh, we've heard that one before," Ringo groaned.

But John, who was already perusing his fan mail article, didn't bother to comment. Whilst the others took the piss out of the merry-eyed editor, he read:

Hello mates! *(Ugh, I* never *wrote that!)*

John Lennon here, and I will *(I'll)* **be answering most of your letters this month — which is only fair since Ringo, George and Paul each have their separate "bit" going in this issue of** *16.* **Got a few "thank you's" to hand out** (*I* never *said that...I think I wrote, "I've got a few thanks goin' out...or* *somethin' of that ilk)* **before I get down to the letters. If your name is not here** *(isn't here),* **it does not mean** *(doesn't mean)* **that I didn't get your birthday card, letter or present.** *(Well, at least they got* that *bit right. Great job, editors!!!)* **It simply means that, as usual, there is not** *(there's not)* **enough room to thank** *all* **of you wonderful** *(fab)* **Beatle people for the nice things you have** *(you've)* **sent to me** *(sent me).* **My** *(M')* **special thanks go to Robyn Jenkins, Fairfax, Calif.,** *(You're not a "nobody," luv.)* *(That's the only part that really mattered here. I hope she read that bit. I meant it.)* **I am** *(I'm)* **more than grateful to Pam Kofoed and Mary McAllister of Logan, Utah, for the invitation to their party, that six-foot-long hand-knit tie, the outline of their feet (what was that for?) and the bottle of stuff so that I could dye my hair blond. Sorry, birds, but the only thing I can put to good use is the tie. I plan to give it to a friend who has a six-foot neck.**[681]

John scanned the rest — an unimaginative list of tedious thank-you's to *16* readers who had sent him birthday wishes from all over America.[682] *I don't care what Stavers says. This is fuggin' awful!* he thought.

So, he moved on to the column of fan mail responses.

Dear John,
How long did you live in London? Where do you live now?
What is the difference between Liverpool and London as a place to live in?

Debbie Phelps
PLYMOUTH, MICH.[683]

- **Dear Debbie,**
  I've bought a house in the lovely *(it's true, but I never said that!)* **county of Surrey, just south of London. Lived right in the capital in an apartment** *(I probably said "mansionette" there. Must not be an American word.)* **most of last year, so it makes a nice change to have a country home away from the noise of the city.** *(None of that shite after "year" is mine! I* loved *the fuggin' noise of the city!)* **I think we all prefer Liverpool to London —** **just because we grew up there and have so many friends**

there *(I think I wrote "y' know" there, but whatever...)*, **apart from anything else — but I must admit it is** *(it's)* **much more convenient to be within easy motoring reach** *(Well, I'm certain I never fuggin' said THAT, but who knows what I said!?)* **of London, because we do so much work in the capital** *(I said "in the Smoke" not "in the capital." No one says "in the capital"! No one I know, anyway.)*, **including most of our television and film dates and all our recording sessions. Night life in London is great, but much more expensive than the clubs we went to** *(Didn't include those last three words)* **in Liverpool. I nearly said "at home in Liverpool," so you can see that we still feel we belong to** *(I would never've said "to")* **Merseyside!**[684]

Yerrokay, not bad, John relaxed a little. *Stavers 'n her group have polished m' work a bit, but at least it rings true, somewhat. Let's have another...*

Dear John,

What do you think of Elvis Presley? The Animals? Would you really like to write a musical for the theater?
                                        Shirley Nunn
                              INDEPENDENCE, MO.[685]

- **Dear Shirley,**
  Elvis is an entertainer we've always admired. *(I think I said, "I've always looked up to...")* **We liked his early records best of all because of their raw, rhythmic quality. It's a pity he's been making the type of records which haven't been clicking with the kids who collect the pops** *("clicking," "the pops!!" I'd never write shite like that!)* **in England just recently. But he'll go** *(I said, "hopefully, he'll go")* **right back to the top of our British charts soon again, I'm sure, when he picks the right material. Elvis deserves the success.** *(Yeah, exactly what I said.)* **He's one of the all-time world-wide great** *(I said, "greats")* **of the show-biz scene...**[686]

"John," Gloria had gathered the others around her recorder. "Mind joining us for a head-to-head…or 'a chat-up,' as I believe you boys say?"

"Why not?" John smirked, "I mean, I'm within 'easy motorin' reach' aren't I?"

And rolling the magazine up for later, John strolled over for an interview that would be *16*'s biggest splash, come March.

Gloria Stavers, the once subscription-clerk who rose to Editor-in-Chief of *16 Magazine*
Photograph from Wikimedia Commons

**The cover of the February 1965 *16 Magazine*
featuring the articles in this chapter**
From the author's collection

Sources:

Barrow, 112-114.
"Those Unfair Evil Beatle Rumors!", 16 Magazine, *Vol. 6, No. 9, Feb.*
1965, 48.
"Fact Sheets on: Cynthia Lennon-Maureen Cox" 16 Magazine, *Vol. 6,*
No. 9, Feb. 1965, 51.
"How Paul Has Changed Jane's Life," 16 Magazine, *Vol. 6, No. 9, Feb.*
1965, 44-46.
"Beatles' Personal Letters," 16 Magazine, *Vol. 6, No. 9, Feb. 1965, 20-*
21.
"George's Hates and Loves," 16 Magazine, *Vol. 6, No. 9, Feb. 1965,*
22.

https://www.gloriastavers.com/ This website traces the career of the
late Gloria Stavers and includes photos of the editor of 16 Magazine.
On the website, her biography is found at:
https://gloriastavers.typepad.com/blog/gloria-stavers.html

https://peoplepill.com/people/gloria-stavers/ This website gives a
concise biography of Gloria Stavers, Editor-in-Chief of 16 Magazine.

[659] http://www.tribune242.com/news/2013/jul/12/when-beatlemania-came-to-the-bahamas/ This is an online reprint of an article by Rupert Missick, Jr. entitled "When Beatlemania Came to the Bahamas," *The Tribune*, Nassau, Bahamas, 12 July 2013. Missick says "…one of these buildings, the one which went by the name of the 'Deauville Cottage' was once the home of four immortals: Ringo Starr, George Harrison, Paul McCartney and John Lennon — The Beatles."

[660] Lewisohn tells us in *The Complete Beatles Chronicle* (p. 185) that on Friday, 26 February, the boys were filmed all afternoon. Ringo shot a scene at the Yacht Basin. Then, George and Ringo were filmed at the kapok tree-house in the gardens of the Royal Victoria Hotel. And finally, John was filmed, running out of the public library, shouting, "Ringo!" So, the meeting and interview with Stavers must have taken place that morning, prior to filming.

[661] Barrow, 112 and https://peoplepill.com/people/gloria-stavers/ It is of note that although Gloria Stavers did not have a college degree in journalism nor any prior experience, she rose from subscriptions clerk at *16 Magazine* to Editor-in-Chief. Her writing style was as respected as were her innovative concepts of marketing. So great was the respect that Stavers engendered that when she died in 1983, her obituary was published in her competitor's magazine, *Rolling Stone.*

[662] Barrow, 114.

[663] Barrow, 112.

[664] https://gloriastavers.typepad.com/blog/gloria-stavers.html This excellent biography of Gloria Stavers is a must-read. She was ahead of her time.

[665] Barrow, 112.

[666] Barrow, 113. Direct quote from Gloria Stavers.

[667] Barrow, 113. Direct quote from Tony Barrow.

[668] Barrow, 113.

[669] Barrow, 112.

[670] Barrow, 113.

[671] "Those Unfair Evil Beatle Rumors!," *16 Magazine,* Vol. 6, No. 9, Feb. 1965, 48.

[672] "Those Unfair Evil Beatle Rumors!," *16 Magazine,* Vol. 6, No. 9, Feb. 1965, 48.

[673] "Those Unfair Evil Beatle Rumors!," *16 Magazine,* Vol. 6, No. 9, Feb. 1965, 48.

[674] "Those Unfair Evil Beatle Rumors!," *16 Magazine,* Vol. 6, No. 9, Feb. 1965, 49.

[675] "Those Unfair Evil Beatle Rumors!," *16 Magazine,* Vol. 6, No. 9, Feb. 1965, 49.

[676] "Those Unfair Evil Beatle Rumors!," *16 Magazine,* Vol. 6, No. 9, Feb. 1965, 48.

[677] "Those Unfair Evil Beatle Rumors!," *16 Magazine,* Vol. 6, No. 9, Feb. 1965, 48.

[678] This became the article "How Paul Has Changed Jane's Life," *16 Magazine*, Vol. 6, No. 9, Feb. 1965, 44-46.

[679] "Fact Sheets on: Cynthia Lennon-Maureen Cox," *16 Magazine,* Vol. 6, No. 9, Feb. 1965, 51.

[680] "George's Hates & Loves," *16 Magazine,* Vol. 6, No. 9, Feb. 1965, 22.

[681] "Beatles' Personal Letters," *16 Magazine,* Vol. 6, No. 9, Feb. 1965, 20.

[682] "Beatles' Personal Letters," *16 Magazine,* Vol. 6, No. 9, Feb. 1965, 20.

[683] "Beatles' Personal Letters," 16 *Magazine,* Vol. 6, No. 9, Feb. 1965, 20.

[684] "Beatles' Personal Letters," *16 Magazine,* Vol. 6, No. 9, Feb. 1965, 20. The original, without John's edits which I supplied, can be found on this page.

[685] "Beatles' Personal Letters," *16 Magazine,* Vol. 6, No. 9, Feb. 1965, 20.

[686] "Beatles' Personal Letters," *16 Magazine,* Vol. 6, No. 9, Feb. 1965, 20. The original, without John's edits which I supplied, can be found on this page.

Saturday, 27 February 1965
Balmoral Island
The Bahamas

Louise had been invited to be — and wanted to be — "the girl on the beach," the lovely young lady playfully pretending to be Paul's guitar in this afternoon's filming. But the instant he'd caught wind of the notion, George had nixed it.[687]

"My sister's not to be filmed in a swimsuit for *anyone!*"[688] he'd snarled, protectively. And having met resistance from Lou and the others, George was now off, having a sulk.

Louise ignored him, chatting cheerfully with John and Paul whilst one hand drew windblown hair from her eyes. John, who hated his forehead exposed, had tugged a blue-jeans Lenin cap almost to his eyebrows, and his pale pink shirt collar was upturned against the crossing winds of the craggy island.[689] He'd worn long sleeves and jeans this morning,[690] but still, he shivered against a nip in the air. And spectators who'd been invited to watch the filming stood with their arms crossed against unseasonal temperatures.[691]

But laughing, winking, and cavourting in a short-sleeved, black T-shirt, Paul seemed oblivious to the chill. He flirted with Jack Atcheler's 8mm camera and carelessly delivered a jaunty rendition of "Another Girl." Rocking back and forth, Paul snickered and made faces at the camera.[692]

When George was finally summoned to perform, his face was expressionless. Without umph, he played his lead line, staring at the frets and solemnly doing the job.[693]

"C'mon George," Louise cajoled her brother, squeezing his arm between takes. "I'm not doin' the 'forbidden bit,' now am I? I'm minding *your* manners, just as prescribed. So, enjoy! Smile a little!" But George barely lifted the corners of his mouth.

Ringo, too, was withdrawn. With his kit wedged up against the water's edge on a rocky purchase of land, he played and never glanced at the camera.[694] In fact, he rarely looked up. In white jeans and a white long-sleeved shirt,[695] Ritchie looked every bit the devoted "good guy," amiably doing what he was called to do when he was asked to do it.

"Awright, Ringo?" Louise tried a bit of Scouse. She loved keeping the boys uplifted.

"Ugh, I'm creased," he yawned. "All this gettin' up at daybreak. I'm not for it, y' know. I haven't got camera-ready smiles." But Louise knew it was more than that. Ringo was always the first to get homesick...for Mo, for his flat, for his familiar surroundings. Ritchie was a homebody.

"Well, if y' haven't noticed, George is rather browned off with me, y' know," Louise confided, trying to draw the drummer out of his maudlin thoughts. "And not just about my wantin' to be 'The It Girl' in this scene."

"Yeah?" Ringo took the bait. "What's he on about now?" He was already forgetting his funk.

"See his jeans?" Louise smiled, conspiratorially. "They're not supposed to be splattered with greyish patches! It's *not* on purpose."[696]

"I thought it was a style," Ringo shrugged. "I'm always the last to know."

"He marred them in the wash, did Havva!"[697] John overheard and threw commentary in.

"Bleach,"[698] Louise chuckled, throatily. "And he thinks *I* should've warned him!"

"'N then," John grinned, wickedly, "he had to do the self-same thing to his other two pair..."[699]

"...for the filmin', y' know," Louise explained. "Continuity...the wardrobe has to match, scene to scene."[700]

"So...*all* of his jeans are blotched, then?"[701] Ringo grinned. Louise had done her job.

"Every last one,"[702] Lou laughed.

"Eck, eck, here he comes!" John warned, out of the side of his mouth.

"Hey, fab kecks, George!" Ringo lit right into him, without mercy.

And cutting his eyes at his sister, George sighed. He'd been well sussed. This was no group in which to commit an error.

"Go on, say what y' will!" George gave it back. "I don't really care. Because as I see it, the way things are goin' with this Beatles thing, everyone'll be wearin' jeans precisely like this in another six months!"[703]

And having had the last word, George stomped away for a cig.

****

10.00 p.m.
John: So, how's the very Queen of *16 Magazine*?
Cynthia: John! (Her voice automatically lit up. But then…) I thought you'd all but forgotten about me. (However, knowing that John despised self-pity, Cynthia quickly righted herself.) How's the film going?
John: I dunno, it's work…8.30 to 5.30-6.00, every day.[704] Not counting bein' up before that, for hair 'n makeup, y' know. We have to be on our fuggin' feet well before 7.00 a.m.[705]
Cynthia: So, just like last time, then. A chore.
John: Yeah but, it's strange, y' know. I mean, we were *the stars* in the last "fil-um"…but from where I stand, this time we're fuggin' ancillary …we're *extras* in our own film![706]
Cynthia: Wait…what do you mean, "The Queen of *16 Magazine*"?
John: I wondered when you'd crack on…they did a story about you, y' know, in this month's issue, gerl! A fact sheet. Hey, wait one. (He grabbed his copy.) All right, says here you're 5' 4" 'n weigh 110 pounds…[707]
Cynthia: *Ugh!* How *very dare* they?!
John: You've blonde hair 'n blue eyes…'n y'er from Hoylake, Cheshire, England.[708]
Cynthia: At least that's not *quite* as invasive.
John: Though now you live in a $60,000 six-bedroom neo-Tudor home in Weybridge, Surrey, 20 miles out of London.[709]
Cynthia: Why not just supply the fans with a pinpointed *A to Zed*?! Wouldn't that be simpler for everyone involved?
John: But then there's *this* bit…(John paused for effect.) "Her husband says of her, 'I like her looks, her cookin' 'n everything

about her. She is the complete opposite of me.'"[710]

Cynthia: (Smiling) Well, *that* part's lovely. I suppose that makes it all worthwhile.

John: Maureen's included as well, y' know. She's 5'3 'n weighs...[711]

Cynthia: Yes, much less than I do...let's move on.

John: Says here she flatly denies she's engaged or even *thinkin'* about marriage to Ringo.[712]

Cynthia: Well, there's a denial whose time has come and gone!

John: So, y' see, y'er not the only one in the public eye, gerl...'n look... they've a *whole article* here on Miss Asher!

Cynthia: Wait a minute, John...how can The Beatles be extras in their own film?

John: One circuitous conversation — this! A fuggin' cat chasin' 'er own tail.

Cynthia: Seriously, how is that even possible?

John: Well, they've recruited a slew of stars, y' know. Leo McKern, Eleanor Bron, Peter Copley, Roy Kinnear, 'n of course, our own Victor Spinetti. 'N *they're* the ones carryin' the ball, as it were...the real actors.[713] We just fill in a line, here 'n there — rather deadpan-idly, if y' ask me.[714]

Cynthia: Well, I'm sure it's much more than...

John: No, not really. We're the mimers of songs 'n the purveyors of slapstick.[715] As Paul told this one reporter, "We're the only ones who *can't* act!"[716]

Cynthia: But on the other hand, I saw Dick Lester quoted as saying that *you,* in particular, are a *great* actor.[717]

John: None of us 're great, Powell. Truth is, in all the so-called "gimmicky, zany, cartoon comedy" goin' on all around us, we're forgettin' who we are, y' know. It's like...it's like havin' clams in a movie about frogs![718]

Cynthia: (Sighing) Haven't you had *any* fun at all, John? There you are, off on a warm, tropical island, whilst here at home, we're freezing to death! Surely, it's not all drudgery.

John: I mean, yeah, they try their best to make things right. Thisavvy, someone gave us these little convertible cars to drive around the sand,[719] 'n a coupla days ago, we went to this go-kart track where we were side-swipin' 'n rammin' one another, y' know...until someone said it was all too fuggin' dangerous for the valuable fuggin' Beatles![720]

Cynthia: Oh, John. (She sighed.) I'm sorry.

John: But after-hours, y' know, we have drinks with Angie 'n Jim Mac…'n with Victor, whose Welsh accent grows *greatly* pronounced as the night wears on.[721] Even ole Donald Zec's a larf, that time of night. He's got all these fuggin' stories no one would believe![722] 'N he's brash. I mean, a coupla nights ago, he was after persuadin' Leo McKern to remove his glass eye…but right when McKern was on the verge of really doin' it, ole Jim reprised his famous motto of, "Toler and moder, son! Toler and moder!"[723]

Cynthia: (Giggling) That's Jim, all right. The very voice of reason.

John: Yeah, even Angie, who thrives on a bit of malarkey, was sayin' to Leo, (Imitating her voice) "*This* line of chatter has gotten out of hand!" (Cynthia laughed.) Speakin' of fun, gerl, how're things in Weybridge?

Cynthia: (Sighing) Well, the renovation goes on and on, eternally…but they *vow* they'll be done in six more weeks.

John: Which is what they've been sayin' forfuggin'ever, isn't it? Fortunately, you'll be free of it all whilst we're in Obertauern.[724] We've still got Lillian mindin' Julian, right?

Cynthia: Yes, and she never lets me forget it. Every day there's some barb about my "jetting off on *yet another* skiing holiday" while she'll be moored here, "minding hearth and home."

John: Y' mean, like the home I bought her? If she doesn't want to be "mired," I could always take it back!

Cynthia: I'm sure it won't come to that, John.

John: Well, we're up early tomorrow, Cyn, so…give Jules a kiss for me.

Cynthia: He misses you, John. (She lied. The boy never asked after his father. John was so seldom home that Julian barely knew him.) We all miss you. I do especially.

John: (Defensively) Yeah, well, it's only a few more days, y' know.

Cynthia: (A pause. Hoping for something more romantic from her husband. But when nothing came…) Well, all right, then. Give my love to the others…and say "Hello" to Brian, Mal, and Neil.

John: I'll do m' best, Powell, but now that Mal's a famous film star…

Cynthia: *What!?*
John: Yeah, we all got together 'n insisted that the writers, a.k.a. *Wooden Beam*,[725] add him in[726] — so they've created this role: Mal as a global swimmer, y' know. Searchin' the wide world over for the elusive Cliffs of Dover.[727]
Cynthia: That's rather…curious, isn't it?
John: I dunno. Is it? I don't know *what's* bizarre anymore! But regardless, Mal's in! He's happy. So, we're all grand with it.
Cynthia: Well, tell him congratulations for me…*and* I want his autograph.
John: (Coyly) Y' can always have mine, y' know.
Cynthia: (Finding her smile) Can I?
John: Yeah, but I'm not after givin' autographs without favours, gerl.
Cynthia: Well, consider it done, then!
John: Cynthia Powell Lennon: favours freely offered…I've jotted it in m' diary…'n I won't forget it. (They both chuckled quietly.) Well…I'm off. Tirsarrah, luv!
Cynthia: Good night, John.

And hoping that her husband's final flirtation was a harbinger of good days ahead, Cynthia gently replaced the receiver.

There was no denying it. John had been different since the turn of the year. Withdrawn. Sullen. Interested in other women.

At Cilla Black's London housewarming party, Cynthia had watched John flirting with almost everyone in a skirt, and devastated, she'd wandered off alone. After a quarter of an hour — when John hadn't come hunting for her — Cynthia had decided to experiment. She'd quietly tiptoed into Cilla's bedroom and closed herself away in the massive armoire, waiting to see how long it would take John to seek her out.[728]

But after an hour, it was Georgie Fame who had stepped up to the armoire and sadly pronounced, "Come on out, Cyn. What's the matter?"[729]

"I'll come out," Cynthia had sobbed into the heavy mahogany door, "when John realises I've gone missing."[730]

And there she'd remained until Cilla — anxious about the lovely, new garments in her wardrobe being crushed by the interloping Mrs. Lennon — came to retrieve her.[731]

"Cyn," Cilla had intoned, as compassionately as possible,

"Please come out. Enjoy the party. Find someone else to chat up, why don't you?" But when Cynthia seemed determined to wait John out, the lovely, auburn-haired, Scouse hostess had grown quite candid. "Listen Cynthia, he's not comin', y' know. He's down there laughin' 'n chattin' 'n having a wonderful time."

And with that, the heavy armoire door had creaked open. Cynthia had stepped out carefully, blinking against the harsh light — and against an even harsher reality.[732] Her husband hadn't missed her at all. If he'd even noticed her absence, he hadn't been a bit concerned.

Cynthia would've given anything then — and now — to recapture the thirst of their college days: her sensual black leather skirts and fishnet hose, her newly-dyed blonde hair, her smoky, charcoaled eyes.[733] And John, with his greased D.A. reeking of smoke and fish'n'chips, his battered guitar slung across his back, and his hands rough with callouses.[734] They were passionate then. They were happy.

But lately, cloistered in the dusty attic of her stockbroker belt mansion, Cynthia felt unloved and unlovely. "Miss Prim," John had called her, back in art school, when she wasn't.[735] But now, the moniker fit. Despite shopping sprees to Mary Quant in King's Road and Biba in Kensington High Street, Cynthia felt every bit the dowdy mum.[736] And she hadn't one strategy in her pocket for winning her husband back again.

Not even the slightest idea.

Notes!

Were The Beatles — as John told Cynthia, Ray Coleman, and many others — "extras in [their] own film" in 1965?

In Beatles at the Movies, *Roy Carr tells us, this time United Artists had secured "a production budget of £500,000" (p. 59) for the making of 'Help!' And "as a means of protecting United Artists' investment, The Beatles would no longer be expected to carry a film entirely on their own. For 'Help!', a highly-experienced team of comic actors, led by Leo McKern and including Victor Spinetti, Eleanor Bron, Bruce Lacey, Patrick Cargill, and John Bluthal, was hired not to appear in 'cameo,' but to play an integral part of the plot, from start to finish." (p. 63)*

Did John really call Cynthia whilst away from home in 1965?

In her 2005 memoir, John, Cynthia Lennon writes, "When John was away our affection for each other intensified. He would phone as often as he could, but he preferred to write — tender, funny letters, filled with anecdotes, musings and long passages telling me how much he missed me and longed to come home." She then proceeds to share one of those letters from 1965. So, it is the 1965 timeframe to which Cynthia is referring. (p. 168-169)

Sources:

Lewisohn, The Complete Beatles Chronicle, *185.*
Lennon, Cynthia, John, *160-161 and 168-169.*
Harry, The Ultimate Beatles Encyclopedia, *299-300.*
Barrow, 62.
McCartney, Angie, 85.
Harrison, Louise, 314.
Miles, The Beatles' Diary, Vol. 1, *190.*
Badman, 142-144.
Norman, Shout!, *662.*
Norman, John Lennon: The Life, *395.*
Coleman, Lennon, *100, 102, 108, and 262.*
16 Magazine, Vol. 6, No. 9, Feb. 1965.
Carr, 59-64.
Schaffner, 42.
Goldman, 179.
Kane, When They Were Boys, *319.*
Egan, The Mammoth Book of The Beatles, *379.*
Trynka, 162 and 164.

https://www.bing.com/videos/search?q=Beatles+film+on+Blamoral+Beach+Bahamas+1965&docid=608041913220079891&mid=674FC69797A70F6BCA53674FC69797A70F6BCA53&view=detail&FORM=VIRE This video takes you on a tour of Balmoral Beach, set to the sounds of a Beatles tribute band. Photos of The Beatles are dropped in at appropriate locations, depicting where and how the boys recorded "Another Girl." You can see George's "uniquely coloured" jeans.

https://www.nytimes.com/1965/03/14/archives/the-beatles-berserk-in-the-bahamas.html You can read the original New York Times article, "The Beatles Berserk in the Bahamas" via the "Time Machine" on this page.

https://www.beatlesbible.com/1965/02/ Information and photos of The Beatles filming their beach scenes in the Bahamas, 1965.

https://www.youtube.com/watch?v=M-_Qu6Jl3S0
This is a short video of The Beatles filming the scenes on Balmoral Beach.
Or use this QR code:

---

[687] Harrison, Louise, 314.

[688] Harrison, Louise, 314.

[689] Carr, 65. Here, you can see an excellent photo of the rocky beach on which The Beatles filmed on this day. You'll also see Paul holding the girl selected to "stand in" as his guitar during the scene. John, by the way, is seated on Ringo's podium.

[690] https://www.youtube.com/watch?v=M-_Qu6Jl3S0 This video, by Beatles accountant Dr. Walter Strach, shows The Beatles filming their "Help!" performance of "Another Girl."

[691] https://www.youtube.com/watch?v=M-_Qu6Jl3S0

[692] https://www.youtube.com/watch?v=M-_Qu6Jl3S0

[693] https://www.youtube.com/watch?v=M-_Qu6Jl3S0

[694] https://www.youtube.com/watch?v=M-_Qu6Jl3S0

[695] https://www.youtube.com/watch?v=M-_Qu6Jl3S0

[696] Harrison, Louise, 314.

[697] Harrison, Louise, 314.

[698] Harrison, Louise, 314.

[699] Harrison, Louise, 314.

[700] Harrison, Louise, 314.

[701] Harrison, Louise, 314 and https://www.youtube.com/watch?v=M-_Qu6Jl3S0 When you watch this video, you can see George's blotched jeans.

[702] Harrison, Louise, 314.

[703] Harrison, Louise, 314. Direct quote from George Harrison.

[704] Miles, *The Beatles' Diary, Vol. 1*, 190.

[705] Badman, 142. Dick Lester says, "We work until the sun goes down…The boys have to be up around 7 a.m. Then they have to go to make-up, which, since we're shooting in colour will take a while longer. We start shooting around 8:30 a.m. and then run though until around 6 p.m."

[706] Norman, *John Lennon: The Life*, 395, Coleman, *Lennon*, 262, Trynka, 162, Carr, 65, and Norman, *Shout!*, 662. "I was an extra in my own film!" is a direct quote from John Lennon to Ray Coleman. Trynka has him saying The Beatles were "bit players in our own movie."

[707] "Fact Sheet on Cynthia Lennon-Maureen Cox," *16 Magazine,* Vol. 6, No. 9, Feb. 1965, 51.

[708] "Fact Sheet on Cynthia Lennon-Maureen Cox," *16 Magazine,* Vol. 6, No. 9, Feb. 1965, 51.

[709] "Fact Sheet on Cynthia Lennon-Maureen Cox," *16 Magazine,* Vol. 6, No. 9, Feb. 1965, 51.

[710] "Fact Sheet on Cynthia Lennon-Maureen Cox," *16 Magazine,* Vol. 6, No. 9, Feb. 1965, 51. Direct quote from John Lennon.

[711] "Fact Sheet on Cynthia Lennon-Maureen Cox," *16 Magazine,* Vol. 6, No. 9, Feb. 1965, 51.

[712] "Fact Sheet on Cynthia Lennon-Maureen Cox," *16 Magazine,* Vol. 6, No. 9, Feb. 1965, 51.

[713] Trynka, 164. Trynka quotes Walter Shenson as saying that The Beatles seemd to resent the professional actors. "The strong supporting cast smothered The Beatles. They felt they were merely puppets being pulled around on strings and that these fine actors, like Leo McKern, were actually the stars."

[714] Egan, Sean, *The Mammoth Book of The Beatles,* 379. In his critique of "Help!", reviewer Keith Tynan agreed with John. He said, "Lester leaves it to his cameraman (David Walker) to create the exuberance, confining The Beatles to deadpan comments, never asking them to react to events with anything approaching emotion. He capitalizes on their wary, guarded detachment."

[715] Barrow, 62.

[716] Badman, 142. Direct quote from Paul McCartney.

[717] Coleman, *Lennon,* 262.

[718] Schaffner, 42. Direct quote from John Lennon.

[719] Goldman, 179 and https://www.youtube.com/watch?v=WqZH603iDkE Goldman says they were "gold cadillacs." You can see in the video that they were small, convertible sports cars.

[720] Harrison, Louise, 311-312. Louise says that the "go-kart facility" had "steep climbs and dangerous curves" and the powers-that-be stepped in to stop the boys from driving it, "due to insurance coverage." She says, "One of the drawbacks to fame was that you couldn't have spontaneous fun."

[721] McCartney, Angie, 85.

[722] McCartney, Angie, 85.

[723] McCartney, Angie, 88. Angie tells us that one of Jim McCartney's most used phrases was "toler and moder," meaning "tolerance and moderation." They were his watchwords.

[724] Harry, *The Ultimate Beatles Encyclopedia,* 299. Harry tells us that The Beatles plus Cynthia, Maureen Starkey, and Pattie Boyd were headed to Obertauern, Austria, on 13 March for more work on the film.

[725] Harry, *The Ultimate Beatles Encyclopedia,* 300. John is using his typical word play here. The screenwriters for "Help!" were Christopher Wood and Marc Behm, from an original story by Behm.

[726] Kane, *When They Were Boys,* 319.

[727] Badman, 144.

[728] Lennon, Cynthia, *John,* 161.

[729] Lennon, Cynthia, *John,* 161. Direct quote from Georgie Fame, according to Cynthia.

[730] Lennon, Cynthia, John, 161. Direct quote from Cynthia Lennon.

[731] Lennon, Cynthia, *John,* 161.
[732] Lennon, Cynthia, *John,* 161.
[733] Coleman, *Lennon*, 102.
[734] Coleman, *Lennon*, 108.
[735] Coleman, *Lennon,* 100.
[736] Lennon, Cynthia, *John,* 160

March 1965

Chart Toppers[737]

"My Girl" — The Temptations
"Eight Days a Week" — The Beatles
"Stop! in the Name of Love" — The
Supremes

In the News[738]

8 March: The first U.S. forces arrive in Vietnam,
on the beaches of Da Nang.

18 March: The "Poppin' Fresh" Doughboy is
announced by Pillsbury.

18 March: Cosmonaut Aleksie Leonov leaves the
Voskhod 2 for 12 minutes to become the first human
to "walk in space."

21 March: Dr. Martin Luther King, Jr. begins the
march for racial equality from Selma, Alabama to
Montgomery, Alabama.

Tuesday, 2 March 1965
Nassau
The Bahamas

John never gave the film's extras much thought. They were just there. They wore their costumes, went through their paces, did their jobs. And rarely did any of The Beatles have contact with the paid "fill-ins." But this kid from Florida who'd sought John out was something different. Mark Vidalis was authentic: as Mimi would say, "No shilly-shally in him!"

The teenager wasn't shy. In fact, for the last quarter-hour on break, he'd regaled John with the entire tale of how he'd been chosen to "star in the movie."[739] And John — mellowed — listened and nodded.[740]

"Yeah, well, I was back home in Florida, just bummin' time away after high school graduation — from West Palm Beach, but you probably don't need to know that — when my dad, well, he suggested that I come down to visit my mom, who works for this big, important law firm down here in Nassau."[741]

So, eager for sun, sand, and "hot chicks," Mark had winged his way to the exotic Bahamas. At first, he'd had fun, lying covered in coconut oil on the beach. He'd slept late and lazily roamed the breezy, open air markets along the docks. He'd listened to calypso and Junkanoo music.[742] He'd bought himself a straw hat and a couple of bright, tropical shirts. One night, he'd gone to the movies, to see Gina Lollobrigida in "Strange Bedfellows," and he'd jotted off a few "wish you were here" postcards to send back home.

"But after two or three days," he told John, "it was just the same ole, same ole." At loose ends, Mark had begun hanging around his mother's office, "makin' a nuisance of myself, I suppose."

"And that's when it happened!" Mark grinned. "My mom's boss came into the empty conference room where I was sitting around, flipping through some old magazines and stuff, and he said, 'Hey Mark, what's going on today?'

"I think I shrugged and said, 'Uhhh, nothin' really. Just hangin' out, I guess.'[743]

"Well, at that point, he put on this mysterious face and leaned on the table and said, 'Well, I know this sounds a bit strange.' Mark imitated the man's slight British accent, 'But our office is currently working with a film production company, and…well, we're looking for bums.'[744] Then he sorta laughed and said, 'Somehow, I thought *you* just might fit that bill.'

"Well, I'm pretty sure I scratched my head and made this *'What?!'* kinda face. I mean, I wasn't sure *how* to take that!

"But my mom's boss gave me this 'I know something you don't know' look and said, 'Mark, I mean that in the best possible way, and if you'll trust me, you'll see what I mean. I can't say any more than that.[745] All right?' Then he had handed me a slip of paper with an address scribbled on it[746] and said, 'Be at this hotel tonight, *before 7.00 p.m.!*'"[747]

"And without any other info, man, I took the bait."

"Intermission. End of Part 1." John yawned and stretched. "'N now, jadies and lents, Part 2."

"That night…" Mark's eyes were bright. He was "on," giving John the complete re-enactment of his adventures — gestures and all. "That night, I was one of a *swarm* of guys about my age and maybe a little bit older, waitin' around for an interview with this British film director named Richard Lester."[748]

"Ah, Lester!" John paraphrased Shakespeare. "A man of infinite jest."[749]

"Well, I don't know about that. He was all right, I guess. Sorta middle-aged, kinda balding, Roman nose…"

"I know him well, Horatio!"[750] John smirked.

Mark smiled politely but barely paused. "So anyway, this Lester…he shook my hand and got right down to it. He said something like, 'Mark, it's great meeting you, and I can see, straight off' — or straight away or whatever it was he said — 'that you'll blend right in. Not too tall. Not too short. Medium. No distinguishing characteristics that'll make you stand out from the others.'[751] Then he really looked me over and said, 'Yes, you'll do quite nicely.'[752]

"Medium!" Mark winced at John, "I don't mind sayin', I was a little bit insulted, you know." The boy stood taller and broader. "But then, I suppose something made Mr. Lester take a closer look, because he told me he guessed I'd been in contact sports, back in school…and he said *that* was 'quite necessary' because the stuff I was gonna be doing was sort of physical[753]…which was cool with me because, as you can probably tell, I was in almost every sport there was, back in West Palm!"

"Hmpf!" John sniffed. "He never asked me if *I* was into contact sports. And unfortunately, y' know, I'm in the same physical film." John over-pronounced each word, his overbite rendering the line comic.

"Yeah, well…" Mark shrugged, pulling his mouth to the side and trying not to laugh, "Sorry about that, man…but uhm…anyway, when Mr. Lester heard I'd played football, he said I was one hundred percent *perfect* for the job! A shoo-in!"

"Cheers, son!" John lifted an invisible toast.

"Yeah, I was pretty pumped about it…even though I still didn't know what the *heck* the interview was for! So finally, I got my courage up and said, 'Uhm, thanks very much, Mr. Lester. I appreciate this 'n all. But uhhh…perfect for *what?*'"

"'Oh,' Lester frowned at me. "I thought you knew!" I guess he assumed that all of us applicants had been "informed" or whatever, when we filled out our paperwork. But he explained, 'You see, we're doing a film…with The Beatles. And this evening, we're selecting several dozen young, male extras — to be soldiers in a rather ragtag, religious sect army.'

"And *that's* when my heart did this *full stop,* man! I just stood there and stared at him, bug-eyed.

"The Beatles!" I kinda gasped, but right away, in like a split second, I slammed the brakes on. I mean, look — you can understand, I was big-time suspicious. I thought, 'Wait a minute…this is *bound* to be some kinda gag!'

"But that Mr. Lester, he didn't even miss a beat. He said, 'Yes, a Beatles film — their second one, with United Artists. You might've seen the first, 'A Hard Day's Night,' did you not?'

"And I said real slowly, 'You're making a Beatles movie *here? Now?'* And I kinda remember looking around, like wondering if I could see some of the cast and crew millin' about, you know. But nope. It was just me and a ton of other guys out in the hallway, waiting to be signed up, too…along Mr. Lester, of course, who glanced at the wall clock, and then started walking me toward the door."

"Ah, the ole' heave-ho, hey?" John muttered.

"Yeah…and I knew he had a ton of other people to talk to, but I still was kinda worried. So, I looked him straight in the eye and said, 'You're not pullin' my leg, are you? This isn't some kind of a joke, like say 'Candid Camera,'[754] is it?'

"And he kinda laughed at that, but instead of answering me, he handed me some papers to sign and got right down to brass tacks. 'Fourteen dollars a day, Mark. Hair and makeup at 7 a.m. — no later. Close of business: 5.30 to 6.30 p.m. And be certain to dress *identically*, without the slightest deviation, every single day. No hair trims. Nothing amiss.[755] Report tomorrow morning, and I'll see you then."

"And man," Mark grinned at John, "that's when I knew it was for *real*…like *really real*! And I just sorta drifted outta that room without even blinking! Maybe without even breathing…and then, once I was out in the hall, I just kinda leaned against the wall for a few minutes and said to myself, 'This is *nuts*! I mean, this is some kinda *nuts*!'

"Here, I'd flown over to Nassau just to relax and hang out with my mom, and all of a sudden — *wham!* — I was *hired to be in a film with The Beatles!* The guys on Ed Sullivan! The guys who wrote 'Eight Days A Week'! I mean, that's *crazy*, man!

"I was…well, I was on top of the world until all of a sudden, it hit me like a ton of bricks: *No one* back at home will ever, *ever* believe this![756] They'll all think I made it all up. Unless…unless I can get a photo with one of those guys — some actual proof that this happened to me!'

"But," Mark sighed "the next few days were kind of a letdown. I mean, last Friday, we filmed a scene at some prison camp, out in the swamp land around Lake Cunningham.[757] But you guys never showed up at all. We heard later that Ringo and George were off doing scenes in the Royal Victoria Hotel gardens, and Ringo was over at the Yacht Basin, too.[758] And you…they told us that you were down at the public library, filming this part where you ran out of the building shouting, 'Ringoooo!'"[759]

"Right," John mangled a piece of chewing gum as he listened.

"I remember it as if it were only yesterday." He pushed his sunglasses higher on the bridge of his nose. "'N, y' know, I wondered where you'd gotten off to. I asked around. I said, 'Where's Mark when we need 'im?'"

Mark sputtered laughter. John Lennon was a riot...even funnier than in movies and interviews. *Real smart aleck!*

"So," Mark hurried on, afraid he'd already worn out his welcome, "we filmed a couple of other times, too, but unfortunately, we never did run into you guys. Until today, that is."

"Well, we didn't want you to get bored of us, now did we?" John flashed a fleeting grin. "Familiarity breedin' contempt 'n all that."[760]

"What?" Mark blinked.

"Quoth the raven, 'Never mind.'"[761]

"So, anyway," Mark had reached the end of his tale, "here we are, at long last...filming the very last scene of the whole movie...together!"

"Yeah, here we finally are." John was amused by the kid. Mark Vidalis was unadorned, natural, the real thing.

"And guess what?" Mark bubbled over. "I solved my problem today, too! I made sure nobody'll ever doubt me! I came up with this ingenious plan, and it worked!"

"Do tell." John crossed his leg and leaned back against a palm tree — his thin, blue-and-grey-striped seersucker jacket[762] failing to buffer him from the spiky bark.

"Well," Mark's face was blotched with battle-paint along his cheeks and beneath his eyes, "in that scene we just shot — you know, where we were told to look the other way and *not* look directly into the camera?"

"Yeah right," John patted himself for another "cig."

"Well, I looked *straight in*," Mark beamed. "And lo and behold, they filmed it anyway![763] So, there you go, man! It'll be right there, in the movie, and no one'll ever be able to say I wasn't a part of all this!"

"Welllllll," John lifted an eyebrow, "y' do know, once they find that bit in production, they'll more 'n likely leave it on the cuttin' room floor, son. I mean, they'll suss you out, won't they?" John imitated scissors with his fingers. He hated to bring the kid down, but it would be worse to let the boy go home and boast to his friends, only to be humiliated with the film came out.

"Oh," Mark frowned. "I hadn't thought about that. *Dadgummit!* I guess you're right."

"So," John took a deep drag. He didn't speak for five or ten seconds, "there's only one viable solution, as I see it. Tomorrow mornin', before they smear on yer paint, we'll nab a photo together, me 'n you. We *have* to do it, y' know…for the sake of historical documentation…for the all-important 'permanent record,' don't we?"

"You'd *do that*?" Mark's heart was racing. Here was the Leader Beatle, the founder of The Beatles, offering to take a photo with him! Earlier, Mark had asked George Harrison for an autograph, and Harrison had abruptly told him to "bugger off."[764] But John Lennon, *the* John Lennon, was actually offering — no, *suggesting* — a photo!

"I don't see a way 'round it," John pretended to sigh, "now that you've fiddle-arsed around 'n looked 'straight into the camera,' as it were. Face it, old son. You'll never make it to the big screen!"

And opening one eye, John threw a wry grin in the boy's direction. But Mark exploded, "Oh my gosh, *thank you*! Thank you so much! That's waaaaay cool! I mean…I can't even thank you enough! First thing tomorrow morning! Oh man, count me in!"

And on Wednesday, 3 March, 1965, Mark Vidalis and John Lennon stood side-by-side and took a colour snapshot that John would quickly forget.[765] But years and years later, when Mark Vidalis' obituary was lovingly written, his family would make sure that the precious moment with John Winston Lennon was recorded as one of the greatest events of his wonderful life.[766]

Notes!

Mark Vidalis "lived the dream" of most Sixties teenagers. But, truth told, he played a role in making it come true. Whilst the other "extras" were reticent to approach the group, Mark walked right over, introduced himself, and chatted with the band. He is quoted as saying that when he met them, "For a couple of minutes, I was in awe. Here were the guys who had people screaming and fighting to get close to them, and I had the chance to shoot the breeze with them."[767] Mark told Beatlefan reporter Richard Evans that after a few minutes he and The Beatles were "making small talk."[768]

The Beatles could always detect honesty and a genuine spirit, and Mark clearly had that aura. John, especially, liked the kid. Mark told Richard Evans, "In between scenes we'd sit around talking as if they weren't the most famous people in the world."[769]

Not only did John and Mark's friendship secure Mark a photo, but Mark was also given a "solo cameo" in "Help!" He is the member of Clang's troop who tosses a coconut down on Paul's head from the top of a palm tree. Unfortunately, the board on which Mark was balanced during the filming of this scene split, and Mark (who was supposed to "pratfall" from the tree) actually fell! Thankfully, the first take was flawless, and Mark didn't have to film the fall again.[770]

*Oh, and by the way, Mark's "straight into the camera" glance at the end of "Help!" was **not** cut from the film. In fact, he told* Beatlefan *reporter Richard Evans that in the scene where "the other bad guys are walking in the ankle-deep surf, having given up their pursuit of The Beatles, 'There's only one extra with his face towards the camera. That's me.'"*

When researching Mark's story, after reading about him on Sara Schmidt's website, http://www.meetthebeatlesforreal.com, I came upon his obituary from 2012. I was saddened not to have been able to meet such a friendly, unique soul, and was not at all surprised when Sara Schmidt, who had talked with Mark in person told me, "His story is one of my very favorite ones that I've found in the years that I've been hosting www.meetthebeatlesforreal.com. I talked to Mark on the phone, and he was a super nice person."

Sources:

The two primary sources for this chapter are:

Meet the Beatles for Real: Search results for Mark Vidalis
This article from Sara Schmidt's "Meet the Beatles for Real" tells the true story of Mark Vidalis and his role in "Help!". This includes the photo of Mark and John.

Evans, Richard, "Meeting The Beatles," Beatlefan, *Aug./Sept. 1982.*

Lewisohn, The Complete Beatles Chronicle, *185.*
Harry, The Ultimate Beatles Encyclopedia, *300.*
Carlin, 116.
Egan, The Mammoth Book of The Beatles, *376-377.*
Buskin, The Complete Idiot's Guide to The Beatles, *199.*
Barrow, 144.
Brown, 170.
Hill, Tim, and Marie Clayton, The Beatles Unseen Archives, *129.*

Borak, John M., John Lennon: Life is What Happens, *74.*
Carling, 116.
Goodden, 56.
Freeman, 129-133. Freeman provides great photos of the beach scenes in which Mark Vidalis took part are shown. Unfortunately, Mark is not in these particular scenes. Nevertheless, you'll get get the flavour of the filming location.

https://www.dailyrepublic.com/all-dr-news/obituaries/mark-j-vidalis-2/ Obituary for Mark Vidalis, 2012.

https://www.youtube.com/watch?v=Fkedw92qOUs This video speaks to the veracity of John's smoking marijuana whilst on break during the filming of "Help!" Both Dick Lester and Eleanor Bron discuss The Beatles' usage of the drug during filming.

http://www.meetthebeatlesforreal.com/search/label/Help%21 This is another video from meetthebeatlesforreal.com on the filming of "Help!"

---

[737] https://en.wikipedia.org/wiki/List_of_Billboard_Hot_100_number-one_singles_of_1965

[738] https://www.onthisday.com/events/date/1965

[739] Evans, "Meeting the Beatles," *Beatlefan* magazine, Aug./Sept. 1982. In his interview with Richard Evans, Mark Vidalis said that he had struck up a friendship with John Lennon and "in between scenes, we'd sit around talking." What they talked about, we can only surmise. Here, Mark is answering a basic question, "How'd you end up in the film?" That is most likely a question John would have posed. And though we don't know Mark's exact words in response, the facts given about his selection for the film are all exactly as they occurred.

[740] Carlin, *McCartney*, 116, Egan, *The Mammoth Book of The Beatles*, 376-377, Buskin, *The Complete Idiot's Guide to The Beatles*, 199, Barrow, 144, Carling, 116, Goodden, 56, and Brown, 170. These sources and others indicate that The Beatles were smoking the special cigarettes (filled by Mal and Neil with deWilde's gifted marijuana) on their breaks in filming. Furthermore, this video shows both Dick Lester and Eleanor Bron discussing The Beatles' usage of marijuana during the filming of "Help!"
https://www.youtube.com/watch?v=Fkedw92qOUs
Finally, Goodden in *Riding So High* states, "The Beatles found filming deeply boring and smoked cannabis to while away the time." (p. 56) There is ample documentation that John would have been smoking marijuana as he listened to Mark talk.

[741] http://www.meetthebeatlesforreal.com/search?q=Mark+Vidalis The original article on Mark Vidalis and his time with The Beatles in the Bahamas, 1965, was researched and written by Richard Evans for the "Meeting The Beatles" feature in *Beatlefan* magazine, Aug/Sept. 1982. Sara Schmidt covered the story on her website, "Meet the Beatles for Real," and she was contacted

by Mark Vidalis himself and given extra information, as well as photos. My sincere thanks to Richard and Sara for sharing this special, true story.
[742] https://en.wikipedia.org/wiki/Music_of_the_Bahamas This website gives the origins of Junkanoo music as well as other forms of music in the Bahamas.
[743] http://www.meetthebeatlesforreal.com/search?q=Mark+Vidalis and Evans, Richard, "Meeting The Beatles," *Beatlefan*, Aug./Sept. 1982. Mark Vidalis is quoted as saying, "One day the lawyer asked me what I was doing. I told him, 'nothing,' and he said, 'Good, we're looking for bums.'"
[744] http://www.meetthebeatlesforreal.com/search?q=Mark+Vidalis and Evans, Richard, "Meeting The Beatles," *Beatlefan*, Aug./Sept. 1982.
[745] http://www.meetthebeatlesforreal.com/search?q=Mark+Vidalis and Evans, Richard, "Meeting The Beatles," *Beatlefan,* Aug./Sept. 1982.
[746] http://www.meetthebeatlesforreal.com/search?q=Mark+Vidalis and Evans, Richard, "Meeting The Beatles," *Beatlefan*, Aug./Sept. 1982.
[747] http://www.meetthebeatlesforreal.com/search?q=Mark+Vidalis and Evans, Richard, "Meeting The Beatles," *Beatlefan*, Aug./Sept. 1982. Mark is quoted as saying, "Then [the lawyer] told me to be at a local hotel that night, but wouldn't tell me why."
[748] http://www.meetthebeatlesforreal.com/search?q=Mark+Vidalis and Evans, Richard, "Meeting The Beatles," *Beatlefan*, Aug./Sept. 1982.
[749] John is paraphrasing William Shakespeare's "Hamlet," Act 5, Scene 1.
[750] John is paraphrasing William Shakespeare's "Hamlet," Act 5, Scene 1.
[751] http://www.meetthebeatlesforreal.com/search?q=Mark+Vidalis and Evans, Richard, "Meeting The Beatles," *Beatlefan*, Aug./Sept. 1982. Mark Vidalis told Richard Evans, "Lester was looking for people who weren't too tall because, 'They didn't want anybody in the movie so big they overshadowed The Beatles.'"
[752] http://www.meetthebeatlesforreal.com/search?q=Mark+Vidalis and Evans, Richard, "Meeting The Beatles," *Beatlefan*, Aug./Sept. 1982.
[753] http://www.meetthebeatlesforreal.com/search?q=Mark+Vidalis and Evans, Richard, "Meeting The Beatles," *Beatlefan*, Aug./Sept. 1982. Here Mark states, "He [Lester] also asked if I'd been involved in contact sports in high school because the part included some very physical work." Vidalis qualified…and got the part.
[754] https://en.wikipedia.org/wiki/Candid_Camera This website provides information about the 1960s hidden camera show "Candid Camera," that caught people in hilarious, unscripted incidents. Naturally, Mark Vidalis might suspect that the chance to "star in a Beatles film" was a "Candid Camera-esque" practical joke.
[755] http://www.meetthebeatlesforreal.com/search?q=Mark+Vidalis
[756] http://www.meetthebeatlesforreal.com/search?q=Mark+Vidalis and Evans, Richard, "Meeting The Beatles," *Beatlefan*, Aug./Sept. 1982. Evans explains that as soon as Mark Vidalis realised that the film opportunity was not a prank, his thoughts instantly flew to: "I bet nobody will believe this when I get back to Florida."
[757] Lewisohn, *The Complete Beatles Chronicle*, 185.
[758] Lewisohn, *The Complete Beatles Chronicle*, 185.
[759] Lewisohn, *The Complete Beatles Chronicle*, 185.

[760] John is quoting the oft-cited "Familiarity breeds contempt" proverb, which has been attributed to numerous sources including Lucius Apuleius (c.124-c.170 A.D.), who is quoted as saying, "Familiarity breeds contempt, but rarity wins admiration," and St. Augustine (354-430 A.D.) in his work, *Scala Paradisi*. Other sources include *Aesop's Fables* and Chaucer's *Canterbury Tales*.

[761] John's pun is created based on Edgar Allan Poe's line in "The Raven": "Quoth the raven, 'Nevermore.'" The poem was published in 1845 in Poe's book, *The Raven and Other Poems*.

[762] Borak, John, *Life is What Happens*. The jacket that John is wearing in this chapter is found on the picture sleeve of Capitol 5476, the 45-single for "Help!" and "I'm Down." You can see a photo in Borak, 74.

[763] http://www.meetthebeatlesforreal.com/search?q=Mark+Vidalis and Evans, Richard, "Meeting The Beatles," *Beatlefan*, Aug./Sept. 1982. Evans quotes Mark Vidalis as saying, "There's only one extra with his face towards the camera [in that scene]. That's me."

[764] http://www.meetthebeatlesforreal.com/search?q=Mark+Vidalis Vidalis recalls [that] George Harrison was the most "tense." Once, he says, he asked Harrison for his autograph, and Harrison refused. "He was a little short-tempered that day," Vidalis said.

[765] http://www.meetthebeatlesforreal.com/search?q=Mark+Vidalis and Evans, Richard, "Meeting The Beatles," *Beatlefan*, Aug./Sept. 1982.

[766] http://www.meetthebeatlesforreal.com/search?q=Mark+Vidalis and Evans, Richard, "Meeting The Beatles," *Beatlefan*, Aug./Sept. 1982.

[767] Harry, *The Ultimate Beatles Encyclopedia*, 300, http://www.meetthebeatlesforreal.com/search?q=Mark+Vidalis, and Evans, Richard, "Meeting The Beatles," *Beatlefan*, Aug./Sept. 1982. Mark's mother's law firm was working closely with the production company for "Help!" Harry tells us that production company was Shenson-Subafilms.

[768] http://www.meetthebeatlesforreal.com/search?q=Mark+Vidalis and Evans, Richard, "Meeting The Beatles," *Beatlefan*, Aug./Sept. 1982.

[769] http://www.meetthebeatlesforreal.com/search?q=Mark+Vidalis and Evans, Richard, "Meeting The Beatles," *Beatlefan*, Aug./Sept. 1982.

[770] http://www.meetthebeatlesforreal.com/search?q=Mark+Vidalis and Evans, Richard, "Meeting The Beatles," *Beatlefan*, Aug./Sept. 1982.

Sunday, 7 March 1965
"The Temple"
New Providence Island
The Bahamas

This afternoon, not even the news that a camera team would be filming The Beatles' August concert in New York's Shea Stadium[771] could make Brian smile. He'd been petulant ever since his former press agent, Derek Taylor, had flown into Nassau four days ago[772] — ironically, on assignment from Los Angeles's wildly popular radio station, KRLA — to interview The Beatles.[773] The bitter enmity between Epstein and Taylor hadn't diminished one iota,[774] and Taylor's L.A. new tan and gleaming smile only made current circumstances worse.

Then, an ill-timed telegram announcing the cancellation of The Beatles' July Parisian concert taping had further darkened Eppy's mood.[775] He'd seen the potential film as an opportunity for a "break-through" with the standoffish French public and, of course, as wonderful publicity for the boys. Now, that opportunity had vanished.

But the unhappy *coup de gras* had been the telephone call informing Epstein that John Lennon's spoken-word recording of *In His Own Write* had been set aside. The news had sent The NEMperor into an uproar.[776] And John — who'd rather looked forward to the project — wasn't much happier. The two men had arrived on set this morning in foul moods.

"John's got rabies," George warned gregarious Connecticut radio journalist Long John Wade, "'n Brian's completely lost the plot, if y' get m' drift. I'd give 'em both a wide berth, if I were you." And though at six feet four inches tall, Wade towered over both Epstein and Lennon,[777] he nodded, heeding the wise advice.

But Dick Lester hadn't been cautioned. Oblivious to the

morning's disappointments, he began chirpily escorting The Beatles around the deeply-wooded, dilapidated iron and frame buildings selected to represent Clang's make-shift Bahamian "Temple."[778] The putrefying structure of the supposedly sacred building was a droll comment on the fabric of fanatic beliefs, Lester thought. "An ideal location, don't you think?" he smiled.

"Ugh yeah, rather grotty, isn't it?" Paul sniffed. The building tilted here and sagged there, and the so-called windows were tiny openings — many far above eye level.

"What *is* this, anyroad…some sort of army barrack?"[779] George wrinkled his nose.

"Yeah, what's this place when it's at home?" Ringo brushed past, touching the walls and quickly withdrawing his hand, moist with pungent mould pong.

"Well, we're not quite sure," Lester shrugged. "Might've been a prison camp, at one time or another. I don't suppose it's much of anything these days. A relic, I presume. But we thought the irony of it serving as the beloved temple…" Lester lifted a palm.

"D' you mean we're addin' social commentary into this 'gimmicky James Bond-esque thriller'?"[780] Paul quoted the newspapers, jumping up to peer inside the filthy windows.

"James Bond wouldn't be caught dead here," John spat, prying open one lower, secured wooden shutter that swung on dangerously rusted hinges.[781]

And that's when he discovered them: a group of emaciated elderly men and women, wearing what could only be described as rags — and a huddle of dirty, terrified children robed in not much better.[782] They clung to one another — their eyes wide and fearful.

"Who're *they*?!" John rasped, taken aback, horrified. He'd never been comfortable with disease, deformity, or dire poverty. But *this*! The conditions were inhumane: a sordid collection of the unlovely and obviously, unloved — tossed into this den medieval. "*Unfuggin'believable!*" John's eyes grew enormous. "Who the fuggin'ell left 'em here like *this*?!" He struggled to talk, turning on Lester. "'N why the fuggin'ell are they locked away in the fuggin' Black Hole of Calcutta?!"

"I uhm," Lester was nonplussed. "I honestly have no idea, John. No one told us a word about *anyone* being on premises, let alone something of this magnitude. Give me a moment, and I'll…I'll…" And bewilderedly seeking answers, the director hurried away.

Slowly creaking the chipped green shutter closed and leaning against the wabbly wooden porch railing, John wrestled for breath. Breath that came too fast, too shallow.

Nothing could have prepared any of them for this level of neglect, but for John, the image of unwanted children, pushed away from sight and mind, was too familiar to bear.[783] He struggled against hot bile rising in his throat. He worked to slow his breathing. John fought to abate rage and to envision, instead, some way for his "star status" to make this right. Someone had to intervene.

****

The Government House[784]
Nassau
The Bahamas

8.00 p.m.

The last thing most of them wanted, after a long day of filming, was a compulsory black-tie dinner with the traditional austere assembly of officials and politicians. But for John, the formal event was serendipitous — just the sort of venue he required to say what he had to say.

Soft calypso music echoed through the exquisite arched and pillared dining room, open to a dazzlingly-lighted, azure pool and an elaborate stone deck dotted with Greek statues and opulent vases of greenery and fresh flowers.[785] The patter of a quartz-carved fountain hovered above the tinkle of silverware on china, clinked crystal, and conversation. Bowls of delicate orchids, sweet oleander, and gaudy, watermelon-hued bougainvillea trailed colour across the tables, and the glittering "Who's Who" of the North West Indies imperiously pawed and prodded their famous British celebrity guests.

Nodding and smiling, Brian chatted quietly with the Mayor of Nassau,[786] whilst Paul made gracious small talk with the Governor General and his once-lovely, manicured wife.[787] Ringo and George were gesturing, laughing, engaged in a lively conversation with American Bob Rowley, Chief of the Bahamas Tourism Board.[788] But John picked at his food and clenched his jaw, mentally rehearsing the bit he'd come to say to anyone who could make a difference.

Fortunately, John had been seated directly across the table from broad-shouldered, rotund Minister of Finance and Tourism, Sir Stafford Sands.[789] And when the dinner plates were removed and coffee poured, John grabbed his opportunity.

"Tell me," he leaned in Sands's direction, "how do y' do it?"

"I'm sorry," Sands lifted his eyes, smiling slightly. He adjusted the large-lens glasses on his wide, jowled face. "Do what exactly?"

"Justify *all this*…account for all this…all this lavishness."[790] John swept his hand at the evening's elegant trappings. "All this…when there're children 'n elderly folks starvin' 'n abandoned, right here on the island!"[791]

"*What?*" Sands blinked. He narrowed his eyes momentarily, sifting through catalogued answers for the perfect, polished response.

"I saw it m' self," John went on. "We all did!" He glanced at Victor Spinetti, seated on his right, "Where we were filmin' today in what we thought was a deserted army barracks. Turms out, it was a filthy place full of old people…frankly, it was disgustin'. How do y' account for that?"[792]

Surreptitiously, Victor carefully nudged John with his foot. He completely agreed with Lennon's campaign. The situation they'd witnessed this afternoon needed righting. But the press, Victor fretted, were chumming for any hint of an incident, and this had the earmarkings of a rather significant one.[793]

John, however, was unfazed. He pressed on, his eyes locked on Sands. "Yeah, y' heard me right. There were old people out there, starvin'…in this decrepit place, not far from here."

Sands took a stalling sip of water. His brow furrowed. "I'm not sure I know what you're talking about," he replied.

"'N children as well," John's voice was rising, "with no one lookin' after 'em…children who're out there *alone* tonight," he threw a pointed finger towards the magnificent open archway, "whilst we're in here with *all this*!"[794]

"F-forgive me," Sands stammered, "I realise there are some

complicated social and civic issues on the island...but I'm completely unaware of..." He lifted a palm and glanced helplessly at those around him. John was cast as the attacker and Sands, the innocent.

"*Unaware!*" John nearly shouted. Sands drew his embroidered napkin to his lips and jowls, carefully daubing. Then folding the white linen and placing it on the table, he edged his chair back from the Beatle. All around them, chatter fell away.

Recently, John had abandoned alcohol — which rendered him acerbic and nasty — in favour of marijuana. But tonight, he'd been regularly topping off his fury with Scotch,[795] and John was livid and uncensored.

"Unaware," John spat the word again. "Then, what's yer job here? 'N how can y' look me in the eye 'n tell me y'er *unaware?*" John threw his own white napkin on the table, but it was hardly a gesture of surrender.

"I'm um...I'm the Minister of Finance and Tourism," Sands responded indignantly, "but no one's said a thing to me about starving children or abandoned elderly people. This is the first I've heard of it. I *assure you*, I'll do everything I possibly can to remedy this awful-sounding situation. But of course, you'll need to give me more detail."

John glared at the man, unconvinced. He'd heard, "I'll look into it" before. He knew when he was being pacified, put off.

But with all eyes focused in his direction, the ungainly, wide-faced Sands went on. "I'm being most sincere here...and I want you to know that I take no salary for my work here in Nassau. I only assumed the post to help bring tourism to the island, to boost the economy, as it were — to make things better. I volunteer my time, you understand... my work's completely *gratis*."

It was John's turn to stare. For a moment, no one in the room moved as the stunned Beatle blinked at his skilled opponent and then slowly lifted his glass to toast the minister he'd just been berating.

"Well, then," John said, sheepishly, "In that case, I suppose y'er doin' much better than I thought you were doin'.[796] Cheers."

And as the justified Sands found a small smile and returned John's toast, the politician began asking questions about what the Beatle had seen earlier in the day...nodding and appearing quite concerned, deeply affected. It was enough to satisfy the onlookers, and around the room, *status quo* claimed its customary residence.

The Beatles, after all, would soon be off and away, and no one would remember this night, other than to say in articles and the few biographies that Lennon might engender that the boy had been brash and reckless. A known hothead.

Who would remember these ugly accusations from a reckless lad a week from now? Who would believe "the wildly exaggerated observations" of a young, inebriated singer from some moptop, rock'n'roll band hailing from Liverpool?

****

The Deauville Cottage
The Balmoral Hotel
Nassau
The Bahamas

10.45 p.m.

If Brian could have blocked Derek Taylor's interview — could have banned the boys from fraternizing with Derek entirely — he would have done. But KRLA wielded great power on America's West Coast, and since The Beatles were slated to play Los Angeles once again in August,[797] Brian grudgingly looked the other way.

Ringo, his black satin bow tie tossed aside and his dress shirt undone, was up first, at Taylor's behest. Paul had trundled off to bed, but John and George listened in, their sock feet up on the white wicker coffee table. Making himself as inconspicuous as possible, sipping brandy by the window, Brian hovered. His lips were pursed, thin lines radiating up to pinched nostrils. He said nothing.

Taylor gave a "four, three, two…" count-in and then pressed the large, red "Record" tab on the front of his unwieldy tape recorder.

Taylor: So, Ringo, tell us…how do you stand the separation from your wife so soon after getting married?[798]

Ringo: Oh, y' know, you've just gotta take it, y' know, 'cause we knew when we were gettin' married that — y' know, I had to leave to come out here for the film. Y' know, we just sorta got used to the idea. It's a bit of a drag, y' know. But there was no point fetchin' Maureen out 'cause, y' know, we're workin' like lunatics, 'n we don't have a day off when we're on location.

Taylor: So, it wasn't a question, then, really of having a Caribbean honeymoon, which is many people's dream?

Ringo: No, no. Well, we — we didn't have an English one, never mind a Caribbean one.

Taylor: How long were you actually away from London?

Ringo: Uhm…we got married on a Thursday, 'n we went back on the Sunday night.

John shook his head and threw his eyes to the ceiling. *Three days, Ritchie! Three whole days, son!* He 'n Cyn had had a set chicken lunch and trifle dessert at Reece's[799] with Brian and the others. But that night, it was off to a gig in Chester's Riverpark Ballroom whilst Cyn unpacked their Falkner flat.[800] *Some honeymoon we had, me 'n Cyn. Three days would've been a fuggin' luxury!*

Taylor: (To Ringo) It was quite a dramatic story, which broke at a very good time of day. How long was it planned before it happened?

Ringo: Well, we decided to get married two…two weeks to the day. And then it started gettin' planned from then, y' know.

Yeah, that's just about what we had…a week. With both Cyn 'n Maureen expectin', there was a bit of hurry-up. John exhaled smoke, slowly. *Not that we didn't love the girls, but it was…well, things weren't really "at our leisure,"as they say.*

Taylor: Well, let me say congratulations, 'cause everyone who knows you — knows you both — is delighted! I think it was a marvellous move. I'm sure you thought so, too, or you wouldn't have done it!

Ringo: (Smiling) Thanks a lot, Derek, and I thought it was a good move!

Edge o' the seat, this chat! John yawned. *I know* I'm *fuggin'*
riveted. John liked Derek; he always had. But this! It wasn't
Taylor's forté — interviewing.

Taylor: It means that at last we won't have to deny or confirm
the query, "Is Ringo married?" So, would you now say, into the
microphone, something for all time, on record: "I married
Maureen Cox."
Ringo: I married Maureen Cox, and I'm very happy, and her
name is now Maureen Starkey.[801]

John glanced over at Brian, and their eyes met. Almost
instantly, John could read Eppy's mind, hear his commentary: *"I*
expected more from a man with Taylor's experience and moxie.
Surely, he realises this is anything *but revelatory."*

And smirking at his manager, John hooted and applauded
wildly when Taylor snapped the recorder off.

"That's right, laugh, Lennon," Derek lifted an eyebrow, "but
as it turns out, you're next! In fact, get over here."

And suddenly, things weren't quite as funny.

****

11.05 p.m.
Whilst John had quickly changed clothes, they'd refreshed
drinks and located the leftover party food from George's birthday
do. Brian had made a wordless exit, and George had traipsed off
to bed. Seated across from Derek at the recorder, John munched a
carrot stick and slipped on a pair of sun shades.

"Hollywood, Derek. Hollywood!" he said, toothily.

Derek chuckled and started the tape.

Taylor: John Lennon, in dark glasses, white trousers, blue
plimsolls, black socks, lilac shirt, and multi-coloured jacket! It's
lovely to see you again, John, after about three months.[802]
John: It's great to see you, Derek, in your grey shirt, blue tie,
grey trousers of a tweedy-thingy, Beatle boots, 'n black socks.
Taylor: (Looking down) They're not Beatle boots.

John: They *will be* to anybody seein' you in the States, Derek.

Taylor: What's the film called, John?

John: They haven't got a title yet, Derek, so if y' can think of one, we'd be pleased to hear from you, Derek. (With a mocking Lennon smirk)

Taylor: (Wagging a finger) I *tried* to help you once with an album cover, but didn't get very far. Have you had any ideas which come close to the title, or have they all been, sort of, laugh ideas?

John: They've all been laughs. (John began batting his eyelashes and quoting in a comical, over-pronounced tone.) "He who laughs...laughs, laughs, laughs, laughs!" Things like that.

Taylor: (Chuckling and shaking his head) I think George had one... which was something to do with Goldilocks!

John: (Nodding) "Who's been sleepin' in my porridge?"

Taylor: That sounds pretty close. Do you think you might use that one?

John: No, 'cause we can't very well sing about, "Who's been sleeping in my porridge?", can we?

Taylor: And will the title also be the title of a song then, do you think?

John: (Holding up a palm, as if the concept was obvious) It'll have to be.

Taylor: Will it?

John: That's what I've heard.

Taylor: How many songs have you written for the film, John?

John: We wrote thirteen. We recorded eleven. We're usin' seven, 'n we need a title song, so all together we'll have written fourteen, but only seven will be actually used.

Taylor: The script (Derek arched a skeptical eyebrow at John.) — which I had a look at this morning — looks a little...eccentric. The aim of the operation, presumably, is to get a *different sort* of film from "A Hard Day's Night."

John: (Clearly questioning the concept as well) Yeah, 'n we've done it, haven't we?

Taylor: Well, by the look of the set, you have! Sitting on the beach in holes in the sand are little people in khaki uniforms, red sashes, and red turbans. Some of them are carrying guns, and some of them are carrying shovels. Over by the water's edge, Leo McKern, the British actor, is standing looking like a Polynesian high priest — the whole scene is pretty wild. (Leaning into the mic) John wasn't doing too much this morning. I presume you got up later than Ringo.

John: (Coughs) Yeah, Ringo got up about 7.00. I got up at 9.00, which is late on a film, but early for me.

Taylor: (Grasping at this topic as something to discuss) How do you come to terms with getting up so early when normally you're late risers and late to bed?

John: (Scratching his right sideburn, mischievously) Well, we just, sort of (glancing conspicuously at an invisible watch on his wrist) go to bed about 12.00 every night. 'N we just go out at 6.00 and pretend it's 11.00 at night 'n then come in at 12.00, y' see. (He flashes a swift grin.)

(Awkward pause, presumably as Taylor tried to settle some other topic.)

Taylor: Are you finding it fairly easy to move around in the Bahamas?

John: Oh yeah, it's not bad at all. Just the usual fat American tourists, 'n apart from that, it's not bad.

Taylor: Somebody was telling me about the sendoff at London Airport.

John: It was me.

Taylor: Was it?

John: (John nods.) Yes, it was very big, 'cause it was a half-day for the schools, so there was about eight or ten thousand there.[803] It was like the crowd we had when we got back from America, the first time. It was very good.

Taylor: That's probably the biggest sendoff! While you've had huge crowds going *in*, normally you don't get a big crowd to see you out.

John: No, that's right, so it was probably *the* biggest sendoff we've had.

Taylor: The Beatlemania level in England — if you'll forgive the phrase, 'cause I know you don't like the phrase — is still pretty high. It's very high in America, too.

John: Good.

Taylor: When are you due back in America?

John: I think it's about the autumn or "the fall," as they call it, I think.

Taylor: There's just a few other things I'd like to talk to you about, John — like killing a few rumours. Is it still true that you only have one child?

John: I only have one child 'n none on the way.

Taylor: There are an awful lot of rumours about you havin' been in Hollywood recently with Cyn, and that wasn't true either, was it?

John: (Shaking his head) No, I haven't been to America since we were last there.

Taylor: When you leave here, where will you be going?

John: England for two days, then to Austria for a week, 'n then back to England for the rest of the film.

Taylor: Do you know how long it will be before the film is released?

John: (Yawning) I haven't a clue — y' know, I've no idea.[804]

John moved his hand back and forth across his windpipe, the signal to cut the tape. Derek frowned, but minded.

"Yes?" he lifted two palms at John.

"Efuggin'nough." John took a long quaff of his drink. "I have to be up, y' know, in only a coupla hours, 'n everyone else is already off to beddie-bye. I've still things to do, y' know."

"Oh yeah, I remember the Lennon drill," Derek smiled, "...all the uhm, rituals, shall we call them: call Cyn, drink Ovaltine, read the nightly novel..."

"...battle the nightly insomnia," John added, sighing.

John had no trouble slumbering, once he was asleep. But dozing off had been a lifelong difficulty. In fact, his childhood mate, Pete Shotton, used to say that the only thing John hated more than going to bed was getting up in the morning.[805] The minute John was still and quiet, ideas, song lyrics, and a myriad of things he should have done or should have said bombarded him. John had never resolved a way to quiet his brain. So, most mornings, he was sleep-deprived, irritable, and raggedly weary.[806]

"All right, then," Derek conceded, "we'll have done...*if* you'll promise to give Cyn my love."

"Already rang 'er, earlier," John yawned, shuffling to the tiny, open kitchen to place his glass dutifully in the sink, as his aunt had taught him. "It's Mim tonight."

"Oh, well, in that case, you haven't *seen or heard* from me!"

Derek used two fingers to cross himself. "For some reason, that woman doesn't approve of me!"

Half-smiling, John flicked off the kitchenette light. "She doesn't approve of me either, Taylor. She only likes Brian 'n Paul."

And chuckling, the two old friends began battening down hatches as another "hard day's night" wound past midnight on the set of "Help!"

****

Monday, 8 March 1965
The Deauville Cottage
Nassau, Bahamas

1.00 a.m.

Mimi: (Resentfully) So, it's Himself, is it?

John: Johnny Lennon, Esquire…in the very flesh, woman.

Mimi: And to what do I owe this singular honour?

John: Well, y' know, I give every girl a whirl, now 'n again.

Mimi: *Hmmmph!*

John: 'N…I thought I'd better say in person that I didn't exactly say those things they're sayin' I did in the "funny papers."

Mimi: You mean, like being, and I'm quoting, "unrepentant for verbally assaulting the Bahamian Minister of Finance and Tourism"?[807]

John: Yeah, well I felt bad about that at the time, but since then, I've found out, he's not as nearly innocent as he seems…

Mimi: Most politicians never are.

John: 'N what I was protestin', y' see, was that they've shut away this group of elderly indigents in some filthy psychiatric hospital, as it were…on the jungle edge of nowhere, Mim. 'N I thought somethin' ought to be done about it, y' know!

Mimi: John, John, John. (His aunt clucked her tongue.) How much longer will you be in Nassau?

John: Two days. We fly home Wednesday.[808]

Mimi: So, you *must* realise that even if this politician pledged vast improvements…

John: (Instantly deflated) …he'll disregard it, once we've gone.

Mimi: Exactly. And you'll have no way of finding out what comes to pass, whilst, in the meantime, the press will make *you* the scapegoat of this ugly affair…the brash, young Beatle who fired away recklessly without a proper target.

John: But Mim, it's a…

Mimi: …hopeless cause, John. Face it. You absolutely *must learn* to curb your enthusiasm.

John: You sound like Spinetti, y' know. That's the very lecture he was after givin' me![809] (John assumed a preachy tone.) "Mind yer tongue 'round the press, Lennon!" That sort of thing.

Mimi: And that's why *he's* an enduring international star. He's learned the hard way, I presume, to — as the Pope once said — "see everything, overlook a great deal, correct a little."[810]

John: Yeah, right, but I'm John, y' know, not Pope John.

Mimi: Yes, well, we're *all* aware of that, aren't we?

John: 'N besides, woman, you've got it all wrong! *I* was the one bein' bashed at that 'do'![811]

Mimi: Employ the English language, John.

John: All evenin' long, those so-called dignitaries 'n their assorted, overweight wives were commentin' freely on m' work 'n m' manners…from the moment we arrived! I mean, they were sayin' things like, "Oh, which one is Ringo? Is he the one with the nose?"[812] 'N then, they'd push on it, just to make sure it was real.[813] It was awful, Mim. But only half as bad as their commentary on our work. They had *nothin'* but open disdain for what we do, for who The Beatles are![814]

Mimi: Which is *precisely* why you must strive to rise above…to prove them wrong.

John: (Shouting) But I couldn't *take it* anymore, Mim! I was *goin' insane*! I felt like swearin' at 'em, y' know![815]

Mimi: (Pausing a moment to let her nephew calm down) John, listen to me. Success is the best revenge.[816]

John: Y'er just a quote a minute, aren't you, woman? (Long pause)

John: (Tentatively) Mim?

Mimi: I'm here…here to help you, if only you'd listen.

John: (Exaggerating a sigh) Yerrokay, go on…

Mimi: Well…the press is *also* reporting that you're "quite taken by" that actress, Eleanor Bron.

John: Well, if "quite taken by" means we're friends, then for once, the press 've got it right.[817] She's smart; she's great.[818] In fact, she's just your type, y' know.

Mimi: *My* type?

John: Cambridge-educated, articulate…a bookworm, as it were.[819] (When there was no response from his aunt, John tried another tack.) 'N besides, Mim, she's ten years older 'n me, y' know! She could easily be m' mother!

Mimi: (Sniffing) I wonder if *your wife* feels that way.

John: *My wife* has become habituated to the rumour-mongers. One week, they say I'm after Alma Cogan, 'n the next, it's Jayne Mansfield, y' know.

Mimi: Yes, I believe *that* was the week you were in Los Angeles…being photographed with her. Quite cosy, if I recall.

John: (Sighing again) *Why* do I even bother ringin' you up?

Mimi: Well, I suppose because I'm smart, educated, a bookworm, articulate, and old enough to be your mother.

John: You rest yer case.

Mimi: I rest my case.

(Pause)

John: Look, Mim…I'll be home from the 10th to the mornin' of 13th. Why don't you take the train down for a coupla days…to see Julian, y' know? We'll send the car 'round to the station to bring you out.

Mimi: (Repeating herself, sarcastically) I wonder if your wife feels that way.

John: She asks you over all the time…I've heard 'er.

Mimi: Yes, but does she *mean* it sincerely?

John: Well, that's not for me to say, now is it? But you've been invited…so there!

Mimi: Duly noted. And goodnight.

John: You're ringin' off?? *I'm* the one who called you. I ring off!

Mimi: (Sighing) Mind your temper, John. It's 6.00 a.m. here! There're cats to be fed, milk bottles to be carted inside before they freeze, breakfast to be prepared for the boarder, and…well, a full day ahead with an *inordinate* number of things to do![820] I can't loll about chatting.

John: (Smirking to himself) Would you be happier if it were an

ordinate number?
Mimi: You've lost the run of yourself, John...go to sleep.
John: You always say that.
Mimi: And I always mean it.
John: 'Night, Mim! Turn out the landin' light![821]
Mimi: (Smiling a smidge) Sleep well, John.
John: Och, aye...

And replacing the heavy, black receiver, John felt the familiar pang of homesickness. No matter how "grown-up" or rich he became, the old loneliness refused to fade away. It was always there, a well-worn stone in a laden heart.

Notes!

Was John in the wrong for lashing out at Sir Sands about the horrid conditions he had observed whilst filming "Help!"?

John certainly never acquired Paul McCartney's gift for diplomacy. But those in the United Artists cast and crew who were present when John and the others discovered a group of ill-treated indigents inside the ramshackle "Temple" outside of Nassau clearly state that John had every reason to protest.

Richard Lester, in Coleman's Lennon, *says that John discovered the hovel containing a group of neglected children and elderly men and women in "a mental hospital where conditions were outrageous." And horrified, John vowed to speak to someone in power about this. That evening, Lester says, The Beatles were invited to "...a black-tie affair with the equivalent of all the hoorays of the Bahamas. John let loose. It was a perfectly justifiable sense of outrage for anyone with a sense of social conscience." (Coleman,* Lennon, *254-255)*

Similarly, actor Victor Spinetti, who also witnessed the atrocious conditions, said that upon finding "a lot of spastics and cripples and old people" in what Spinetti says was a deserted army barrack, "John was shocked that they had been shoved away under this terrible corrugated-iron army hut." Spinetti chastised John for speaking without restraint at the gala, but in principle, he agreed with John entirely. (Coleman, Lennon, *255)*

Indeed, Richard Lester says that "even as a multi-millionaire pop and film star, [John Lennon] was not likely to be conned into high society." He says "One didn't want to have a tongue lashing from John." (Coleman, Lennon, *254) All sources agree that although John was vitriolic with Sir*

Sands, the Beatle was not without just cause.

Furthermore, although John was for years castigated for speaking rudely to Sands at the Government House dinner, Sands was not — as he led John to believe — "unaware" of the horrific conditions all around him.

Born and reared in Nassau, Stafford Sands was an integral part of the United Bahamian Party. He had served in many capacities in the heavily Caucasian Bahamian government from 1950 on. One biography of him states: "During his brilliant tenure as an important figure in Bahamian society, Sir Stafford served as a member of the Board of Education, Agriculture and Marine Products Board, Board of Health, Public Board of Works, Airport Board, and the Town Planning Committee. Sir Sands was, indeed, very aware of every aspect of Bahamian life. See:: http://www.bahamasb2b.com/bahamas/bahamians/stafford-sands.html

In fact, in 1967, after it had been revealed that politicians such as Sands had been actively working "to keep the Negro masses suppressed," Sands and other politicians of his era were carefully investigated. During the investigations into the illegal practices that had taken place throughout the early 1960s, Sands fell under particular scrutiny by the Royal Commission of Inquiry. He and the United Bahamian Party for whom he worked were accused of receiving large payments from casino interests for preferential treatment.

Rather than face these charges, Sands opted to self-exile in Spain, taking his considerable fortune with him. In short, Sands's reputation for being the selfless civil servant he had pretended to be to John Lennon was questioned. Accusations against Sands alleged that he had been quite cognizant of the conditions of the poor on the island, whilst the privileged class ruled without restrictions. https://en.wikipedia.org/wiki/Stafford_Sands

In the years that have followed, several unfavourable biographies have been penned about Sands. However, some Beatles biographies continue to paint John Lennon as "out of line" for his stance at the Government House black tie dinner. Nothing could be further from the truth, as it turns out. John was right. And as early as 1965, he was already a champion of those in need, no matter the ramifications and the consequences to his own reputation.

Sources:

Lewisohn, The Complete Beatles Chronicle, 185.
Lewisohn and Howlett, In My Life: John Lennon Remembered, 34.
Harry, The Encyclopedia of Beatles People, 72-73.
Norman, John Lennon: The Life, 389, 395, and 399.

Miles, The Beatles' Diary, Vol. 1, *68 and 190.*
Gunderson, Some Fun Tonight!: The Backstory of How The Beatles Rocked America: The Historic Tours of 1964-1966, Vol. 2, *5.*
Badman, 143.
Lennon, Cynthia, A Twist of Lennon, *80-81.*
Lennon, Cynthia, John, *96-97.*
Coleman, Lennon, *27, 194.*
Schaffner, 42.
Margotin and Guesdon, 474.
Turner, A Hard Day's Write, *159.*
Riley, Tell Me Why, *271.*
Riley, Lennon, *272.*
Connolly, 231.
Carr, Roy, Beatles at the Movies, *65.*
Mulligan, Kate Siobhan, The Beatles: A Musical Biography, *85.*
Thomas, Gareth, John Lennon: An Illustrated Biography, *99.*
Trynka, 166.
Freeman, 143. There is a photo of George Harrison in front of the "Temple" building where the indigent elderly were being housed in the Bahamas.
Thomas, 99. There is an excellent photo of John with Eleanor Bron on location.

http://www.tribune242.com/news/2013/jul/12/when-beatlemania-came-to-the-bahamas/ *This is an online reprint of an article by Rupert Missick, Jr., "When Beatlemania Came to the Bahamas," The Tribune, Nassau, 12 July, 2013.*

https://www.bing.com/videos/search?q=derek+taylor+interviews+Beatles+Bahamas+1965&view=detail&mid=1A9D8697F9EC3C6ADF1D1A9D8697F9EC3C6ADF1D&FORM=VIRE *This is Derek Taylor's interview with John in Nassau, March 1965. The text was carefully transcribed by* **Suzie Duchateau** *of* https://www.beatlesinterviews.net *Thank you so much, Suzie, for the gift of your time and talent!!*

https://www.beatlesbible.com/1965/03/07/filming-help-13/ *This website gives a day-to-day account of what occurred during the filming of "Help!" including the location of "The Temple" on New Providence Island.*

Articles on Sir Stafford Sands include:

https://en.wikipedia.org/wiki/Stafford_Sands *This website carries a concise biography of Sir Stafford Sands.*

http://www.bahamasb2b.com/bahamas/bahamians/stafford-sands.html

https://bahamianology.com/stafford-sands-and-the-nazi-who-laid-out-the-vision-for-the-modern-bahamas/ *This is an in-depth report on the rather questionable business dealings of Sir Stafford Sands in the Bahamas.*

---

[771] Miles, *The Beatles' Diary, Vol. 1*, 190.

[772] Miles, *The Beatles' Diary, Vol. 1*, 190 and http://www.tribune242.com/news/2013/jul/12/when-beatlemania-came-to-the-bahamas/ This article by Rupert Missick in *The Tribune*, Nassau, "When Beatlemania Came to the Bahamas," includes one of Taylor's interviews with The Beatles and dates his interview as 4 March. Thus, I am using that as the date of his arrival. It could possibly have been 3 March.

[773] Miles, *The Beatles' Diary, Vol. 1*, 190 and Harry, *The Ultimate Beatles Encyclopedia*, 644.

[774] In late September 1964, Taylor had resigned from his post with NEMS due to repeated angry outbreaks and accusations from Epstein. Taylor stayed on with NEMS until the end of 1964, but could no longer work with The Beatles' volatile manager.

[775] Miles, *The Beatles' Diary, Vol. 1*, 190.

[776] Miles, *The Beatles' Diary, Vol. 1*, 190.

[777] http://www.broadcastpioneers.com/longjohnwade.html This is an excellent biography of Connecticut's Long John Wade. However, it is incorrect in stating that Larry Kane and Long John Wade were the only two journalists on the complete 1964 North American Tour. Ivor Davis foreign correspondent for the *Daily Express* was on the tour from beginning to end as well.

[778] Lewisohn, *The Complete Beatles Chronicle*, 185.

[779] Badman, 143.

[780] Schaffner, Nicholas, *The Beatles Forever*, 42. The words "gimmicky thriller" are Schaffner's. He calls "Help!" "a surreal parody of the expensive gimmicky thrillers that were so popular at the time."

[781] Badman, 143. Spinetti says, "John lifted this wooden shutter, and we looked through this hole, and this hut was full of spastic kids and old people."

[782] Lewisohn, *The Complete Beatles Chronicle*, 185 and Norman, *John Lennon: The Life*, 395. Lewisohn calls the place "a ramshackle hospital for handicapped children and old people, the state of which disgusted The Beatles." Norman identifies the building as "a psychiatric institution where old people and children were crowded together."

[783] Lewisohn, *The Complete Beatles Chronicle*, 185 and Norman, *John Lennon: The Life*, 395. Norman says "All of The Beatles were sickened by it."

[784] Norman, *John Lennon: The Life*, 395.

[785] Badman, 143. Victor Spinetti describes the party setting as "...it was like something out of Hollywood...a huge house built around a swimming pool, so that you could fall off your dining chair right into the pool and swim under and come out the other side. There were Greek statues all around..."

[786] Miles, *The Beatles' Diary, Vol. 1*, 190. John says they were talking with the "Mayor of the Bahamas." It was, more than likely, the Mayor of Nassau.

[787] Badman, 143.

[788] http://www.tribune242.com/news/2013/jul/12/when-beatlemania-came-to-the-bahamas/ This is an online reprint of an article by Rupert Missick, Jr. entitled "When Beatlemania Came to the Bahamas," *The Tribune*, Nassau,

Bahamas, 12 July 2013. Missick tells us that it was Bob Rowley who found lodging for The Beatles and their staff as well as the United Artists cast and crew "in Nassau, which was already bulging at the seams with its usual influx of high-season tourists."

[789] Norman, *John Lennon: The Life*, 395, Badman, 143, and http://www.tribune242.com/news/2013/jul/12/when-beatlemania-came-to-the-bahamas/ This is an online reprint of an article by Rupert Missick, Jr. entitled "When Beatlemania Came to the Bahamas," *The Tribune*, Nassau, Bahamas, 12 July 2013. Missick supplies the name of the Minister of Finance for the Bahamas, 1965.

[790] Badman, 143 and http://www.tribune242.com/news/2013/jul/12/when-beatlemania-came-to-the-bahamas/ This is an online reprint of an article by Rupert Missick, Jr. entitled "When Beatlemania Came to the Bahamas," *The Tribune*, Nassau, Bahamas, 12 July 2013. Missick refers to *The Beatles, A Biography* by Kate Siobhan Mulligan in which Mulligan states of the night in question, "John asked [the Minister of Finance] to justify such lavishness when there were children and elderly folks starving and abandoned on the island."

[791] Badman, 143 and http://www.tribune242.com/news/2013/jul/12/when-beatlemania-came-to-the-bahamas/ This is an online reprint of an article by Rupert Missick, Jr. entitled "When Beatlemania Came to the Bahamas," *The Tribune*, Nassau, Bahamas, 12 July 2013.

[792] Badman, 143. Direct quote from John Lennon, according to Victor Spinetti.

[793] Riley, *Lennon*, 272. Afterwards, according to Riley, Victor had a talk with John about "popping off in public."

[794] Norman, *John Lennon: The Life*, 395. Norman says "So, at the dinner, John rounded on the nearest official, who happened to be the Bahamian Minister of Finance...John really tore into this guy."

[795] Miles, *The Beatles' Diary, Vol. 1*, 190. John says that he was drunk when he insulted the Minister of Finance.

[796] Norman, *John Lennon: The Life*, 395 and Badman, 143. Direct quote from John Lennon.

[797] Gunderson, *Some Fun Tonight!, Vol. 2*, 5.

[798] http://www.tribune242.com/news/2013/jul/12/when-beatlemania-came-to-the-bahamas/ This is an online reprint of an article by Rupert Missick, Jr. entitled "When Beatlemania Came to the Bahamas," *The Tribune*, Nassau, Bahamas, 12 July 2013. This is the first line of an interview between Derek Taylor and Ringo Starr conducted in March 1965 in the Bahamas. I'm not going to endnote every line, but will endnote again at the end of the interview. Here I added the words, "So Ringo, tell us..."

[799] Miles, *The Beatles' Diary, Vol. 1*, 68, Lennon, Cynthia, *A Twist of Lennon*, 84, and Lennon, Cynthia, *John*, 96. In *A Twist of Lennon*, Cynthia refers to her wedding lunch at Reece's as a "run-of-the-mill set luncheon." (p. 84) This story is told in great detail in Vol. 2 in **The John Lennon Series**, *Shivering Inside*, on Kindle: https://www.amazon.com/Shivering-Inside-Jude-Southerland-Kessler-ebook/dp/B007V9BFJS

[800] Miles, *The Beatles' Diary, Vol. 1*, 68, Lennon, Cynthia, *John*, 97. Both sources say that John's gig was in Chester. Miles lists the location as the

Riverpark Ballroom. Cynthia asserts that although John invited her to accompany him to his gig that evening, "I decided to stay in our new home and sort things out to be ready for when John got back." In both of her books, Cynthia calls her new home the "Falkener flat." However, I have been to the flat and until recently, had a close friend, June Furlong, who lived on that street. It is named Falkner.

[801] http://www.tribune242.com/news/2013/jul/12/when-beatlemania-came-to-the-bahamas/ This is an online reprint of an article by Rupert Missick, Jr. entitled "When Beatlemania Came to the Bahamas," *The Tribune*, Nassau, Bahamas, 12 July 2013. This is the last line of an interview between Derek Taylor and Ringo Starr conducted in March 1965 in the Bahamas.

[802]

https://www.bing.com/videos/search?q=derek+taylor+interviews+Beatles+Bahamas+1965&view=detail&mid=1A9D8697F9EC3C6ADF1D1A9D8697F9EC3C6ADF1D&FORM=VIRE This is the first line of Derek Taylor's interview with John in Nassau, March 1965. The text was carefully transcribed by Suzie Duchateau of https://www.beatlesinterviews.net I am not going to endnote every line, but will endnote again at the end of the interview.

[803] Miles, *The Beatles' Dairy, Vol. 1,* 190. John is exaggerating a bit here. I'm sure the crowd felt like eight to ten thousand fans, but Miles tells us that "1,400 fans waved goodbye."

[804]

https://www.bing.com/videos/search?q=derek+taylor+interviews+Beatles+Bahamas+1965&view=detail&mid=1A9D8697F9EC3C6ADF1D1A9D8697F9EC3C6ADF1D&FORM=VIRE This is the last line of Derek Taylor's interview with John in Nassau, March 1965. The text was carefully transcribed by Suzie Duchateau of https://www.beatlesinterviews.net Thank you so much, Suzie, for the gift of your time and talent.

[805] Margotin and Guesdon, 474. Direct quote from Pete Shotton.

[806] Turner, Steve, *A Hard Day's Write*, 159, Riley, *Tell Me Why*, 271, and Margotin and Guesdon, 474. The older John became, the more his insomnia increased to a serious problem. During the making of *The White Album*, he said that he didn't sleep for three weeks. In "I'm Only Sleeping," John refers to sleeping as "floating upstream." He struggled to relax and block distracting thoughts. Even as a child, his imagination became very active and creative after Mimi or George turned off the light at night.

[807] Coleman, *Lennon*, 255, Badman, 143, and Mulligan, Kate Siohban, *The Beatles: A Musical Biography*, 85. Mulligan suggests that: "The next day after the party, The Beatles were asked to leave the Bahamas." Badman quotes Victor Spinetti as saying, "…the next day, there were headlines in the paper, 'John Lennon Insults The Governor General,' and we were practically thrown off the island."

[808] Lewisohn, *The Complete Beatles Chronicle*, 185 and Miles, *The Beatles' Diary, Vol. 1,* 190. The Beatles were to fly home to London on Wednesday, 11 March.

[809] Riley, *Lennon*, 272 and Badman, 143.

[810] Direct quote from Pope John XXIII, 1881-1963.

[811] Miles, *The Beatles' Diary, Vol. 1,* 190.

[812] Badman, 143. Direct quote from John Lennon.

[813] Badman, 143.

[814] Miles, *The Beatles' Diary, Vol. 1*, 190. John is quoted as saying, "The most humiliating experiences were like sitting with the Mayor of the Bahamas when we were making 'Help!' and being insulted by these fuckin' junked-up middle-class bitches and bastards who would be commentin' on our work and commentin' on our manners. I was always drunk, insultin' them. I couldn't take it. It would hurt me. I would go insane, swearin' at 'em."

[815] Miles, *The Beatles' Diary, Vol. 1*, 190. Direct quote from John Lennon.

[816] https://www.goodreads.com/quotes/46105-the-best-revenge-is-massive-success Mimi is parphrasing Frank Sinatra who said, "The best revenge is massive success."

[817] Coleman, *Lennon*, 254 and Harry, *The Encyclopedia of Beatles People*, 72-73.

[818] Harry, *The Encyclopedia of Beatle People*, 72-73. Bill Harry, one of John's closest lifelong friends, observes, "[Bron] formed a close friendship with John Lennon. They spent a lot of time together drinking in hotel bars, discussing politics and philosophy."

[819] Harry, *The Encyclopedia of Beatles People*, 72 and Connolly, *Being John Lennon*, 231. Connolly states, "John always liked intelligent, educated women — Eleanor Bron, with whom he had been friendly when she had appeared in 'Help!' had studied at Cambridge and Maureen Cleave had been at Oxford..."

[820] Norman, *John Lennon: The Life*, 389. Norman says, "Mimi was now nearing sixty and...remained as energetic and self-reliant as ever living at Mendips."

[821] Coleman, *Lennon*, 27. Coleman quotes Mimi Smith as saying of John's childhood during World War II, "We weren't short but we weren't rich, and I couldn't bear waste, particularly of electricity. [John's] little voice would shout down on so many nights, 'Turn the landing light out, Mim!'"

Wednesday, 10 March 1965
Nassau International Airport[822]
Nassau

The flight home would be another night-into-day excursion.[823] The Beatles were departing on Wednesday, 10 March from Nassau and landing in London Airport at 7.05 a.m. on the 11th.[824] So, John had dressed as casually as Brian would allow. For the last fortnight, he and the others had been required in hair and make-up no later than 7.30 a.m., and they'd worked steadily until just after sundown.[825] Now, John craved sleep and the forgetfulness it afforded. He couldn't wait to claim a blanket and pillow, all his own.

But just as on every return flight of his life, scads of troublesome "what-if's" and their answers forced him awake. And The Beatles' early morning breakfast meeting with Brian had "gotten on his wick" anyway.

Begrudgingly, Brian had shared the grim news that as soon as they returned from Austria, a number of BBC interviews would be wedged into their already hectic diaries. Eppy had apologised, confessing his regret that The Beatles were being tugged in dozens of directions. But although Brian had made it clear to the BBC's Donald MacLean that the boys were inundated by the making of their second United Artists film as well as the writing and recording of the concurrent soundtrack, no excuses were being accepted.

In fact, MacLean had now engaged the support of Light Entertainment Booking Manager Patrick Newman, who had widely hinted that legal ramifications were not out of the picture if The Beatles refused to star in several pre-arranged Bank Holiday specials. Telephone calls, telegrams, and tense moments ensued as Brian had pushed back against the BBC's assumption that The

Beatles were theirs — for Easter, for Christmas, and for the August bank holiday.[826]

"So quite unfortunately," Eppy had sighed, "I've been compelled to relent for Whit Monday.[827] Believe me, I had no choice whatsoever. It's nearly nuclear war with them, you understand.[828] Very like."

And thus, despite a slate of other engagements, The Beatles were pledged to several BBC lunchtime and evening interviews throughout their upcoming time in Twickenham Studios.[829] It made John weary, merely considering it. Every week, it seemed, something new was added to his list, and nothing was ever, ever removed. If he began dwelling on all that was expected of him, his breath shallowed.

So, pulling the prickly airline blanket against his face, he tried to shut out the world and crawl into sleep.

****

The world, however, was constantly waiting for John...and his mates. Already, at London Airport, fans were gathering. Overnight, the numbers of banner-carrying Beatlemaniacs had fanned out across the observation decks, and at first light, the crowd began to sing — brightly coloured "bairds" heralding the morning sun.

When at last, at 6.56 a.m.,[830] the incoming plane was spotted circling around to land, a vortex of screams arose.[831] Gusty winds lifted voices and tossed hand-painted signs, poster boards, and decorated bedsheets into the faces of the girls who had created them.[832] Only one banner proclaiming, "It's Great to Have You Back, BEATLES!!!" remained secured and readable as the BOAC Boeing-707's wheels hit the tarmac[833] and rolled ponderously to a halt.

At 7.05, after the gangplank had been manually wheeled over and the door to the aircraft opened, there was a freighted pause.[834] The Beatles were layering clothes upon clothes against the British weather, delaying that first dreadful step back into frosty reality.

But finally — solemn-faced — George emerged.[835] His heavy overcoat and black turtleneck did little to diminish the look of discomfort on the boy's gaunt face. Barely acknowledging the fans, he hurried down the stairs, only pausing mid-way to encourage John and Paul, behind him, to hurry along.[836] Ringo, carting two large suitcases and bringing up the rear, squinted. His grimace spoke volumes about the pointlessness of heavy topcoats in England's ragged, spring wind. The drummer was clearly miserable.

Halfway down the stairs, Paul stopped to wave and throw vigourous "thumbs ups" to the shrieking fans. And hunched against the cold, John, too, briefly waved. Then, hunkering down and letting George block the wind for him, John grinned and waved once again before employing his BOAC flight bag to nudge George along.[837]

Standing a bit apart in a smart tweed topcoat, tucked cashmere scarf, and sunglasses,[838] Brian watched this reunion with pride. His eyes misted — as they always did — at the rare and thrilling phenomenon that was The Beatles. And although cheerless newsmen continued to insist that "an imminent end to Beatlemania" was at hand, Brian saw little change in the fans' fervour. Only his boys, he mulled, had altered.

Though Ringo and Paul still donned the traditional "travel suit and tie," John and George now regularly chose the ease of turtlenecks and "corduroy kecks." All of their haircuts, especially Ringo's and John's, were much longer and uncoifed. And these days, the stunned look of wonder had fled their faces.[839] The Beatles — though appreciative and grateful — now expected receptions like these. This early morning gathering was, quite honestly, "the norm."

But most of all, as Brian watched George juggling a sack full of wrapped presents for Pattie Boyd, and Ringo struggling with "prezzies" for Maureen,[840] he acknowledged that the boys these days had their own private lives. As their months together became years, the four were maturing and growing tired of the road. They were men now, craving time at home — time for their families, time for themselves, time for their music. Like it or not, Brian's role as manager was, undeniably, changing.

And he feared the worst.

Sources:

Lewisohn, The Complete Beatles Chronicle, *136.*
Lewisohn, The Beatles: Day by Day, *59.*
Winn, Way Beyond Compare, *307.*
Miles, The Beatles' Diary, Vol. 1, *191.*
Schultheiss, 130.
Trynka, 166.
Hill, John, Paul, George & Ringo: The Definitive Illustrated Biography, *190.*
Wiener, 47.
Robertson, Lennon, *39.*

https://www.beatlesbible.com/1965/03/10/travel-bahamas-london/
This webpage discusses The Beatles' departure from the Bahamas.

http://www.meetthebeatlesforreal.com/2021/01/leaving-bahamas.html
Great *rare fan photos of The Beatles leaving the Bahamas can be seen here.*

https://vimeo.com/152416608 This is a home-made video of The Beatles returning to England from the Bahamas.
Or use this QR code:

---

822 https://www.beatlesbible.com/1965/03/10/travel-bahamas-london/
823 http://www.meetthebeatlesforreal.com/2021/01/leaving-bahamas.html
Great fan photos of The Beatles departing the Bahamas are shown here. These are shots you probably have never seen before. Thanks, Sara Schmidt!
824 Lewisohn, *The Complete Beatles Chronicle*, 185 and Miles, *The Beatles' Diary, Vol. 1*, 190.
825 Badman, 142. Dick Lester is quoted as saying, "We work until the sun goes down…It is a pretty strenuous day. The boys have to be up by about 7 a.m. They have to go to hair and make-up, which as we are shooting in colour will take a little while longer. We want to start shooting around 8.30 a.m.and then run through until about 6.00 p.m."
826 Howlett, *The Beatles at the BBC*, 67-69.
827 https://en.wikipedia.org/wiki/Whit_Monday If you're not familiar with Whit Monday, this article gives details about the day, also known as Pentecost

Monday, the day after Pentecost, which varies on the calendar according to the date of Easter. It is a holiday in Europe and the United Kingdom.

[828] Howlett, *The Beatles at the BBC*, 67. The categorization of BBC and NEMS relations as nearly "nuclear war" is Howlett's own.

[829] Howlett, *The Beatles at the BBC*, 69.

[830] Lewisohn, *The Complete Beatles Chronicle*, 186 and Miles, *The Beatles' Diary, Vol. 1*, 191. The boys landed at 7.05 a.m., and it takes about eight minutes to land and slow to a halt.

[831] Lewisohn, *The Complete Beatles Chronicle*, 186 and Miles, *The Beatles' Diary, Vol. 1*, 191.

[832] *https://vimeo.com/152416608* Most of the descriptions of The Beatles' return landing at London Airport on 11 March 1965 come from this live video.

[833] Winn, *Way Beyond Compare*, 307 and https://www.antiquestradegazette.com/news/2018/menu-signed-by-all-four-beatles-from-a-flight-when-getting-high-was-the-refreshment/ This article shows The Beatles leaving for the Bahamas on this plane. It's safe to assume they used the same BOAC plane, returning home. Winn says that in a silent 1.03 video by ITV, Ringo sees the sign mentioned here and begins to sing the line from "Hello, Dolly!": "It's so nice to have you back where you belong!"

[834] *https://vimeo.com/152416608*

[835] *https://vimeo.com/152416608*

[836] *https://vimeo.com/152416608*

[837] *https://vimeo.com/152416608*

[838] *https://vimeo.com/152416608*

[839] *https://vimeo.com/152416608*

[840] *https://vimeo.com/152416608*

Thursday, 11 March 1965
Kenwood
Weybridge, Surrey
England

The first night home was always awkward. Cynthia, her beloved housekeeper Dot Jarlett,[841] and Julian had established their own familiar routine, and welcoming John back to Kenwood always seemed "a wonderful intrusion." They made the extra effort to fit him into household proceedings, but all of them — especially John — felt him an outsider.

"So, Mal was actually in the film, then?"[842] Cynthia stood at the tiny third-floor table to carve the roast she'd asked Dot to help her prepare.[843] Dressed in a newly-purchased, white mohair jumper-dress, she smiled and flirted with her husband. Cyn's thick, shoulder-length blonde flip had been teased high, just the way John liked it. And using fingernail scissors, she'd carefully trimmed her own blunt fringe.

"Yeah, right," John nodded, yawning. He was wretchedly jet-lagged. "Whilst we were all whingin' about our parts, y' know, he was on fuggin' Cloud 9. He said bein' in the film was 'one of the most excitin' moments of his life!'"[844]

"And what did you say he did? Appear in a scene or two, sorting the gear?"

"No, like I told you when I rang, Powell, he was supposed to be this world-class swimmer, as it were, 'n he did this scene that'll be at the very end of the film where he emerges from the ocean, still tryin' to reckon his way — as his character does throughout — tryin' to locate the White Cliffs of Dover."

"Umm," Cynthia ladled cooked carrots, pearl onions, and peas onto John's plate whilst Julian, in his Poddy Pants,[845] rolled a toy fire engine to and fro on the braided rug.

"Whilst filmin' the other day, he was out there treadin' in fairly deep water, forfuggin'ever it seemed, when Lester — who decided he wasn't goin' to take the shot right away after all — called out for Mal to swim in."[846]

Cynthia added a nudger and handed John the plate. Her familiar perfume swept over him, the scent of home.

"Ta," he nodded. And taking an enormous bite of the crusty bread, he went on, "But as he was swimmin' in, y' know, Lester sort of casually looked over at him 'n shouted, 'Oh, 'n by the way, there's a big stingray, right behind you, y' know!'[847]

"Well, the four of us all laughed, thinkin' it was some kind of Dick Lester gag, what have you, but Mal turned 'round 'n saw the fuggin' thing, *for real*...'n he started power-strokin' as if he really *were* some world-champion athlete, as it were! Truth is, Powell, I've never seen him move that fast!"[848]

The Lennons laughed, even Julian, who waved his hands and giggled. Reaching down to muss her son's hair and tossing her own happily, Cynthia turned to serve her own plate. "I can just see it now!" Her eyes glinted. "I'll bet Mal left quite a wake!"

John grinned and shoveled in food as if they'd starved him on location. "Hey, did I tell y' Ted Kennedy was in our hotel for a coupla days?"[849] he bragged. Even with all his fame, John still yearned to impress his aunt, his sisters, and his wife.

"No, but the newspapers were full of it."

"Yeah," John sliced into the roast, "'n accordin' to Mim, they were also full of reports about me 'n Eleanor Bron." He slid his eyes to Cyn.

"Well, yes," Cynthia shrugged, "but *I know*. I know everything you do or say is being recorded, repeated, analysed,[850] and more often than not, misconstrued."

"Right, well, we're friends, Cyn — me 'n Bron." John stuffed beef in his mouth and talked as he chewed. "Good friends.[851] I mean look...one afternoon, we were all performin' this song that Paul wrote...recordin' it for the film down on this sort of rocky beach, what have you...with this group of girls in bikinis. Extras." He shrugged and took another bite. "Well, the press, they were after forcin' her — Bron, that is — to strip 'n pose for her own 'bikini shot' with the four of us.[852] But, quite clearly, she wanted nothin' to do with it.[853] I mean, she's above that sort of thing, isn't she?"

Cynthia finally took a seat next to her husband at the table. "I'm actually shocked they'd even suggest something of that nature! I mean, I know the press, but Eleanor Bron's well beyond that!"

"Yeah, well, it wasn't even a suggestion, Powell...they were mad about it! I mean, they kept after her 'n after her, no matter what she tried to say!" John took a sip of the wine that Cynthia had sent Alf out to purchase. "So finally, I gave 'em what for! I turned 'round 'n dealt with it!"[854]

Cynthia patted his arm proudly. "Just as you did that Bahamian Minister, I hear..."

"Yeah, right," John now attacked his vegetables, "'n *that's* the other story I've been wantin' to set straight..."

And whilst a banshee wind howled outside their third-storey window, John was the centre of attention. He was "on" in a candle-lit third floor garret, starring in a very private one-man show. Around him were his two most ardent fans in the world — one of them silently praying that this happy camaraderie would last.

Sources:

Harry, The John Lennon Encyclopedia, *133 and 410.*
Harry, The Encyclopedia of Beatles People, *72-73 and 123.*
Badman, *143.*
Lennon, Cynthia, A Twist of Lennon, *141-142.*
Lennon, Cynthia, John, *151, 170-171.*
McCartney, Angie, *83.*
Norman, John Lennon: The Life, *396.*

https://johnandcynthialennon.blogspot.com/2019/06/the-household-help.html *This website includes an account of her time in Kenwood by Dot Jarlett and a photo of Dot and her husband.*

https://www.dailymail.co.uk/news/article-2952113/Never-seen-papers-John-Lennon-s-bitter-1968-divorce-rare-insider-s-account-Beatle-s-drug-abuse-affair-Yoko-Ono-aggressive-behaviour-young-son.html *Jarlett's early and later days at Kenwood are outlined in this article from the Daily Mail.*

http://www.meetthebeatlesforreal.com/2021/02/white-cliffs-of-dove-part-2.html *Sara Schmidt's excellent website offers great photos of Mal Evans on the set of "Help!"*

https://www.theguardian.com/stage/2015/nov/23/eleanor-bron-i-didnt-want-to-be-like-other-little-girls-interview This 2015 Guardian _interview with Eleanor Bron (featuring a photo of John and Eleanor together) will shed more light on why John liked this smart, interesting woman so much._

---

[841] Harry, _The John Lennon Encyclopedia_, 410. Harry gives a full biography of Dorothy "Dot" Jarlett. Also, see "John and Cyn's Household Help," which features a photo of Dot Jarlett here:
https://johnandcynthialennon.blogspot.com/2019/06/the-household-help.html
[842] http://www.meetthebeatlesforreal.com/2021/02/white-cliffs-of-dove-part-2.html Great photos of Mal Evans in "Help!" are available here.
[843] Harry, _The John Lennon Encyclopedia_, 410. Harry tells us that Dot Jarlett was "initially hired to look after Julian…but soon she began taking on all the household chores, ranging from cooking and cleaning to checking the fan mail…" Pete Shotton, furthermore, observed that Dot "helped Cyn with the cooking, and even took many of her meals with her boss, who insisted she called him by his Christian name." See "John and Cyn's Household Help" found at:
https://johnandcynthialennon.blogspot.com/2019/06/the-household-help.html
[844] Badman, 143. Direct quote from Mal Evans.
[845] Dot Jarlett mentions that Cynthia was happy with letting Julian play at home in his "Poddy Pants" or diapers. See
https://johnandcynthialennon.blogspot.com/2019/06/the-household-help.html
[846] Badman, 143.
[847] Badman, 143.
[848] Badman, 143.
[849] McCartney, Angie, 83.
[850] Lennon, Cynthia, _A Twist of Lennon_, 142. Direct quote from Cynthia Lennon.
[851] Harry, _The Encyclopedia of Beatles People_, 72.
[852] Norman, _John Lennon: The Life_, 396, Harry, _The Encyclopedia of Beatles People,_ 72 and Harry, _The Ultimate Beatles Encyclopedia,_ 123.
[853] Norman, _John Lennon: The Life_, 396 and Harry, _The Encyclopedia of Beatles People,_ 72. Harry states that a photo was later released of a brunette standing with Paul with her back to the camera, and the press claimed it was Eleanor Bron. But both Paul and John denied that she had ever posed for that shot.
[854] Norman, _John Lennon: The Life_, 396. Norman says that when Bron was confronted, John "dealt with them in no uncertain manner."

Saturday, 13 March 1965
London Airport
Heathrow

11.00 a.m.

The Beatles hadn't yet recovered from their Bahamian jet lag, but here they were again, right where Alf Bicknell had deposited them,[855] on the all-too-familiar tarmac of London Airport — waving and smiling and departing for Austria.

The boys were somewhat blasé, but Cynthia, Maureen, and Pattie Boyd[856] were giddy — their heads together, giggling over ski instructors, moonlit sleigh rides, and the possible glimpse of famous Salzburg sites from the West End hit, "The Sound of Music." For months, America's 20th Century Fox had been turning the London (and Broadway) theatrical production into a film,[857] and the girls were hoping to explore the Von Trapps' Austria, first-hand.

This morning, the fans were giddy as well. Getting a chance to see "their boys" off on a weekend day was rare; the crowd was enormous. Cheering, chanting, and singing, the happy Beatlemaniacs overwhelmed the airport overlook, whilst on the ground a horde of journalists, photographers, reporters, and documentary filmmakers pressed ever closer, hoping for a serendipitous interview or candid shot.[858]

To John's left, Walter Shenson had been pressed into giving a quick, shouted statement: "Yes, uhm...the film is essentially a holiday picture...filmed in two totally contrasting holiday resorts. We're traveling from calypso to yodel, you see...with a lot of 'Yeah, yeah, yeah!' thrown in."[859] The reporter nodded and grinned, and then pressed for more, but Shenson quickly retreated.

Before the frustrated journalist could corral another victim, the cabal of cast and crew began moving steadily towards the aircraft. One more flight. One more press conference. One more hotel stay. One more stop *en route* to a successful film. For most of those boarding the plane this morning, this routine was "old hat." Only The Beatles' ladies smiled in anticipation. For them, the week ahead would be sheer holiday.

****

Hotel Österreichisher Hof
Salzburg, Austria

As always, it had all happened at a sprint. They had landed in Salzburg Airport, by all reports, to the squeals and shouts of over 4,000 European fans[860] — and this time, to the objections of a few grumblers as well. A small contingent of solemn-faced, hatted young men in business suits hoisted a hand-painted banner (lettered in English) that demanded, "Beatles Go Home!"[861] But the resentful Austrian lads were well in the minority. Other than a pressman or two, no one paid the grousers a whit of attention; their jealous efforts were for naught.

With Brian at their back, the boys had exited the BEA twin prop and paused at the top of the stairs. Hair wildly askew beneath his Lenin cap, John had waved briefly and then, seeing the girls react gleefully, he'd waved once more, friendlier.[862] When the mammoth crowd extemporaneously broke into song, John had chewed gum and conducted them. Then, after a few bars, he'd sung along, smiling with gusto.[863]

But consulting his watch, Brian had urged the boys on — down into the churning sea of reporters.[864] After a few courteous poses and answered questions, the boys had been pressed into a large, waiting station wagon, ready for transport into the heart of historic Salzburg.[865]

Cyn, Pattie, and Maureen had been rapidly relegated to a second car, with Mal's promise to look after them during the press conference. In fact, he'd been "gently persuaded" to make sure the girls had "a good look" around the famous city.

Moments later, John, Paul, George, Ringo, and Brian were

part of a motorcade traveling swiftly to Salzburg's gem, Hotel Österreichisher Hof, one of the most elegant pre-war landmarks in the city.[866] Built on the edge of the River Salzac,[867] the ornate, four-storey, domed edifice had been a stopping point for visitors and dignitaries for years. And today was no exception. The Beatles were permitted to snap photos.

Inside, in the ground floor restaurant/meeting room — with its high, wide windows gracefully overlooking the river and a growing throng of spectators — long tables had been pushed together and microphones assembled for the highly-anticipated Beatles news conference.[868] A single red rose and a cluster of white carnations in crystal had been artfully placed along the linen-draped dais. Menus in silver holders and iced pitchers of water awaited the famous British boys.[869]

At first, John was seated to the far left, followed by Ringo, Paul, and George.

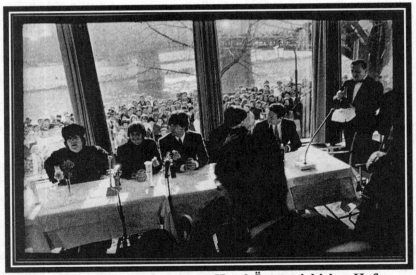

Beatles Press Conference at Hotel Österreichisher Hof, Salzburg, 13 March 1965
The original seating arrangement of The Beatles for the Salzburg press conference. Once Eleanor Bron is seaated, however, John will be moved into Ringo's position. You can see the river, the crowds, and the champagne about to be served.

But then, someone had suggested moving Eleanor Bron into the centre of events, and John had been quickly relocated to one side of the star; Paul, to the other.[870] As constant flashbulbs exploded, the exotic, brunette actress laughed, thoroughly delighted with the pomp of it all. And seizing her good humour, the boys smiled as well.

Beatles Press Conference at Hotel Österreichisher Hof, Salzburg, 13 March 1965
The Salzburg press conference seating arrangement after Bron was seated.
Note the Coca-Cola bottles and champagne.
Both photos purchased from Alamy.com, IY1957649

As reporters fired the customary queries at the lads, outside the window, fans jumped and waved and hurled snowballs at the glass. Pretty Austrian girls tried everything to induce their heart-throbs to turn around and notice them. Once — to instant screams — John lifted a Coca-Cola bottle in their direction. And George swiveled to bestow a wink, now and again. Paul was requested to sign the cast of a little girl who had broken her leg, and he agreed, gladly.[871] Ringo was asked to wiggle his rings for the flashing cameras.

In Salzburg, it was an afternoon Beatles fête. The boys were served champagne as well as soft drinks, and gradually, the four of them fell into the happy spirit with which Salzburg had greeted them. It wasn't 90 degrees here, and the Bahamian banquet of tropical flowers had been replaced by ice and snow, but in Austria, the Liverpool boys were received most royally. The lovely land of the Alps was ecstatic to have been selected for yet another major movie set, and their enthusiasm showed.

****

Hotel Edelweiss
Obertauern, Austria

"Well, it isn't the Palace Hotel, now is it?" John sniffed, flinging open their large, battered suitcase and fishing for "knickers and slippers." Mimi had taught him never to tread on "common hotel floors," so he always entered the shower, prepared to exit and dress on a clean bath mat.

"No," Cynthia shrugged, contented simply to have escaped the musty garret she'd been living in since August, "but, I didn't expect it to be. It's a sport hotel...for skiers."[872]

Hotel Edelweiss was clean, sunlit, and roomy with a theme of rough, exposed beams and wide stone fireplaces.[873] Everything about the lodge shouted healthy and athletic, whereas the Palace Hotel in St. Moritz had whispered romantic and serene. At the Edelweiss, one planned to hit the slopes early and stay out 'til sunset. Nestled at the base of the majestic Gamsleiten 2, the hotel was a convenient resting place between outdoor adventures.[874] Its beauty could only be discovered with eyes wide open, not lost in nocturnal bliss.

"Yeah, well, I'm all out of sport." John trudged to the loo and turned the shower full on. "I haven't an ounce left in me...especially when I imagine what's ahead, y' know."

"Then don't," Cynthia's face clouded, empathetically. She knew her husband was frazzled.

John grabbed a clean, rolled towel and unwound it, looping it over the shower bar. He clenched his jaw.

"I think that sounded unfeeling," Cynthia backtracked, "but what I *meant* was, try not to look at the big picture, John. Try focusing on small increments — on moments, as it were."

"Easier said..." John reached in and tested the water.

Cynthia leaned against the loo door, watching as John slowly unwrapped a bar of soap. "Well, I believe someone once said, 'You can eat an elephant, one bite at a time.'[875] Right?"

"Except I've always wondered who'd want to!"

"But you get my point, John. I mean, take 'takes,' for example," Cynthia reached over and handed John the tiny bottle of complimentary shampoo. "You know, Take 1, Take 2, that sort. Takes are doable. You can manage takes, but if they told you that you had to film everything all at once, from beginning to end — or sing an entire song perfectly from beginning to end — you'd be hard pressed to do that, right?"

John peeled off his shirt and said nothing.

"So," his wife went on, "think in 'takes,' as opposed to wandering out so far into the future."

"You're fairly canny, aren't you, Powell?" John begrudged a small smile. "One of those girls the professors approved."

"Well, I *was* known for my ability to do stellar lettering homework, especially for this *one* particular student back in art college." She lifted a meaningful eyebrow. "I mean, as far as I know, he never voiced any complaints."

"None thus far," John grabbed her by the wrist and pulled her towards the shower. Their eyes met. "But let's see how it goes...care for a shower, Mrs. L?"

"Well," she smiled shyly, "I might do."

"This is, after all," John Cheshire grinned, "a sport hotel."

****

Sunday, 14 March 1965
On the slopes
Obertauern, Austria

For the next eleven days, John zeroed in on moments — small

increments of time, tasks that could be accomplished and checked off his list.

On Sunday, The Beatles were introduced to their ski instructor, the lovely Miss Austria 1964, Gloria Mackh.[876]

"Things 're rather lookin' up!" Paul muttered, out of the corner of his mouth.

"Right yeah. Cheers!" George nodded.

"Now, John here already knows how to ski," Dick Lester explained to the long-haired model. "But the others, well..." He swept a hand, hopelessly, in Paul's direction.

"But wait! I've been told I'm a *natural* skier!" Paul batted his eyelashes at the girl.[877] And beneath a chorus of rowdy laughter, there were assorted mumbled comments — for Beatles only.

John was taken to meet his stunt double. He lowered his sunglasses slowly at actor Joe Dunne and spat, "You don't look a bit like him!"[878]

But Dunne[879] — who had John's nose, if not his stature — missed the "Hard Day's Night" reference entirely and seemed to take offense.

"It's a joke, son." John nudged the shorter man, playfully. "A line from the last film, y' know. This lady said it to me about *me*."

"Oh," Dunne shrugged and smiled a fraction. "Well, all right, then. Great."

And all forgiven, Dunne pivoted and introduced John to Paul's double, Peter Cheevers; Ringo's double, Mick Dillon; and George's stunt man, Cliff Diggins.[880]

"Y' know, y' remind me of someone, old son," John confided to Dillon, who, except for a heavier jaw, truly did resemble the famous Dingle drummer.[881]

"Right, so I've been told! Quite frequently! But fortunately, by gorgeous girls, not ugly Scousers!" Flourishing his Surrey inflection, Dillon wiggled ten gloved fingers just as Ringo ordinarily displayed his rings.[882]

The group chortled. Even John.

"All right, then," Dick Lester plowed over, followed by Paul, George, and Ringo — all four breathing heavily in the deep snow. "Here's what we're doing, lads. I want you stunt men up on this horse-drawn sleigh." The actors immediately began to climb aboard. "And then, what I'd like is..." he panted, "...we'll set the vehicle in motion, and I'd like you to..."

But John tuned out the rest. He turned and, for the first time since he'd arrived in Austria, slowly absorbed the sheer immensity of Gamsleiten 2: its white sweeps, deep blue hollows, and amethyst shadows. He tilted his head to the sky and followed the trek of aimlessly wandering clouds. Intentionally relishing deep breaths of brisk, icy air, John sought peace — for just a moment.[883]

****

Monday, 15 March 1965
On the slopes
Obertauern, Austria

It was a rather tricky manouever. "The Beatles" — skillfully portrayed, in crucial instants, by their stunt doubles — were to share a ski lift, whilst "Ringo," wearing a tight black jumper with white rings around the sleeves[884] and bellowing "Help!" for all he was worth, was to dangle perilously from a faltering line beneath the wooden chair.[885]

"I'm only thankful it's you 'n not me," the real Ringo confided to Dillon, honestly. "I mean, no amount of money, y' know!"

Mick laughed. "And no amount of money could get *me* up on a stage surrounded by two zillion hysterical girls, either — all hurlin' objects right at m' head!"

"Yeah, well," Ringo smiled weakly, "I'm not much in favour of *that*, either...or of performin' in a hurricane..."[886]

"...but what's a Beatle to do, eh?" John cackled in his famous geriatric voice.

"All right, men," Lester commanded, "let's try the lift bit again." And without delay, the group was at work once more.

****

Wednesday, 17 March 1965
On the slopes
Obertauern, Austria

"Top o' the mornin'!" George grinned madly at the others. Over cups of early morning tea, they turned and stared at him blearily. "Top - o' - the - mornin'!" he repeated, slowly. And when they failed to "cop on," he shouted, "It's St. Paddy's Day!"

"Oh, to be in England," John wryly paraphrased Browning, "now that Paddy's here!"[887]

"Uh, t' be in *Liverpool*, y' mean," Ringo corrected, "the *real* Capitol of Ireland!"[888]

"Where today," John orated, "the streets run every likely (and unlikely) shade o' green!"

"Y' got that right!" George's eyes twinkled with memories of the many feral nights they'd spent together on 17 March, back in the early days.

"That bein' said," Paul looked over the collar of his new sealskin jacket.[889] "What's on tap *today*…in the real world?"

"Norra Guinness," George sighed, still in St. Paddy's mode. "Unfortunately."

"Some bit, they said, at a curlin' rink, " Ringo informed them.

"Another vain attempt on our Ringo's life, as it were," John pulled his black cape lined with white satin[890] up under his eyes and arched his eyebrows, fiendishly.

It was the usual morning patter whilst the boys idly waited to film. Hot tea, Scouse humour, camaraderie.

"Well," Dick Lester pattered up, beaming. "It's officially official, boys! Being announced *everywhere* this morning! We're calling the film 'Eight Arms to Hold You'! Ringo's very own moniker!"[891]

"Well, don't look to *us* for a title song, then," Paul wagged a finger between John and himself.

"Yeah, we've said a hundred times, Lester…we can't write a song about somethin' like that!" John hissed. "We've told y' over 'n over. It won't work!"

"Well, I'm sure," Dick cajoled, "you'll find some way…brilliant as you both are!"

"I'm sure we won't." Paul was polite but pragmatic.

Nevertheless, the announcement was already going out, worldwide. And the very last people to have "a say" in the press release were seated right here, in this very spot. They sat waiting to act and sing and write the songs that would make the film's investment of 1.5 million dollars the achievement it had to be.[892]

Success hung entirely on The Beatles. Nevertheless, they hadn't a vote in much of anything, not even the film's quippy title.

****

Ray Coleman had flown into Obertauern to record a *Melody Maker* interview, set for release at month's end.[893] And though the interview was an exclusive with Paul McCartney,[894] John was overjoyed to see his long-time journalist friend again. The two sat in the restaurant of Hotel Edelweiss and chatted over a glass of wine and a plate of cheese.[895]

At first, they focused local, commiserating over the myriad pressures on Brian these days — the likely source of his increasingly alarming insomnia.[896] Then, they branched out, covering affairs a world away, in Vietnam.[897] At last, the two talked music.

"Word is," Coleman wasn't sure if the boys had been informed; he glanced around for listening ears. "Word is you're being nominated for *six* Grammy awards!"[898]

"Do tell." John crushed his cig in a red, oblong ashtray.

"I hear you're up for 'Record of the Year' for 'I Want to Hold Your Hand'..."[899]

"That old thing!" John waved Coleman off, pseudo-modestly.

"...and 'Best Rock'n'Roll Recording of the Year,' again for 'that old thing,' 'I Want to Hold Your Hand.'"[900]

"Go on..."

"Then, 'Song of the Year' for 'A Hard Day's Night.'"[901]

"Mine."

"And 'Best Performance by A Vocal Group.' Same song."[902]
John couldn't staunch the smile.

"And then," Coleman grinned as well, 'Best New Artist of 1964.'"

"*New*!" John's eyebrow arched. "We've been at it for the last forty years, y' know!'"

"Well yes, *I* know that but…" Coleman shrugged.

"Look, they were screamin' for us in Litherland Town Hall way back in December 1960,"[903] John pointed out. "'N *that* was a fuggin' half-decade ago!"

"Still…it's wonderful, right?" Ray coaxed. "Being recognized so broadly after all this time?"

Sliding his empty glass aside, John pulled out a thin stick of gum and unwrapped it. He offered one to Ray, who shook his head.

"And last but not least," Coleman had a flair for the dramatic, "'Best Original Score Written for a Motion Picture or TV Show.'"

"Yeah right, well, that's George Martin," John admitted, "not us. And what did he get for it, eh? Lester wouldn't even have him back on the film this time!"[904]

"Yes, I'd rather noticed," Coleman nodded. "Shame — that. But still, congratulations, John! Those of us who've been with you all along are bursting with pride."

"Ta," John nodded. "You're one of the ones who really means that, Coleman."

And in all sincerity, he did.

****

Ray Coleman: Tell me boys, would you ever live permanently outside of Britain?[905]

George: Leave England? Never! Best country in the world to live in!

Paul: No, definitely not. Out of everywhere I've been, I like England best.

Coleman: How would you like to be remembered as The Beatles when you are old?

Paul: With a smile.

John: I won't be interested in bein' remembered. I'll be in a mental home, and *Melody Maker* will run articles sayin', "Now, direct from the mental home, we present "John Lennon in Blind Date." (Laughter from all, including Coleman) No…I'd like to be remembered as the one with the twinkle in his eye.[906]

****

Victor Spinetti had been ill for days — flu, the rumour was. Unable to appear on set and growing steadily worse, Spinetti was primarily suffering alone. So, as soon as Coleman wound up the short group chat, the boys headed off for their co-star's suite.[907]

"It's a good thing Brian's asleep," George was right. The NEMperor wouldn't have permitted "his Beatles" to be infected by anyone, not even the Queen herself.

"*He* wouldn't let us do this for a big clock!" John chuckled over the shrewd Scouse-ism.

"Well, I'm not sure we really should," Paul was wisely reticent. "I mean, Spinetti's quite ill, from what I hear.[908] 'N we've got a film to..."

"Ah, c'mon Macca!" Ringo tugged at his arm. "It's Victor! He needs us."

But when the boys filed into the actor's hotel suite and saw the man — pale, unshaven, swathed in a stained bathrobe, and smelling of disease — none of them were glad they came.

"Let's hope you're better than you look, Sonny Jim!" John barked, appalled. Victor covered his mouth and coughed, deep and wet. The sound set them back a couple of steps.

"I've brought you milk 'n cookies!"[909] George proffered his prezzies. "'N look, you've already got a whole tray of nice, refreshin' beverages."

"Go on. Have some fruit juice," Victor croaked. Then, he let his head fall helplessly onto the pillow.

"Could we get you anythin', then?" Paul clicked his cheek, twice. "Aspero? A gorgeous nurse, perhaps — or two?"

"Care for a naughty limerick?" John offered.

But Victor didn't even break a smile. "No, nothing," he almost whispered.

Certainly, the situation appeared far more grim than the four had been led to believe. Despite the presence of his distinguished visitors, Spinetti had hardly opened his eyes.

But spotting the huge Room Service menu, Ringo grabbed the bound portfolio and pulled up a chair. Taking a seat, the drummer cleared his throat and confidently began, "Once upon a time, there were three bears..."[910]

Within seconds, Victor began to snicker. The snicker turned to a coughing laugh, and the coughing laugh, to genuine laughter. And within a quarter hour, The Beatles had their friend propped up on pillows and drinking tepid orange juice.[911]

"And thus," Victor finished Starr's fairytale for him, "with a little help from his talented friends, the old ogre recovered, happy ever after."

"To the livin' end!" John pronounced.

It was, indeed, a moment.

****

Friday, 19 March 1965
Hotel Edelweiss
Obertauern, Austria

The girls had been told not to expect their lads back until well after the dinner hour. The Beatles were slated for a long day of filming ahead, followed by an 8.00 p.m. telephone interview with their old friend, Brian Matthew.[912] Matthew had taken a shine to the four back in their early days, when being asked on Matthew's "Saturday Club" was a genuine thrill. So tonight, he'd been asked to capture The Beatle's phone conversation for the BBC.

"We really ought to rename it the 'Beatles Broadcasting Company,'"[913] Matthew had once quipped. But these days, *only* the BBC saw things that way. Trying his best to appease the powerful corporation without overextending his boys, Eppy had conceded to a string of "convenient interviews," in lieu of personal appearances. This was one of them.[914]

"Telephone chats are a perfectly effortless way to keep everyone happy," Brian explained pedantically, over a hair-and-makeup breakfast. "You can sit in the luxury of your own hotel room…"

"…rather than relaxin' of an evenin'." John wasn't buying it.

"…or goin' down to the bar to chat up everyone else," George seconded.

"…or takin' in whatever the hell else is goin' on," John

relished the give-and-go banter.

But Brian had heard enough.

"You can sit in your room and do a *brief* interview," he spat, peevishly, "as a gracious show of goodwill, and you can play nice with the BBC…or we can all spend *months* acquitting ourselves from a slew of legal entanglements!"

"Yeah well, it's always one brief *somethin'* 'n that, isn't it?" John objected over buttered toast and currant jam. But all of them knew that protest was worthless. Complaining might make them feel better, but in the end, The Beatles would do what they were told. They always did.

By 8.00 a.m., Epstein's command of the four had been overtaken by Lester's. The director had the boys enacting a short scene out on the hotel terrace, whilst crowds of onlookers pressed ever closer. Every time "Cut!" was called, another parent requested that the boys sign another child's cast or autograph book.[915] Another mother asked them to "say a few words" to their "biggest fan," her pig-tailed daughter. And some self-important dignitary was always lurking, waiting for an autographed group photo. Some gawky teenager, who'd won a "Meet the Beatles" contest, lingered to present a plaque and get a "snap." Throughout the long day of "dos and redos," there wasn't one solitary moment of quiet. The Beatles were constantly on display.

It's fuggin' runnin' me ragged! John seethed. *Every fuggin' bit of it!!*

Over a far-too-short lunch break, he said as much to Ray Coleman. "Look, it's quite annoyin' when people turn 'round 'n say, 'But we *made you*, you ungrateful swine!' I mean, *they did,* in a way, but there's a limit, y' know, to what we're bound to do, as if it's a duty!"[916]

"Yes, I quite agree, of course." Coleman nodded. He nibbled at his *Tyrolean Gröstl*[917] and let John unburden himself.

"When I had black windows put in m' car, for example, a fan actually wrote to me 'n said, 'You're hidin', turnin' your back 'n runnin' from the very people who made you!' Well, I say, '*Rubbish!*' If I go to a shop down the road 'n buy a bunch of roses, I don't expect the bloke to be so grateful that he spends his life bowin' 'n scrapin' to me! I like roses, so I buy 'em, 'n *that's that*!"[918]

"True, it's certainly not a *quid pro quo* arrangement."

Coleman summed up the argument.

"Right," John sighed. "Look I don't want to sound as if we don't *like* bein' liked. We do, 'n we appreciate it! But we can't spend our lives bein' dictated to!"[919] John gnawed at the Austrian hot dog[920] — heavily slathered with spicy mustard — of which he'd become so fond. Chewing, he went on, "Listen, people pay six shillings 'n eight pence for a record. Because of *that*, do we have to do what they say, like a Jack-in-the-box!?"[921]

"Actors, on set, please!" a voice announced from some distant megaphone.

"Well, Coleman, it appears it's time for me to pop out o' the fuggin' box again!" John pushed his plate away. "Pop goes the weasel, son!" And pulling a face, John jumped to his feet, waggled his arms like a toy clown, and stomped off, back to work.

****

Fortunately, the last item on the day's diary wasn't another "brief something." After the lads' long-distance chat with Brian Matthew, Dick Lester — to fête the birthday of his assistant, Clive Reed — had generously scheduled an elaborate cast party, complete with tiers of lavish refreshments and a rather unique band.[922]

Never too weary to eat or gin out rock'n'roll, John brought out his guitar, and Paul commandeered the drums. After a couple of drinks, Dick Lester scrubbed up the courage to jump in and join the boys on piano. Whilst the film's Director of Photography, David Watkin, snapped personal photos, the gig was on![923] In a two-hour extemporaneous show that included Cavern favourites such as "Young Blood" and "Summertime," Lester, Lennon, and McCartney got the room on its feet.[924]

Cynthia danced with Pattie and Maureen, and over her shoulder she sent her coy "come hither" glances to her husband. But sweating in his party suit, John barely noticed. He was lost in a passion he'd almost forgotten, captivated by rock'n'roll.

John had hastily loosened his tie and unbuttoned his shirt, and he sang with a recklessness Cyn hadn't seen in ages. He shouted insults to the audience, Scouse style. He began songs and heedlessly abandoned them, half-way through. He screamed and shook his wet hair and revived the old *mach schau*. Everything that Brian had taught The Beatles *not* to do, John did.

Tonight, there wasn't a single "Thank you very much." There wasn't one "For our next song, we'd like to…" There wasn't a single bow from the waist. Tonight, John was John. The Jack-in-box jumped, but only when he pleased.

Notes!

Pattie Boyd is mentioned as being on this Austrian sojourn with Cynthia and Maureen. However, Pattie isn't included in the official photos in London Airport. Was she present?

Although Pattie does not cover this holiday with George in Wonderful Tonight, *she was there. Please take a look at these photos of Pattie Boyd in Austria with George and the others:*

https://tinyurl.com/uusuh6h This is Pattie waiting to board the plane for Austria with the group.

https://tinyurl.com/rqxp394 This is Pattie and George playing cards in the lunchroom set up for the cast and crew at Hotel Edelweiss.

https://tinyurl.com/t9afza3 This is Pattie with Cynthia and Maureen at Hotel Edelweiss.

Note: There is a photo of Maureen, Cynthia, and Pattie in the back seat of a limo together in Stokes's The Beatles, *p. 154. It is probable that this shot was taken on this particular day.*

Sources:

Lewisohn, The Complete Beatles Chronicle, *29 and 186.*
Lewisohn, The Beatles: Day by Day, *60.*
Harry, The Ultimate Beatles Encyclopedia, *299.*
Miles, The Beatles' Diary, Vol. 1, *191.*
Barrow, *62.*
Womack, Maximum Volume: The Life of Beatles Producer, George Martin, *216.*
Coleman, The Man Who Made The Beatles, *215.*
Coleman, Lennon, *256 and 258.*
Howlett, The Beatles at the BBC, *67.*
Yule, *102.*

Badman, 144-145.

Pawlowski, How They Became The Beatles, *69.*

Greenwald, 104.

Carr, 59.

Bicknell, 34.

Schultheiss, 130.

Riley, Lennon, *271.*

Trynka, 166.

Stokes, The Beatles, *54.*

Freeman, 139. Bob Freeman captured a great photo of Ringo's stunt double as Paul, John, George, and Rick Dillon are posed atop a sled grinning for the camera.

https://www.beatlesbible.com/1965/03/13/travel-london-austria/ I used all of the pages in Beatles Bible pertaining to The Beatles' time in Austria.

http://www.beatlesarchive.net/the-beatles-filming-help-in-obertauern-austria-in-march-1965.html Many photos of The Beatles in Obertauern, Austria are found here.

https://www.tapatalk.com/groups/solobeatlesphotosforum/13-march-1965-london-austria-salzburg-obertauern-t6803.html Many photos of The Beatles, plus Maureen Starkey and Cynthia Lennon, leaving London Airport, can be found here.

https://www.blog.tirol/en/2014/12/tyrolean-groestl-the-original-recipe-to-try-at-home/ This website has information on the Austrian dish Ray Coleman was eating, Tyrolean Gröstl.

https://tinyurl.com/rqc4nv3\ This site gives additional information on Ringo's stunt double, Mick Dillon.

https://simkl.com/tv/6835/whats-my-line/season-15/episode-46/ This site provides information about Gloria Mackh, The Beatles' Austrian ski instructor.

https://tinyurl.com/vvgp9b3
This is an excellent pre-war photograph of Hotel Edelweiss.

https://www.luerzer.at/en/hotel-obertauern/sporthotel-edelweiss/home/ Additional information on Hotel Edelweiss, Obertauern, and Austria can be found here. There are also photos of the hotel today.

https://en.wikipedia.org/wiki/The_Sound_of_Music
This site gives information about the 1965 box office hit "The Sound of Music," filmed in Salzburg, Austria.

https://www.bing.com/videos/search?q=beatles+arriving+salzburg+aust ria&view=detail&mid=F52C86FDF44A0D6F3A9BF52C86FDF44A0D6F 3A9B&FORM=VIRE This is a video of The Beatles landing at Salzburg Airport and being driven to Hotel Österreichisher Hof for their press conference.
Or use this QR code:

Photos used for accurate descriptions:

https://tinyurl.com/uy6h7cl This is a photo of John eating a hot dog on the set of "Help!" in Austria.

https://www.imdb.com/title/tt0059260/fullcredits This is the complete IMDb listing for the United Artists cast and crew of "Help!"

https://tinyurl.com/vjtem8k2 This is a photo of The Beatles with their stunt doubles for "Help!" George's stunt double is not in the photo, but George is.

Video of The Beatles in Austria making "Help!":

https://www.youtube.com/watch?v=yobxwD1G_aE This video of The Beatles in Austria. It also includes shots from the filming on Salisbury Plain.
Or use this QR code:

---

855 Bicknell, 34. Alf says he "did the run around, picking the boys up again." He goes on to say, "They are off to do some skiing for the film."
856 The presence of Pattie Boyd isn't mentioned in any of the biographies on The Beatles, but two photos of her at London Aiport and boarding the plane

for this trip can be found here:
https://www.tapatalk.com/groups/solobeatlesphotosforum/13-march-1965-london-austria-salzburg-obertauern-t6803.html Many other photos were found at the end of the chapter. She was clearly with Cynthia and Maureen throughout the trip.

[857] https://en.wikipedia.org/wiki/The_Sound_of_Music London's highly acclaimed and popular West End production of "The Sound of Music" had opened at the Palace Theatre in 1961. In the autumn of 1965, the film of "The Sound of Music" would be released with Julie Andrew and Christopher Plummer. For more information on places in Salzburg where the movie was filmed, go to: https://www.sound-of-music.com/experience-salzburg/the-city-of-salzburg/

[858] Lewisohn, *The Complete Beatles Chronicle*, 186, Harry, *The Ultimate Beatles Encyclopedia,* 299, and Miles, *The Beatles' Diary, Vol. 1*, 191.

[859] Harry, *The Ultimate Beatles Encyclopedia*, 299.

[860] Lewisohn, *The Complete Beatles Chronicle*, 186, Miles, *The Beatles' Diary, Vol. 1*, 191, and https://www.beatlesbible.com/1965/03/13/travel-london-austria/

[861] Trynka, 166 and https://www.youtube.com/watch?v=QGSg5EixJaA. This short video of The Beatles landing in Austria has sound. You can see the perturbed "Beatles Go Home!" contingent in this one.

[862] https://www.youtube.com/watch?v=Lv4AObEcOcE There is no sound on this longer video of The Beatles arriving in Austria.

[863] https://www.youtube.com/watch?v=QGSg5EixJaA

[864] https://www.youtube.com/watch?v=Lv4AObEcOcE You can see the reporters surging towards The Beatles here.

[865] https://www.youtube.com/watch?v=Lv4AObEcOcE

[866] https://tinyurl.com/vvgp9b3 This is an image of the hotel during its heyday.

[867] https://en.wikipedia.org/wiki/Salzburg

[868] Miles, *The Beatles' Diary, Vol. 1*, 191, Lewisohn, *The Complete Beatles Chronicle*, 186, and https://www.beatlesbible.com/1965/03/13/travel-london-austria/

[869] You can see these details in the chapter photos and in this video: https://www.youtube.com/watch?v=Lv4AObEcOcE

[870] https://www.youtube.com/watch?v=Lv4AObEcOcE

[871] https://www.youtube.com/watch?v=Lv4AObEcOcE You can see Paul signing the little girl's cast in this video.

[872] https://www.luerzer.at/en/hotel-obertauern/sporthotel-edelweiss/home/ This is the current website for Hotel Edelweiss, and the pictures are of the renovated lodge. But the description of the hotel as a "sport hotel" was as accurate in 1965 as it is today.

[873] https://www.edelweiss-obertauern.at/en Although the décor is new, the fireplaces and beams have not changed since 1965.

[874] https://www.luerzer.at/en/hotel-obertauern/sporthotel-edelweiss/home/

[875] https://www.barrypopik.com/index.php/new_york_city/entry/how_do_you_eat_an_elephant This expression was first credited to Frank Cody in 1921, but it

became very popular in the 1940s and 1950s, when it was thought to be a Chinese proverb.

[876] Trynka, 166. Trynka spells her name as "Gloria Makk." On many websites and when she appeared on the 1960s TV show "What's My Line?" (Season 15, Episode 46), she spelled her name "Mackh." To see the "What's My Line?" program where she explains her role at The Beatles' ski instructor for "Help!" go to: https://simkl.com/tv/6835/whats-my-line/season-15/episode-46/

[877] Miles, The Beatles' Diary, Vol. 1, 191. Barry Miles states, "Paul turned out to be very good on skiis and was said, by his instructor, to have the makings of a professional."

[878] Owen, Alun, line from the screenplay of "A Hard Day's Night," United Artists Films, 1964.

[879] Lewisohn, The Complete Beatles Chronicle, 186 and https://www.imdb.com/title/tt0059260/fullcredits. To see John with his stunt double and ascertain the degree of "similitude," go to: https://tinyurl.com/ueqw8qm

[880] Lewisohn, The Complete Beatles Chronicle, 186 and https://www.imdb.com/title/tt0059260/fullcredits

[881] https://tinyurl.com/rqc4nv3 This is a photo of Ringo and his stunt double, Mick Dillon.

[882] https://www.imdb.com/name/nm0227042/bio This webpage supplies more information on Mick Dillon, Ringo's double.

[883] Lewisohn, The Complete Beatles Chronicle, 186. Lewisohn additionally tells us that on this day, The Beatles also filmed "a toboggan hire sequence" that wasn't used in the film. They also filmed a shot of themselves falling backwards into the snow.

[884] Harry, The Ultimate Beatles Encyclopedia, 300.

[885] Lewisohn, The Complete Beatles Chronicle, 186.

[886] Ringo is referring here to The Beatles' performance in Jacksonville, FL just after Hurricane Dora in September 1964. Ringo's podium had been secured to the stage with lines and he had performed in 40-mile-an-hour winds. This event is covered in detail in Vol. 4 in **The John Lennon Series**, Should Have Known Better, pp. 539-547. Also, see Chuck Gunderson's remarkable work, Some Fun Tonight!, Vol. 1, 223 and A. J. Rayl's very thorough work, Beatles '64: A Hard Day's Night in America, 184.

[887] https://en.wikipedia.org/wiki/Home_Thoughts_from_Abroad Browning, Robert, "Home, Thoughts From Abroad," written in Italy in 1845 and included in his collection of poetry, Dramatic Romances and Lyrics. To read the poem, go to: https://www.bartleby.com/246/647.html

[888] According to the 22 September 2015 Liverpool Echo article "12 Reasons Liverpool is Ireland's second capital," the city achieved that nickname in the 1800s "…because of the huge numbers of Irish immigrants to the city. In 1851, there were more than 83,000 Irish-born people recorded in the Liverpool census return – 22% of the population. As many had large families, their proportion of the city's population was probably closer to 50%."

[889] Harry, The Ultimate Beatles Encyclopedia, 300.

[890] Harry, The Ultimate Beatles Encyclopedia, 300.

[891] Lewisohn, *The Complete Beatles Chronicle*, 186, Miles, *The Beatles' Diary, Vol. 1*, 191, and https://www.beatlesbible.com/1965/03/17/filming-help-19/. Additionally, in *Maximum Volume: The Life of Beatles Producer, George Martin,* author Ken Womack tells us that "Eight Arms to Hold You" was not the only title considered at this stage. He lists "...Lester's suggestion of calling the feature film *Beatles 2,* Harrison's tongue-in-cheek suggestion of *Who's Been Sleeping in My Porridge,* and Shenson's oddly forlorn recommendation of *The Day the Clowns Collapsed."* (p. 257)

[892] Harry, *The Ultimate Beatles Diary,* 299, Greenwald, Ted, *The Beatles Companion,* 104, Carr, 59, Trynka, 162, and Coleman, *The Man Who Made The Beatles,* 215. Coleman says that "Help!" cost £400,000 and Trynka agrees with this number. Carr says that "Help!" had "a production budget of £500,000 or approximately one million dollars."

[893] Badman, 144.

[894] Badman, 144.

[895] Badman, 144.

[896] Norman, *Shout!,* 255.

[897] Coleman, *Lennon,* 256. Coleman (like Art Schreiber before him on the 1964 North American Tour) said that John loved discussing politics and philosophy.

[898] Miles, *The Beatles' Diary, Vol. 1,* 191.

[899] Miles, *The Beatles' Diary, Vol. 1,* 191.

[900] Miles, *The Beatles' Diary, Vol. 1,* 191.

[901] Miles, *The Beatles' Diary, Vol. 1,* 191.

[902] Miles, *The Beatles' Diary, Vol. 1,* 191.

[903] Miles, *The Beatles' Diary, Vol. 1,* 26, Pawlowski, Gareth, *How They Became The Beatles,* 69, and Lewisohn, *The Complete Beatles Chronicle,* 29. Pawlowski says that the fans, on this night, "surged the stage" for the first time in Beatles history. And Mark Lewisohn states, "If any one live performance in The Beatles' career could be described to be the turning point, it would be this, their penultimate engagement in 1960. Their career was not without hiccups in the future, but really, the group never looked back after this night."

[904] Womack, *Maximum Volume: The Life of Beatles Producer, George Martin,* 256 and Margotin and Guesdon, 216. Years later, George Martin is quoted as saying, "Dick Lester and I didn't hit it off well on 'A Hard Day's Night,' and the fact that I got an Academy Award nomination for musical direction didn't help."

[905] Badman, 145. This is the first line of a group interview that Ray Coleman conducted in March 1965 in Obertauern, Austria for *Melody Maker.* He had recorded an extensive interview with Paul McCartney prior to this, but when the other Beatles joined Paul, Coleman recorded this short conversation. I'm not going to endnote every line, but will endnote again at the end.

[906] Badman, 145. This is the last line of the group interview that Ray Coleman conducted in March 1965 in Obertauern, Austria for *Melody Maker.*

[907] Barrow, 62 and Riley, *Lennon,* 271. Riley sets this incident in the Bahamas.

[908] Barrow, 62 and Riley, *Lennon,* 271. Barrow called it a "flu-like bug that had kept [Spinetti] in his hotel bed for days."

[909] Riley, *Lennon,* 271.

[910] Barrow, 62.

[911] Barrow, 62. Barrow says, "Spinetti roared with laughter and later credited Ringo with speeding along his recovery."

[912] Lewisohn, *The Complete Beatles Chronicle*, 186, Miles, *The Beatles' Diary*, Vol. 1, 191, and https://www.beatlesbible.com/1965/03/19/filming-help-21/ Goodden on BeatlesBible.com calls this "the penultimate day of filming in Austria." The lads were indeed busy from 6.30 a.m. to midnight.

[913] Howlett, *The Beatles at the BBC*, 67. Several employees of the BBC take credit for this quote. It was a well-circulated pun.

[914] Lewisohn, *The Complete Beatles Chronicle*, 186 and Howlett, *The Beatles at the BBC,* 67.

[915] Miles, *The Beatles' Diary, Vol. 1*, 191.

[916] Coleman, *Lennon*, 258. Direct quote from John Lennon.

[917] https://www.blog.tirol/en/2014/12/tyrolean-groestl-the-original-recipe-to-try-at-home/ This is the classic Austrian ski lunch. To see a photo and get the recipe, use the link provided.

[918] Coleman, *Lennon*, 258. Direct quote from John Lennon.

[919] Coleman, *Lennon*, 258. Direct quote from John Lennon.

[920] This is a photo of John eating a hot dog on the set of "Help!" in Austria https://tinyurl.com/uy6h7cl

[921] Coleman, Lennon, 258.

[922] Miles, *The Beatles' Diary, Vol. 1*, 191 and Yule, 102. Yule quotes Lester as saying that years later, Reed confided to him that the party "was one of the highlights of his life." Miles says that "The Beatles gave a party for the cast and crew," but Yules states that it was given by Lester for Clive Reed.

[923] Trynka, 166.

[924] Trynka, 166.

Sunday, 21 March 1965
Hotel Edelweiss
Obertauern, Austria

John awoke to the unseasonal Christmastide sound of church bells pealing and echoing, despite the early hour.

"What's the time?" John sat up, raking a hand across his face.

"Only 10.00 a.m., luv," Cynthia mumbled, pulling her husband back under the satin duvet. "Go back to sleep. It's your one and only day off."

Lester had taken the cast and crew over to Radstadt Station for the morning, and later this afternoon, they were filming in a tunnel route to Salzburg.[925] But happily, The Beatles weren't required. The boys were given one entire day to rest, eat, and do exactly as they pleased.

"I've been thinkin' 'bout Pete," John got up and pulled the curtains tighter, blocking the shine of sun-off-snow.

"Shennon, you mean?" Cynthia smiled, snuggling into her pillow. John and his childhood mate, Peter Shotton, had become so notoriously inseparable in Quarry Bank Grammar that the duo had earned the unholy moniker "Shennon and Lotton."[926]

"Yeah," John sat on the edge of the bed and drained the last from the hotel's crystal water tumbler. "Shennon. I hadn't heard *that one* in forever."

"Why're you awake and traipsing down memory's path?" Cyn yawned.

"The market opened yesterday.[927] Big ceremony 'n all that."

"Ah, the Hayling Supermarket." Cynthia rolled towards John and stroked his arm. "It was lovely of you to do that, John. You're a true friend."[928]

"Well, it's a great shop, y' know…with its own post office, food 'n drink area…even a hardware section, as it were![929] 'N besides…Pete would've done the same for me, if things were the other way 'round." John crawled back under the thick, luxurious covers. "''N Pete's a born entrepreneur. He worked hard at the Old Dutch caff,[930] 'n he'll be even more remarkable as a store owner. It's a great investment, as it were."

"*Investment*?" Cynthia propped up on one arm, the cold air of the room invading her bundle of sheets and blankets. "So…you stand to make a bit on the venture, then?"

"Not really. I mean, I just kicked in the £20,000 to get the store for Pete," John pushed his pillow further under his neck, "but I mean, it's all his. George 'n me are listed as 'directors' of Hayling Supermarkets, Ltd., but in reality, that's…well, it's just our promise to stand behind Pete — not somethin' for either of us, as it were." John was honest with his wife. The world would hear nothing of his role in the Hayling venture; he'd mention it to no one.

"Besides, y' know, me 'n Pete…I'm invested in what he does, 'n he feels the same. He's always been there for me — especially when Uncle Ge'rge passed…'n when m' mum…"

A strained silence.

"I know." Cynthia's brow furrowed. She hurt to see John still so wounded by Julia's loss. She doubted that the jagged, raw scars would ever vanish. Even now, she saw her husband clutching at drugs as an escape, a way to forget. But Cynthia clung stubbornly to the hope that she could heal him, eventually, with unconditional love.[931] She threw an arm across his chest and kissed the base of his neck. "And if memory serves, Pete was also the very first member of your very first band…your one and only washboard player, right?"[932]

"Yeah, back in the good ole Black Jack 'n Quarry Men days."[933]

"Way back when." Cynthia snuggled against John — her head on his chest. She yawned again, and so did he. "Tell me the story…" she sorted through her favourite tales, deciding which to resurrect as a curative. "Tell me the story of the time that you and Pete decided to 'swear off swearing.'"[934] She closed her eyes, giving John her complete attention.

"You've heard it a hundred times, Powell."

"Humour me. Make it a hundred and one."

"Yerrokay." John pretended to sigh, but began the story

anyway. "Well, as near as I can recall, we were like 10 or 11, somewhere in there.[935] Maybe it was Lent or somethin' like that, but I had this streak of conscience, I suppose, 'n I decided we needed to stop swearin'."

"Ummmhmmm…"

"I told Pete, I said, 'We're so used to swearin' that we might start comin' out with it in front of our parents. I might just be havin' me tea and suddenly go, 'Pass the fuggin' salt, Mimi.' 'N I'd be in right fuggin' trouble then!'"[936]

No matter how many times she heard it, the yarn made Cynthia grin. She did, and John gained momentum.

"So, I said, 'What say we have a bet with each other, yeah? Stake each other a toffee apple, as it were?' 'N Pete — who loved sweets as much as I did — was in!"[937]

"And?" Cynthia was the perfect "straight man."

"'N the next two hours were spent in *dead fuggin' silence*. We couldn't talk, could we? Tryin' to communicate with one another without bein' who we were! It was like spendin' the day with your fuggin' parents, y' know!"[938]

"On your very best behaviour," Cynthia murmured.

"Right." John yawned. "So finally, I threw up me hands 'n said, 'Fuck it! I can't be bothered with this nonsense anymore! Let's go back to normal!'"[939]

"Making Pete the winner of the bet, then?"

"Yeah, but I don't recall ever payin' up. I mean, he was so fuggin' *relieved* that he never even asked me! It'd almost ruined us both — that bet."

"Well, I hope the distinguished owner and manager of Hayling Supermarkets can do without his…uhm, colourful language when the customers are about," Cynthia teased.

"Y' mean the way John Lennon does in press conferences 'n radio interviews?" John scratched one bushy eyebrow and yawned once more.

"Precisely."

"Well, one does what one has to do, Powell." John tugged the covers higher around his neck, "'n right now, one has to fuggin' rest."

"Right, Mr. Director, sir."

And wandering back through carefree days on the Tip and warm, sunny afternoons with Pete — riding bikes down the tree-lined dual carriageway of Menlove Avenue or climbing the stone wall at Strawberry Field — John drifted from memory to memory and gradually, to sleep.[940]

Notes!

In his book, John Lennon: In My Life, *Pete tells the story of John's purchase of the Hayling Supermarket in full detail. He notes that John had promised to bankroll any business venture that Pete wanted to try, but Pete "had yet to find anything suitable." (p. 99) Then, over the Christmas holidays 1964, Pete and his wife Beth spent some time with Pete's "sister Jean and her husband Frank in Fareham, near the south coast of England." (p. 99)*

Pete goes on to say: "After several days of lounging around the house, I grew slightly restless, and decided to go into Fareham for (of all things!) a haircut — the haircut, as it turned out, that changed my life. Upon emerging from the barber's, I happened to spot a business transfer agency nearby, and impulsively popped in to see what they had to offer. Though I hadn't, thus far, even considered the possibility of going into business outside Liverpool, I thought it might be mildly instructive to learn what was available...After ascertaining that I was looking for something in the range of £20,000, the agent launched into a lyrical description of a holiday trade supermarket, complete with sub-post office, on a place called Hayling Island." (p. 99)

Pete says that although he had never been "the least bit interested in supermarkets," for some reason, he took the information the agent handed him and brought the idea up to his brother-in-law at dinner that evening. Upon hearing about the opportunity, Frank was ecstatic. Pete writes: "'Hayling Island!' he exclaimed, '... It's a really neat little resort, with beaches and all the rest.'" (p. 99) And an idea had formed.

After checking out the property with his brother-in-law, Pete says: "I fell in love with Hayling Island...and announced: "This is it." (p. 99) He "rang up John's accountants, told them about the supermarket, and asked them to check the place out. A few days later, they returned the verdict that was a fine business, and that John and I could hardly hope for a better investment." (p. 99)

Over the next few weeks, the Hayling Supermarkets, Ltd. corporation was formed and by 18 March, Pete had a new career.

Although John would have funded any project that Pete was interested in, Bill Harry in The John Lennon Encyclopedia *wisely observes that "the supermarket was only an hour's drive from Weybridge" and says that Pete began regularly visiting John on the weekends. (p. 809)*

Pete states, "I was to spend all of my free weekends with John (unless, of course, he happened to be out of town on Beatle business). He even designated a special room for me at Kenwood: the Blue Room, so called for its uniformly blue wallpaper, furnishings, and decorations." (Shotton and Schaffner, p. 100)

Clearly, John's backing of Pete's new business venture didn't change the dynamics of their relationship. Pete states, "I never regarded myself as John's lackey. (He always despised mere hangers-on in any case.) Had our relationship not been grounded in mutual respect, it could hardly have flourished as it did for over three decades. We were, in short, one another's best mates." (Shotton and Schaffner, pp. 26-27) He goes on: "Indeed, John never allowed his status as a Beatle to interfere in any way with the rapport we had developed so many years earlier...our relationship was as firmly grounded as the Rock of Gibraltar." (p. 100)

Sources:

Lewisohn, The Complete Beatles Chronicle, *12.*
Lewisohn, The Beatles: Day by Day, *60.*
Harry, The Ultimate Beatles Encyclopedia, *606-608.*
Harry, The John Lennon Encyclopedia, *808-809.*
Harry, The Encyclopedia of Beatles People, *289-290.*
Harry, The John Lennon Encyclopedia, *809.*
Miles, The Beatles' Diary, Vol. 1, *191.*
Coleman, Lennon, *60 and 602.*
Davies, The Quarrymen, *109.*
Connolly, *195.*
Womack, The Beatles Encyclopedia, Vol. 2, *836.*
Shotton and Schaffner, *21, 26-27, 29, 51-52, and 99-100.*
Goldman, *191.*
Kane, Lennon Revealed, *55 and 58.*
Friede, Titone, and Wiener, *194.*

Tributes paid after John Lennon's best friend Pete Shotton passes away - Liverpool Echo This article from the Liverpool Echo *shows photos of John and Pete and discusses John's 1965 purchase of the Hayling Supermaket.*

18 March 1965 - Hayling Supermarkets - Beatles & Solo Photos & Videos Forum (tapatalk.com) This website briefly discusses John's purchase of the Hayling Supermarket and shows an excellent photo of it.

Absolute Elsewhere: The Spirit of John Lennon | Articles: My Friend John
This website provides a wonderful article from Beatles biographer Hunter
Davies on the relationship between John and Pete.

---

[925] Lewisohn, *The Complete Beatles Chronicle*, 186 and Miles, *The Beatles' Diary, Vol. 1*, 191.

[926] Shotton and Schaffner, 21, Womack, *The Beatles Encyclopedia*, 836, and Harry, *The John Lennon Encyclopedia*, 808,

[927] Miles, *The Beatles' Diary, Vol. 1*, 191. Miles tells us that Pete Shotton's Hayling Supermarket opened on 18 March 1965.

[928] Lewisohn, *The Beatles: Day by Day*, 60, Miles, *The Beatles' Diary, Vol. 1*, 191, Shotton and Schaffner, 99-100, Harry, *The Encyclopedia of Beatles People*, 289, Harry, *The Ultimate Beatles Encyclopedia*, 607, and Harry, *The John Lennon Encyclopedia*, 809. Hayling Supermarkets Ltd., located on the summer resort of Hayling Island, Hampshire, was to be managed by Pete Shotton. The corporation's directors were listed as Peter Shotton, John Lennon, and George Harrison. In his book, Pete Shotton tells the complete story of his purchase of the supermarket. He says that John was eager to make good on the "new life that John had so magnanimously promised to bankroll." In purchasing the Hayling store for Pete, John did just that.

[929] Davies, *The Quarrymen*, 109. Also on this page, Pete Shotton comments that John kept insisting that Pete find some business that he could purchase for his friend. Pete states, "He said money was raining on him, so it was about time I had something that would make money for me. I should find something really good. Something around £20,000."

[930] One of Pete's earliest jobs, after he left the Liverpool Police force, was working in the Old Dutch Café on Smithdown Road, Woolton. In Liverpool, it was fondly referred to as "the Ol' Dutch caff." By the late 60s, it became a biker hang-out known as "Dutch Eddies." When my husband and I visited Liverpool in 1993, I was driving Smithdown Road when I spotted it. Here is the Old Dutch in 1993:

The Old Dutch Café 1993
Photograph used by kind permission of Rande Kessler

931 Kane, *Lennon Revealed*, 55 and 58. Kane, who was particularly close to John in 1964 and 1965, said that John repeatedly told him that Cynthia was "a source of great stability" and "an enormous source of strength." (p. 58)
932 Lewisohn, *The Complete Beatles Chronicle*, 12, Shotton and Schaffner, 51-52, Harry, *The John Lennon Encyclopedia*, 808, Harry, *The Ultimate Beatles Encyclopedia,* 606-607, Womack, *The Beatles Encyclopedia, Vol. 2,* 836, Coleman, *Lennon*, 60, and Pawlowski, 6.
933 Lewisohn, *The Complete Beatles Chronicle*, 12, Shotton and Schaffner, 51-52, Harry, *The John Lennon Encyclopedia*, 808, Harry, *The Ultimate Beatles Encyclopedia,* 606-607, Womack, *The Beatles Encyclopedia, Vol. 2,* 836, Coleman, *Lennon*, 60, Brown, 23, and Pawlowski, 6. It is interesting to note that in his book, Pete Shotton never mentions the Black Jacks. The first name

Pete links with a "band" including John and himself is the Quarry Men (two words, not one).

[934] Shotton and Schaffner, 26.

[935] Shotton and Schaffner, 26.

[936] Shotton and Schaffner, 26. Direct quote from John Lennon.

[937] Shotton and Schaffner, 26.

[938] Shotton and Schaffner, 26.

[939] Shotton and Schaffner, 26. Direct quote from John Lennon.

[940] Shotton and Schaffner, 29.

Wednesday, 24 March 1965
Twickenham Studios
London

The Beatles had every reason to be impressed. Twickenham Studios — their indoor location for both "A Hard Day's Night" and now "Eight Arms to Hold You" — was the best London had to offer. Founded in 1913 as St. Margaret's Studios, it was the largest facility of its kind in the city.[941] Housed in a former skating rink, Twickenham — the brainchild of Dr. Ralph Jupp — was a mammoth building, equipped with state-of-the-art film production capabilities, as well as an impressive art department and superb prop and costume stores.[942] The studio was, undeniably, Beatles-worthy.

But John, Paul, George, and Ringo were insensible to the fact that the historic studio, from Day One, had always been a cut above. (In fact, Twickenham's very first film had starred the august Ivor Novello,[943] whose memorial award for entertainment excellence the boys had captured in 1964.)[944] The Beatles saw their days in Twickenham as mere "drudge work." And today was no exception.

Promptly at 8.30 a.m.,[945] the boys blocked and then filmed an escape scene inside "the Temple" in which they found themselves inadvertently trapped beneath ground — near the dreaded sacrificial altar.[946] Urged by their secret ally Ahme (Eleanor Bron) to plunge inside the ornate, water-filled altar and swim to safety, John had held his nose and charmingly quipped, "I can't swim!" But "swim," he was compelled to do. And the four hapless boys were rapidly closed inside the ornate, holy table, only seconds before Clang and his blood-thirsty henchmen swarmed into the cave-like room.

Had Lester taken the time, he could have explained to The

Beatles that the very first day's filming, weeks ago in Nassau, had been the completion of this very adventure. When The Beatles — rather miraculously — had emerged, topside, in a resort hotel swimming pool, they had been surfacing from *this* "great escape" inside the Temple.

Unfortunately, the director, always fixated on making "Eight Arms to Hold You" better than "A Hard Day's Night,"[947] was far too preoccupied with his own challenges to connect the dots for the boys. So, The Beatles had no concept of how their assorted scenes were interlaced. Working without any tangible comprehension of the plot, the four lacked "buy-in." They only worked because they were prompted to do so; there was no enthusiasm involved.

As John had confided, days earlier, to Ray Coleman, "…it's like doin' *nothin'* most of the time but still havin' to rise at 7.00 a.m. We've all become fuggin' bored!"[948]

"Yeah," Paul had nodded agreement, "we're just not motivated, really. I'm not sure anyone even knows the script. We try to learn it on the way to the studio, but…"[949] He took a drag on his cig and drifted away.

"'N if we don't…" Ringo had shrugged, "we don't."

Initially, the boys had been minimally interested in the new project; whilst on location, they'd seemed to enjoy it. But here — back in their customary London *milieu* — they were jaded. Dead creased.

Typical filming at Twickenham Studios, 1960s
Photograph from Wikimedia Commons

****

Sunday, 28 March 1965
Alpha Television Studios
Aston, Birmingham

Sundays were no excuse, anymore, for lying in. Almost as if Brian hoped to swill out the memory of the boys' one day off in Austria, he now pressed them into a gust of activity.

They'd risen early for the trek with Alf Bicknell[950] up to Birmingham, where a rehearsal of the boys miming three taped songs — "Eight Days a Week," "Yes It Is," and "Ticket to Ride"[951]

— would be followed by the taping of their last personal appearance on *Thank Your Lucky Stars*.[952] Finally, to close the day, Paul and Ringo were to be interviewed by the show's host, Brian Matthew.

"Well, why not a skit or two thrown in as well?" John suggested snarkily to Eppy.

Epstein nervously brushed the back of his hand across his lips, ignoring the barb. "Let's leave that for another day, shall we?"

"*Hmpf*!" George monosyllabically sided with John.

The boys were unanimous; they'd had enough. But irked or not, The Beatles were in it. And as usual, they "turned to."

****

For a year now, Brian had refused to waiver on one steadfast rule: NEMS would "accept no bookings for audience shows of any sort, due to problems of crowd control."[953] Over at the BBC, Don MacLean was well-aware of this imperative. But today, MacLean had swept aside the order, and Epstein was forced into concord.[954] Because sitting on the Alpha Television Studio stage, almost on top of The Beatles, (on a four-tiered bleacher draped with a black-and-white striped skirt) were well over 100 fans.[955] Winners of a *Birmingham Mail* contest,[956] these fortunate "Beatlemaniacs," as they were now being labeled, roosted only feet from John, Paul, and George, and only inches from Ringo.[957]

"A bit too close for comfort," George muttered, disconcertedly, as he entered the studio.

"Norra bit good," Mal scrutinized the ecstatic group of bedecked, perfumed girls and enthusiastic, suited young men and shook his head.

"We'll keep them at arm's length, boys." Neil sounded confident. He was already formulating an escape plan. Thus far the fans were animated, but under control. *Thus far,* he thought as he strategized.

Wearing the traditional black suits, white shirts, and narrow black ties they'd always worn for studio travel, Ringo and Paul were clearly taken aback by the close-quartered throng. John, who had dressed down in a black turtleneck beneath his suit, stopped and stared. "Where'd *they* come from?" he swiveled to Neil.

"Oh, c'mon John," Neil tried to scrub it off, "surely y' know of the birds 'n the bees by now!"

But having survived rash, spontaneous stampedes during the 1964 North American Tour, Ringo refused to grin. The Beatles' eyes darted about uneasily, and only hesitantly did they move towards their microphones.

The boys had starred on *Thank Your Lucky Stars* eight times since their first happy appearance on 13 January 1963[958] — a fortuitous programme that had propelled them to television fame.[959] But with each show, the likelihood that one or all of the boys would be set upon had increased. Today, the immediate proximity of the fans made that eventuality seem all but inescapable. Ringo, especially, felt vulnerable; eyes wide, he offered thin grins as he situated himself on the rostrum.[960]

Grabbing his black-and-white Rickenbacker,[961] John strummed a few chords and tried to concentrate on the words to his songs. Remembering had always been his nemesis. When singing lyrics live, he was free to deviate. If he forgot a line of two, he could always repeat a verse or simply laugh and improvise. But miming to a record was altogether different. It required accuracy. John had to get the words right — and from the 1957 Woolton Garden Fête on, he'd rarely done so.[962]

Today, all three songs on the docket were his. The spotlight would be squarely on him. And though he relished the recognition of his talent, John was nervous. Singing from a raised stage yards and yards away from a rambunctious, screaming tour audience covered a multitude of sins. But singing straight into a camera was utterly unforgiving.

John was almost glad the *Birmingham Mail* fans were here, to draw at least *some* of the attention away from him. He pivoted and pulled a face at the punters, dancing and encouraging them to wave and wail. If the crowd was permitted to remain in place for the show's actual taping, his ruse might work. His devotees would be his cover.

****

The afternoon rehearsal session commenced with Brian in a swivet. Arriving to find George decked out in blue jeans and a tan cashmere jumper,[963] the manager had grown petulant. And when George had refused to respond to Epstein's ire, the NEMporer had accused the boy of "quiet defiance."

Brian wasn't far wrong.

The other three had complied with Eppy's expectations and had worn the requisite travel suits, but they, too, were aggrieved. Eight days ago — last Saturday — they'd spent eight hours filming in Austria. Later that evening, John and Ringo had been interviewed by Radio Luxembourg's popular host Chris Dennings for his programme, *The Beatles*. Then they'd taped a telephone interview with today's host, Brian Matthew.[964]

Only days later, they'd flown directly home to London and with a mere 24 hours' rest, they'd immediately jumped into the Twickenham scenes for "Eight Arms to Hold You," putting in a full day, every day. Now in the week ahead — by this Tuesday — their diary not only held filming but also a long evening in EMI as well, recording Paul's "That Means a Lot."[965]

The Beatles worked each weekday. They worked of a Saturday. They worked of a Sunday. Frequently, they worked twice a day. Sometimes, more.

And George, in faded jeans and a soft cashmere jumper, said it with conviction: the boys didn't like the drift their lives were taking. And it was time to do something about it.

****

The Birmingham crowd — though tightly wound and restive — seemed manageable. Girls held hands and jiggled about. They pointed and grabbed their faces. They sang and wept, but they remained seated.[966]

John, often cleverly swiveling his head from the camera to "sing" directly to the fans, amplified their shrieking. But still, the crowd seemed harmless enough.

One heavy-set, stern-faced mother in a blue suit and bright red floral hat, sat squarely between her two daughters. Her arms crossed and lips tight, she was ready to quell "any nonsense."[967]

A teacher on the front row — wearing low heels, glasses, and a sensible brown suit with white lapels — sat firmly cross-armed beside her giddy students.[968] She was prepared to stand in the gap, if need be. No harm would come to anyone.

To Paul's right, up on the second row, a rotund father perched proudly beside his lovely, brunette daughter. And smack in the middle of the front row, directly behind Ringo, a young mother in a chic sleeveless blouse sat beside her eight-year-old son, sporting his own "travel suit." The boy grinned and shook his hair, a mop proudly combed in a Beatle coif.[969]

It was an exuberant but innocuous crowd. However...

As The Beatles took a break and changed into matching black turtlenecks and double-breasted grey pin-striped suits, the crowd was changed as well.[970] The afternoon *Mail* winners were efficiently escorted out, and the evening's audience was escorted in.

This later crowd had nothing in common with the afternoon's younger, more sedate gathering. Comprised predominantly of unescorted teenagers — rabid fans — the evening audience was fervid from the moment they entered the room.

When John kicked off "Eight Days a Week," two girls on the far-right end of the first tier flew into jarring shrieks. They held hands and doubled at the waist, leaning as near to Lennon as they possibly could. They cried out in utter delirium.[971]

As Paul and George mimed close harmony with John on "Yes It Is," a young brunette in a red print dress and long, pointed, white collar, lifted an arm above her head and screeched devotion, whilst beside her, a skinny coed in dark hose and a short, tweed skirt sat mesmerized.[972] Ringo took it all in, glancing over his shoulder as two girls in Beatles sweatshirts flew into a frenzy.[973]

Mal watched the momentum building as well — observing closely as The Beatles' lip-synced under hot, glittering stage lights. The ABC cameras rolled in for close-ups, and for each ecstatic fan, fat monitors provided intimate glimpses of the boys. Mal felt the intensity mounting as John mouthed, "She's got a ticket to ride...but she don't care!!!!"

But it was Brian who first saw them take flight: three daredevil girls headed straight for Ringo: a strawberry blonde in a belted, floral dress and two fringed brunettes in dark hose and Beatles gear. The trio spanned the stage in an instant and were on top of

Ringo before anyone could counter.[974] By the time Brian strode onto the boards to protect his lads, John, Paul, and George had vanished. Indeed, as Mal and Neil wrangled with the assailants — tugging girls towards the stage wings — the other Beatles (guitars still around their necks) were almost to the dressing room.

And not heedlessly.

Following their three brash, female leaders, the Birmingham crowd swarmed the stage. Ten or fifteen fans forged a path towards the Dingle drummer, who huddled determinedly against his kit.[975] As stage security mobilized, photographers filled the floor, hungrily snapping the moment for tomorrow's press. And whilst Brian ruefully pinched his lips in "I-told-you-so" disgust, Mal swiftly returned to the boards, shepherding Ringo off to safety — to the Green Room where "his brothers" were already guffawing at his expense.

"Ringo for President!" Paul winked, as Ringo tumbled in.

"We love Ringo!!!" George crowed, doing his signature stomp dance.

"Ringooooooo!" John cupped his hand around his mouth and borrowed a line from the latest film.

The Beatles were busy turning fear into whistle-in-the-dark hysteria.

Collapsing onto a folding chair, Ringo nervously patted himself for a cig. "It's always *me*, isn't it?" His hands were shaking. "Knocked down in Sydney...knocked down in Dallas...singled out for that unsolicited haircut in the 'Ambassadors do'! Those girls 're 'goin' Bismarck,' out there!"

"Ah, givvus a kiss, Ringo!" John batted his eyelashes in the drummer's face.

"Gerroff, Lennon!" Ringo tossed him a backhanded V. "Sure, you've no worries...no one wants *you*!"

And though John cackled at the comeback, the zinger stung. For months, John had felt less popular than the others. Certainly, less appealing. There were more banners for Paul these days — a good many for Ringo as well. And on tour, George always had some luscious "tsart" on his arm.

But John felt fleshy and staid...not worth hurtling across a stage for. It had been a long time since a "baird" had recklessly flown at him, since he'd seen some desperate girl weeping his name. Pulling his famous Eccles face, he wiped down his Ric and tossed out swift retorts to the others. But sharply cutting his eyes towards the narrow Green Room mirror, John truly despised what he saw.[976]

Sources:

Lewisohn, The Complete Beatles Chronicle, *186-187.*
Lewisohn, The Beatles: Day by Day, *60.*
Harry, The Ultimate Beatles Encyclopedia, *648-649 and 671-672.*
The Beatles, The Beatles Anthology, *167.*
Howlett, 67-69.
Miles, The Beatles' Diary, *Vol. 1, 191-192.*
O'Donnell, Jim, The Day John Met Paul, *99.*
Bedford, David, Liddypool, *110.*
Womack, The Beatles Encyclopedia, *949-950.*
Spitz, 95.
Brown, 169.
Hill, John, Paul, George, & Ringo, *191.*
Schultheiss, 130.
Robertson, John, "Help! The End of the Beginning," Trynka, ed. The Beatles: Ten Years That Shook the World, *167.*
Bicknell, 36.

For information on Twickenham Studios:

https://www.visitrichmond.co.uk/thedms.aspx?dms=3&venue=3517770

https://thestudiomap.com/uk/listing/twickenham-studios/

https://www.yahoo.com/entertainment/news/twickenham-studios-home-beatles-silent-stars-hollywood-elite-120030240.html

For information on The Beatles receiving the Ivor Novello Award, 1964:

https://en.wikipedia.org/wiki/List_of_awards_and_nominations_received_by_the_Beatles

General chapter information:

Bentley, David, "Beatles in Birmingham," Birmingham Mail, 10 October 2014, found at https://www.birminghammail.co.uk/news/nostalgia/gallery/beatles-in-birmingham-7402830

https://www.beatlesbible.com/1965/03/28/television-thank-your-lucky-stars-8/ This webpage furnishes details of The Beatles' 28 March appearance on Thank Your Lucky Stars.

http://www.beatlesarchive.net/the-beatles-in-birmingham.html This website offers a synopsis of The Beatles' many visits to Birmingham, including the 1965 appearance on Thank Your Lucky Stars. Click on the link for the 1965 visit to see the excellent photo of the boys performing with the fans on the stage with them.

http://www.45spaces.com/the-beatles-on-tv/r.php?r=thd130717 Several good photos of the fans on the stage during the 28 March Thank Your Lucky Stars can be seen on this site.

https://www.youtube.com/watch?v=-tjHIFPTwVk For those of you unfamiliar with the character, Eccles, or "The Goon Show," one of John's favourite childhood programmes, you might enjoy this clip!

https://tinyurl.com/y4xu5xcl This is a video compilation of an excellent collection of colour photos from this last performance on Thank Your Lucky Stars.
Or use this QR code:

---

[941] Womack, *The Beatles Encyclopedia*, 949-950, Harry, *The Ultimate Beatles Encyclopedia*, 671-672, and https://www.visitrichmond.co.uk/thedms.aspx?dms=3&venue=3517770

[942] https://thestudiomap.com/uk/listing/twickenham-studios/ This website provides information about Twickenham Studios.

[943] https://www.yahoo.com/entertainment/news/twickenham-studios-home-beatles-silent-stars-hollywood-elite-120030240.html This website goes into greater detail on the history of Twickenham Studios.

[944] According to https://en.wikipedia.org/wiki/List_of_awards_and_nominations_received_by_t he_Beatles in 1964, The Beatles were nominated for three Ivor Novello Awards and won three. They won a "Special Award for Outstanding Services to British Music," and "She Loves You" captured the "Most Broadcast Work of the Year." They were nominated for "The Year's Outstanding Song" for "All My Loving," but failed to capture that prize.

[945] Lewisohn, *The Complete Beatles Chronicle*, 186-187.

[946] Lewisohn, *The Complete Beatles Chronicle*, 187.

[947] Brown, 169.

[948] The Beatles, *The Beatles Anthology*, 167.

[949] The Beatles, *The Beatles Anthology*, 167.

[950] Bicknell, 36.

[951] Lewisohn, *The Complete Beatles Chronicle*, 187, Miles, *The Beatles' Diary, Vol. 1*, 192, and https://www.beatlesbible.com/1965/03/28/television-thank-your-lucky-stars-8/

[952] Lewisohn, *The Complete Beatles Chronicle*, 187 and Harry, *The Ultimate Beatles Encyclopedia*, 648-649. These Beatle experts made a careful distinction here that this is The Beatles' last "personal appearance" on *Thank Your Lucky Stars*. In 1966, the boys do supply two taped promo clips for *Goodbye Lucky Stars*, the 25 June 1966 final episode of the programme. However, this March appearance is their last one in which the boys appeared in person.

[953] Howlett, Kevin, *The Beatles at the BBC*, 67.

[954] Howlett, Kevin, *The Beatles at the BBC*, 67-69. Direct quote from Brian Epstein from p. 67.

[955] https://www.bing.com/videos/search?q=Beatles+last+Thank+Your+Lucky+Stars+March+1965&docid=608032871924631337&mid=E7ED919569B8B0ED0A42E7ED919569B8B0ED0A42&view=detail&FORM=VIRE The number of fans may not be exact. You can see the *Thank Your Lucky Stars* fans in this video. I counted four rows of 14 fans behind The Beatles and four rows of 9-10 fans to Paul's right. There appear to be around 130 fans, but this number may be low.

[956] https://www.birminghammail.co.uk/news/nostalgia/gallery/beatles-in-birmingham-7402830 This article shows many appearances of The Beatles in Birmingham, but four of the photos are excellent shots of the boys on the 28 March *Thank Your Lucky Stars* programme.

[957] https://www.bing.com/videos/search?q=Beatles+last+Thank+Your+Lucky+Stars+March+1965&docid=608032871924631337&mid=E7ED919569B8B0ED0A42E7ED919569B8B0ED0A42&view=detail&FORM=VIRE This is an excellent compilation video of quite a few colour photos from The Beatles' final appearance on *Thank Your Lucky Stars* on 28 March 1965. You can see the raised platform on which the fans are seated in very close proximity to the boys.

[958] Harry, *The Ultimate Beatles Encyclopedia*, 648-649.

[959] Lewisohn, *The Complete Beatles Chronicle*, 187, Lewisohn, *Day by Day*, 11-12, and Miles, *The Beatles' Diary, Vol. 1*, 82. In his *Complete Beatles Chronicle*, Lewisohn states that the boys' first appearance on *Thank Your Lucky Stars* "launched [The Beatles] on national television."

[960] https://www.bing.com/videos/search?q=Beatles+last+Thank+Your+Lucky+Stars+March+1965&docid=608032871924631337&mid=E7ED919569B8B0ED0A42E7ED919569B8B0ED0A42&view=detail&FORM=VIRE

961

https://www.bing.com/videos/search?q=Beatles+last+Thank+Your+Lucky+St
ars+March+1965&docid=608032871924631337&mid=E7ED919569B8B0ED
0A42E7ED919569B8B0ED0A42&view=detail&FORM=VIRE
962 Lewisohn, *The Complete Beatles Chronicle*, 16, O'Donnell, Jim, *The Day
John Met Paul*, 99, Spitz, *The Beatles*, 95, and Bedford, David, *Liddypool*,
110. When Paul saw John on stage live for the first time at the Woolton
Garden Fête, John was singing what Spitz describes as "a mangled version" of
the Del Vikings' "Come Go with Me." Jim O'Donnell describes John's lyrics
that first day this way: "The teenager [John Lennon] didn't know the words, so
he makes some of them up. No one in the Quarry Men is surprised. His
bandmates never know what he is going to do next when he picks up a guitar."
963

https://www.bing.com/videos/search?q=Beatles+last+Thank+Your+Lucky+St
ars+March+1965&docid=608032871924631337&mid=E7ED919569B8B0ED
0A42E7ED919569B8B0ED0A42&view=detail&FORM=VIRE
964 Lewisohn, *The Complete Beatles Chronicle*, 186-187, Lewisohn, *The
Beatles: Day by Day*, 60, Miles, *The Beatles' Diary, Vol. 1*, 191, and
Schultheiss, 130.
965Lewisohn, *The Complete Beatles Chronicle*, 186-187, Lewisohn, *The
Beatles: Day by Day*, 60, Miles, *The Beatles' Diary, Vol. 1*, 191, and
Schultheiss, 130.
966

https://www.bing.com/videos/search?q=Beatles+last+Thank+Your+Lucky+St
ars+March+1965&docid=608032871924631337&mid=E7ED919569B8B0ED
0A42E7ED919569B8B0ED0A42&view=detail&FORM=VIRE
967

https://www.bing.com/videos/search?q=Beatles+last+Thank+Your+Lucky+St
ars+March+1965&docid=608032871924631337&mid=E7ED919569B8B0ED
0A42E7ED919569B8B0ED0A42&view=detail&FORM=VIRE
You can see this woman in the third row between Paul's left shoulder and
George's right shoulder in many of the photographs.
968

https://www.bing.com/videos/search?q=Beatles+last+Thank+Your+Lucky+St
ars+March+1965&docid=608032871924631337&mid=E7ED919569B8B0ED
0A42E7ED919569B8B0ED0A42&view=detail&FORM=VIRE
Again, this lady is over Paul's left shoulder on the bottom row.
969

https://www.bing.com/videos/search?q=Beatles+last+Thank+Your+Lucky+St
ars+March+1965&docid=608032871924631337&mid=E7ED919569B8B0ED
0A42E7ED919569B8B0ED0A42&view=detail&FORM=VIRE
The long-haired brunette daughter beside her father is in the second row on
Paul's right. She has on a white long-sleeved dress. You can't miss the young
mother and her eight-year-old son behind Ringo. They are front and centre.
You can also see the mother and son in a photograph (#02) on this website:
http://www.beatlesarchive.net/the-beatles-in-birmingham.html
970

https://www.bing.com/videos/search?q=Beatles+last+Thank+Your+Lucky+St

ars+March+1965&docid=608032871924631337&mid=E7ED919569B8B0ED
0A42E7ED919569B8B0ED0A42&view=detail&FORM=VIRE
971

https://www.bing.com/videos/search?q=Beatles+last+Thank+Your+Lucky+St
ars+March+1965&docid=608032871924631337&mid=E7ED919569B8B0ED
0A42E7ED919569B8B0ED0A42&view=detail&FORM=VIRE
972

https://www.bing.com/videos/search?q=Beatles+last+Thank+Your+Lucky+St
ars+March+1965&docid=608032871924631337&mid=E7ED919569B8B0ED
0A42E7ED919569B8B0ED0A42&view=detail&FORM=VIRE
973

https://www.bing.com/videos/search?q=Beatles+last+Thank+Your+Lucky+St
ars+March+1965&docid=608032871924631337&mid=E7ED919569B8B0ED
0A42E7ED919569B8B0ED0A42&view=detail&FORM=VIRE
974

https://www.bing.com/videos/search?q=Beatles+last+Thank+Your+Lucky+St
ars+March+1965&docid=608032871924631337&mid=E7ED919569B8B0ED
0A42E7ED919569B8B0ED0A42&view=detail&FORM=VIRE
975

https://www.bing.com/videos/search?q=Beatles+last+Thank+Your+Lucky+St
ars+March+1965&docid=608032871924631337&mid=E7ED919569B8B0ED
0A42E7ED919569B8B0ED0A42&view=detail&FORM=VIRE

976 Robertson, John, "Help! The End of the Beginning," Trynka, ed. *The Beatles: Ten Years That Shook the World*, 167. Robertson says that during the making of "Help!", John was enduring a period of "depressive self-analysis."

April 1965

Chart Toppers:

Freddie and the Dreamers - "I'm Telling You Now"
Wayne Fontana and the Mindbenders - "Game of Love"
Petula Clark - "I Know a Place"
The Kinks - "Tired of Waiting for You"
Herman's Hermits - "Mrs. Brown, You've Got A Lovely Daughter"

In the News

5 April: At the Academy Awards, "My Fair Lady" wins eight Oscars, including "Best Picture."

7 April: President Lyndon Johnson delivers his "Peace Without Conquest Speech," explaining U.S. military escalation in Vietnam.

9 April: The Beatles' song "Ticket to Ride" is released as a single in the U.K.

26 April: Manchester United wins England's football championship, breaking a standings tie with Leeds United.

29 April: Robert Menzies, Prime Minister of Australia, announces that he is sending troops to fight in the Vietnam War.[977]

Saturday, 3 April 1965[978]
The Home of John Riley
2 Strathearn Place, Hyde Park[979]
Bayswater
London

It was a social obligation and the last thing any of them wanted to do on a Saturday night. In fact, although John Riley[980] — who catered exclusively to London's "beautiful people" — was their dentist,[981] he was truly only George's friend.[982] Moreover, John, Cynthia, Pattie, *and* George had all heard rather disturbing rumours about the man[983] — intimations that he and his girlfriend, Cyndy Bury[984] (who carefully chose the girls for London's Playboy Club),[985] were involved in kinky sex and orgies.[986] The Beatles and their ladies had accepted Riley's dinner invitation with a healthy amount of reserve and suspicion.

"I thought we were after seeing Klaus's new trio down at the Pickwick,"[987] John piped up from the back seat of the new, orange Mini, Pattie's birthday "prezzie" from George.[988]

"We are. We still are!" George nodded, motoring Pattie's "baby" carefully through the posh London suburb of Bayswater. Once more, he double-checked the address he'd scribbled on a torn paper bag and leaned out the car window,[989] trying to read the nine-foot-high, iron street signs. "We'll leave right after the meal, yeah? I mean, the band doesn't even start 'til 10, does it?"[990]

"Well, regardless," Cynthia injected a positive note, "it's a lovely evening and a gorgeous neighbourhood — I adore this part of town: the manicured gardens, the fountains, the old brick high-rises."

"Well, at the prices our host charges to make *us* appear presentable," Pattie giggled and wrinkled her nose, "the *whole evening* should be absolutely flawless!"

"Yeah, right." John leaned forward, squinting — peering at the iron-railed Victorian buildings towering around them.[991]

Since The Beatles, these days, were photographed constantly and closely, they'd become extremely conscious of their teeth. Being a model, Pattie had always paraded a stunning smile, but the others had recently invested in a bit of Riley's acclaimed cosmetic work.[992]

"Here we are." George slowed the vehicle. "Strathearn Place.[993] Now, if only we can luck into a parking slot."

And ten minutes later — including a short stroll — the four stood nervously outside the painted hardwood door of #2. George glanced at the others, shrugged, and rang the bell.

****

"Haven't seen you 'round the clubs lately, have I, George?"[994] Riley was making drinks for all: Scotch and Coke for the men, champagne for the ladies.[995]

"No." George lingered at the window, watching night fall over Hyde Park. "We've just returned from Austria...'n before that, y' know, the West Indies..."

"Yes, yes...I was there, remember?" Riley nudged him. "Wanted to see you boys in action *and* to escape these brutal winter climes."[996]

"Oh, that's right, you *were* there!" John nodded from the sofa. "It's hard to recall, y' know...what with all the odd sods 'n' bods droppin' by...reporters, film actors, politicians... assorted family members..."

"You jet setters, you!" Cyndy Bury smiled, toasting them with the Bohemian crystal champagne glass Riley had just handed her.

"Actually, it isn't as glitzy as it sounds," Pattie smiled. "People don't realise the boys work virtually all the time, especially on location. I mean, we hardly saw them at all in Austria. They filmed all day long...and recorded shows and interviews at night."

"*Not* that we're complaining," Cynthia quickly interjected, returning Cyndy's toast. "It's just that most people think being a

Beatle is all play and no work...and nothing could be further from the truth, really."

By the time the six took their places in Riley's chandeliered dining room, they'd all relaxed. The meal was sumptuous; the drinks, many;[997] and the conversation flowed naturally. They critiqued "Hello, Dolly!" in Drury Lane, discussed the replacement of Eric Clapton in the Yardbirds with Jeff Beck, and debated the recently-healed rift between Queen Elizabeth and the Duchess of Windsor.[998]

Riley — discovering that both John and he had read "A Visit to Inner Space" in November 1963's *Playboy* [999] — went on a bit about America's emerging drug culture and the controversial "in drug" called lysergic acid diethylamide or LSD.[1000]

"I thought Alan Harrington's piece on the matter presented the pros and cons of 'acid,' as they're calling it, quite handily, didn't you?" Riley placed his knife and fork atop his plate and folded his napkin.

"Yeah well," John hesitated, "I think it'll take a bit more research 'n evidence to determine whether the drug's the 'wave of the future' or 'a nasty, deadly menace' or somethin' in between."[1001]

"Come on, John!" Riley smiled. "A good many intelligent people — Timothy Leary and Aldous Huxley, notably — seem to endorse it rather heartily."[1002]

"Right yeah, but Harrington himself had a 'bad trip,' as they say, didn't he?" Lennon countered. "I mean, look, the drug's clearly not for everyone...."

And debating, the six adjourned to the drawing room.

"So, what do you make of the recent citation of Mick, Brian, and Bill for urinating on that public wall in Stratford?"[1003] Riley strode towards the mantlepiece where a neat row of six sugar cubes were lined up, decoratively.[1004]

"Well, personally, I think they had every motivation." George smiled wryly, looking for an opening to announce their imminent departure. He could tell the others were antsy, ready to leave. "Y' can't refuse someone the right to use the loo, just because y' think their hair's over-long, can you?"

"No." Riley hurried over to assist Cyndy who entered, carrying a tray laden with a coffee pot, sugar bowl, creamer, spoons, and six lovely china cups and saucers, "But I'm rather certain our three friends'll be charged anyway. Public display, you know. There's no getting around it."

"Uhm, I'm really sorry," John spoke up. "It's all been great, y' know, but we promised this friend of ours from Hamburg, Klaus Voormann, that we'd be there tonight to hear his band down at the Pickwick."[1005]

"Oh no!" Cyndy pouted, genuinely disappointed. "You four *must* stay for coffee! It's all prepared, isn't it?" She immediately began to pour.

"Well..." Cynthia cut her eyes at John. The Hoylake girl was ill-at-ease with being ungracious.

"But we promised we'd be there *before* the ten o'clock show." George was firm. "They're holdin' a table for us."

"Just a quick one, then." Bury handed the first cup to Riley, who ceremoniously dropped one of the mantlepiece sugar cubes inside. He ostentatiously stirred the sweet in and then handed the brew to Pattie. One at a time, Riley repeated the dramatic performance, presenting a sugared cup to Cynthia, one to John, and finally, one to George. At last, Cyndy and John Riley sipped sugared coffees of their own.[1006]

"Ooh, all of a sudden I feel a tad odd." Pattie touched her temple, attempting to place her cup carefully on the ornately-carved end table.

"No, no, finish it, now," Riley urged the cup back into her hands. "Come on, finish it!"[1007]

"We must go." John was increasingly wary. The eccentric sugar cube performance had raised the hair on the back of his neck. Now Riley's insistence that they drink the entire cup felt "off." "These friends of ours..."[1008]

"Paddy, Klaus & Gibson," George explained, suddenly thick-tongued.

"...they'll be on soon," John stood, feeling unbalanced. "It's their first night y' know. We've *got to go...*"[1009]

"At least finish your coffee, first,"[1010] Riley prodded. He lifted his own, in example.

"Come on." George stood as well. "It's late. We've got to go."[1011]

"But you *can't* leave!"[1012] Riley was now on his feet. His face was blanched and grave.

"Why not?[1013] What're y' talkin' about?"[1014] John barked, his eyes dangerously narrowed. *Now we're gettin' to it,* John steeled himself. *This is where he'll insist on a fuggin' orgy.*[1015]

"Because," Riley leaned closer to John and lowered his voice, "you've just had LSD."[1016]

"No, we haven't!"[1017] John snarled.

"Yes, you have," Riley repeated deliberately. "It — was — in — the — coffee!"[1018]

For a moment, John stood stunned, silent. But when Cyn — thinking she might have food poisoning[1019] — groaned, John was instantly back. "How *dare* you fuggin' do this to us?!"[1020] His nose pinched.

"But...it's all the thing!"[1021] Riley chuckled, shrugging nonchalantly.[1022]

John swiveled to the others. "We've had LSD!"[1023] he informed them, raggedly — navigating to his wife's side, slowly pulling her to her feet.

"Well, what's *that*?"[1024] George lifted a shoulder. He was hearing everything as though through a megaphone. *"So what? Let's go!"*[1025]

Never dreaming that the drug might be more potent than pot or pills, Harrison — demanding their coats — led the others to the front door.[1026] The girls were right on his heels, desperate to escape.[1027] But enraged that his rights had been so flagrantly violated, John threw febrile glares at the poshy dentist.[1028]

"I'd advise you not to leave,"[1029] Riley cautioned, fighting his own array of lights and colours.[1030]

"How fuggin' *dare you*?!" John snarled again, taking a step forward.

"John, please! Please, let's go," Cynthia tugged at his arm. "I'm — really very ill."

"Look, if you insist on departing, then at...at least let me drive you to the Pickwick,"[1031] Riley stammered, concern and confusion sweeping alternately over him. He could just imagine the gruesome morning headlines: "Beatles Seriously Injured in Drug-Induced Car Crash."

"No, no," George raised a firm hand of refusal, "we'll go in my car."[1032] And he led the way.

But taking Cynthia's hand and moving towards the lift — John glowered back over his shoulder. And he deeply regretted that this wasn't the time or the place for Northern, rancorous, "eye-for-an-eye" violence.[1033]

****

The thing that terrified them most, as George careened towards the Pickwick Club, was that Riley and Bury were following them in another car.[1034]

"He's a demon! *My God, he's a demon!*"[1035] Cynthia shrieked. She peeked out beneath hands clasped over her eyes.

"The car's *shrinking!*"[1036] Pattie screamed, pushing her feet as hard as she could against the front passenger seat. "Smaller and smaller and smaller and…!!!!"[1037]

"He's the devil!" Cynthia wailed, lapsing into tears.

"Drive faster," John demanded, saying little but expecting much.

"I *am* drivin' faster, John…I think!" George took a screeching turn, skidding up onto a curb.[1038] "Actually, I don't know if I'm goin' two miles an hour or two hundred…but I'm tryin'!"[1039]

"He's *still following us!*" Cynthia glanced back again. "Hurry, George! Hurry! He's evil!"[1040]

"Look, there," John pointed, his hand quivering, "the Pickwick." And those were the last words they remembered, before the haze.

****

"Downstairs at the Pickwick"
Newport House
Leicester Square
London

In and out of focus: colours coursing into colours.[1041] A front row seat.[1042] The table stretching longer and longer and endlessly longer.[1043] Lights tumbling down and bubbling up. The entire room pulsating to the beat of Paddy, Klaus & Gibson.[1044] People

— with heads or bodies of animals — surging and fading away.[1045] Images shifting.[1046] Melting. Sweeping. Colliding against the bright landscape around them.[1047]

George: "Suddenly, I felt the most incredible feelin' comin' over me...like a very concentrated version of the best feelin' I've ever had in m' whole life...*FANTASTIC!* I fell in love, not with anythin' or anybody in particular but with everythin'. Everythin' was perfect, 'n I had an overwhelmin' desire to go 'round the club tellin' everybody how much I loved them — people I'd never seen before!"[1048]

Pattie: "We were completely out of it! People kept recognizing George and coming up to him, but they were going in and out of focus...we clung to each other, feeling surreal."[1049]

Cynthia: "Plants talked. Other people looked like ghouls. And time stood still. It was *horrific.*"[1050]

John: "It was just terrifyin', but it was fantastic!"[1051]

Cynthia: "It was a horrifying experience — one I will never forget.[1052] For John, the mind expansion, the discovery of oneself within, the check on one's ego, the release, the heightening of his perception were not just the perfect backdrop for the vibrancy of Swinging London...the drug's ability to detach him from the mundane and transport his mind into a kind of Nirvana was, he told me, 'an answer to prayer'...It seemed to be all right for him, although I was *totally against it.*[1053]

"John was still searching, whereas I thought I had found what I wanted out of life[1054]...but that night, I finally realised...I was on my own." [1055]

****

At first, they thought a bomb had taken the roof of The Pickwick right off.[1056] Unforgiving exposure. Glaring light.

Elbows across their eyes.

It was George who finally grasped that The Pickwick was closed. Klaus and the others had packed up and gone. The waiters had stripped the tables and were loudly plunking chairs upside down on the scarred, wooden tops. No music. No revelry. No one left...except George and Pattie and Cynthia and John.[1057]

"Oops," George giggled, "we'd better leave..."[1058]

John, who never wanted a party to end, suggested going on to the Ad Lib Club.

The Ad Lib was The Beatles' haunt, their hangout, their "usual." John and Ringo had been the first to discover the shadowy, mirrored, many-nooked night spot, but rapidly, they'd been joined by Paul and George —— by managers, booking agents, photographers, and newsmen of all stripes...and by other luminaries of Swinging London: rock stars, models and their trusted stylists and boutique owners, actors, artists, writers, composers, architects, rich, carefree bachelors, and young, willing groupies.[1059] For London's wealthy elite, this was "the place." As Paul had once assessed, "It was 'the pub.' That's what it really was."[1060]

So right now, the Ad Lib seemed the safest place to be. And fortunately, it was only blocks away. The four could walk there.[1061]

****

Sunday, 4 April 1965
The Ad Lib Club
7 Leicester Place
London

Moving leadenly, John, Cyn, George, and Pattie concentrated, threading a cautious path amidst annoying, flickering lights, screeching horns, and throngs of strangers stirring about in thick, mask-like makeup — aliens teeming through London.[1062]

"It's *Alice in Wonderland,*" George muttered to himself as they plodded along Regent Street.[1063]

"Let's smash the store windows!"[1064] Pattie flung her arms wide and shouted to the night sky.

"C'mon now, don't be silly!"[1065] George fumbled for her hand. He wanted to pull her closer, but as he scrabbled to connect, they suddenly rounded the corner into Leicester Place.

Immediately, the Ad Lib's brilliant marquee assaulted them: a furore of colour above the commotion of Saturday night. Partiers plugged the street. Laughter and conversation swelled around them.[1066]

"*Shit!* What's goin' on here?"[1067] John staggered and shielded his eyes.

"Must be a film première,"[1068] Cynthia blinked, trying to tolerate the noise and muddle.

"Just move inside," George struggled to sound coherent, but the words fell like stones from his lips. "Fourth floor," he managed to say.

And somehow, they complied.

But once the lift's heavy metal doors slid shut, enclosing the four inside the tight and shiny space, terror erupted. The red light on the emergency button reflected, refracted, and swelled to an enormous flame.[1069]

"*Fire!*" one of them shouted.[1070]

"*Fiiiiiiiire!*" They crouched on the floor or against the walls, their arms flung across their faces.[1071]

"*Aaaaaaaaahhhhhh!*" Their screams were horrid: the sickening sound of those about to die.[1072]

Had only one of them experienced the flames and heat, they might have seen it for what it was: an illusion. But all of them were engulfed in the inferno. None of them doubted it for a second. George was sure they were bound towards hell.[1073]

When the lift finally opened, they were shrieking pitifully.[1074] Crawling off the lift in panic,[1075] they shouted warning: "The lift's on fire! The lift's on fire!"[1076]

Stumbling into Mick Jagger, Marianne Faithfull, and Ringo, John shouted dire notice in his friend's face, but Ringo only smiled.[1077] "Don't take a blind bit o' notice o' Lennon here," Ringo patted John's shoulder fondly. "I don't."

And chuckling, Mick, Marianne, and Ritchie entered the lift, which slid silently away, whilst the very shaken John, Cynthia, George, and Pattie were shown to The Beatles' table — that sacrosanct spot saved for rock'n'roll's unquestioned royals.[1078]

In stunned relief, they collapsed into their chairs and tried to breathe, to focus. Someone ordered drinks.

A few seconds or a great while later, a tentative voice stammered at John's elbow. "Excuse me. Can I...uh, sit next to you?"[1079]

Pivoting his head sluggishly, and then waiting for the room to cease spinning, John eyed the club's young singer — a devotee, no doubt.

It could be me, John thought, *approachin' Little Richard or Roy Orbison on that fuggin' bus...wherever it was. Whenever it was.*

"Yeah, right...go on." John was kind. "Only if you *don't* talk...I can't think."[1080]

I don't know what's *goin' on,* John sat and drank and chewed his lip. He tried to see sense in anything. *We're all goin' crackers, aren't we?*[1081] He eyed Cynthia, next to him, weeping.[1082] George, smiling at the ceiling. Pattie, draped in gaudy noise and umber silence.

And the next thing John realised, he was inside George's cramped Mini, trundling slowly into the shadowy, remote countryside towards Esher.[1083]

****

En route to Kinfauns
The Bungalow of George Harrison
and Pattie Boyd
Esher

The night held a zillion stars, and then none.

George was driving. He never swerved his head but focused solely on the winding road that led to the walled and gardened bungalow he shared with Pattie. The waxing crescent moon afforded little light,[1084] and outside the puddle of amber that his headlamps offered, darkness reigned.

"Let's jump out and play football!"[1085] Pattie squealed.

"There! *There!* There're those big rugby poles!"[1086]

"No, I can't stop." George plowed on, prodigiously. "We have to get there."

John — who, in addition to "the curious cube" had also taken speed — rattled off a colourful series of Scouseisms.[1087]

"Look, don't make me laugh! Oh God!"[1088] George sputtered, craning closer to the windscreen. "We *have* to get there, don't we?"

But when Cynthia stuck her head out the window, jamming her fingers down her throat and trying to vomit, George relented.[1089] He slowed almost to a halt.

"I can't rid myself of it!" Cynthia keened. "It won't work! Nothing works!"

For a time, John was cackling madly,[1090] then he was banging his head against the window and sobbing.[1091] George had brief glimpses of lucidity, and then — *like that!* — he was elsewhere entirely.[1092]

But at unbelievably long last[1093] — just as the sun glinted off an endless sweep of dew[1094] — they found themselves nearing the Kinfauns front gate.[1095]

"Pattie," George articulated as if she were hard of hearing, "Get out, and once I've motored in, close 'n lock the chain behind us. We can't have Margaret[1096] comin' in 'n findin' us this way."[1097]

"Margaret?" Cynthia frowned, looking around — more confused than ever.

"The cleaner," John said from far, far away. "We're famous friends!"[1098]

Pattie, slowly doing what she was told, found the effort useless. *No one would recognize* me, *anyway. I'm wholly changed...and that's fine, but...how will I ever explain this to my friends? How will I say, "Look, it's me? It's **still** me!"?*[1099]

Over the next half hour, they parked the car, navigated the front walk, unlocked the door, put the cat into another room, and then collapsed onto the trendy, backless sofas around the place. John scrounged pens, pencils, and paper and set to drawing. But Cynthia — mumbling over and over, "God *knows* how we made it! God *knows* how we made it!" — was coming apart. She tried alternately to sleep or retch.[1100] But there was nothing for it. And the fear that this utterly foolish prank might somehow separate her from her child haunted her. It broke her heart.[1101]

****

Finally, they all quieted. John wasn't sure if the others were sleeping or milling about in another room, and he didn't care. He was hunched over his paper, biting his tongue and putting finishing touches on a sketch of four faces, bearing the sardonic inscription: "We all agree with you!"[1102] It was John's tongue-in-cheek commentary on Beatledom: the ever-expected response to any command.[1103] Admitted tonight to a land of sharp enlightenment, John saw the privileged mop-top world for what it truly was: an elegant but hollow prison. And more than anything, John craved escape.

But wait...there it was: THE WAY OUT!

In an instant, Kinfauns was transformed into a splendid submarine, and John was graciously bidden to take the helm. Supernaturally guiding his sleeping friends up and over an 18-foot underwater wall, John navigated the cerulean deep in intense silence.[1104] Eyes, straight ahead. Breathing, calm. Raison d'etre, clear.

Like his father before him, John was "the son of a son of a sailor." He'd always known that he'd been born for this: John had chosen to navigate the boat.

Notes!

1. When did the encounter with LSD in this chapter occur?

The date listed in most reference books for this first encounter that George, Pattie, John, and Cynthia had with LSD is Saturday, 27 March 1965. However, that date cannot be accurate. Let's look logically at the events of Saturday evening and Sunday morning, 28 March:

When the four left London on Saturday evening (actually early Sunday morning) and motored towards George and Pattie's home in Esher, the sun was beginning to come up. Both George in The Beatles Anthology, p. 177, and Pattie in Wonderful Tonight, p. 102, state that it was **daylight** when they arrived at Kinfauns.

After entering Kinfauns, the four friends busied themselves with various activities. Cynthia tried to vomit and sleep. George played his guitar for a while and then went to bed. Pattie curled up with the cat. And John *sketched before taking command of a large "submarine" with all four of them aboard.*

Then, later in the morning, Cynthia tells us in her book, John: "John and I found our way home wearily and fell into bed to catch up on the sleep we'd missed." (p. 182)

If the four had indeed taken LSD on 27 March, then all of this activity would have been taking place on the morning of Sunday, 28 March 1965. And on that morning, according to Mark Lewisohn in The Complete Beatles Chronicle, *The Beatles were bound for ABC Studios in Birmingham to film the episode you just read in the previous chapter of this book, The Beatles' last live appearance on* Thank Your Lucky Stars. *(p. 187)*

Indeed, their driver, Alf Bicknell, writes in his Beatles Diary: *"Sunday 28. March 1965...Drove up to Birmingham with the boys for a spot on the* Thank Your Lucky Stars *show, at the ABC studios, and I think they were looking forward to performing again." (p. 36)*

Had John taken LSD the night before, stayed up all evening, "commanded a submarine" at dawn, and sketched all morning, he would have been physically unable to travel to Birmingham on Sunday, 28 March.

Logistically, it was also virtually impossible for John to be in two places at one time on that Sunday morning, 28 March. The boys were due in ABC Studios for an afternoon rehearsal, and the drive from London (and the suburbs around London) to Birmingham is 2 hours, 39 minutes currently.[1105] (It would have been a longer trip in 1965.)

So, the latest that John could have left Kenwood was around 10.00 a.m. Yet Cynthia says that after John and she left Kinfauns in the mid-to-late morning and drove home, they went to bed and slept. Therefore, John would still have been in Esher or motoring home to Kenwood or asleep well into the afternoon of 28 March. And George, as well, would have been "sleeping it off" in Esher with Pattie.

Thus, 27 March could not have been the correct date for the all-night experience that the four faced.

Looking ahead to the weekend of Saturday, 10 April and Sunday, 11 April, as a possible date for what George called "The Dental Experience"[1106] — their first LSD trip — the schedule also seems impossible. The Beatles were slated to appear at the 1964-1965 New Musical Express *Annual Poll Winners All-Star Concert in Wembley...and it was an* **afternoon show.** *So again, John and George could not have logistically traveled to the concert, given the timeline of evening events* *during the LSD evening in question.*

*But on the weekend of Saturday night, 3 April and Sunday, 4 April, The Beatles had **no engagements for Sunday. Thus, this weekend appears to be correct date that the incident occurred.***

2. What were the individual reactions of George, Pattie, Cynthia, and John to the use of LSD?

The reactions of John, Cynthia, George, and Pattie to the events of this historic evening are widely diverse.

In The Beatles Anthology, *George called it "a spiritual experience" in which "the question and answer disappeared into each other." He said, "...in ten minutes I lived a thousand years. My brain and my consciousness and my awareness were pushed so far out that the only way I can begin to describe it is like an astronaut on the moon, or in his spaceship, looking back at the Earth." (p. 179)*

In Wonderful Tonight, *Pattie Boyd says, "At the time, we thought nothing of it. We didn't consider that [the drugs] might be harmful. They were just fun. They could be scary, but most of the time, they made us feel like a million dollars, see wonderful psychedelic images, and hear everything much more acutely...Every sensation was heightened." (102)*

But Cynthia, in her 2005 book, John, *says, "It was horrific: I hated the lack of control and not knowing what was going on...John felt differently: although he'd been as shocked and scared as the rest of us, he was also fascinated. He enjoyed the lack of control and the weirdness. What for me had been the end was for him only the beginning." (p. 182) "When John was tripping I felt as if I was living with a stranger. He would be distant, so spaced-out that he couldn't talk to me coherently...I hated the fact that LSD was pulling him away from me." (p. 182) Finally, she concludes: "The biggest change in our lives at this time, and the biggest single factor that led to our break-up, was John's deepening interest in drugs." (p. 181)*

As Cynthia aptly points out, for John, LSD was a lifeline. And Pete Shotton, John's lifelong mate, concurs, stating, "[This evening] was the beginning of [John's] three-year love affair with LSD. He saw acid as a godsend — a magical key to uncharted regions of his own imagination, and a potential cure for most of his psychological problems. It gave almost tangible form to his lifelong perception of the world as a surrealistic carnival, and it enabled him — instantaneously, effortlessly, and without leaving his chair — to experience the semblance of mystical visions and even communion with God." (p. 117)

Sources:

Lewisohn, The Complete Beatles Chronicle, *187-188.*
The Beatles, The Beatles Anthology, *177-179.*
Goodden, Riding So High, *77-98.*
Lennon, Cynthia, A Twist of Lennon, *142-144.*
Lennon, Cynthia, John, *181-183.*
Boyd, Pattie and Junor, Penny, Wonderful Tonight, *79 and 100-102.*
Harry, The John Lennon Encyclopedia, *570.*
Shotton and Schaffner, 117-118.
Norman, Shout!, *244-245.*
Norman, John Lennon: The Life, *462-463.*
Badman, 146-147.
Miles, The Beatles' Diary, *Vol. 1, 192.*
Miles, The Beatles in Their Own Words, *115.*
Spitz, 546-548 and 565-568.
Wenner, Lennon Remembers, *73-76.*
Coleman, Lennon, *226-227 and 322.*
Gould, Can't Buy Me Love: The Beatles, Britain, and America, *316.*
Goldman, 196-197.
Brown, Peter, 172-174.
Connolly, 199-200.
Brown, Craig, Glimpses of The Beatles, *267-269.*
Buskin, The Complete Idiot's Guide to The Beatles, *217.*
Mulligan, 85.

To hear John and George talk about what happened on this night, go to:
https://www.youtube.com/watch?v=aOAEEiqcbkg

To read the article by Alan Harrington on LSD that both John Riley and John Lennon had read prior to this evening, go to: https://allaboutheaven.org/observations/alan-harrington-a-visit-to-inner-space-1-012221/221

To see the 1965 advertisement and artwork for Harrington's LSD article, go to: https://www.retrospace.org/2011/09/vintage-reads-31-few-books-from-70s.html

https://www.beatlesbible.com/1965/01/20/ringo-starr-proposes-maureen-cox/ This article contains additional information on the Ad Lib Club.

http://webgrafikk.com/blog/uncategorized/paddy-klaus-gibson/ This website, managed by Roger Stormo, gives excellent information on Paddy, Klaus & Gibson.

https://www.freemaptools.com/how-far-is-it-between-london_-uk-and-

birmingham_-england.htm This website calculates driving distances between destinations in the U.K.

https://www.calendar-12.com/moon_calendar/1965/april This website calculates phases of the moon in April 1965.

https://en.wikipedia.org/wiki/March_1965 This website chronicles the news headlines of March 1965.

From Rolling Stone magazine, *here is John talking about the experience of that night: https://www.rollingstone.com/music/music-news/beatles-acid-test-how-lsd-opened-the-door-to-revolver-251417/ Or use the QR code:*

This is a very interesting video of George and Pattie visiting Kenwood, just around this time, in the Spring 1965:

---

977 https://en.wikipedia.org/wiki/April_1965

978 The "traditional" date selected for this event by Beatles scholars has long been Saturday, 27 March 1965. See the discussion of this at the end of the chapter to explain the date used in this chapter.

979 Goodden, *Riding So High*, 77. For years, this LSD story had more gaps than facts. The date, the name of the dentist, the events following the ingestion of LSD…much of it was vague and contradictory. But Joe Goodden has done incredible research in his 2017 work that gives us every detail we need to know, including the address where this episode took page. I could not have written this chapter without Joe's superb research. I highly recommend purchasing *Riding So High*. (Spitz does list the address in *The Beatles*, p. 564, but lists it as Edgeware Road.)

980 Boyd, Pattie and Penny Junor, *Wonderful Tonight*, 101, Goodden, 77, and Norman, *John Lennon: The Life*, 463.

[981] Wenner, *Lennon Remembers*, 73, Goodden, 77, and https://www.youtube.com/watch?v=aOAEEiqcbkg. Goodden says that Riley only catered to "high profile patients." George, in the video, talks about the dentist.

[982] Wenner, 73, Goodden, 77, Norman, *Shout!*, 244, Lennon, Cynthia, *A Twist of Lennon*, 144, Connolly, 199, and Lennon, Cynthia, *John,* 181. Ray Connolly quotes John as saying, "It was the flat of some trendy, swinger dentist, y' know the sort of people who George hangs out with..." (p. 199) In *A Twist of Lennon*, Cynthia says, "a friend of George's...slipped us an LSD 'mickey-finn.'" (p. 144) And in her 2005 book, *John*, Cynthia says the event occurred at a dinner party "we'd gone to with George and Pattie, a friend of theirs, and his wife." (p. 181)

[983] Boyd, and Junor, *Wonderful Tonight*, 102, Brown, 172, and Goodden, 77. In *Wonderful Tonight*, Pattie Boyd says of Riley: "I had always thought John Riley was rather odd. No matter what he was going to do in our mouths, he would give us intravenous Valium...We would go into a deep sleep and wake up not knowing what he had done...he could have done anything to us while we were out." (p. 102)

[984] Goodden, 77.

[985] Goodden, 78, Connolly, 199, and Brown, 172. Connolly quotes John as saying "[Riley's] wife chose the bunnies for the Playboy Club or somethin'." Brown calls Cyndy Bury "a curvaceous blonde who hired the bunnies for the Playboy Club." Goodden and Brown are accurate in noting that Bury is Riley's girlfriend, not his wife, though as Goodden points out, the two do marry later. Goodden tells us that she was 21 years old at the time of this incident.

[986] The Beatles, *The Beatles Anthology*, 177, Goodden, 80, Brown, 172, Brown, 174, Badman, 146, Spitz, 564, and Goldman, 196. In *The Beatles Anthology*, George Harrison states, "I'm sure [Riley] thought LSD was an aphrodisiac. I remember his girlfriend had enormous breasts, and I think he thought there was going to be a gang bang and that he was going to get to shag everybody. I really think that was his motive." (p. 177) Badman quotes John as saying, "We all thought he was trying to keep us for an orgy in the house, and we didn't want to know!" (p. 146)

[987] Goodden, 79 and 81, Goldman, 196, Brown, 172-173, and Connolly, 200. Coleman mentions the Pickwick Club but doesn't mention Paddy, Klaus & Gibson. Goodden tells us that George was "keen on seeing the band." (p. 79)

[988] Boyd, Pattie and Penny Junor, *Wonderful Tonight*, 101 and Harry, *The John Lennon Encyclopedia,* 180. Pattie says, "The four of us went to London in my little Mini Cooper S — George had bought me a fabulous orange one for my birthday."

[989] Lennon, Cynthia, *John*, 181, Harry, *The John Lennon Encyclopedia*, 870, Norman, *Shout!*, 244, Goodden, 80, Shotton and Schaffner, 117, Goldman, 196, and Connolly, 200. Goodden identifies the vehicle as "Pattie Boyd's Mini Cooper." (p. 80) And Bill Harry calls it "George's black Mini." (p. 870) Cynthia Lennon, in *John,* states, "George had driven us there in his brand new Mini." (p. 181) Connolly simply says "George's car." (p. 200) Goldman says

they are in "George's Aston Martin DB6." (p. 196) Shotton doesn't say which car it is, but does confirm that George is driving.

[990] Spitz, 546.

[991] Goodden, 77.

[992] Brown, 172.

[993] Goodden, 77.

[994] Boyd and Junor, 100, and Goodden, 77. Pattie Boyd says, "We [George and she] knew [Riley] quite well and had been to a few clubs with him in the past."

[995] Goodden, 177 and Lennon, Cynthia, *A Twist of Lennon*, 109. Goodden makes a point to say that Bury did not take drugs. In fact, she only "drank a little glass of champagne." Cynthia refers to herself drinking wine, socially, for "a bit of Dutch courage."

[996] Goodden, 77. Goodden says that Riley flew to the Bahamas whilst The Beatles were there.

[997] Boyd and Junor, 101. Pattie says "We had a lovely meal and plenty to drink…"

[998] https://en.wikipedia.org/wiki/March_1965 This website outlines the major events of March 1965.

[999] Harry, *The John Lennon Encyclopedia*, 570, Brown, 174, Connolly, 200, and Goodden, 79. Goodden tells us, "Cynthia Lennon said [LSD] had been mentioned in general terms over dinner that evening."

[1000] Goodden, 89 and Wenner, 73. Wenner emphasizes that Riley didn't understand the implications of giving the two Beatles and their ladies LSD. He quotes John saying, "…[Riley] didn't know what it was, it's all the thing with that sort of…Middle-class London swingers, or whatever had heard about it, and they didn't know it was different from pot or pills…".

[1001] https://www.retrospace.org/2011/09/vintage-reads-31-few-books-from-70s.html You can see the advertisement for Alan Harrington's article here, including the artwork. And you may read the entire LSD article that Riley and Lennon read here: https://allaboutheaven.org/observations/alan-harrington-a-visit-to-inner-space-1-012221/221

[1002] Goodden, 88-89, Harry, *The John Lennon Encyclopedia*, 570, and https://allaboutheaven.org/observations/alan-harrington-a-visit-to-inner-space-1-012221/221

[1003] https://en.wikipedia.org/wiki/March_1965

[1004] Goldman, 196, Miles, *The Beatles' Diary, Vol. 1*, 192, and Goodden, 81. Goldman specifically says there were "six hits" supplied to Riley for the occasion, not four. Both Miles and Goodden point out that all six people at this dinner party took the LSD sugar cubes, not just The Beatles and their ladies.

[1005] Goodden, 79, Brown, 172-173, Spitz, 564, and Connolly, 200.

[1006] Goldman, 196 and Goodden, 98. Goldman says there were "six hits," not just four. This is confirmed by Cyndy Bury's information in Goodden's research. She says that Riley and she took LSD as well and after a short time were "unable to drive" so they took a taxi home that night. (p. 89)

[1007] Brown, Peter, 172. Direct quote from John Riley.

[1008] Goodden, 79. Direct quote from John Lennon.

[1009] Goodden, 79. Direct quote from John Lennon.

[1010] The Beatles, *The Beatles Anthology*, 177. This is a direct quote from George Harrison, remembering the events of the evening.

[1011] Boyd and Junor, 101 and The Beatles, *The Beatles Anthology*, 177. Direct quote from George Harrison.

[1012] Brown, Craig, *150 Glimpses of The Beatles*, 268. According to Pattie Boyd, this is a direct quote from Riley.

[1013] Goodden, 79. Direct quote from John Lennon.

[1014] Brown, Craig, 268. According to Pattie Boyd, direct quote from John Lennon.

[1015] The Beatles, *The Beatles Anthology*, 177, Brown, 174, and Badman, 146.

[1016] Boyd and Junor, 101, The Beatles, *The Beatles Anthology*, 177, Goodden, 79, Coleman, *Lennon*, 196 and 322, Brown, Peter, 174, Badman, 146, Spitz, 564, Shotton and Schaffner, 117, Harry, *The John Lennon Encyclopedia*, 570, Miles, *The Beatles' Diary, Vol. 1*, 192, Brown, Craig, 268, and Connolly, 200. Accounts vary here on who was told about the LSD. Pattie Boyd, who was there, has Riley telling John about the LSD first; John then tells the others. Goodden, Spitz, Badman, and Connolly agree. All other sources have Riley telling the group all at once.

[1017] Boyd and Junor, 101 and Brown, Craig, 268. Direct quote from John Lennon, according to Pattie Boyd.

[1018] Boyd and Junor, 101 and Brown, Craig, 268. Direct quote from John Riley, according to Pattie Boyd.

[1019] Lennon, Cynthia, *John*, 181.

[1020] Boyd and Junor, 101 and Goodden, 80. Direct quote from John Lennon, according to Pattie Boyd.

[1021] Goodden, 79 and https://www.youtube.com/watch?v=aOAEEiqcbkg.

[1022] Lennon, Cynthia, *John*, 181. Cynthia says Riley "no doubt…thought [LSD] was hip and harmless." She says that when the four guests insisted on leaving the party, "our **laughing hosts** enlightened us" about what they'd been given.

[1023] Spitz, 565. Direct quote from John Lennon.

[1024] The Beatles, *The Beatles Anthology*, 177 and Goodden, 80. This is a direct quote from George Harrison.

[1025] The Beatles, *The Beatles Anthology*, 177 and Goodden, 80. This is a direct quote from George Harrison.

[1026] Lennon, Cynthia, *John*, 181.

[1027] Lennon, Cynthia, *John*, 181.

[1028] Brown, *150 Glimpses of The Beatles*, 268. Pattie Boyd is quoted as saying that John was "absolutely furious."

[1029] Goodden, 80, Brown, 172, Spitz, 564, Norman, *Shout!*, 244, Connolly, 200, and https://www.youtube.com/watch?v=aOAEEiqcbkg. Both Goodden and Connolly use the exact same wording for Riley, "I advise you not to leave." George Harrison repeats this phrase in the video. Norman, in *Shout!*, quotes Cynthia as saying: "…this man told us we couldn't leave." (p. 244) I'm sure that's exactly how it felt.

[1030] Spitz, 565.

[1031] Boyd and Junor, 101.

[1032] https://www.youtube.com/watch?v=aOAEEiqcbkg In this video, that is precisely what George Harrison says he said.

[1033] Boyd and Junor, 101, Shotton and Schaffner, 117, and Connolly, 200. Connolly says John told him that he "liked to be the one to decide when he took drugs and to know what he was taking." (p. 200) Pattie Boyd adds that "John was absolutely furious." (p. 101)

[1034] Goldman, 196, Brown, Peter, 172-173, Badman, 146, Spitz, 565, Shotton and Schaffner, 117, and https://www.youtube.com/watch?v=aOAEEiqcbkg. There is a great deal of disagreement about whether Riley, terrified for the safety of John, Cynthia, George, and Pattie, followed his guests in a taxi or in his car. Badman quotes Cynthia Lennon saying, "We'd somehow got away in George's mini, but [Riley] came after us in a taxi." (p. 146) Shotton and Schaffner, Brown, and Spitz simply say the dentist followed them, but gives no mention of a vehicle. Goldman and Goodden state that Riley followed them in his own car. Goodden, who interviewed Cyndy Bury, was told by her that both Riley and she followed their four guests and made it to the Pickwick, where they joined them at a table. But later, Riley and Bury left the club in a taxi because they were "no longer able to drive." (p. 81) And finally, in the video, George Harrison says that Riley "came [to the Pickwick] as well in his car."

[1035] Norman, *Shout!*, 244. Direct quote from Cynthia Lennon.

[1036] Boyd and Junor, 101 and Brown, Craig, 268.

[1037] Boyd and Junor, 101, Brown, Craig, 268, and Goodden, 80. Direct quote from Pattie Boyd.

[1038] Brown, Peter, 172-173

[1039] Shotton and Schaffner, 117. Pete Shotton says that George told him later that he was "unable to gauge whether he was driving at two miles per hour or two hundred."

[1040] Norman, *Shout!*, 244. Cynthia says, "Our host seemed to change into a demon. We were all terrified. We knew it was something evil…"

[1041] Spitz, 565 and Brown, *Craig*, 269.

[1042] Brown, Peter, 173.

[1043] The Beatles, *The Beatles Anthology*, 177, Wenner, 74, Goldman, 196, and Goodden, 81.

[1044] Brown, Peter, 173.

[1045] Boyd and Junor, 101.

[1046] Boyd and Junor, 101, Brown, Craig, 169, and Goodden, 81. Pattie Boyd says, "…people were going in and out of focus" and "people looked like animals. We clung to each other, feeling surreal."

[1047] Connolly, 200.

[1048] The Beatles, *The Beatles Anthology*, 177.

[1049] Boyd and Junor, 101-102.

[1050] Lennon, Cynthia, *John*, 182. Direct quote from Cynthia Lennon.

[1051] Wenner, 74, Connolly, 200, Badman, 146, and Gould, *Can't Buy Me Love: The Beatles, Britain, and America*, 316. Direct quote from John Lennon.

[1052] Lennon, Cynthia, *A Twist of Lennon*, 144.

[1053] Coleman, *Lennon*, 322. Direct quote from Cynthia Lennon.

[1054] Norman, *John Lennon: The Life*, 462.

[1055] Lennon, Cynthia, *A Twist of Lennon*, 144. Direct quote from Cynthia Lennon.

[1056] The Beatles, *The Beatles Anthology*, 177 and Goodden, 82. In *The Beatles Anthology*, George says, "...then suddenly, it felt as if a bomb had made a direct hit on the nightclub and the roof had been blown off. 'What's going on here?' I pulled my senses together and I realized [sic] the club had actually closed...all of the peole had gone..."

[1057] The Beatles, *The Beatles Anthology*, 177 and Goodden, 82. In *The Beatles Anthology*, George goes on to say, "...the waitresses were going around bashing the tables and putting the chairs on top of them. We thought, 'Oops, we better get out of here!'"

[1058] The Beatles, *The Beatles Anthology*, 177 and Goodden, 82. Direct quote from George Harrison.

[1059] Spitz, 546.

[1060] Spitz, 546. Spitz says the Ad Lib was also the meeting place for the Hollies, Stones, Moody Blues, Yardbirds, John Mayall, the Searchers, and Georgie Fame.

[1061] Boyd and Junor, 102, The Beatles, *The Beatles Anthology*, 177, and Goodden, 87. Some sources say the four took the car to the Ad Lib, but as George points out in *The Beatles Anthology*, "It [the Ad Lib] was just a short distance, so we walked." Pattie Boyd also says, "It [the Ad Lib] wasn't far from the Pickwick, so we walked..." (p. 102)

[1062] The Beatles, *The Beatles Anthology*, 177, Spitz, 565, Norman, *Shout!*, 244-245, Goodden, 82, Goldman, 196, Brown, 178, and Connolly, 200. Norman quotes Cynthia as saying, "Everybody seemed to be going mad..."

[1063] The Beatles, *The Beatles Anthology*, 177. Direct quote from George Harrison.

[1064] Boyd and Junor, 102, Norman, *Shout!*, 244-245, Goodden, 82, Brown, 174, Goldman, 196, Connolly, 200, Brown, Craig, 169, and Badman, 147. In Badman and in Norman's *Shout!*, Cynthia is quoted as saying that Pattie wanted to "smash all the windows along Regent Street." And Pattie herself says that as they walked to the Pickwick "...on the way, I remember trying to break a shopwindow." (p. 102) Goldman has this occurring as the four drove to Esher, later in the evening, but every other source has it happening *en route* to the Ad Lib.

[1065] The Beatles, *The Beatles Anthology*, 177. Direct quote from George Harrison.

[1066] The Beatles, *The Beatles Anthology*, 177.

[1067] Brown, Peter, 174. Direct quote from John Lennon.

[1068] The Beatles, *The Beatles Anthology*, 177, Brown, 174, Spitz, 565, and Goodden, 82. In *The Beatles Anthology*, George describes the scene this way, "Then we got round the corner and saw all the lights and taxis. It looked as if there was a big première going on..."

[1069] Boyd and Junor, 102, The Beatles, *The Beatles Anthology*, 177, Wenner, 73, Goldman, 196, Brown, 174, Badman, 146, Goodden, 82, and https://www.youtube.com/watch?v=aOAEEiqcbkg. John told Wenner, "We all thought there was a fire on the lift. There was just a little red light, and we were all screaming. The lift stops and the door opens, and we're all going,

'Aaaaaaaahhhh!', like that, and we just see that it's the club and we walk in and sit down…" Similarly, in *The Beatles Anthology*, George says, "We went up into the nightclub, and it felt as if the elevator was on fire and we were all going into hell…and at the same time, we were all in hysterics and crazy." The video shows both John and George discussing this phenomenon.

[1070] Wenner, 73 and Goodden, 82.

[1071] Wenner, 73 and Goodden, 82.

[1072] Wenner, 73 and Goodden, 82.

[1073] https://www.youtube.com/watch?v=aOAEEiqcbkg In this video, both John and George talk about this "fire" experience, and George says they thought they were "going into hell."

[1074] Boyd and Junor, 102, The Beatles, *The Beatles Anthology*, 177, Wenner, 73, Goldman, 196, Brown, 174, Badman, 146, Harry, *The John Lennon Encyclopedia*, 570, Brown, Craig, 269, and Goodden, 82. John told Wenner, "We all thought there was a fire on the lift. There was just a little red light, and we were all screaming. The lift stops and the door opens, and we're all going, 'Aaaaaaaahhhh!', like that, and we just see that it's the club and we walk in and sit down…" Similarly, in *The Beatles Anthology*, George says, "We went up into the nightclub, and it felt as if the elevator was on fire and we were all going into hell…and at the same time, we were all in hysterics and crazy." Pattie Boyd, too, says: "…we thought the lift was on fire because there was a little red light inside."

[1075] Boyd and Junor, 102, The Beatles, *The Beatles Anthology*, 178, and Spitz, 546. Ringo says that he was in the Ad Lib and that they screamed at him, "The lift's on fire!" Pattie says the four of them "'crawled out' of the elevator" and "bumped into Mick Jagger, Marianne Faithfull, and Ringo." She goes on to say that John "told them we'd been spiked." (p. 102)

[1076] Boyd and Junor, 102, The Beatles, *The Beatles Anthology*, 178, and Spitz, 546.

[1077] Spitz, 566 and Connolly, 200.

[1078] Brown, Peter, 173, Brown, Craig, 269, and Goodden, 82. Goodden says: "The Beatles were treated like royalty there [in the Ad Lib] with their own table." **Note:** Proof that this night was extremely confusing and blurry to them all is the fact that Cynthia doesn't even mention going to the Ad Lib. In her 2005 book, *John*, she has them going directly to George and Pattie's home in Esher. (p. 181) Pete Shotton, also, has them going directly to Esher. (p. 117) In Wenner's *Lennon Remembers*, John sums it up by saying, "Well, it seemed to go on all night. I can't remember the details." (p. 74) The complete story of this evening must be pieced together from various sources.

[1079] The Beatles, *The Beatles Anthology*, 177, Wenner, 74, Badman, 147, Goodden, 82, Goldman, 196, and Brown, 173. This information is directly from John.

[1080] The Beatles, *The Beatles Anthology*, 177, Wenner, 74, Badman, 147, Goodden, 82, Goldman, 196, and Brown, Peter, 173. Direct quote from John Lennon.

[1081] Spitz, 566. Direct quote from John, according to Spitz.

[1082] Norman, *Shout!*, 244. Cynthia says that for her, "it was a nightmare that wouldn't stop, whatever you did."

[1083] The Beatles, *The Beatles Anthology*, 177, Wenner, 74, Goodden, 82-83, Goldman, 196, Brown, Peter, 174, Badman, 147, Shotton and Schaffner, 117, Connolly, 200, Lennon, Cynthia, *John*, 182, and Harry, *The John Lennon Encyclopedia*, 570. George says that he remembers driving "about 18 miles an hour" home to Esher.

[1084] https://www.calendar-12.com/moon_calendar/1965/april This website supplies the phases of the moon for April 1965.

[1085] The Beatles, *The Beatles Anthology*, 177, Wenner, 74, Badman, 147, Brown, Peter, 174, Harry, *The John Lennon Encyclopedia*, 570, and Goodden, 82-83. John Lennon says this is a quote from Pattie Boyd.

[1086] The Beatles, *The Beatles Anthology*, 177, Wenner, 74, Badman, 147, Brown, Peter, 174, and Goodden, 82-83. John Lennon says this is a quote from Pattie Boyd.

[1087] The Beatles, *The Beatles Anthology*, 177, Wenner, 74, Badman, 147, Brown, Peter, 174, and Goodden, 82-83. John says, "I was getting all these sort of hysterical jokes coming out like speed, because I was always on that, too."

[1088] The Beatles, *The Beatles Anthology*, 177, Wenner, 74, Badman, 147, and Goodden, 82-83. Direct quote from George Harrison, according to John Lennon.

[1089] Norman, *Shout!*, 244-245 and Brown, 174.

[1090] The Beatles, *The Beatles Anthology*, 177 and Gould, 316. Direct quote from John Lennon.

[1091] Norman, *Shout!*, 245 and Badman, 147. Cynthia says, "John was crying and banging his head against the wall."

[1092] The Beatles, *The Beatles Anthology*, 177, Goodden, 83, and https://www.youtube.com/watch?v=aOAEEiqcbkg. In the video, George talks about his moments of clarity followed by unexpected sweeps back into the madness.

[1093] Boyd and Junor, 102 and Brown, Peter, 174. Brown says that the typically 42-minute trip from London to Esher took hours. Pattie says, "The journey took hours…"

[1094] Boyd and Junor, 102 and https://www.youtube.com/watch?v=aOAEEiqcbkg. In the video, George states that they arrived around "daylight." Pattie says, "…it was daylight by the time we got home." (p. 102)

[1095] Boyd and Junor, 102, The Beatles, *The Beatles Anthology*, 177, and Goodden, 83. George says, "It was daylight and I drove everyone home…we got home safe and sound."

[1096] Boyd and Junor, 79.

[1097] Boyd and Junor, 102, Brown, Peter, 174, and Goodden, 83. Brown adds that they locked the windows at Kinfauns as well.

[1098] Boyd and Junor, 79. Pattie says that Margaret loved John Lennon because he gave her speed.

[1099] Brown, 174.

[1100] Boyd and Junor, 102, Lennon, Cynthia, *John,* 182, Badman, 147, Goodden, 83, and Norman, *Shout!*, 245. Cynthia Lennon's "God knows how we made it!" is a direct quote.

[1101] Lennon, Cynthia, *A Twist of Lennon*, 144. Cynthia was extremely fearful that drug use that night or any night might place Julian in danger. In *A Twist of Lennon,* she said, "Julian's position in this new set up gave me a great deal to worry about. A threat of kidnapping had [already been] revealed to us by the local police" and caused "many a sleepless night." Because of this, she "wanted desperately to hang on to sanity" while John "needed to escape his reality." Cynthia felt that as a mother she needed to "stand apart." (p. 144)

[1102] The Beatles, *The Beatles Anthology*, 178, Wenner, 74, Goodden, 83, Brown, Peter, 174, Badman, 147, Goldman, 196, and Harry, *The John Lennon Encyclopedia*, 570. Note: John says that he gave his drawings from this evening to Ringo.

[1103] Miles, *The Beatles' Diary, Vol. 1*, 192. Miles says that the drawing of four faces depicted "The Beatles as a hydra-like creature, with each head pronouncing, 'We all agree with you!'" (p. 192)

[1104] The Beatles, *The Beatles Anthology*, 178, Wenner, 74-75, Goodden, 83, Brown, Peter, 174, Badman, 147, Shotton and Schaffner, 117, and Harry, *The John Lennon Encyclopedia*, 570-571.

[1105] https://www.freemaptools.com/how-far-is-it-between-london_-uk-and-birmingham_-england.htm This website figures driving distances between destinations in the U.K.

[1106] The Beatles, *The Beatles Anthology*, 177. Direct quote from George Harrison.

Wednesday, 7 April 1965[1107]
Kenwood
Weybridge, Surrey

When the buzzer went, Cynthia frowned. She hadn't been expecting a soul. John was away in Twickenham, filming what sounded like a fairly risky scene — a pub cellar encounter between the besieged Ringo and a supposedly ferocious Bengal tiger named "Raja."[1108]

"Look, y' know we'd never be in peril!" John had thrown his eyes to the ceiling when Cyn had fussed over it. "The underwriters wouldn't have it, would they? No doubt the maneater'll be sedated — or at least somewhat, y' know."

"Well, one would hope." Cynthia had pulled her hair into a low ponytail and donned one of John's old shirts over a pair of jeans. This morning, Dot and she were moving John's "most beloved items" into the house below. Partridge had — at long last — "nearly completed" his renovations, and Cyn couldn't wait to vacate the attic, clear away the chalky dust below.

"Dot? Are we expecting a delivery of some sort?" Cynthia set John's dogeared collection of *Just William* books on the bedside shelf beside the Lewis Carrolls.

"Not that I recall." Dot Jarlett was carrying a few of John's Scalextric cars up to the "racing room."[1109] "But let me get the door. Could be another covey of fans who've sussed you out."

"More than likely," Cynthia sighed, reaching for the small, framed photo of Quarry Bank Grammar that John routinely hung above his reading lamp. John had rarely had a good word to say about the place back when Pete Shotton and he had spent their high school years there. But here it was again, in the usual place of honour.

John had left specific instructions as to where "his things" were to be situated. Cyn was sure he'd have drawn a detailed chart, if only he'd had the time.

He was very "hands on." It was John who had selected the living room's deep-pile black carpet and demanded a private, ebony-walled study featuring a gentleman's bar shaped like a world globe.[1110] John had been downright persnickety about where his mother's upright piano would stand, and he'd carefully hand-selected the spaces where Stu's paintings would hang.[1111] He'd also insisted upon displaying his suit of armour topped with a gorilla head, and the colourful, much-beloved 48-play jukebox, chockfull of his favourite Fifties hits.[1112] John had almost demanded a separate gaming room, loaded with pinball machines, and the morning room was laid out to meet his exact specifications.[1113] Cynthia — who despised the modern, Hollywood kitchen that was far too complicated to operate[1114] — thought John had clearly gotten the better end of the bargain in this mock-Tudor monstrosity. She looked around now and shook her head.

But Dot was back at the bedroom door — her eyes wary. "Erm, you'd better come and greet *this one*, Cynthia," she said. "It's above me."

Lifting an eyebrow as she set down the feather duster, Cynthia pushed stray hairs from her cheeks. "Something awry, Dot?" She always expected the worst.

"Well," the housekeeper evaded, cleverly, "I'm afraid you'll have to be the judge. I'd call this situation fairly unique."

****

The stranger, twisting a frayed bowler in his hands, rocked foot-to-foot just outside the doorway. Greasy grey hair fell long and unkempt beneath a bald pate, and his shiny suit was as vagabond-tatty.[1115] But when his eyes met Cynthia's, he threw out a bold, defensive grin: a charmer.

"Hello, Cyn!" Her eyes widened as the diminutive man[1116] with John's face employed John's moniker for her.[1117] "I'm John's dad, 'n you haven't seen me before!"[1118] Then stepping spryly into the reception foyer before she had a chance to object,[1119] he gibbered on in John's voice,[1120] "I've been dyin' to meet my daughter-in-law 'n the kiddie,[1121] y' know. I've read all about you!"

Bewildered and bowled over by the uncanny resemblance, Cynthia stuttered, "Was…was John expecting you?"

"Oh no, we met ages ago…last year, it was. But I'd love to see him again, Cyn! I want *very much* to see him!"[1122]

Cynthia glanced into the empty drive, searching in vain for the man's transport. "How did you…"

"Well y' see, I was in this pub a day or so ago, 'n this man comes up to me 'n says, 'If y'er Fred Lennon, I drive your son.' And so, I said to him, I said, "Oh? Well, give me a lift to his house, then. I'd like to see him!"' Fred grinned and threw his arms out dramatically. "'N he did, 'n here I am!'"[1123]

"Well!" Cynthia closed the door slowly, engineering a smile and trying to decide what to do. Fred gave her time. He casually surveyed the magnificent entryway, whistling his appreciation of the grand decor. "He's done all right, our one!"

"Yes, John works very hard," Cynthia returned. "Very hard, and…" She wasn't sure what to say, what to share with this stranger.

Fred coughed, uncomfortably. His bright eyes darted here and there, taking in everything. And noting Cynthia's jeans and ratty shirt, Fred smiled at her sadly. His eyes held sympathy.

"Oh! Oh, I've been dusting, actually," Cynthia quickly explained. "You see, we're moving in after months and months of renovation, and…well, to be honest, I could use a bit of a break. Care to join me in a cup of tea and some cheese on toast?"[1124]

"A cuppa!" Fred was delighted. "I could easily be persuaded!"

And chuckling merrily, the tiny, ebullient man followed Cynthia into the sunroom — a cosy, wide-windowed, welcoming gallery overlooking the garden. From what he could remember, it was an almost exact replica of the one in Mendips, except here the garden was much larger and more resplendent.[1125]

"Hmm, looks a lot like Calderstones Park!" Freddie had fond memories of his days with Julia in the lush Liverpool suburbs.

"Yes." Cynthia stood beside him. "To be honest, I think that's what drew John to it as well…that and the resemblance to Mendips, of course."

"Our Johnny's done all right for himself, hasn't he?" Freddie smiled. And drawing a deep breath, he found himself feeling quite at home.

****

Whilst the tea was being poured, Freddie rambled on, scattershot, about his latest job as a hotel dishwasher near Esher. "It's not the best, Cyn...but well, I've always been far too happy-go-lucky to roost in one place — to strike for a vocation, as it were."[1126] "I've always got the wind at m' back, haven't I? Unfortunately."

Cynthia smiled and listened. It seemed the best arrangement.

"That's why m' eldest brother, Stanley..." Freddie dunked the corner of his toast liberally into his tea, "That's why he's never had the time of day for me, has he? Now, Charlie, on the other hand...well, we're thick as thieves, us two."[1127]

Cynthia cut her eyes at the clock. She was torn between a desire to let Fred stay and meet Julian, and the perhaps wiser decision to move John's dad along before John returned.[1128] Her heart of hearts whispered that John wouldn't be thrilled with this unexpected pop-in, but she was equally convinced that it wasn't her place to determine whether or not John was afforded the opportunity to reunite with his father.

"Quite the place — this!" Freddie's fingers drummed on his knees. His eyes were everywhere. "I mean some houses are Queen Mary on front 'n Queen Mury Ann on back, but this..." Implicit in his observation was envy. No one could miss it.

"Well, it hasn't been a snap," Cynthia said, soberly. "We've been renovating since last August. For months, it's been a complete tip."

"But surely, you've been elsewhere for the duration..."

"No." Cynthia shook her head. "Other than a brief Swiss skiing holiday back in January and some time on set with John in the Austria a few weeks ago, I've been right here...living in the servants' quarters — in the attic."

"A stingy space, eh?" Freddie's eyes clouded. "I know all about that life."

"Well..." Cynthia turned her palms up. She hated to complain. "John and I needed to get out of London quickly, you see. We couldn't continue to live there whilst the renovations were done. The fans, you know…"

"Err…point me at the loo, Cyn," Freddie interrupted, blushing with embarrassment.

"Oh, of course," she fumbled to her feet, "Right this way."

And whilst Freddie was indisposed, his daughter-in-law located Dot and asked her to bring down "Mr. Lennon's grandson." It was, she had decided, high time the two met.

****

"Julian, tell your grandfather what tomorrow is," Cynthia prompted.

"My birthday,"[1129] the freckled-faced, auburn-haired toddler divulged quietly.

"*Your birthday!*" Freddie roared, beaming. "Now *how* did I know that? Why, I've arrived just in time for your special anniversary, haven't I, Sonny Jim?!"

"My name's Julian," the child corrected, soberly. "John Charles Julian Lennon." Clinging to his mother's side, the boy had found his confidence.

"Well, that's a-lot-of-name for a wee lad like you," Fred laughed. He looked to Cynthia, "Charles, is it? For m' brother, Charlie?"

"My father's name was Charles," Cynthia explained. "And my eldest brother's Charles as well."[1130]

"Oh well…" Freddie studied Julian with tender eyes. "Julian, then." He sighed. "He does look so much like her. But *no one* resembles Julia as much as our Johnny does."

"Really? You think so?" Cynthia furrowed her brow. "*I think* John looks identical to *you!*"[1131]

"No, no, no, no, no…" Freddie shook his head, "he's *so* much like his mother, I was quite astounded! He even wears the same kind of scowl his mother might have done…"[1132] For a moment, Freddie's voice trailed away. His eyes were far off. "I would really like to see John again, Cyn. I would. He's tough altogether, just as she was…but I'd like to explain things to him, my way."[1133]

Cynthia nodded, wondering what she would do if John didn't

materialise in the next hour or so. She'd no idea how late he would be, and her catalogue of conversation was almost thumbed-through. But then, Freddie tugged a lank lock of hair behind his left ear.

"I know!" Cynthia piped up, as if they'd both been considering how to best use their spare time. "I once dreamed of going to beauty school, and I've always enjoyed styling hair. I used to do my mum's when we lived together. It's sort of a hobby for me, as it were. So, if you wouldn't mind, I'd love to cut yours…in the interim, before John arrives.[1134] We could have another cup of tea and…"

"It wouldn't do!" Freddie raised his hands, feigning reluctance.

"No, really, I'd love to!" Cynthia thought that a quick transformation might make Freddie a bit more palatable to his son.

"Well," Freddie grinned, "no skin off mine…if y' really mean it!"

"Done then!" Cynthia smiled. "And rest easy, Freddie…you're in good hands."

Within minutes, Freddie was draped in two large bath towels and seated on a three-legged, wooden stool, atop an old sheet. Cynthia concentrated, snipping away, whilst "the old sea dog" delighted her with yarns and a few of his favourite "vocal selections." Beside them, Julian played, trying to sing along.

"Anywhere I turn up, matey," Julian's grandfather winked and ruffled the lad's Beatle cut, "*fun* is destined to follow!"[1135]

And falling over in a high-pitched giggle, the child became a believer.

****

Thursday, 8 April 1965
Kenwood
Weybridge, Surrey

A little more than 24 hours into Freddie's "extended stay," almost no one else was happy,[1136] not even Cynthia, who had devised the plan.[1137] Lillian thought Freddie "a pathetic hobo," and barely gave him the time of day. Dot thought him another mouth to feed, another bed to make — an extra burden during the already-trying process of moving into Kenwood.

Mimi, who'd rung for Julian's birthday and learned the shocking news of "the unexpected house guest" from Cynthia, was horrified. No one in the Stanley family had ever found a single redemptive quality in the man.[1138] "Well, aside from the fact that he's a charmer,"[1139] Mimi had admitted, begrudgingly. But everything else about Fred Lennon, she'd hissed, was revolting.

Even the man's Scouse accent repulsed her. "When John was young, I went out of my way," she railed on, "to train him to speak proper English. I *never* wanted him to speak like a ruffian,[1140] or to be associated with…the lower classes! But now, you two have one *living* under your very roof — carping on, I'm sure, in that vulgar dialect!"[1141]

"It's only for a few days, Mimi." Cynthia tried to mitigate the imagined damage.

"We always knew," Mimi went on, unfazed, "that Alfred Lennon would *never* be of use to anyone — certainly not our Julia![1142] And now, he's latched on to you, more's the pity."

"Well, to be fair, John barely makes contact with him. I mean, John's off filming all day, and tonight we're invited to the official opening of a new London night club.[1143] So…"

Mimi was hardly listening. "It makes me utterly *ill* to think of John rubbing shoulders with that rough type![1144] Surely you must know, Alf Lennon's gold-digging."[1145]

"As a matter of fact," Cynthia struggled to remain civil, "Freddie hasn't asked for a thing. Of course, if he does, I'm sure John will help him." She enjoyed hearing Mimi huff. "John helps everyone. He always says, 'Money flows in, and money flows out!' That's his attitude."[1146]

"Ugh!" Mimi was almost speechless. "Just have John ring me before you go to that…function tonight!"

"I will, if he comes home to dress, but often he just asks me to meet him…"

"Have him ring me," was the stern directive. And without even the courtesy of a "goodbye," Mary Elizabeth rung off.

****

Over the telephone, John had defended his father, but Mimi's calculated words lingered. They always did.

Even as John chatted with "A Hard Day's Night" co-actor John Junkin and Michael Crawford at the Pickwick,[1147] his aunt's diatribe hovered. And later, on the long, quiet ride home — as Cynthia napped on his shoulder — John began to see everything his father had said or done from Mimi's perspective.

At home, in bed, John whispered, "Mim says Freddie's a cadger.[1148] She says he earns good money, but somehow or another, he's always broke."[1149]

"And how does *she* know how much he earns?" Cynthia was instantly wide awake. Though she, too, was growing weary of Freddie's songs and stories and imitations of Al Jolson, Mimi's prejudiced judgements always offended her.[1150] "Your aunt resents *everyone*, John! She resents me! She tolerates Paul, hates George, despises Ringo...she even calls Pete 'a cadger,'[1151] and he's your best friend!"

"Yeah, right." John listened. He pulled the covers up higher and tried to get comfortable in the gigantic new bed he'd ordered. After their snug double in the attic, he felt lost in it.

"Look, John," Cynthia threw a leg over her husband, snuggling in, "if your father *is* in search of a handout, then he's completely awful at it...because he hasn't said a word. Or even hinted. And, if you must know, the reason I invited him to stay..."

"Y' mean, when I glared at you as if t' say, 'Do you realise what y'er doin'!?!'"[1152] John cut in.

"Yes," Cynthia sighed, "when I invited him and you glared at me...when you were clearly uncomfortable around him and kept going in and out of the room like a cat on a hot tin roof..."[1153]

"Yeah, I recall. Go on."

"Well, the real reason I invited him to stay was that I thought it might be good for *you*, not him.[1154] I thought that you might use this time as an opportunity to talk things out...to ask him the questions you've always wanted to ask."

"Hmmm." Cynthia could feel John deliberating. He rarely ever dismissed an idea out-of-hand. He considered all things possible.

"I know you haven't wanted to open a quarrel, luv," Cynthia went on, "but this is the perfect opportunity to sort things out...isn't it?"

And over the next few hours, whilst Cynthia snored softly beside him, John mulled it over. He developed a strong line of questioning and made a plan.

Tomorrow evenin', he promised himself, *I'll stop being a rejected little boy 'n find out why m' dad left me...'n never came home again.*

This time, John wouldn't be put off. He'd find out.

****

Friday, 9 April 1965
Kenwood
Weybridge, Surrey

It had been a long day of filming. Again. Starting early, they'd shot and reshot a scene: a clash between The Beatles — protected by Superintendent Gluck (the wry Patrick Cargill) and seven of his most stalwart policemen — and the undaunted Clang and his naughty henchmen.[1155] Waiting in a dank, spring-chilled warehouse[1156] whilst the scene was blocked and filmed, and then altered a bit and filmed again, The Beatles had been bored, cold, and hungry. And the experience had left John well-scuppered.

But now, there was a fire and drinks — Fred nursed a pint of lager; John, a Scotch and Coke. Unobtrusively on the sofa, Cynthia sipped...not Earl Grey. It was time.

"So. Where've y' been for the past twenty years?"[1157] John leaned forward, repeating the self-same question he'd asked Freddie last April, in Brian's office.[1158] It was as good a starting place as any.

"But..." Fred frowned, "we've been all through that, Johnny! I told you my story last year! I explained...I was at sea...arrested at one point, thrown in prison...'n very complicated 'n long story short, your Mary Elizabeth 'n my Stanley didn't think I was the 'right sort of influence' for a boy like you. They told me to stay away from you. Mary Elizabeth warned me to stop writin' you letters or else! She said they'd only upset you in the end 'n that you were happy 'n content with her 'n George. She said you didn't need the apple cart upset by the likes o' me is what she said."

"Why did you leave Julia?"[1159] John blurted out, livid. His eyes were narrowed; his jaw, taut. "She would have had you back, y' know."[1160]

"*What's this*?!" Freddie rubbed the aching legs that rickets had badly stunted years ago.[1161] It was his nervous twitch. "How *could I*, John? Julia left *me*!! I didn't leave Julia!"[1162]

In his heart, John knew this. He knew all about his mother's love of the dashing John Dykins from Liverpool's Adelphi Hotel. He remembered the giddy life she'd lived at 1 Blomfield Road, Allerton…with "Bobby," as she called him, and their two precious little girls, John's adoring half-sisters, Jacqui and Julia.[1163] John had been a part of it all, in and out of the house quite regularly.

But that wasn't the scenario in which John wanted to believe. It wasn't the childhood fantasy he'd invented in Mendips's upper room. John had always seen his father as a swashbuckling Errol Flynn, a hero who would suddenly swoop down on Liverpool, claiming his wayward bride and their little son.[1164] And, living happily ever after, the three would settle down together, their family unity restored at last.

"She would have welcomed you back!"[1165] John insisted, barking at the tiny facsimile of himself seated across the sunroom. "She would've rebuilt the marriage!"[1166]

"Where's this comin' from, John?" Freddie looked to Cynthia for answers. He sighed heavily and shook his head. Finally, he fired back. "Julia found another man whilst I was at sea, John! She didn't want me back![1167] Believe me, I know. I tried! I *pleaded*!"

But there was nothing for it. John didn't want to hear this version of the story. The truth.

"I wish…" John jumped up and eyed at his father, "I wish Mimi had told me what kind of father I really had![1168] I wish I'd known from the start."

And refusing to disillusion John further, Freddie said nothing more. He hung his head as John swept up his drink — spilling a quarter of it on the table and rug — and almost ran from the room.

"I'll be goin' tomorrow, Cyn," Freddie said, in a half-sob.

"Yes," Cynthia nodded, "I think it's for the best. But despite all of this, Freddie, I want you to know that John informed me last night that you're 'all right.' He even said you're 'a bit wacky, like him.' He said that watching you over the last few days, he can see where he 'got things.' He told me that with you here, he's begun to know "where he came from."[1169]

"Well, then," Freddie stood, "there's that."

And without another word, the senior Mr. Lennon mizzled off to pack the little drawings and treasures that Julian and Cynthia had given him during his all-too-brief stay in Kenwood.

****

John collapsed on the bed and grabbed his guitar. Brooding, he leaned against the massive headboard and strummed the Jumbo quietly, playing the opener that he'd just written for the film.[1170]

He knew that Martin and the others would make the song into a fast-paced rocker, the sort of rumbler that could open an adventure "flick," as they now called them.[1171] He'd knew the powers-that-be wanted an energetic backdrop for their pseudo-James-Bond-Ringo-escaping-the-villains romp.[1172]

But as it stood, the song wasn't fun, and it wasn't happy.[1173] And the way he sang it now, you could tell.

"Help me, if you can," he sang slowly, "I'm feelin' down…"

Cynthia shuffled in, removing her earrings and the wispy, black scarf she'd tied into her teased flip. She bit her lip, trying not to well up at the painful, candid words.

John crooned, softly, his voice cracking as he held the note on "grou-ound."

When Cynthia doffed the overhead light, the room fell dark, save one small orange splotch from the bedside lamp.

"Won't you please," John sang, earnestly, "please…help me."

And in the room's weighted shade, Cynthia brushed her hair, trying to think of a way that she *could* help. Gradually, John was drifting into a deep, isolated depression.[1174] They were both high and dry these days, and for weeks, she'd found no way to cross over to her husband. She was alone. John was alone. It was a frightening impasse.

No, she bit her lip. *It's petrifying. We have no one.*

Notes!

1. Were there, in fact, two meetings between John and Freddie Lennon, and if so, when did they occur?

There were, in fact, two meetings between Fred and John — the first on 1 April 1964 in the London NEMS office and then twelve months later, a second meeting in April of 1965. Many biographers combine the two meetings into one event.

Cynthia never mentioned the 1964 meeting between father and son in her first book, A Twist of Lennon. But in her 2005 book, John, Cynthia says that when Fred showed up at Kenwood in April 1965, John told her that his father and he "had met briefly a few weeks earlier when [Freddie] turned up in John's dressing room…" (p. 180) Cynthia says that until the 1965 meeting, she had never heard a word about the initial encounter between father and son. It's possible that John truly forgot that the reunion had occurred the year prior; it's also possible that John purposely minimized the length of time since the 1964 reunion because he had never, in all that time, told his wife about the event.

Cynthia's account of Fred's 1965 three-day visit to Kenwood is completely different in her interview with Ray Coleman for his master-work, Lennon (1984), and in her 2005 account of that same event in John. In John, she says that John never turned up at Kenwood on the day that Fred arrived unexpectedly, and so "A couple of hours later, with no sign of John, [Fred] went on his way." (p. 180)

However, in Coleman's book, Lennon (pp. 302-304), Cynthia supplies vivid details about Freddie's three-day 1965 visit in Kenwood, even sharing the story of John's emotional confrontation with his father, which is repeated in this chapter.

Both the 1964 and the 1965 reunions between Freddie and John occurred, as both Pauline Lennon in Daddy Come Home and Tim Riley in Lennon concur. Cynthia did invite Fred to stay for three days. Cynthia told Ray Coleman (in 1984) that with Fred in their house "the pressures on [John] mounted so much that he was out more often than he was at home, leaving [her] with the unpleasant job of talking to his father." (Lennon, p. 304) She did encourage John to confront his father, and after what Cynthia calls "a fruitless discussion" about Fred's failure to save his marriage to Julia, Fred agreed to leave. (Coleman, Lennon, 304)

2. Has history treated Freddie Lennon fairly?

John's dear friend, Bill Harry, in The Encyclopedia of Beatles People, says that Fred Lennon, "has been maligned in Beatles books much more than is warranted." (p. 90) He goes on to say, "In 1946, when Fred *docked in Southampton, he contacted Mimi and asked if he could take John to Blackpool. He then decided that he and John could forge a new life for themselves in New Zealand and was making plans when Julia arrived, demanding the return of John. As John wanted to go with his mother, Fred agreed." (p. 91)*

Ray Coleman, in Lennon, *tells us, "Julia delivered [John] back to Liverpool, safe into the loving arms of her sister Mimi, who was to care for him with conscientiousness, strictness — and passion." (p. 22) It had been decided that John was to live with Mimi and George in Mendips.*

As Pauline Lennon summarizes in Daddy Come Home, *"So, John settled in at 251 Menlove Avenue where he was to spend the remainder of his childhood with the forty-three-year-old Mimi Smith...who had now achieved her ambition to rear him as her own...Mimi's home was large and spacious...But psychologically, [John] was devastated. The confusion of the last few months had proved bewildering to John. In choosing to be with his mother at the expense of his parting from his father, John had, in fact, ended up losing both parents...*

"John was not to see Freddie again throughout his childhood, and he received no information about him from Mimi...no matter how often he pressed his aunt to talk to him about his father, she simply pursed her lips and left his questions unanswered. By Mimi's standards, Freddie was a failure, and she felt the less said about him, the better...Freddie's name was never mentioned." (Lennon, Pauline, pp. 83-84)

Fred did write to John in the months after his departure but his letters were never shown to his son. He wanted to stay in contact with John and would have visited him when his ship docked in England. After all, why would a man who had planned to take his son to New Zealand to live together as father and son suddenly abandon the child? However, Mimi, who did not have legal guardianship of the child, was (as Pauline Lennon writes in Daddy Come Home*) "only too well aware that, as his natural father, Freddie could turn up at any time to snatch the boy away to the other side of the world..." (p. 90)*

So, Pauline Lennon goes on to say, "For her own security as John's guardian...she [wrote] to Freddie in stern tones, informing him that John was now living with her and advising him to keep out of his son's life." (p. 90)

Mimi's letter to Fred is quoted as saying: "You must resign yourself to the fact that you have now completely severed any hopes you may have had of obtaining custody of the boy...You have made an absolute shamble of your life and have brought shame and scandal upon your family. If you have a shred of decency left in you, I advise you to...put your past life behind you...Surely you don't want your son to know you've been in jail." (Lennon, Pauline, p. 90)

And with that, Fred Lennon's letters to John ceased.

But John's relationship with his mother flourished after the death of his Uncle George in the summer of 1955. Returning to John's life as a "best friend," Julia became his constant companion. They spent countless hours together as she taught John to play banjo, inspired him to form a skiffle band, and told him that he had "music in his bones." Julia played her rock'n'roll records for the boy and introduced him to Elvis and Little Richard, as they "rocked around the clock."

Julia, however, never mentioned Freddie either. She didn't tell John that his father had wanted him and had tried to win him away from her. Nothing was said about "the invisible man," one way or the other.

When Fred returned to John's life in 1964 and then again in 1965, John was clearly faced with a sticky wicket: If he believed Freddie, then he would be admitting that Mimi — and possibly, his beloved mother as well — purposely side-stepped the truth about his father.

And so, John did exactly what Hunter Davies did when presented with both stories. As John's dear friend Bill Harry writes in The Encyclopedia of Beatles People: *"When Fred was interviewed by Hunter Davies for his authorized Beatles biography, Fred's version of events was vetoed and Mimi's version was put to the fore." (p. 191) And that is exactly what happened in John's mind. Once again, he chose Julia.*

In my Liverpool interview with John's Uncle Charlie Lennon, he said, "Well, Fred said he was willing to settle down and take young John to live with him. But we all found it hard to believe. After all, he was a rover, was Fred. But he was never given the chance to be proven wrong, was he? And so, we'll never know, one way or t' other. But I do know this: when Johnny became famous, our Fred didn't try to push himself on his son. In fact, he ran from the press. Only after they hounded him for a story did our Fred get in touch with John. I believe Fred was happy living as he was. He didn't want anything from John..."

The story unfolding in 1965 was complicated. John's relationship with his parents had always cast a shade over his life and continued to do so.

3. Was the upbeat title song for The Beatles' second United Artists film "Help!" truly a mournful autobiographical song from John Lennon?

In The Beatles Encyclopedia, *author Dr. Kenneth Womack states, "Written largely by Lennon, "Help!" was originally a slow-tempo composition that evoked the anxiety of Lennon's lyrics. The song's tempo was intentionally sped up in the studio to make it more commercially viable — a move that Lennon deeply regretted."*

Dr. Womack, along with Dr. Walter Everett in The Beatles as Musicians: The Quarry Men Through *Rubber Soul, 296, Tony Barrow in* John, Paul, George, Ringo & Me, *146, Spitz in* The Beatles, *555, Badman in* The Beatles: Off the Record, *99, Margotin and Guesdon in* All the Songs, *220, and many others cite John's very revealing quote:*

"The whole Beatle thing was just beyond comprehension. When "Help!" came out, I was actually crying out for help. Most people think it's just a fast rock'n'roll song. I didn't realize it at the time; I just wrote the song because I was commissioned to write it for the movie. But later, I knew I really was crying out for help. So, it was my fat Elvis period. You see the movie: He...I...is very fat, very insecure, and he's completely lost himself. And I am singing about when I was so much younger and all the rest, looking back at how easy it was...I go through deep depressions where I would like to jump out of the window...Anyway, I was fat and depressed, and I was crying out for help."

Sources:

Interview with Charles Lennon, The Grapes Pub, Liverpool, 1995.
Interview with Julia Baird, June, 2021.

Lewisohn, The Complete Beatles Chronicle, *187.*
Harry, The Ultimate Beatles Encyclopedia, *372-373.*
Harry, The Encyclopedia of Beatles People, *190-191.*
Harry, The John Lennon Encyclopedia, *190-191, 373, and 476.*
The Beatles, The Beatles Anthology, *180.*
Lennon, Cynthia, John, *14-15 and 179-180.*
Lennon, Cynthia, A Twist of Lennon, *7.*
Lennon, Pauline, Daddy Come Home, *83-84, 90, 113, and 123.*
Baird, Julia, John Lennon: My Brother, *12, 21-22, and 95.*
Baird, Julia, Imagine This: Growing Up with My Brother, John Lennon, *23-24.*
Coleman, Lennon, *20, 273-274, 288, and 302-304.*
Norman, Shout!, *243.*
Norman, John Lennon: The Life, *103, 391, and 397-398.*
Goldman, *28 and 287.*
Barrow, *146-147.*
Badman, *99.*
Brown, *167, 171.*
Miles, Paul McCartney: Many Years from Now, *30-32 and 169-170.*
Miles, The Beatles' Diary, Vol. 1, *139, 193.*
Womack, The Beatles Encyclopedia, *375-376.*
Womack, Maximum Volume: The Life of Beatles Producer, George

Martin, *275.*
Womack, Long and Winding Roads: The Evolving Artistry of The Beatles, *107.*
Everett, The Beatles as Musicians: The Quarry Men Through *Rubber Soul, 296.*
DuNoyer, We All Shine On: The Story Behind Every John Lennon Song, 1970-1980, *27-28.*
Kenny, Francis,166.
Spitz, 21-23, 497, and 555.
Robertson, John, "Help: The Beginning of the End," Trynka, The Beatles: Ten Years that Shook the World, *167.*
Connolly, 208.
Turner, 74-75.
Margotin and Guesdon, 220.
Bicknell, 37.
Buskin, 113-114.
Riley, Lennon, *252, 272.*
Schultheiss, 132.

https://en.wikipedia.org/wiki/Alfred_Lennon This website gives a very accurate account of Fred's life, clearing up many urban legends about the man.

https://www.bing.com/videos/search?q=video+of+John+Lennon+talking +about+Kenwood&&view=detail&mid=1E8BB3B39A4D6630EDCE1E8 BB3B39A4D6630EDCE&&FORM=VDRVSR This is an audio tape (accompanied by a few photos) of Cynthia reading from her book, John. In this clip, she is describing Kenwood — what it was like when John and she discovered it, what the renovations involved, and how it looked afterwards.

https://www.youtube.com/watch?v=KkcBqKwZKNM This is a 1965 video of John talking about Kenwood and its furnishings.

https://kenwoodlennon.blogspot.com/2013/01/kenwood-1965.html This website gives you a wonderful glance at Kenwood when Cynthia and John were moving into it, renovated, in the spring of 1965. Enjoy!

http://triumphpc.com/mersey-beat/beatles/unclecharlie.shtml This website, authored by Bill Harry, gives a brief interview on the background of the Lennon family in an interview with John's Uncle Charlie.

https://web.archive.org/web/20080614235259/http://www.lennon.net/fa milytree/sub/pauline_lennon.shtml This website gives additional information about Freddie Lennon and Pauline Lennon.

**Sam Flannery, the author, John's Uncle Charlie Lennon, and
Eddie Porter in The Grapes, Mathew Street, Liverpool**
Photograph used by permission of Rande Kessler

**Jude and Julia Baird
at the New York Fest for Beatles Fans, 2014**
Photograph used by kind permission of Rande Kessler

[1107] Robertson, John, "'Help!' The End of the Beginning," Trynka, *The
Beatles: Ten Years that Shook the World,* 167. Robertson says that "almost

simultaneously" with the evening that John and George experimented with LSD for the first time, "John was visited at home by an unwelcome reminder of his past, his long-vanished father." All accounts of this second meeting have it happening just a few days after the LSD experience. And all accounts have John away in Twickenham, filming for the greater part of the day, with Cynthia having to entertain Fred.

[1108] Lewisohn, *The Complete Beatles Chronicle*, 187.

[1109] Miles, *Many Years From Now*, 169 and Spitz, 383. Miles says that John so enjoyed the Scalextric model racing car set that the boys had set up backstage during the 1964 North American Tour that he came home and purchased 20 sets of his own for Kenwood. In this 30 November 1965 BBC interview, John says that he set up a separate bedroom in the house as a "racing room": https://www.youtube.com/watch?v=KkcBqKwZKNM

[1110] Miles, *Many Years From Now*, 169.

[1111] Miles, *Many Years From Now*, 169-170 and https://www.youtube.com/watch?v=KkcBqKwZKNM.

[1112] Miles, *Many Years From Now*, 169-170 and https://www.youtube.com/watch?v=KkcBqKwZKNM

[1113] Miles, *Many Years From Now*, 169-170 and https://www.youtube.com/watch?v=KkcBqKwZKNM

[1114] Miles, *Many Years From Now*, 169 and Spitz, 383. Miles says, "There was a Hollywood Modern kitchen so complicated that someone had to be sent from London to show Cynthia how to use it."

[1115] Lennon, Cynthia, *John*, 179 and Coleman, *Lennon*, 304. Cynthia told Ray Coleman that Freddie had on "a shabby suit." In *John*, she calls Fred's appearance "down-at-the-heel."

[1116] Harry, *The John Lennon Encyclopedia*, 476, Brown, 167, Lennon, Cynthia, *John*, 179, and Goldman, 287. Cynthia calls him "a tiny man," and Bill Harry explains that childhood rickets had stunted the growth of Fred's legs. He says Fred was 4' 4". (p. 476)

[1117] Lennon, Cynthia, *John*, 179. Cynthia says that although he looked like a "hobo," Fred, "alarmingly, had John's face."

[1118] Coleman, *Lennon*, 302. According to John's report of this event to Ray Coleman, this was Fred Lennon's exact quote.

[1119] Coleman, *Lennon*, 302.

[1120] Goldman, 287. Goldman says, "When Freddie opened his mouth to speak, he projected the very sound of John's voice with the same Liverpudlian intonation, but with a rather more cosmopolitan accent because the former merchant mariner had spent so much of his life in foreign travel." To hear the sound of Fred's voice, listen to his spoken record, "That's My Life," found here: https://www.youtube.com/watch?v=azAiSG09FBk

[1121] Coleman, 288. Direct quote from Fred Lennon.

[1122] Lennon, Cynthia, *John*, 179.

[1123] Coleman, *Lennon*, 302. Coleman is quoting Cynthia's version of the story, told to him by her.

[1124] Lennon, Cynthia, *John*, 179. Cynthia says, "Once I got over the shock, I asked him in, gave him a cup of tea and some cheese on toast."

[1125] Spitz, 383.

[1126] Spitz, 21.

[1127] Spitz, 21 and interview with Charlie Lennon, The Grapes Pub, Liverpool, 1995.

[1128] Lennon, Cynthia, *John*, 179 and Coleman, *Lennon*, 302. In *John*, Cynthia writes, "I was a little anxious about John's reaction, but I felt I couldn't shut the door in his father's face." She also told Ray Coleman, "I had no alternative but to ask [Fred] to wait for John to return."

[1129] Julian was born on 8 April 1963.

[1130] Lennnon, Cynthia, *John*, 14-15 and Lennon, *A Twist of Lennon*, 7.

[1131] Lennon, Cynthia, *John*, 179.

[1132] Goldman, 287. Direct quote from Fred Lennon.

[1133] Goldman, 287. Other than the words, "He's very tough altogether," this is a direct quote from Fred Lennon.

[1134] Lennon, Cynthia, *John*, 180. Cynthia says, "I'd always enjoyed hairdressing — I used to do Mum's when we lived together — so I was itching to take the scissors to Alf's long, stringy locks. He agreed."

[1135] Spitz, 21. Spitz says, "anywhere Fred turned up always meant fun was about to start."

[1136] Riley, *Lennon*, 272 and Coleman, *Lennon*, 302. Riley says that Fred stayed at Kenwood for three days. Although in Cynthia Lennon's 2005 book, *John*, she says that Fred left Kenwood before John came home, she had told Ray Coleman much earlier, for his 1984 biography, *Lennon*, that in April of 1965, "John came home to find his father sitting in his lounge, drinking a cup of tea."

[1137] Riley, *Lennon*, 272 and Coleman, *Lennon*, 302.

[1138] Kenny, Francis, *The Making of John Lennon*, 166 and Spitz, 21. Spitz quotes Leila Stanley Harvey, John's cousin, as saying the Stanleys "wanted nothing to do with [Fred] from the start."

[1139] Spitz, 23.

[1140] Kenny, 166. Direct quote from Mimi Smith.

[1141] Kenny, 166.

[1142] Spitz, 21. Direct quote from Mimi Smith.

[1143] Miles, *The Beatles' Diary, Vol. 1,* 193 and Bicknell, 37. Although the club had been open for some weeks, The Beatles were all attending the official opening of "Downstairs at the Pickwick" on the evening of 9 April.

[1144] Kenny, 166. Kenny states that Mimi thought it degrading enough that John had associated himself with "two from the council estates" (George and Paul) and then later with "one from the Dingle! God forbid!" (Ringo) But now, he had a dishwasher living under his very roof. For her, this was "the last straw."

[1145] Lennon, Cynthia, *John,* 180.

[1146] Connolly, 208. "Money flows in and money flows out" is a direct quote from John Lennon.

[1147] Miles, *The Beatles' Diary, Vol. 1,* 193 and Bicknell, 37.

[1148] Connolly, 208.

[1149] Coleman, *Lennon*, 303.

[1150] Spitz, 23. Spitz says that Fred "had Al Jolson down cold, with all the gesticulations."

[1151] Connolly, 208.

[1152] Coleman, 303. Cynthia says this was a direct quote from John Lennon when she invited Fred to stay at Kenwood a few days.

[1153] Coleman, 303. Direct quote from Cynthia Lennon.

[1154] Lennon, Cynthia, *John*, 180. Cynthia says that she knew John "still hoped for a father-son relationship."

[1155] Lewisohn, *The Complete Beatles Chronicle*, 187.

[1156] Lewisohn, *The Complete Beatles Chronicle*, 187. Mark Lewisohn reminds us that this was one clip that was filmed but not included in "Help!"

[1157] Trynka, 167, Riley, *Lennon*, 272, Coleman, *Lennon*, 302, and Buskin, 113.

[1158] Lennon, Pauline, *Daddy Come Home*, 107-111, Lewisohn, *The Beatles: Day by Day*, 44, Badman, 99, Miles, *The Beatles' Diary, Vol. 1*, 139, Spitz, 497, Norman, *John Lennon: The Life*, 103, Harry, *The John Lennon Encyclopedia*, 373, Goldman 287, and Riley, 252. For more about this 1964 meeting on 1 April 1964, see Vol. 4 in **The John Lennon Series**, *Should Have Known Better*, pp. 169-183.

[1159] Coleman, *Lennon*, 303. According to Cynthia, this is a direct quote from John Lennon to his father at Kenwood, April 1965.

[1160] Coleman, *Lennon*, 303. According to Cynthia, this is a direct quote from John Lennon to his father at Kenwood, April 1965.

[1161] Goldman, 287 and Harry, *The John Lennon Encyclopedia*, 476. Harry says that, as a child, Freddie "had to wear irons on his legs because he was afflicted with rickets."

[1162] Coleman, *Lennon*, 303. This is a direct quote from Fred Lennon to his son, according to Cynthia Lennon's interview with Ray Coleman.

[1163] Coleman, *Lennon*, 20 and Baird, *John Lennon: My Brother*, 12 and 21-22.

[1164] Coleman, *Lennon*, 303. Cynthia says that John had always held an image of his seafaring father as "an Errol Flynn type...romantically sailing around the world." She says that John refused to accept that Julia had left Freddie, and kept asking Fred why he had abandoned Julia.

[1165] Coleman, *Lennon*, 303. This is a direct quote from John Lennon to his father, according to Cynthia Lennon's interview with Ray Coleman.

[1166] Coleman, Lennon, 303. Direct quote from John Lennon to his father, according to Cynthia Lennon's interview with Ray Coleman.

[1167] Coleman, *Lennon*, 303. These two sentences are direct quotes from John Lennon to his father, according to Cynthia Lennon's interview with Ray Coleman.

[1168] Coleman, *Lennon*, 304. Coleman says that John phoned Mimi the next day and said, "How could my mother marry a man like that!? Why didn't you tell me what kind of father I had?" And Mimi responded, "Oh dear boy, how would I know what kind of father you had? I didn't know him well myself. Did you want me to bring you up telling you he was a bad man who left you? Would that have made you happier? You've always been happy, haven't you?" And John's heart-breaking response was, "Yes, I'm the happiest person in the whole family."

[1169] Lennon, Cynthia, *John*, 180. These are direct quotes from John Lennon, according to Cynthia Lennon.

[1170] Margotin and Guesdon, 220, Schultheiss, 132, and Turner, 74-75. For those who call this song a collaboration, Paul clears the air. He is quoted,

saying, "My main contribution [to 'Help!'] is the counter-melody to John."
Margotin and Guesdon clearly point out that "John composed the eponymous
song." Similarly in *A Hard Day's Write*, Steve Turner says, "The lyric
reflected John's dissatisfaction with himself. 'I needed help,' [John] said, 'The
song was about me.'" Schultheiss points out that John and Paul wrote the song
on 4 April 1965.

[1171] Womack, *Maximum Volume: The Life of Beatles Producer, George
Martin,* 257. Womack aptly observes, "When John sat down to bring the title
track to fruition, he was in the act...of making a literal cry for help through the
auspices of his music...In its original incarnation, 'Help!' was a downbeat,
piano-oriented tune."

[1172] Womack, *Maximum Volume: The Life of Beatles Producer, George
Martin,* 257, Badman, 162, Margotin and Guesdon, 220, Spitz, 555, Norman,
John Lennon: The Life, 397-398, Schaffner, 42, and Barrow, 146. In *Off the
Record,* Keith Badman quotes John Lennon as saying about the song "Help!",
"I meant it. It's real! It's just me singing, 'Help!' and I meant it. I don't like
the recording that much. We did it too fast, to be commercial. When 'Help!'
came out, I was crying for help." Tony Barrow includes the same quote in his
book, but after John's words, "I was crying out for help," Barrow quotes John
as saying additionally that he was going through "deep depressions where I
would want to jump out of the window." (p. 146) In April 1965, John was in
emotional pain. In *All the Songs*, Margotin and Guesdon sum the song's
message up by saying, "[John] poured all his dark and unhappy thoughts into
his song on the ['Help!'] album."

[1173] Badman, 162, Margotin and Guesdon, 220, Spitz, 555, Norman, *John
Lennon: The Life,* 397-398, and Barrow, 146.

[1174] Barrow, 146. Direct quote from John Lennon. Also, Womack in *Long and
Winding Roads: The Evolving Artistry of The Beatles,* says, "['Help!''s]
nostalgia emerges from John's wistful yearnings for a simpler past...Married
and isolated in the London suburbs, he felt alienated and lost with 'Help!'
becoming his literal cry for emancipation and assistance." (p. 107) In *The Love
You Make,* Beatles friend Peter Brown observes that John wrote "Help!" "out
of loneliness and despair much greater than the previous, 'I'm A Loser.'" (p.
171)

Sunday, 11 April 1965
En Route to Teddington Studio Centre
Teddington, London

"Will w' have to call y' Father Ringo, now?" George took the mickey out.

"Well, I'm not one yet, am I?" Ringo scowled and looked out the limousine window.[1175] Becoming a father was a double-edged sword.[1176] It was wonderful, of course, but would take some getting used to. For the first time, Ringo felt intimidatingly old.

"How's Maureen, then?" Paul clicked his cheek.

"Awright, y' know," Ringo nodded sideways, "but if she eats a bice, she..."

"Don't remind me," John intervened. "I remember."

The official announcement had been made in the newspapers last Wednesday.[1177] And ever since then, fans had been sending cards, blankets, and booties to the Starkeys' London flat. With months to go before the birth, Ringo's contingent was already planning the baby's future.

"Another motivation for movin' to Weybridge." For weeks, John had been hurling hints in Ringo's direction.

"Or Esher," George murmured.

"Yeah, might do." Ringo and Maureen had been seriously mulling the move over. They got on famously with John and Cyn. In fact, when the four had lived in London, they'd spent lots of free time together. And now, as the only two married Beatles, John and Ringo held even more in common.[1178] "Brian says we're gettin' an agent to show us 'round."

"I'm still lookin' at that three-storey Regent in Cavendish Avenue." Paul had no desire to vacate to the country. He loved London's theatre, opera, and varied city nightlife.[1179] "It's historic, y' know. Rather Dickens. It has a high brick wall 'n sturdy, black metal gates.[1180] 'N it's only a short walk to EMI..."[1181]

"Though *you'll* never walk it," John said.

"Well, y' never know, do you, John?" Paul countered. But really, none of them could walk anywhere anymore (unless they attempted it, rather recklessly, in the small hours of the morning — as John and Neil had recently done, after partying with Mick Jagger and Keith Richards).[1182]

"I suppose you heard Pete Best's band just broke up?" George's face was solemn. Although all of them knew that Ringo — who was the star of this second film as well as the first — had been perfect for them, none of them lived without guilt in the Best matter.

"Yeah," John nodded, "a week past."[1183]

For a few minutes, they rode in bumpy silence.

"Alf, the radio,"[1184] John advised. And as Denny Laine of the Moody Blues belted out "Go Now!",[1185] the boys kept their uneasy thoughts to themselves.

"I know...Winners and Losers!"[1186] Paul announced as the song ended. The noisy travel game was their favourite distraction on the road. "EMI!" he kicked things off.

"Winner!" they yelled, almost in unison.

"Decca!" Paul called out.

"Loser!" was the keen cry.

It was John's turn. He attempted a French accent. "Frrrance!"

"Losers!" the boys cried back, in their own tongue.

"America!" John raised an enthusiastic fist.

"Winners!" the others agreed.

"Coca-Cola!" George took the lead.

"Winner!" they applauded their beverage of choice.

"Pepsi?" George lifted an eyebrow.

"Loser!" It was unanimous.

"Los Angeles!" Ringo knew this answer.

"Loooooser!" The Beatles had despised much of their time there in 1964. The "command performance" ice cream social with scads of uppity Hollywood stars and their children had tipped the balance for the worst.

"New York!" Ringo countered, with a deep chuckle.

"Winner!"[1187] the others concurred.

And smiling at memories of two magical nights in Forest Hills Tennis Stadium and their "interesting" evening with "Mr.

Zimmerman" (as John called Bob Dylan), The Beatles were back to being Beatles again.

Babbling over one another about the rowdy crowd of 10,000 fans at the *New Musical Express* Poll Winners All-Star concert earlier that afternoon[1188] and their "kick" of receiving the *NME* award from New York's musical don, Tony Bennett,[1189] the boys were once again caught up in the bright business of today…and suddenly hazy about the murky events of tomorrow or yesterday.

****

Teddington Studios, Richmond-on-Thames, London,
where The Beatles appeared on
"The Eamonn Andrews Show," 11 April 1965
Original 1960s photographer unknown

Teddington Studio Centre
Teddington, London

6.30 p.m.

People rarely gave a thought to whether or not The Beatles had had sustenance. Minds were focused, instead, on equipment, run-throughs, sound levels — that sort. The moment that they had arrived in Teddington, Brian had traipsed off to parley "the important details."

"We're starvin' here, y' know," the "Quiet Beatle" insisted to a frowning stage hand, when they filed into the sparse dressing room.

"Y' see," Paul explained, more politely, "when we were supposed to be havin' somethin' to eat, earlier...we had this interview with 'the Fifth Beatle.'"[1190]

"Murray the K," John elucidated, "a self-nominated Beatle, a self-enshrined 'important American deejay.'"[1191]

"So," Ringo picked up the narrative, "if there's a place to muck in..."

"Right, right." The assistant's assistant nodded. "Let me see what I can do."

Whilst the boys washed up and changed clothes, a nearby take-away was found and meals retrieved[1192] by Alf Bicknell. Perched in front of the long, narrow dressing room vanity, the boys scarfed down greasy, lukewarm fish and chips, just prior to the 7.30 p.m. blocking and camera run-through.[1193]

"Who's this Wolf Mankowitz when he's at home?" Ringo scanned the typewritten list of co-stars on the evening's programme as he ate.

"Author, critic...primarily a playwright," John smoked, flicking ashes onto the sodden plate. He'd devoured his food in minutes. "He wrote that book, *Expresso Bongo*, that was made into the Cliff Richard film. And he did the script for *The Millionairess* with Peter Sellers..."[1194]

"...*and* Sophia Loren!" George flashed his soft half-grin.

"Well, awright then!" Ringo flashed a "thumbs up" and read on, narrowing one eye. "Katharine Whitehorn? Who's she?"

"Journalist." Paul knew the press. "She posed for that famous Lucozade advertisement before she started her writin' career. These days, she's with the *Observer,* isn't she?"[1195]

"How should I know?" Ringo lifted a shoulder. "I'm the one askin' you, son!"

"All right, boys," Neil appeared in the doorway. "Time to go, then."

"But I haven't finished m' chips!" Ringo protested.

"Bad luck, that!" Neil chuckled.

"He's been talkin' too much!" George slapped Ringo on the back as he followed Aspinall into the hall.

"I'm filin' a grievance!" Ringo vowed, following them reluctantly. His voice was fringed with fatigue.

"Oh, really? I've never been so unconcerned!" Neil laughed. "How 'bout you lads?"

They all yawned loudly, feigning indifference. Not one of them was, apparently, on Ringo's side. You had to be tough to be a Beatle.

****

Studio 1[1196]
Teddington Studio Centre
Teddington, London

11.05 p.m.

It had just gone eleven. The boys, who'd done well in the 8.45 to 9.30 p.m. dress rehearsal, were gathered in the wings, primed for the walk-on and pre-performance chat with tall, broad-shouldered Irish entertainer, Eamonn Andrews.[1197]

John and Ringo were similarly attired, in dark polos topped with dark suits. Ringo had chosen his velvet-lapeled jacket whereas John — who'd been sternly directed to remove his gum — was more casual. Paul and George were dressed in matching garb. But Paul was all polish. He'd selected a loose-weave tweed jacket and polo and had combed his hair to perfection, whereas George — scratching in an itchy, tight-weave, beige wool — seemed ill-at-ease. His overlong fringe hung directly into his eyes, and he chewed the inside of one gaunt cheek.[1198]

"Now remember," Brian cautioned them, "you're here to promote the new single...our first of the year, you realise."[1199]

"When's *that* comin' out?" John kept a straight face.

"'Ticket to Ride' was released *two days ago*, John!"[1200] Brian's neck instantly mottled. Once again, John had spun him into high dudgeon.

"Did it, now?" John sneered.

"He knows it did." George calmed the kerfuffle.

"Well then why…" Brian began sternly, but the sound of Andrews's theme music rescued John from censure. As the programme's emcee announced: "From London…The Eamonn Andrews Show!",[1201] John swiveled away to face the stage.

"Tonight, Eamonn's guests are," the announcer went on, "Katharine Whitehorn, Wolf Mankowitz, John Lennon, Paul McCartney, Ringo Starr, George Harrison."[1202]

"Why 'm *I* last?" George bemoaned.

"It's usually me," Ringo whispered.

"*Shhh!*" Brian hissed.

"And now," the announcer paused for effect, "Here's Eamonn Andrews!"

The live audience cheered and whistled. Someone yelled "Aieeeeee!" as if in pain, and laughter rose over the applause.[1203]

Andrews, curly-haired and thick-jawed, was a former boxer and a seasoned performer, and he knew what audiences wanted. The moment he strode onto stage, he got right to it. "And…welcome!" he beamed into the camera, "Yes, ladies and gentlemen, it is…The Beatles!"[1204]

Tossing a Cheshire grin at Brian, John led the others onto the stage with a sharp cry of "Crackerjack!"[1205] Andrews beamed appreciatively at the clever reference to his weekly children's game-and-variety show.

Immediately, the smartness of The Beatles brightened Andrews's unimaginative, beige-curtained backdrop and his budget-conscious, pseudo-wooden desk, with its tufted, faux-leather front panel.[1206] With the boys there, the paltry set seemed almost fantastic. The Beatles were directed to sit around a low coffee table where microphones were strategically placed. John sat beside Eamonn at the host's desk. Ringo and George shared a sofa. And Paul was given his own swivel chair.[1207]

In the audience, Alf Bicknell caught Paul's eye.[1208] Paul offered a brisk backwards nod, and Alf grinned broadly — well-chuffed.

"Thank you, boys!" Eamonn sat, quickly making the superstars at home. "I'm absolutely delighted! As you know, later we're going to be joined by Katharine Whitehorn and Wolf Mankowitz, talking about what you or they or anyone else feels like talking about, but I can't begin the show without starting off and congratulating Ringo…Ringo, congratulations!"[1209]

The ABC studio crowd, not all of them aware of the fact that Ringo had been publicly proclaimed "an expectant father," flew into applause, nevertheless. The Beatles were always doing *something* worth congratulating.

"Congratulations!" Paul winked at the drummer.

"Congratulations!" George echoed.

"Congratulations!"[1210] John freighted his compliment with irony.

The boys were having fun.

"How does it feel to be an expectant dad?"[1211] Eamonn grinned in the direction of Ringo and George.

"Not so bad, y' know," Ringo said, "Not so bad. I hope it's a boy or a girl!"[1212]

Whilst the audience snickered, Paul asked, "What'd he say? What'd he say?" And George gave his friend a "Ha-ha, ha-ha, ha-ha…"[1213]

In high spirits, John leaned towards the drummer and suggested, "It might be an eye!"[1214]

Eamonn shook his head at the banter. The boys were just as he'd heard — untamed. "When it *does come*, boy or girl, George, you might go to John here for some good advice…"[1215]

"I'm not George,"[1216] Ringo muttered.

"That's *my name*!"[1217] George tapped his chest. "That's me!"

"True, true," Eamonn blushed, working quickly to cover his blunder. He glanced over at John, "*Will you* be able to give him some good advice?"[1218]

But instantly, John was in no mood to assist Andrews with the awkward situation. The fact that their host didn't know The Beatles apart, hadn't sorted out their identities prior to the programme galled him. The slight was absurd.

The day had been long and challenging. After working the better part of yesterday in Riverside Studios, filming a *Top of the Pops* performance, promoting "Ticket to Ride"/"Yes It Is,"[1219] the boys had risen early again this morning for the trek to the *NME* concert. In Wembley, they'd taken photographs, sat for interviews, and performed on stage — the whole gamut. But instead of enjoying the remainder of their Sunday evening at home, they'd hurried on for the return trip to London and this late-night Andrews gig.[1220]

And *that* was the irritant. Whereas The Beatles were expected to hit every mark, answer every query, and do everything every day professionally, the host of a prominent television programme couldn't tell them one from another...couldn't or didn't care to. Either way, for John, it was a bruised moment.

Thinning his lips and softening his tone — all the more foreboding, if one knew John Lennon —a curt "No" was all he said.[1221]

Scrambling to make amends for the *faux pas*, Andrews pandered, "Anyway, I know you're working on your new film, and that means you've less time to spare than you ever had before, and I'm very delighted that you gave me some of your spare time tonight."[1222]

Batting his eyelashes rapidly and employing a mocking, upper crust accent, John returned, "It'sapleasurecoming. Good night!"[1223]

The audience roared, but Paul, who'd come to know John's moods over the years, heard more than a comical phrase. He stepped in.

"Now, this is your second film..."[1224] Eamonn was still looking towards John.

"Yes,"[1225] Paul quickly cut across them, claiming the question.

Andrews shifted his eyes to this new Beatle. "The first film — let's address this to you, Paul, so there's no confusion — the first one was compared to The Marx Brothers. Remember it?"[1226]

"Oh, I..." Paul wasn't certain if Andrews was asking if he remembered "A Hard Day's Night" or if he remembered that particular critic's observation. So, noncommittally, he said, "Yes, yes, well..."[1227]

Observing Paul's hesitation, Eamonn lifted an eyebrow. "Have you ever *seen* The Marx Brothers?"[1228]

Now, it was Paul's turn to be insulted, but tactfully, he covered it well. "Yes," McCartney nodded. "Nothin' like 'em!"[1229]

"*Nothing* like you?" Eamonn pressed.[1230]

Paul smiled brightly, but refused to budge. "We're nothin' like that, no."[1231]

"Well," the host let the boy have his way, "what sort of thing — and this is addressed to all of you — what sort of thing makes you fellas laugh?"[1232]

"Uh," Paul looked directly into the camera and smirked. "The Marx Brothers!"[1233]

In a shower of snickers, giggles, and applause, The Beatles won the volley. And John, pleased to see Andrews bested, uncrossed his arms.

Emboldened, Andrews attempted to engage John again. "John, do you have any…any…any preferences when you go to the cinema?"[1234]

"I like to see Ringo." John distinctly pointed to the "expectant drummer," reviving the identity issue. "Seems everybody is now."[1235]

"You do?" Andrews wasn't sure if John was putting him on.[1236]

"Yes." John remained largely aloof.[1237]

So, turning to Starr, Andrews asked, "Ringo, any preferences in comedy: slapstick or smart talk or what?"[1238]

"Laurel and Hardy!" Starr said, without pause.[1239]

"Slapstick," Andrews categorized it.[1240]

"Yeah."

"George?" Eamonn identified him correctly this time.[1241]

"Uh, well," George let bygones be bygones, "just recently, we've seen the last few Peter Sellers films. I like all that, y' know."[1242]

"What he said," John agreed.

"Peter Sellers…" Paul piped up, and then, as the others over-talked, he added, "Peter Cook![1243] What, good last week Peter!"[1244]

"Very good," George said.

Relaxing his fit of pique, John leaned in. "I like ole Lionel Bunting, or whatever his name is."

"Lionel Jeffries?" Paul suggested.

"Which one of you, in the film," Andrews scanned them all, "is the best actor?"[1245]

"Me!"[1246] John piped up, flashing his famous Eccles face. The audience roared.[1247]

Eamonn chuckled, relieved to have Lennon back in the fray. "Why are you the best actor, John?"[1248]

"'Cause Ringo said."[1249] John thumbed toward Starr whilst Ringo solemnly nodded.

"I always say he's the best." Ringo bit off a smile, "He pays me."[1250]

This Liverpool combo, Eamonn mused, *has the audience eating out of their hands. Are they always this quick on their feet? It's as brilliant as the singing!*

"Now," Eamonn lifted his palms, including them all, "in these two films — this one and the one before — you *are* playing yourselves, The Beatles. Do you have any...any thoughts of the future, you know, in a separate way, to be actors of...other parts besides the parts of The Beatles?"[1251]

"No," John shook his head. "Couldn't do it!"[1252]

"We can't act, y' know!"[1253] Paul was honest.

John was once again their spokesman, and he spelled it out plainly. "Whoever cuts it makes it look as though we're nearly actin', but...we're not!"[1254]

With a wry grin, George suggested, "Paul's goin' to play Cathy in that...that..."[1255]

"*Wuthering Heights?*" Andrews filled in the blanks.

"Yeah, *Wuthering Heights,*" George fell into giggles. "Paul's Cathy!"[1256]

Ignoring them, Paul went on. "We're not 'good enough' as actors, y' know, because they get — as John says — they get people around us in the film 'n just stick us in a little bit...'n it's all a big pile of actin'...'n it looks as though we can act."

"But we *can't!*" John summed it up.[1257]

"It's a good director," George suggested.[1258]

"I hope he's watchin'!"[1259] Ringo chuckled.

"Well, they say directors are important, but..." watching the drummer's face, Eamonn played a hunch. "...don't *you* have any ambitions to be an actor? Ringo?"[1260]

The hunch played out, and the drummer nodded, "I'd like to be an actor."[1261]

"Do you see yourself in any particular kind of part?"[1262] Andrews was intrigued.

"Any part!" Ringo smiled.

"You can have 'em all!" John muttered, and the others scoffed.

But refusing to be dissuaded, Ringo insisted. "It's good fun, y' know!"[1263]

"Well, even if you don't see yourselves as actors...boys... everyone is interested in what you have to say and what you think about. How do you…how do you see the future…you know, the long-distance future like when you're thirty-five or forty?"[1264]

"Through a glass,"[1265] John alluded to either the New Testament, 1 Corinthians, or to Lewis Carroll.

"Darkly,"[1266] Eamonn bet on the scripture reference.

"We're not planners…"[1267] John began.

"We've never planned, y' know." Paul shook his head. "And we're not planning now…still."[1268]

"Do you really mean that?" Andrews wrinkled his wide brow. "That you don't…don't think about the future?"

"We don't think about…"[1269] John tried to find the right words as the others babbled around him.

"We play it by ear," George firmly asserted. "That's what our press representative tells us."[1270]

"What's he say?" Ringo asked.

"We play it by ear," George repeated.[1271]

"Do we?"[1272] John was now devil's advocate.

"*I* do," George shot back, "I've got big ears. Listen to this!"[1273] The audience guffawed.

"But surely," Andrews insisted, "at least two of you — Ringo now and you, John — as married men, you *must* give some concern to the future…"[1274]

John hoisted his kecks up, straightened his tie, and sniffed. "Ah, well, we do have a bit more responsibility than the others…"

"Well, at least we keep Paul and George in hand,'" Ringo laughed, "Go along!"[1275]

"Now how about this, Ringo…Do you, genuinely, do you think now, 'What am I going to be in ten- or fifteen-years' time?'" Eamonn kept pressing for a sincere answer.[1276]

"No," Ringo shook his head, "'cause I know, y' know…"[1277]

"Older!" John cut across them, supplying the answer.[1278]

"The only thing I'll be in ten years," Ringo finished, "is old!"[1279]

"'N withered," John injected.

"'N Withered Heights!" Ringo grinned. But when the audience only chuckled a smidge, Ringo added, "It was funny when someone said it before!"[1280]

Unsympathetic to the drummer's comedic failure, Eamonn moved on. "Well, well, your success anyway, obviously, is assured. What…what do you think…you must get a great smile at all the psychologists and journalists and social thinkers who try and analyse the reason for your success. You know, they've written…"[1281]

Paul reclaimed a spot in the conversation. "It's rubbish, y' know. I think so."[1282]

"We owe it all to our manager."[1283] George droned out the company line.

"Pardon?" A bit annoyed at being interrupted, Paul only glanced at the lead guitarist before going on. "Y' know, I don't know *what* they're talkin' about, y' know, 'cause they just try to analyse, y' know, and it's not that deep. They try 'n go into it…there's nothin' *there* really."[1284]

"Isn't there?"[1285] John sniffed.

"Well," Eamonn nodded at John, "of course, there's a great deal there! Have you ever sat down yourselves and said, 'What…what apart from your musical ability…what is it that's made us such — because you are, you know — such a phenomenon? What caused it?'"[1286]

When the boys didn't answer instantly, Andrews added, "It's a big word, isn't it?"[1287]

John was already answering as the insulting words left Eamonn's lips, so his response was amiable, "We don't know at all. We're always asked, y' know, but we don't have a clue. I don't think anybody has."[1288]

But Paul, who had clearly heard Andrews' insinuation that they didn't comprehend the word "phenomenon," was irritated. "What made *you,* Eamonn?"[1289] he fired back.

Adept at sidestepping sticky situations, Eamonn manoeuvered his way out with, "Ah, that's a good question."[1290] He smiled and retrieved a sheet of paper, quickly holding it up for Paul to see. "But I have a quote here from somebody who said…a famous New York psychologist said, The Beatles 'symbolically kill off the older generation. They show how neglected and misunderstood they believe themselves to be.' What does that mean?"[1291]

"I don't know what it means! Ask him!" John shook his head. To the laughing audience he snarled, "It's a lot of rubbish, that!" And straight into the camera, he added, "A lot of rubbish, New York psychologist!"[1292]

"I don't know what it means." Eamonn put the paper aside, "But...but you 'symbolically kill off the older generation.'" He shrugged. "What? What? Do you have any feelings that..."[1293]

Paul had heard enough. "It's *not true*, y' know! They think that we're sort of going around choppin' everyone to bits 'n things, but we're not! All right, Dad?!"[1294]

"Is your dad here?" John feigned surprise, taking the mickey out of Paul.[1295]

"Yeah no, he's at home," Paul looked into the camera. "All right, Dad?"[1296]

"It's all right, Dad." Eamonn spoke into the camera. He understood Paul's message. "He's *not,*" the Irish host explained, "going to kill off the older generation. Is that what you mean, Paul?"[1297]

Paul nodded. "No, no, I'm not," he affirmed. "No."[1298]

"But," Eamonn, who was pushing for some "definitive" cause-and-effect explanation, pushed on, "there *must be* some answer that has occurred to you that has made this success, apart from the music, as I say, that you sing and play. Have you seen any single quote that...that said, 'That's it! That must be why we did it!'?"[1299]

John puffed himself up, professorially, and said, "Well, the way *I* look at it is..." and the audience burst into giggles. When the laughter died away, John pretended to be concluding a lengthy exhortation with, "...well, that's how I see it, anyway."[1300] And the audience guffawed again.

"George," Andrews still sought an answer, "do you think they're just looking for reasons that don't exist?"[1301]

"Ummm," George chewed his lip for a moment. "Nobody likes to think there isn't any 'real reason.'" He used air quotes. "But y' know, I'm sure they're wrong because we've done it the same way as everybody else. But we've just had a laugh 'n a smile 'n a smile 'n a laugh, haven't we?"[1302]

"'N a laugh 'n a smile," John said, a little wistfully.[1303]

"'N just played it by ear," George repeated.[1304]

"You *said that*!" John teased.[1305]

"'N I'm sayin' it again!" George grinned.[1306]

"He's tryin' to get a catch-phrase!" Paul muttered to John, having fun with it.

Unable to keep from chuckling at the rapid Scouse-give-and-go, Eamonn leaned over to Ringo, "At what point did it begin to surprise you? When would you sit back and be amazed, or was it too gradual? Did it creep up on you?"[1307]

"Hmpf!" Ringo's eyes twinkled. "I was amazed the day we got paid!"[1308]

"Ringo speaking!" John clarified,[1309] and with that, the conversation had come full circle.

****

The Beatles didn't mind being interviewed, but they always felt most at home performing their songs. And since the interview had not — as Brian required — "promoted the new single," this was their shot.

Though John despised lip-syncing — and had said so repeatedly — he realised that more and more these days, their songs were becoming complicated: built upon intricate layers of instrumentation, experimentation, and double tracking. It was becoming difficult to reproduce a Beatles number on stage, one that truly replicated their sound in the studio.[1310] On tour, screams could hide the deficiencies, but on television, The Beatles were forced to rely upon pre-recorded tracks.

Tonight's performance was especially nerve-wracking. John was tasked with lead vocal on both of his songs, "Ticket to Ride" and "Yes It Is." So, in the few minutes before the boys took the performance stage to sing — whilst the others changed into their matching suits, doodled on guitar, and talked — John stood apart, reminding himself of subtle word changes in the verses.

"You *must* realise," Brian had chastened him earlier, "that the camera won't be focused on *you* the entire time, John." But that was little relief. Bobbling even one word in a close-up would be, John thought, calamitous. Fans liked to believe he was singing live and straight from the heart. To be unmasked miming somehow implied duplicity. So, he continued to worry, as he worried about almost everything these days.

For weeks, John had felt anxious because "Ticket to Ride" was the slowest A-side The Beatles had ever released.[1311] But the single was doing remarkably well. It had entered *Record Retailer* on 15 March at Number 11, based on pre-sales.[1312] And now that it was actually in stores, rumour whispered that in only a few days *Melody Maker* was going to announce it as the next Number One.[1313]

Trying to breathe deeply, John struggled into the new, tan British military-style jacket that he'd worn earlier, for the *NME* Poll Winner's Contest concert in Wembley.[1314] But he waited for the "one-minute warning" to button it over his polo.

It's overwarm in this studio, John thought. The fleshiness he'd acquired, coupled with Teddington's bright stage lights, made the heat nauseating.

"All right then." The assistant's assistant was back once more. "Ready when you are."

"Shall we?" Paul lifted an eyebrow at the four.

"We shall." John still made the decisions. And fastening their buttons tight, the boys were bound for "the boards."

****

Once the songs had been sung, The Beatles were given water and a swift make-up retouch whilst Andrews was up in the live audience, chatting with a cluster of giddy fans.

"When I was listening to The Beatles and talking to them earlier on," he said to the girls, "I was beginning to wonder whether I agreed or not with a quote I made a note of here of Brian Epstein's description of The Beatles from his book, *A Cellarful of Noise*. He said, 'One of them has the glamour. One, the command. One, the little man's quaintness, and one, the boy next door.' Well," he glanced at a nervous young woman in a smart, tomato-red shift, "I've never met this lady-next-door before here. Um, what's your name?"

"Jackie," the abashed audience squiggled a smile.

"Jackie, would you like to try to work it out for me — if you haven't read the book — which is the one who has the glamour?"[1315]

Giggling softly, the interviewee ducked her head. "I'd have to say Paul," she offered.

Andrews turned to the fans around them and asked, "Everyone agree with that?"

There were immediate shouts of "John! John!" One lone but enthusiastic voice cried, "George!"

"George, is it?" Andrews smiled. "All right." Then, he turned back to the selected fan. "Which one," he asked, "has the command?"

"Uhm," she turned up her palms as if the answer were patently obvious, "John!"

There was much chatter from the audience, but not a peep of dissention this time.

"You'd say 'John,'" Andrews confirmed, "I see. Well, the one with the 'little man's quaintness'?"

"Ringo," the reserved young lady asserted with a smile.

There was some laughter and someone — possibly Ringo from the stage — shouted Ringo's name in a crackly voice.

"And the boy next door?" Andrews lifted an eyebrow.

"George," the charming interviewee responded.

"George," Andrews confirmed. "Well," he smiled at her warmly, "the girls behind you got it wrong, but *you* got it right! You're absolutely right. That's the way it goes. And," Andrews began to stroll back to his stage desk, "I'm going to join the four of them now."

The Beatles were already smiling from their places on set. Ringo and George shared the settee, and Paul was now seated with John and Eamonn at the desk. The swivel chair was open, ostensibly for Eamonn's next guest.[1316]

"But we're also being joined," Andrews took his place, "by *Observer* columnist — delighted to welcome her back — Katharine Whitehorn." The audience applauded wildly, and Whitehorn beamed with joy. "And also, by writer Wolf Mankowitz." The audience gave a cordial welcome as the London playwright joined Ringo and George on the sofa.

As Whitehorn and Mankowitz greeted The Beatles, the audience began to fall silent.

"He's been on before?" John thumbed towards Mankowitz.

"He has, indeed, and I hope you'll be on again, too."

"He won't," Mankowitz swiped, "if he carries on the way he's been carrying on tonight!"

Taken aback, but trying to keep things light, Paul winked and said, "Tell him, Wolf!"

But John, feeling the jab, released a loud, derisive Lennon cackle.

"Terrifying giggle he's got tonight," Mankowitz pummeled John again. It was clear that the sometime-critic was seeking a sparring partner, and for a few minutes, John artfully bobbed and weaved without throwing an answering punch.

For a few minutes, the conversation moved into the realm of complimenting the parents of ugly babies, and things remained copacetic.

But Andrews, watching from the safety of the sidelines, decided to make things a bit more interesting. "Wolf, you too, like Katharine, joined the ranks of the Sunday columnists today. And apart from what you just said about John's giggle, I quote you. You also said that 'although The Beatles today make a cult of casualness, I don't think The Beatles are at all modest.' Would you care to repeat that now in front of them?"

"I don't think The Beatles are at all modest," Mankowitz spat, without a moment's flinch.

Not ready to exchange blows yet, John tried to ferret out common ground. "He's right," John nodded.

"Neither do we!" Ringo agreed.

"He spotted it, didn't he?" John said.

"Well," Katharine leaned over and affectionately patted Paul's arm, "what have they got to be modest for?!"

"I think they're four highly..." Mankowitz wrinkled his blocked forehead. He cut his eyes at the audience packed with fans and measured his words. "Well, I mean, much of their publicity points out their modesty — which derives from their casualness — which derives from the *contempt* with which they treat their audiences, essentially."

This audience fell silent. None of them felt wronged by The Beatles. All around Alf, men, women, and teens were wide-eyed at Mankowitz's asperity.

But Andrews pushed the point. "*Do you* think they treat their audiences with contempt?" he asked Mankowitz, point-blank.

"Oh yes," Mankowitz leaned back, interlacing his fingers. "They're so *assured* of the reaction of the audience that they..."

And that was the end of John's tolerance. "Y'er *jokin'!*" he exploded. "You're *wrong* there! We mightn't be modest...but for instance, today we did a show…it's the first time we've done anythin' for months live…'n we were petrified!"

Mankowitz threw sardonic, unbelieving eyes to the ceiling. "Why is *that*?"

"'Cause," John said, "we've been makin' a film, y' see, actually…'n it's on United Artists, 'n we were *petrified* today!" He could see Mankowitz was still widely skeptical. "We always are!" John insisted. "So, we're not *that* immodest!"

"But I mean…" Mankowitz hesitated a moment. He hadn't expected to be challenged and hadn't prepared an exhaustive debate. "Personal appearances don't actually 'hurt' the sales of your records." It was an off-topic argument, but the only one Mankowitz could locate, at the moment. "I mean, your last record pre-subscribed 350,000."

John cut him off. "That doesn't mean to say it's gonna jump in, like everybody thinks!"

"'Cause those…" Paul tried to assist.

"That means," John went on, "that dealers have ordered…" and then, realising he'd interrupted Paul, he deferred, "Sorry 'bout that, Paul."

"It's all right, John." Paul rolled a hand for John to carry on.

"The dealers," John narrowed his eyes at Mankowitz, "have *ordered* that many. But it doesn't mean to say people are gonna *buy them*!" He let the fact sink in for a moment. "It's when they've ordered them 'n then people come in 'n buy them from them that…"

"Three records ago," Wolf cut across John, "it was pre-subscribed one million!"

"I know," Paul tried to explain, "but that's…"

"So sorry about that, Wolf!" George was heavily sarcastic. Resentment that The Beatles were doing well from another successful professional was the last thing the boys had expected on this programme.

"*I* don't mind!" Mankowitz shot back, although clearly, he did.

"That's only *dealers*!" Paul tried to distinguish between the pre-orders placed by record dealers and the actual sales. "That's not the…"

"It's still only the dealers!" John echoed Paul's logic. "It's not actual people puttin' their names down to buy a record!"

"I'm just saying," Mankowitz raised a hand, refusing to listen, "it's not symptomatic of a 'modest regard for the audiences' that artists appear on television in front of some ten million possible buyers of records. I mean, I'm not knocking you. I'm just being realistic."

Andrews, who could see that both The Beatles and his audience were being offended, stepped in. "You've switched the subject, Wolf, in a way."

Katharine Whitehorn was similarly sympathetic with the band. After all, The Beatles were being condemned for their success, for their phenomenal pre-sales. "Well, look Wolf," Katharine said sternly, "you're leaving *us* out, aren't you? They," she swept her hand at the Liverpool boys, "do it for the money just like anybody else...might be you or me!"

"Right, Missus!" Paul nodded vigourously. "Right on!"

"But," Andrews turned to Wolf directly, "you were saying that they're *deliberately* mixing modesty with assurance in front of an audience. I don't believe that!" The audience cheered. "As John has said...not even The Beatles, with all their experience, will go out in front on an audience and be *assured* they've got a good audience."

Paul was still nodding. "Every time we..." he began.

"And the better..." John said simultaneously. "Oh, sorry, Paul!"

"It's all right, John," Paul continued. "Every time we release a record, we *really are terrified* that it's not goin' to make it. Honest!"

Wolf smirked and shook his head. "Well, why is *that,* do you think?"

"People expect it!" John tried to explain, but it was almost impossible to tell an outsider about the immense pressure placed on them.

And Mankowitz gave no quarter. "With the size of the 'success machine' that you've now amassed behind you, why do *you* have to be nervous?"

"Well," John took a breath and tried to make the London writer understand, "it's *worse* for us than other people, 'cause we've got to keep doin' what we've done before! If we don't do it as well, people'll knock you. Even though y'er doin' better than anybody else, if y'er not doin' it *as well* as you did before...y'er in trouble!"

Mankowitz wasn't appeased. In fact, John's comment reminded him of a second complaint he wanted to air. "But now," Mankowitz leaned forward, "now you're a serious incursion into the film business!" His voice raised. "Your last film grossed very big money in the box office!"

"Yeah," Paul shrugged, his usually breezy visage now solemn, "but that doesn't mean to say that our *next* film isn't goin' to be the biggest flop out, y' know. Could be! You can't pre-subscribe to things like films or the 'goodness' of records!"

Wolf scoffed, "There's a certain algebra to these things! It's known, for example, that though James Bond films will eventually drop off, they will build an accumulative audience based upon the business they did before. Similarly, the next Beatles film must do something very near to the business of the last Beatles film..."

"Yeah, but what..." Paul scrubbed his hand across his face. It was fruitless to argue sensibly when the argument kept changing course. "You weren't sayin' that before! You were sayin' that the thing about the pre-subscribed thing is that it doesn't matter whether it's good or bad!" Even Paul, who rarely ever lost his diplomacy, was wearing thin. "But it *does*, y' see! It really does! If the word gets 'round that this next film's a bad film — however 'pre-subscribed' it is — it'll be a flop, y' know. 'N the third one will really finish us!"[1317]

"Even if the third one's very good," John added, "if the second one doesn't make it..."

This time Paul was the one to cut across his friend. "You *can do* bad things, y' know. I mean, maybe you think we do now..."

Wounded feelings were highly contagious on the set. The Beatles were folding arms, leaning back, closing ranks. And the host saw it.

"I think," Andrews intervened, "that The Beatles are in the situation of the...to use a metaphor I'm used to...a boxer who's never been beaten.[1318] Each fight gets tougher because he hasn't had a defeat."

Mankowitz smiled as if Andrews had made his point for him. "So, for *that* reason," the writer swept his hand at the four boys, "you need to have a *genuine* modesty towards the audience! That's what we're arguing!"

They were clearly all talking at cross purposes, but as the

unofficial public relations spokesman for the group, Paul lowered his voice and gave it one more honest shot. "Yeah, the modesty thing is…"

Rousing at the scent of blood in the water, Mankowitz interrupted the boy: "…You're frightened of the audience!"

"Well, it's…" Paul thought for a second, truly trying to set things right, "sort of…as opposed to 'conceited,' really. You can't be conceited 'n still worry that every time you go on that people aren't goin' to like you."

But at that moment, John, who was rarely an appeaser, caught Brian's horrified face in the stage wings. "The Eamonn Andrews Show" was widely viewed, and tonight, things had gone horribly astray. The newspapers tomorrow would be full of it. Despite their best efforts to defend themselves, The Beatles would be accused of false modesty and conceit.

So, trying a different tack to smooth things over, John said, "Well, I think you can. I think you can be 'conceited,' but still worry. I've met lots of conceited people who're worried before they go on. I don't think the two things connect at all, y' know. You can be conceited 'n still worry yerself sick."

By this point, Eamonn Andrews was thoroughly confused. Now, even Paul and John seemed to be diametrically opposed. "You can't be conceited *and* worried!" the host insisted. "If you're totally conceited, you don't worry!"

"Oh, I don't know," Katharine Whitehorn returned to the fray, trying to bring things to a close. "What about Alfred Lunt? When they…"

"Who's that?" John asked her, out of the side of his mouth.

"Yeah, what about him?!" Ringo echoed vehemently, though like John, he had no inkling of who Alfred Lunt was.

"Yeah, what about *him*, eh?" John batted his eyelashes, comically. The audience chuckled uneasily.

Katharine laughed, and then informed the audience — although she was really informing The Beatles, "You might have heard of him. He was a century-and-a-half before your time, maybe. But…there was a story about him and his wife, Lynn Fontanne, and he was saying, 'How was I in this evening's performance?' And she said, 'You were just fine. You were marvellous! I was absolutely terrible. You did look a *little* tired, but you were a terrific actor! But I was ghastly…I was appalling.

I don't know how I got through it.' And when she'd finished depraving herself, he said, 'I was a little tired, was I?' So…you could call *him* conceited!"

Paul smiled. "Yeah."

There was murmur of agreement in the audience. Heads nodding. Whitehorn appeared to have saved the day.

Seeing this, Andrews quickly moved to bring the debate round, full circle. "Well Wolf there, a moment ago, mentioned the 'algebra' of the box office, which you…" he swiveled towards Paul.

"Right," Paul urged him on.

"…you picked up straight away," Andrews finished.

"He mentioned that," John grinned.

Hearing the Scouse phrase 'straight away," Paul chuckled. " Straight away,' eh, Eamonn. You 'n me, eh? Education!"

Enjoying the *détente*, the audience roared laughter.

Smiling now, Eamonn picked up his copy of Brian's *Cellarful of Noise* and showed it to the audience. "So, before we go any further, I'm just going to quote from Brian's book here."[1319]

In the wings, Brian bit his lip. He prayed that nothing he'd said to ghost writer Derek Taylor had inadvertently confirmed Mankowitz's untoward accusations.

"In *Cellarful of Noise*, he describes you as 'four young men in their early twenties, who left school before they should, who can neither read music nor write it. Who care not a fig or a damn or a button for anyone, save a tight, close-guarded clique of less than a dozen.'"

Brian sighed. They were harsh words when taken out of context from the rest of the chapter. He had been trying to illustrate The Beatles' exceptional singularity and isolation from the rest of the world.

"Oh, it's twenty-four now." John was droll. "We've met some more people." The audience loved it.

"Have you?" Eamonn's eyes twinkled. He relished the boy's dry wit. "But…is that still basically true? The last part of it?"

"Well," Paul tried one final time to explain who they were and what they felt, "it's true with most people, isn't it? That you've got your circle of friends, y' know…"

The other three nodded and said, "Umm-hmm."

"But it's not," Paul hurried on, "that we don't 'care a damn about anyone.' We care *more particularly* for our circle of friends, I think. But I think that's true about anyone, really, isn't it?"

"Well, what..." Andrews began.

"Or have I slipped up, Eamonn?" Paul was beginning to get irritated with the intimidating interview. This was supposed to have been a relaxed conversation at the end of a very long and arduous day. The boys all knew that Eamonn Andrews's show was a late-night, adult programme focused on serious subjects, but this had been a battle royal.

"No, I was..." Andrews began again, as regretful as Paul that the evening had soured this way. "Well," Eamonn set the book down and tried to find a way to soften Epstein's words. He shrugged and smiled at the camera. "It's got up to twenty-four, John says!" The audience chuckled, and letting the mirth works its charms, Andrews turned to John. "Who *are* these twenty-four? What sort of people are they that you have time for? Because really, you haven't much time in your lives, anyway. What sort of people are your friends? Who *is* this clique?"

"Well, y' know..." Paul began.

But brushing aside the "correct" answer, John sought to leave the viewers laughing. "I can't think of *anyone* that loves us, really!" He peered down his nose into the camera.

And guffaws of genuine relief broke out in Teddington, as George quickly piped up, "People like us! Well, people in the same business as us..."

"People with the same interests, really." Paul tried to give Eamonn an honest, thoughtful explanation. "'Cause we don't get a chance to talk about other things. Y' know, we talk 'shop' a lot of the time." He thought for a moment before adding, "Like the Stones, y' know...we're always chattin' to them about records..."[1320]

And having rescued his special guests from ugly accusations — intended and unintended — Andrews led the boys into a few moments of easy patter.

Ringo nodded and listened. George, relieved that they had waded out of the argument none the worse, smiled a tad. Paul — after a good half-hour of fence-mending — desperately yearned for a smoke.

But John sat back and watched with hawkish eyes. He had been strangely invigourated by the evening's caustic banter.

Andrews, Whitehorn, and Mankowitz had made him think. They'd challenged a mind tending, these days, towards decay. This had been far more exhilarating than the acceptance of an award or a pat response designed for some slick magazine. This had been an adventure.

John wasn't sure that Wolf Mankowitz even believed the things he'd been asserting this evening. But like John, the writer obviously enjoyed a vigourous discussion and the clash of ideas.

For The Beatles, that sort of thing was all too rare. More often than not, they encountered, "When was the last time you had a haircut?" or — as in their first segment with Andrews — the slightly more philosophical, "Where do you see yourselves in five to ten years?" Few people had the *chutzpah* to challenge The Beatles' authenticity in the way Mankowitz had done.

Oddly enough, John admired the man.

****

1:30 a.m.

By the time Alf had said goodnight to John in the Kenwood drive, it was into the small hours. The show had concluded just shy of midnight,[1321] and then the boys had changed into travel clothes and enjoyed a quick smoke, to unwind.

Nervously scratching his neck, Brian had repeatedly apologised for the errant wording in his biography. "You see, I was trying to depict you as independent — singular and beholden to no man. I wasn't implying you were unappreciative or odious. I would never…"

"'N I didn't do a great job of pluggin' the record, either." John had offered up his own shortcomings in recompense.

"Well…" Brian had smiled a bit at the generosity. "Next time, then."

And once again, the two had found equal footing.

Now, at the heavy front door of Kenwood, Cynthia stepped out, wrapped in a pale blue chenille robe. Alf threw her a wave, and she responded with a sleepy smile.

"See you in just a few hours, John," Alf reminded his employer as John plodded towards the front door, "Quarter past six?"

"Half-past." John felt sorry for Bicknell, who still had to motor home. "What can they do, eh, if I'm late for hair 'n make-up, right? Me double's back in the Alps. There're *stuck* with me!" Chuckling, Alf rolled up the window and dialed the radio station to BBC *Light Programme.* Free of the stress of taking care of the boys,[1322] he loosened his tie and began to croon, "Have You Looked Into Your Heart?" along with Jerry Vale.[1323] And as the long limo rolled away, Alf caught a last glimpse of the weary Liverpool boy hugging his wife in a dim shaft of foyer light.

Notes!

As it turned out, when Alf Bicknell finally made it home, his wife Joan informed him that he had been on television that evening. As he wrote in his Beatles Diary, *"the cameras caught me in the audience, enjoying the show." (p. 38) He was delighted with his 5 seconds of fame!*

And as an interesting aside, later that month, Wolf Mankowitz asked John and Paul to collaborate with him on a musical, one that he hoped would reach Broadway.[1324] The impression that The Beatles made on the playwright/critic on "The Eamonn Andrews Show" must have been far more favourable than Mankowitz was willing to demonstrate on 11 April 1965.

Finally, as we've seen earlier in this book, Brian was extremely hard-pressed to book The Beatles on television shows in 1965. The boys were simply too busy. Furthermore, he especially did not permit them to do live shows. So, how is it that Epstein agreed to let the four appear on "The Eamonn Andrews Show"?

My speculation is that Andrews had an "in" with the group since his 1956 spoken-narrative hit record, "The Shifting, Whispering Sand, Parts 1 and 2" had been produced by none other than George Martin! (If you'd like to hear this award-winning, narrative record, here it is: https://tinyurl.com/y4sodfyr)

Final note: **The dialogue in this chapter is taken word-for-word from the recorded and the transcribed television interview. Nothing is conjecture.** *I have carefully endnoted this as well.*

Sources:

Lewisohn, The Complete Beatles Chronicle, *188.*
Lewisohn, The Beatles: Day by Day, *60.*
Harry, The Ultimate Beatles Encyclopedia, *432.*
Winn, Way Beyond Compare, *312-313.*
Epstein, A Cellarful of Noise, *91-92.*
Miles, The Beatles' Diary, *Vol. 1, 193.*
Miles, Many Years from Now, *254.*
Badman, 150-151.
Coleman, Lennon, *256 and 259.*
Spizer, The Beatles for Sale on Parlophone Records, *45.*
Best, Pete and Doncaster, Patrick, Beatle! The Pete Best Story, *179-183.*
Schultheiss, 131-132.
Hill, John, Paul, George & Ringo, *195.*

http://beatlesinterviews.org/db1965.0411.beatles.html *The entire transcript of the 11 April 1965 Eamonn Andrews show has been transcribed by Jay Spangler and is on this website now co-owned by the author and Suzie Duchateau. Rande Kessler and I spent hours re-listening to the audio and made several tweaks to Jay's excellent work.*

https://www.imdb.com/name/nm0542554/bio?ref_=nm_ov_bio_sm *This website gives a full biography of Wolf Mankowitz, one of the guests on "The Eamonn Andrews Show" with The Beatles.*

https://tinyurl.com/ybumm7lv *This website provides the entire audio recording of The Beatles on "The Eamonn Andrews Show." There is no video, but there are photos of the event.*

https://tinyurl.com/y2jk8r22 *This is an audio recording of "The Eamonn Andrews Show" with The Beatles on 11 April 1965. Again, there is no video, but this is a great collage of photos from that day.*

https://tinyurl.com/y2w5pxxg *This is a link to information on The Beatles on "The Eamonn Andrews Show" from* *https://www.beatlesbible.com*

https://en.wikipedia.org/wiki/List_of_Billboard_Easy_Listening_number_ones_of_1965 *This website lists the #1 Easy Listening Hits for 1965.*

https://en.wikipedia.org/wiki/Jerry_Vale *This website supplies biographical information and a discography for Italian American singer Jerry Vale.*

https://en.wikipedia.org/wiki/Go_Now *This website supplies information about the January 1965 hit "Go Now!"*

https://www.bbc.com/historyofthebbc/anniversaries/september/crackerj ack This website gives information about the hit BBC children's series "Crackerjack!" that Eamonn Andrews hosted from 1955 to1964 and to which John Lennon is alluding as he steps on stage for "The Eamonn Andrews Show" in 1965.

https://en.wikipedia.org/wiki/Eamonn_Andrews This website gives biographical information about Irish sportscaster and later prominent U.K. television host Eamonn Andrews.

https://tinyurl.com/y4sodfyr This is the recording of Eamonn Andrews's award-winning narrative record, produced by George Martin.

[1175] Bicknell, 38. Alf says he drove "the boys" first to the *New Musical Express* concert and then on to Teddington Studios for "The Eamonn Andrews Show."

[1176] Miles, *The Beatles' Diary, Vol. 1*, 193,

[1177] Miles, *The Beatles' Diary, Vol. 1*, 193 and Badman, 150.

[1178] Coleman, *Lennon*, 259.

[1179] Miles, *Many Years From Now*, 254. Miles quotes Paul McCartney as saying, "I still was enthralled with London...I was eager to stay there, to be near the theatre, to be near everything."

[1180] Miles, *Many Years From Now*, 254.

[1181] Miles, *The Beatles' Diary, Vol. 1*, 193, Miles, *Many Years from Now*, 254, and Bicknell, 39-40. Miles, in *The Beatles' Diary, Vol. 1*, says that Paul purchased the 3-storey Regent house at Cavendish Avenue, St. John's Wood, London on 12 April, 1965. The cost was £40,000.

[1182] Schultheiss, 131. No precise date is given, but Schultheiss says this occurred in April 1965. Schultheiss says that John and Neil, who took a subway and then walked, went "unrecognized by the workmen and cleaners who inhabited the early morning subway."

[1183] Schultheiss, 131, Best, Pete and Patrick Doncaster, *Beatle! The Pete Best Story*, 179-183. During this timeframe, the Pete Best Combo had worked extremely hard to score hits in London and America, but Pete says he felt as if there was "an invisible shield" aound them saying "So far and no further!" He said that even his contacts in Liverpool, including Bob Wooler, "began to close around me." Pete says that Decca "shelved" his group, and there wasn't a kind word from anyone he'd known in Liverpool. At one point, he attempted suicide. The Beatles, experiencing an unparalleled rise to fame, must have felt some discomfort at their differences. It was a subject never discussed between them for more than a brief moment.

[1184] Bicknell, 39.

[1185] https://en.wikipedia.org/wiki/Go_Now Though "Go Now!" had been Number One in the U.K. in January 1965, in early April, it was still getting plenty of airplay. Written by Larry Banks and Milton Bennett, the song had been initially recorded in 1964 by Bessie Banks, but it flew to fame under the auspices of The Moody Blues, with Denny Laine on guitar and lead vocals. In the U.S., the song didn't even enter the charts until mid-February 1965.

[1186] Coleman, *Lennon*, 256. This is an actual game played by The Beatles, according to John Lennon in a conversation with Ray Coleman, 1965. I have used *the exact categories* that John detailed to Coleman. The selections are not my own. I am not going to footnote every item in the game, but will footnote again at the end.

[1187] Coleman, *Lennon*, 256. This is the end of the game, "Winners and Losers," that Ray Coleman cited in his book, in direct quote from John Lennon. Each topic was mentioned specifically by John. I only omitted "tea" (winner) and "coffee" (loser).

[1188] Everett, *The Beatles as Musicians: The Quarry Men Through* Rubber Soul, 296.

[1189] Lewisohn, *The Complete Beatles Chronicle*, 187, Lewisohn, *The Beatles: Day by Day,* 61, Spizer, *The Beatles on Parlophone Records*, 47, Miles, *The Beatles' Diary, Vol. 1*, 193, Riley, *Lennon*, 275, and Schultheiss, 132. To see a photo of The Beatles peforming at the 1964-1965 *New Musical Express* Poll Winners All-Star Concert on 11 April 1965, go to p. 47 of Bruce Spizer's *The Beatles for Sale on Parlophone Records.*

[1190] Schultheiss, 132.

[1191] Schultheiss, 132.

[1192] Lewisohn, *The Complete Beatles Chronicle*, 188.

[1193] Lewisohn, *The Complete Beatles Chronicle*, 188.

[1194] https://www.imdb.com/name/nm0542554/bio?ref_=nm_ov_bio_sm This website gives a full biography of Wolf Mankowitz, one of the guests on "The Eamonn Andrews Show" with The Beatles.

[1195] https://www.imdb.com/name/nm0542554/bio?ref_=nm_ov_bio_sm This website gives a brief biography and several photos of Katharine Whitehorn, one of the guests on "The Eamonn Andrews Show" with The Beatles.

[1196] Lewisohn, *The Complete Beatles Chronicle*, 188 and Winn, *Way Beyond Compare*, 312.

[1197] Lewisohn, *The Complete Beatles Chronicle*, 188 and Winn, *Way Beyond Compare,* 312.

[1198] https://tinyurl.com/y2jk8r22 All descriptions of The Beatles, Andrews, and the set in this chapter come from this excellent collage of photos from "The Eamonn Andrews Show" on 11 April 1965.

[1199] Miles, *The Beatles' Diary, Vol. 1*, 193 and Bicknell, 38. Miles tells us that on 9 April 1965, "'Ticket to Ride'/'Yes It Is' was released in the UK as Parlophone R 5625."

[1200] Miles, *The Beatles' Diary, Vol. 1,* 193, Spizer, *The Beatles for Sale on Parlophone Records,* 45, Lewisohn, *The Beatles: Day by Day*, 60, and Schultheiss, 132.

[1201] https://tinyurl.com/ybumm7lv This detail comes from a second, longer YouTube video of "The Beatles on 'The Eamonn Andrews Show,' 11 April 1965." All of the words spoken from this point on come verbatim from that recording and from the transcript carefully compiled by Jay Spangler on http://beatlesinterviews.org/db1965.0411.beatles.html Suzie Duchateau and I assumed ownership of this site in 2018 and have made only minimal changes to Spangler's original transcript.

1202 https://tinyurl.com/ybumm7lv and http://beatlesinterviews.org/db1965.0411.beatles.html

1203 https://tinyurl.com/ybumm7lv and http://beatlesinterviews.org/db1965.0411.beatles.html

1204 https://tinyurl.com/ybumm7lv and http://beatlesinterviews.org/db1965.0411.beatles.html

1205 https://tinyurl.com/ybumm7lv and http://beatlesinterviews.org/db1965.0411.beatles.html and https://www.bbc.com/historyofthebbc/anniversaries/september/crackerjack What John probably shouted here (although it can't be heard completely) was "It's Crackerjack!" He's saying this because Eamonn Andrews was the host of the very popular BBC children's series that aired first on Wednesday early evenings and later, on Friday evenings live from King's Theatre in Hammersmith Road, London. It was a *very lively* series that featured kids' contests, quizzes, songs, and comedy routines, and several years into the series, the opening chant became, "It's Friday…It's 5 to 5…it's Crackerjack!" Andrews hosted the show from 1955 to 1964, and John is acknowledging that as he takes the stage.

1206 https://tinyurl.com/ybumm7lv and http://beatlesinterviews.org/db1965.0411.beatles.html

1207 https://tinyurl.com/y2w5pxxg This is a link to BeatlesBible.com where the exact seating arrangement for The Beatles in interview #1 and interview #2 with Andrews is delineated.

1208 Bicknell, 38. Alf writes, "I was on television tonight! I wasn't meant to be but the boys appeared on 'The Eamonn Andrews Show,' and the cameras caught me in the audience, enjoying the show…"

1209 Badman, 150, https://tinyurl.com/ybumm7lv and http://beatlesinterviews.org/db1965.0411.beatles.html Badman includes an abbreviated transcript of the show in his *Beatles: Off the Record.* Not all of the lines spoken in the lengthy interview are included in the abridged account.

1210 https://tinyurl.com/ybumm7lv

1211 Badman, 150, https://tinyurl.com/ybumm7lv, and http://beatlesinterviews.org/db1965.0411.beatles.html. Eamonn Andrews says "dad," not "father."

1212 Badman, 150, https://tinyurl.com/ybumm7lv, and http://beatlesinterviews.org/db1965.0411.beatles.html

1213 https://tinyurl.com/ybumm7lv and http://beatlesinterviews.org/db1965.0411.beatles.html

1214 Badman, 150, https://tinyurl.com/ybumm7lv, and http://beatlesinterviews.org/db1965.0411.beatles.html

1215 https://tinyurl.com/ybumm7lv and http://beatlesinterviews.org/db1965.0411.beatles.html

1216 https://tinyurl.com/ybumm7lv and http://beatlesinterviews.org/db1965.0411.beatles.html

1217 https://tinyurl.com/ybumm7lv and http://beatlesinterviews.org/db1965.0411.beatles.html

[1218] https://tinyurl.com/ybumm7lv and
http://beatlesinterviews.org/db1965.0411.beatles.html
[1219] Lewisohn, *The Complete Beatles Chronicle*, Lewisohn, *The Beatles: Day by Day,* 61, 188, and Miles, *The Beatles' Diary, Vol. 1*, 192.
[1220] Lewisohn, *The Complete Beatles Chronicle*, Lewisohn, *The Beatles: Day by Day,* 61, 188, and Miles, *The Beatles' Diary, Vol. 1*, 192.
[1221] Badman, 150, and https://tinyurl.com/ybumm7lv and
http://beatlesinterviews.org/db1965.0411.beatles.html
[1222] Badman, 150, and https://tinyurl.com/ybumm7lv and
http://beatlesinterviews.org/db1965.0411.beatles.html
[1223] https://tinyurl.com/ybumm7lv and
http://beatlesinterviews.org/db1965.0411.beatles.html
[1224] Badman, 150, and https://tinyurl.com/ybumm7lv and
http://beatlesinterviews.org/db1965.0411.beatles.html
[1225] Badman, 150, and https://tinyurl.com/ybumm7lv and
http://beatlesinterviews.org/db1965.0411.beatles.html
[1226] Badman, 150, and https://tinyurl.com/ybumm7lv and
http://beatlesinterviews.org/db1965.0411.beatles.html
[1227] Badman, 150, and https://tinyurl.com/ybumm7lv and
http://beatlesinterviews.org/db1965.0411.beatles.html
[1228] Badman, 150, and https://tinyurl.com/ybumm7lv and
http://beatlesinterviews.org/db1965.0411.beatles.html
[1229] Badman, 150, and https://tinyurl.com/ybumm7lv and
http://beatlesinterviews.org/db1965.0411.beatles.html
[1230] Badman, 150, and https://tinyurl.com/ybumm7lv and
http://beatlesinterviews.org/db1965.0411.beatles.html
[1231] Badman, 150, and https://tinyurl.com/ybumm7lv and
http://beatlesinterviews.org/db1965.0411.beatles.html
[1232] Badman, 150, and https://tinyurl.com/ybumm7lv and
http://beatlesinterviews.org/db1965.0411.beatles.html
[1233] Badman, 150, https://tinyurl.com/ybumm7lv and
http://beatlesinterviews.org/db1965.0411.beatles.html
[1234] https://tinyurl.com/ybumm7lv and
http://beatlesinterviews.org/db1965.0411.beatles.html
[1235] https://tinyurl.com/ybumm7lv and
http://beatlesinterviews.org/db1965.0411.beatles.html
[1236] https://tinyurl.com/ybumm7lv and
http://beatlesinterviews.org/db1965.0411.beatles.html
[1237] https://tinyurl.com/ybumm7lv and
http://beatlesinterviews.org/db1965.0411.beatles.html
[1238] Badman, 150 and https://tinyurl.com/ybumm7lv
[1239] Badman, 150 and https://tinyurl.com/ybumm7lv
[1240] https://tinyurl.com/ybumm7lv
[1241] Badman, 150, https://tinyurl.com/ybumm7lv, and
http://beatlesinterviews.org/db1965.0411.beatles.html
[1242] Badman, 150, https://tinyurl.com/ybumm7lv, and
http://beatlesinterviews.org/db1965.0411.beatles.html

[1243] https://tinyurl.com/ybumm7lv and http://beatlesinterviews.org/db1965.0411.beatles.html

[1244] Winn, *Way Beyond Compare*, 313. Winn says that Paul adds this comment.

[1245] Badman, 150, https://tinyurl.com/ybumm7lv, and http://beatlesinterviews.org/db1965.0411.beatles.html

[1246] Badman, 150, https://tinyurl.com/ybumm7lv, and http://beatlesinterviews.org/db1965.0411.beatles.html

[1247] Badman, 150, https://tinyurl.com/ybumm7lv, and http://beatlesinterviews.org/db1965.0411.beatles.html

[1248] Badman, 150, https://tinyurl.com/ybumm7lv, and http://beatlesinterviews.org/db1965.0411.beatles.html

[1249] Badman, 150, https://tinyurl.com/ybumm7lv, and http://beatlesinterviews.org/db1965.0411.beatles.html

[1250] Badman, 150, https://tinyurl.com/ybumm7lv, and http://beatlesinterviews.org/db1965.0411.beatles.html

[1251] Badman, 150, https://tinyurl.com/ybumm7lv, and http://beatlesinterviews.org/db1965.0411.beatles.html

[1252] Badman, 150, https://tinyurl.com/ybumm7lv, and http://beatlesinterviews.org/db1965.0411.beatles.html

[1253] Badman, 150, https://tinyurl.com/ybumm7lv, and http://beatlesinterviews.org/db1965.0411.beatles.html

[1254] Badman, 150, https://tinyurl.com/ybumm7lv, and http://beatlesinterviews.org/db1965.0411.beatles.html

[1255] Badman, 150, https://tinyurl.com/ybumm7lv, and http://beatlesinterviews.org/db1965.0411.beatles.html

[1256] George is referring to the 1847 Gothic novel classic by Emily Brontë, *Wuthering Heights,* in which Cathy Linton falls into a very complicated love entanglement with the hero, Heathcliff.

[1257] https://tinyurl.com/ybumm7lv and http://beatlesinterviews.org/db1965.0411.beatles.html

[1258] Badman, 150, https://tinyurl.com/ybumm7lv, and http://beatlesinterviews.org/db1965.0411.beatles.html

[1259] Badman, 150, https://tinyurl.com/ybumm7lv, and http://beatlesinterviews.org/db1965.0411.beatles.html

[1260] Badman, 150, https://tinyurl.com/ybumm7lv, and http://beatlesinterviews.org/db1965.0411.beatles.html

[1261] https://tinyurl.com/ybumm7lv and http://beatlesinterviews.org/db1965.0411.beatles.html

[1262] https://tinyurl.com/ybumm7lv and http://beatlesinterviews.org/db1965.0411.beatles.html

[1263] Badman, 150 and https://tinyurl.com/ybumm7lv

[1264] https://tinyurl.com/ybumm7lv and http://beatlesinterviews.org/db1965.0411.beatles.html

[1265] https://tinyurl.com/ybumm7lv and http://beatlesinterviews.org/db1965.0411.beatles.html

[1266] https://tinyurl.com/ybumm7lv and http://beatlesinterviews.org/db1965.0411.beatles.html

[1267] https://tinyurl.com/ybumm7lv and
http://beatlesinterviews.org/db1965.0411.beatles.html
[1268] https://tinyurl.com/ybumm7lv and
http://beatlesinterviews.org/db1965.0411.beatles.html
[1269] https://tinyurl.com/ybumm7lv and
http://beatlesinterviews.org/db1965.0411.beatles.html
[1270] https://tinyurl.com/ybumm7lv and
http://beatlesinterviews.org/db1965.0411.beatles.html
[1271] https://tinyurl.com/ybumm7lv and
http://beatlesinterviews.org/db1965.0411.beatles.html
[1272] https://tinyurl.com/ybumm7lv and
http://beatlesinterviews.org/db1965.0411.beatles.html
[1273] https://tinyurl.com/ybumm7lv and
http://beatlesinterviews.org/db1965.0411.beatles.html
[1274] https://tinyurl.com/ybumm7lv and
http://beatlesinterviews.org/db1965.0411.beatles.html
[1275] https://tinyurl.com/ybumm7lv and
http://beatlesinterviews.org/db1965.0411.beatles.html
[1276] https://tinyurl.com/ybumm7lv and
http://beatlesinterviews.org/db1965.0411.beatles.html
[1277] https://tinyurl.com/ybumm7lv and
http://beatlesinterviews.org/db1965.0411.beatles.html
[1278] https://tinyurl.com/ybumm7lv and
http://beatlesinterviews.org/db1965.0411.beatles.html
[1279] https://tinyurl.com/ybumm7lv and
http://beatlesinterviews.org/db1965.0411.beatles.html
[1280] https://tinyurl.com/ybumm7lv and
http://beatlesinterviews.org/db1965.0411.beatles.html
[1281] https://tinyurl.com/ybumm7lv and
http://beatlesinterviews.org/db1965.0411.beatles.html
[1282] https://tinyurl.com/ybumm7lv and
http://beatlesinterviews.org/db1965.0411.beatles.html
[1283] https://tinyurl.com/ybumm7lv and
http://beatlesinterviews.org/db1965.0411.beatles.html
[1284] https://tinyurl.com/ybumm7lv and
http://beatlesinterviews.org/db1965.0411.beatles.html
[1285] https://tinyurl.com/ybumm7lv and
http://beatlesinterviews.org/db1965.0411.beatles.html
[1286] Badman, 150, https://tinyurl.com/ybumm7lv, and
http://beatlesinterviews.org/db1965.0411.beatles.html
[1287] Badman, 150, https://tinyurl.com/ybumm7lv, and
http://beatlesinterviews.org/db1965.0411.beatles.html
[1288] Badman, 150, https://tinyurl.com/ybumm7lv, and
http://beatlesinterviews.org/db1965.0411.beatles.html
[1289] Badman, 150, https://tinyurl.com/ybumm7lv, and
http://beatlesinterviews.org/db1965.0411.beatles.html
[1290] https://tinyurl.com/ybumm7lv and
http://beatlesinterviews.org/db1965.0411.beatles.html

[1291] Badman, 150, https://tinyurl.com/ybumm7lv, and http://beatlesinterviews.org/db1965.0411.beatles.html

[1292] https://tinyurl.com/ybumm7lv and http://beatlesinterviews.org/db1965.0411.beatles.html

[1293] Badman, 150, https://tinyurl.com/ybumm7lv, and http://beatlesinterviews.org/db1965.0411.beatles.html

[1294] Badman, 150, https://tinyurl.com/ybumm7lv, and http://beatlesinterviews.org/db1965.0411.beatles.html

[1295] https://tinyurl.com/ybumm7lv and http://beatlesinterviews.org/db1965.0411.beatles.html

[1296] https://tinyurl.com/ybumm7lv and http://beatlesinterviews.org/db1965.0411.beatles.html Since John's comic line is not in Badman's account, this line is incorporated into Paul's previous quote.

[1297] Badman, 150, https://tinyurl.com/ybumm7lv, and http://beatlesinterviews.org/db1965.0411.beatles.html

[1298] https://tinyurl.com/ybumm7lv and http://beatlesinterviews.org/db1965.0411.beatles.html

[1299] https://tinyurl.com/ybumm7lv and http://beatlesinterviews.org/db1965.0411.beatles.html

[1300] https://tinyurl.com/ybumm7lv and http://beatlesinterviews.org/db1965.0411.beatles.html

[1301] https://tinyurl.com/ybumm7lv and http://beatlesinterviews.org/db1965.0411.beatles.html

[1302] https://tinyurl.com/ybumm7lv and http://beatlesinterviews.org/db1965.0411.beatles.html

[1303] https://tinyurl.com/ybumm7lv and http://beatlesinterviews.org/db1965.0411.beatles.html

[1304] https://tinyurl.com/ybumm7lv and http://beatlesinterviews.org/db1965.0411.beatles.html

[1305] https://tinyurl.com/ybumm7lv and http://beatlesinterviews.org/db1965.0411.beatles.html

[1306] https://tinyurl.com/ybumm7lv and http://beatlesinterviews.org/db1965.0411.beatles.html

[1307] https://tinyurl.com/ybumm7lv and http://beatlesinterviews.org/db1965.0411.beatles.html

[1308] Badman, 152, https://tinyurl.com/ybumm7lv, and http://beatlesinterviews.org/db1965.0411.beatles.html

[1309] https://tinyurl.com/ybumm7lv and http://beatlesinterviews.org/db1965.0411.beatles.html

[1310] Spizer, *The Beatles for Sale on Parlophone Records*, 46. As Spizer so aptly observes, "The Beatles were evolving into true 'recording artists' as opposed to mere performers."

[1311] Spizer, *The Beatles For Sale on Parlophone Records*, 46. That "Ticket to Ride" is the slowest A-Side ever released by The Beatles is John Lennon's exact observation. But he goes on to say, "It's still us. It's no more unusual than we are."

[1312] Spizer, *The Beatles for Sale on Parlophone Records*, 45.

[1313] Spizer, *The Beatles for Sale on Parlophone Records,* 45. You can see photos of the original Parlophone 45 RPM of "Ticket to Ride"/"Yes It Is" on p. 48 of Spizer's book.

[1314] https://www.beatlesuits.com/shea-jacket.html To see the exact suit John wore and to learn about all of The Beatles' suits, visit this one-of-a-kind website by Russ Lease. You can even order a suit of your own! To see a close-up video showing this jacket in all its detail, go to https://www.youtube.com/watch?v=_rmeys-jfJI

[1315] The second half of the 11 April interview on "The Eamonn Andrews Show" begins here. It will be first an audience scene with Andrews and Beatles fans, and then a discussion between Andrews, The Beatles, Katharine Whitehorn, and Wolf Mankowitz. I am not going to endnote every line, but **all words spoken are verbatim from the interview** in these sources: https://tinyurl.com/ybumm7lv and http://beatlesinterviews.org/db1965.0411.beatles.html I will endnote again at the end of the last quoted line.

[1316] Lewisohn, *The Complete Beatles Chronicle*, 188.

[1317] Winn, *Way Beyond Compare*, 313. Winn does an admirable job of explaining what is going on here. He says, "…Mankowitz…attacked The Beatles for being immodest and treating their audiences with contempt. They agree up to a point, but insisted that they are not as confident as they appear, revealing that before their concert appearance earlier that day, they were quite nervous, not having performed live in months. Mankowitz stubbornly reiterates that their records garner huge presales, while Paul makes several futile attempts to explain to him that no matter how many copies dealers order, it can still be a flop if the public doesn't like it."

[1318] Eamonn Andrews says this because early on in his career, he was a successful amateur boxer. In fact, in 1944, he won the Middleweight Irish Championship. It propelled him into a career as a sportscaster which then evolved into a career as a television host.

[1319] Brian's biography, *A Cellarful of Noise*, had been published by Souvenir Press, London, 1964.

[1320] This is the last line in the Eamonn Andrews interview between The Beatles, Katharine Whitehorn, and Wolf Mankowitz on 11 April 1956. The audio and transcript may be found in https://tinyurl.com/ybumm7lv and http://beatlesinterviews.org/db1965.0411.beatles.html

[1321] Lewisohn, *The Complete Beatles Chronicle*, 188. Lewisohn tells us that "The Eamonn Andrews Show" broadcast from 11.05 to 11.50 p.m.

[1322] Bicknell, 19. The pressures of being "responsible" for The Beatles were intense. Bicknell wrote in his *Beatles Diary*, "…it used to cross my mind when I had all four of them in the car with me [that] the responsibility was incredible….just supposing what would happen if I had a 'blowout' or crashed…I was always conscious of the rear view mirror, and who was behind and who was following us. Things in those days used to worry me…what could happen."

[1323]

https://en.wikipedia.org/wiki/List_of_Billboard_Easy_Listening_number_ones_of_1965 This website lists the #1 Easy Listening Hits for 1965 and https://en.wikipedia.org/wiki/Jerry_Vale supplies biographical information and a discography for Italian-American singer Jerry Vale.

[1324] Harry, *The Ultimate Beatles Encyclopedia*, 432 and Miles, *The Beatles' Diary, Vol. 1,* 192.

Monday, 12 April 1965
Kenwood
Weybridge

Whilst coping with "the magically reappearing Dad," starring in a full-length motion picture, debating literary greats and their ilk on television, giving myriad interviews in his "free time," and writing a bevy of new songs (some for The Beatles and others for Billy J. Kramer, Tommy Quickly, and the lovely Cilla Black)[1325], John was also finalizing his upcoming book. The release date for *A Spaniard in the Works* was now 24 June,[1326] and the "*poseurs-that-be*" at Jonathan Cape Publishers in London were fretful.

In order to "hit the mark," the manuscript had to be "in hand, Mr. Lennon, in the next week-and-a-half." So, John had been tasked with "looking over" some of the bits he'd written months ago. "Just needs a bit of light excision," the Suits had chortled over his protests, but The Literary Beatle hadn't found them a bit humourous.

John had always firmly believed that artistic endeavours, at the very heart, demanded spontaneity. He despised tweaking and editing; he thought it almost always ruined things. In fact, Paul and he had bitterly argued this point since the moment they'd met.[1327]

And now, after a very long day of filming — involving slow-motion running down a corridor in a very realistic "Buckingham Palace," struggling against the disorienting rays of Professor's Foot's "Relativity Cadenza"[1328] — John was even more reluctant to sit up late, making changes to work he'd done when he was sharper and more relaxed.

"Snore Wife and Some Several Dwarts," the piece he'd composed last spring aboard the grimy Tahitian boat they'd generously dubbed "a yacht," still made him smile. Back then, filled with starch, sleep, sex, and sunshine, John had (rightly so) fancied himself fairly witty.[1329] Suntanning off Papeete, he'd scribbled:

"Once upon upon in a dizney far away - say three hundred year agoal if you like - there lived in a sneaky forest some several dwarts or cretins; all named - Sleezy, Grumpty, Sneeky, Dog, Smirkey, Alice? Derick - and Wimpey. Anyway they all dug about in a diamond mind, which was rich beyond compère. Every day when they came hulme from wirk, they would sing a song - just like ordinary wirkers - the song went something like - 'Yo ho! Yo ho! it's off to wirk we go!' - which silly really considerable they were comeing hulme. (Perhaps ther was slight housework to be do.)[1330]

And *there* was the problem: *compère* and *Hulme*.[1331] Jonathan Cape's editors had requested "a minimization of British expressions with which readers in America would be rather unfamiliar."

But "compare" and "compère" is the joke! John objected. Everythin' depends on it! Let the Americans learn a new word, hey!

John saw no sense in changing the verbiage now. As Tony Barrow had recently observed, "John has forthright opinions on everything which concerns him directly or indirectly."[1332] And this new book mattered to him; it was personal.

Similarly, in "I Believe, Boot…", the publisher had expressed "apprehensions about the rather disrespectful nature of the piece."

*At least they didn't say "blasphemous," John consoled himself. And trying to remain objective, he read the piece again:

𝔄man came up to me the other day and said - 'Tell me bicar - tell me the deafinition of sin?' - and you know, I couldn't answer him! Which makes me think - do you ever wonder (and what do we mean by the word wonder?) what an ordinary man (and what - I ask myself do we mean by an ordinary man?) who works in office or factory - goes to church on Sunday (what exactly do we mean by Sunday?) who is also a sinner (we are all sinners). People are always coming up to me and asking - 'Why, if Griff is so good and almighty - why does he bring such misery into the world?' - and I can truthfully say St. Alf - th 8 verse 5 - page 9. 'Griff walks in such mysterious ways His woodwork to perform' (what do we mean by perform?) Which leads me neatly, I feel, to our next guest for tonight - A man whom is stickle trodding the pathway to our beloved Griff - slowly but slowly I am here to help with the bridges he must surely crooss. - 'Welcome to our studios tonight Mr Wabooba (a foreigner)'[1333]

Even as worn as he was tonight, John smiled. *How can this be anythin' but fun!? A whimsical spoof on the well-meanin' but bumblin' vicar, minister, priest, whatever...y' know the one we all know...the one who rambles on 'n on from vagary to digression to quotation to sense? There's* nothin' *disrespectful here! It's fuggin' hilarious, if I do "sway" so m'self.*

So, stacking the collection of papers carefully on the sunroom coffee table and inserting them into the wide manilla envelope provided, John sighed. *This is as good as it's bound to get, mates,* he said, licking the gummed flap to seal the parcel. He promised himself to dispatch it tomorrow morning, when his foggy brain could retrieve the address. But for now…

Foot-by-heavy-foot, John pulled himself upstairs reciting his favourite poem from the new collection, "The Wumberlog (or The Magic Dog)":

"Whilst all the tow was sleepy
Crept a little boy from bed
To fained the wondrous peoble

Wot lived when they were dead.

He packed a little voucher
For his dinner 'neath a tree,
'Perhumps a tiny dwarf or two
Would share abite with me?' "[1334]

And reaching the top stair, John whispered to no one, presumably, there:

" 'What are you digging all the time?'
He asked them like a brother.
Before they answered he could see
They really dug each other."[1335]

I'm not changin' a fuggin' word of that, John confirmed his decision, flipping off the foyer light. *If it's good enough for the Wumberlog, it's good enough for thee.*

And yawning, the author called it a day.

Notes!

Did John really despise editing and resist it?

In Harry's John Lennon Encyclopedia, *John is quoted from his promotional appearance for this book on the BBC's "World of Books" programme. He said, "I'm selfish about what I write or big-headed about it. Once I've written it, and the publishers sometimes say, 'Should we leave this out or change that?' I fight like mad because once I've done it, I like to keep it. But I always write it straight off. I might add things when I go over it, before it's published, but I seldom take anything out, so it's spontaneous." (p. 833)*

Years later, in The Beatles Anthology, *John is quoted as saying: "I'm not very keen on being disciplined. (It seems odd, being a Beatle, we're disciplined but we don't feel as though we are. I don't mind being disciplined and not realising it.)" (p. 176)*

John and Paul had always debated about the best way to write music, John preferring extemporaneous creativity. And this penchant remained with him throughout his life. In John Lennon in 1980, Kenneth Womack finds John still, at the end of his life, preferring "inspired" music rather than carefully crafted songs. He says, "As John observed so many times before, it was his preferred means of composition — the sudden moment of inspiration, the bolt out of the blue."

Though John always considered his penchant toward extemporaneous creativity a positive, it was as grating to Paul as Paul's tendency to "worry a thing to death" (as John phrased it) was to John. McCartney biographer Chris Salewicz says, "Though one might consider Lennon's creativity largely positive, the energies that seethed and thrashed within him [were]...largely undirected." Salewicz also refers to John's "permanent indiscipline."

To read a very early encounter between John and Paul about the nature of creativity, see Vol. 1 in **The John Lennon Series***, Shoulda Been There, pp. 186-189.*

Sources:

Lewisohn, The Complete Beatles Chronicle, *188.*
Harry, The John Lennon Encyclopedia, *830-834.*
Harry, The Encyclopedia of Beatles People, *64, 186, and 263.*
The Beatles, The Beatles Anthology, *176.*
Robustelli, I Want to Tell You: The Definitive Guide to the Music of The Beatles, 1962-1963, *155-156.*
Lennon, John, A Spaniard in the Works, *22, 44, 47, 49, and 89.*
Womack, John Lennon 1980, *194.*
Miles, The Beatles' Diary, Vol. 1, *199.*
Coleman, Lennon, *78-80.*
Salewicz, McCartney, *48-49.*
Barrow, Meet The Beatles, *5.*

Womack, Ken, "50 Years of Beatles: John Lennon's In His Own Write,*"* Penn State News, *2014. (Also covers* A Spaniard in the Works.*) Found here:* https://news.psu.edu/story/307744/2014/03/14/society-and-culture/50-years-beatles-john-lennons-his-own-write

https://en.wikipedia.org/wiki/A_Spaniard_in_the_Works *This website offers information about the release of* A Spaniard in the Works *and the nature of Lennon's second book.*

[1325] Robustelli, *I Want to Tell You: The Definitive Guide to the Music of The Beatles, 1962-1963*, 255-256 and Harry, *The Encyclopedia of Beatles People*, 64,186, and 263.

[1326] Miles, *The Beatles' Diary, Vol. 1*, 199.

[1327] Coleman, *Lennon*, 79-80 and Salewicz, *McCartney*, 48-49. Salewicz refers to John's penchant for creating this extemporaneously as "permanent indiscipline."

[1328] Lewisohn, *The Complete Beatles Chronicle*, 188.

[1329] Coleman, *Lennon*, 242.

[1330] Lennon, *A Spaniard in the Works*, 22.

[1331] A *compère* is the British term for "deejay" and *Hulme* is an inner city area in Manchester. These were allusions Americans would not easily understand, hence the concern from Jonathan Cape publishers.

[1332] Barrow, *Meet The Beatles*, 5.

[1333] Lennon, John, *A Spaniard in the Works*, 89.

[1334] Lennon, John, *A Spaniard in the Works*, 44.

[1335] Lennon, John, *A Spaniard in the Works*, 49.

Tuesday, 13 April 1965
EMI Studios
St. John's Wood, London

6.45 p.m.

Although John had composed the film's title track as an introspective, melodic, piano tune,[1336] he knew from its inception that his intent would never hold.[1337] George Martin, Dick Lester, and the others required a pounding theme song for the James Bond-esque adventure-spoof.[1338]

"I'm sure you realise," Martin spoke gently after the informal run-through on John's 12-string Framus acoustic,[1339] "that the theme song must needs be…well, commercial, as they say." When John only quirked his mouth to the side thoughtfully, Martin expanded. "Think of the sound of 'From Russia with Love.' That sort of thing. And when I worked with Shirley Bassey on 'Goldfinger,' we both agreed that a spy thriller demands a bold powerhouse, as it were. So, that's what we aimed for."[1340]

He cut his eyes at John, who although unenthusiastic, allowed the producer to finish his thought. "To my way of thinking," Martin continued, "we always have to ask what we're aiming for when producing a record, John. You know…who's listening?[1341] And here, you've gotten the lyrics exactly right — this sincere cry for 'help!' But now — for the film's purposes — we need to paint a picture in sound,[1342] as it were, a picture of these four madcap victims being hotly pursued by a cutthroat gang of somewhat bumbling religious fanatics!"

John snorted and looked away. "Help!" would never be the personal song he'd wanted it to be.[1343] Like "I'll Cry Instead" or "It Won't Be Long," the pain would be swabbed with a lather of rousing upbeat. People would hear it as just another "get-up-and-dance" tune.[1344] And then, they'd ask him why he never wrote about his life, why he never wrote from the heart.[1345]

"Listen," Martin pulled his high, three-legged stool closer to John, "I know what you're after here, and you can still have it. It's all in the way you use your voice, you see. If we pick up the tempo, then you can sing as if you're pressured, pushed, out of breath, panicked..."[1346]

"...movin' so fast I can't keep up."

"That's it." As 7.00 p.m. approached and the booth was readied for recording, Martin began to roll up his crisp, white sleeves. "And in doing that, what you'll get, you see, is very similar to what you'd originally intended. The listener will hear your desperation, if not what lies behind it."

"Yeah, right," John conceded. But he still hated betraying what he considered to be the best song he'd ever written.[1347] And moreover, he didn't want to be typecast into a mould: the band's perpetual rocker.

Years ago, John had seen that old 20th Century Fox musical about John Phillip Souza — fondly known to his contemporaries as "The American March King" — who had tirelessly composed lullabies and ballads, only to have them transformed, time and time again, into marches, no matter what he said about it.[1348]

Well, here we are again, Mr. Sousa, John thought. *Marches for you; rock'n'rollers for me. I suppose we'll both have to make the best of it.*

And as Paul hoisted his Höfner, and Ringo doffed his cig and ambled towards the drums, John reluctantly nodded at George Martin and stood up to stretch.

With minutes to spare, the producer tossed out cheers and small talk to the others and then, filed up the stairs for another night of creativity, assessment, and work.

****

7.00 p.m.[1349]

The Beatles were well-acquainted with "Plan B." When a well-devised exit scheme was somehow thwarted, Neil always found another, and the boys rapidly adapted. When a bit of a song wouldn't work, they devised an alternative line — tried another instrument. And tonight, with a little help from his friends, John was determined to sing the romping song George Martin needed as the fraught cry for help that John wanted it to be.

But as yet, nothing was cooperating. Just after the Take 1 intro, a contrary string on John's Framus broke, and though the booth kept recording, the boys below fizzled out.[1350] Not understanding what had happened exactly, Norman Smith announced "Take 2" within seconds, but John cupped his mouth and shouted, "String gone!" to buy him the necessary minutes.[1351]

Whilst John repaired, The Beatles smoked, and the booth waited.

Then, at a word from the boys, Take 2 was re-slated, but it, too, broke down almost immediately.[1352] George Harrison was struggling with the descending riff at the front of the song.[1353] Frustrated, the angular lead guitarist shook his head, and a halt was called.

Take 3 let the group wade a bit deeper into Lennon's original before the songwriter — transitioning from the chorus into the second verse — changed chords a tad too early.[1354] Swearing under his breath, John stopped playing, and the song fell apart.

Using this break as a chance for suggestion and commentary, George Martin counseled Harrison about the distinctive descending riff that the boy had devised to introduce each verse. "It's not sounding clean up here," Martin said, as tactfully as possible. "Perhaps we should consider overdubbing it separately."[1355]

"Right, yeah," George lifted his face to the glassed wall above, "but if we're after double-trackin' the vocals — which knowin' John I'm sure we are — then, there'll only be the *two tracks* remainin' on the tape…which means I'll have to sing 'n play the lick at the same time, which is *even more difficult* than what I'm doin' right now."[1356]

And realizing both the validity of the boy's complaint and the struggle George was having with the riff in real time, Martin asked Second Engineer Ken Scott to stop the tape so that the issue could be hammered out.[1357]

Whilst the producer and lead guitarist batted ideas back and forth, John stood with Paul, discussing the sound he wanted from the song's reverse call-and-answer technique. "I want the call, as it were, to doorstep m' lyrics…y' know, *shove* them along."

John wanted Paul and George's blended call to serve as a callous chorus, pushing him stumblingly ahead, thwarting any attempt to pause and speak his mind. He wanted the call to "slant towards overpowerin' me," leaving him somewhat disregarded.

But he couldn't — or wouldn't — explain why. He didn't want to whinge that people only saw him as "the Smart Beatle" or the pithy writer or the brash rocker, but never saw John Lennon. Even when he'd told them, "I'm a loser, and I'm not what I appear to be," they had just giggled and batted their eyelashes at the dreadfully lost boy whose dream of success had gone terribly awry.[1358]

Daily, a million "Bravos!" shouted him down. Screams and applause drowned him out. And John wanted this song to illustrate that. He wanted his response line so closely inserted to Paul and George's call that it seemed stifled, interrupted.[1359] Indeed, almost cancelled.

I want it to sound, he thought, *as if every time I try to plead my case…off goes the world without me…never lettin' me finish my train of thought before they're on to the next line or off to the next big thing.*[1360]

But he didn't say that, and he didn't need to. Paul got it. In fact, many days he felt the same way. And so did George, and so did Ringo. They knew what John was after. And without a word, they had his back.

After a few minutes of give-and-go (Paul offering to mark out the beats on the tape for George and John saying that he'd already been "poundin' out the beats visibly" on his guitar body), a solution was reached. For now, Harrison would leave off the descending lead line, and they'd proceed ahead, coming back around later with some sort of remedy.[1361] Then, content with negotiations, the boys stepped back into place and waited for the red light to flash on.

"'Help!', Take 4," Norman Smith announced, and once again, the song lifted off.

This time, smiling despite the dark lyrics, the group made it all the way through, with only minor errors from Ringo. "Sorry, one 'n all," Ringo rolled the tension out of his shoulders.

"Must be contagious, ha!" George barked.

And as the booth readied Take 5, George lowered his head,

practicing over and over.[1362]

"All right boys, here we go!" Martin had a good feeling about this one.

"'Help!' Take 5," Smith announced, and the tape rolled.

The producer's instincts had been spot-on. This time, everything worked. Right words, right chords, right backbeat — right! Towards the very end of the recording, however, John's guitar began to slip a bit out of tune. *But not enough,* he thought, *to mar the work.*[1363]

However, when George Martin failed to announce, "Great work! Let's have that one, then," John instinctively leaned over the Framus and began the grueling tuning process.

Moments later, as the red light flashed on, Paul – unaware of John's dilemma – began the count-in to Take 6. But unable to join the others, John merely blinked and watched them charge into the first verse without him. Martin, seeing all from above, smiled, shook his head, and called things off.

"Sorry about that, John" the producer offered over the 1MC.

"Do we really need him, yeah?" Harrison found a grin. And everyone, except John, who was genuinely struggling to tune the Framus, laughed.

Muted conversation about Paul's house purchase, earlier in the day,[1364] resumed in a corner of the room as John bit into his lower lip and fought to achieve a pleasant sound from the Hootenanny. Tuning had never been his forté. In fact, part of Paul's initial appeal, at the 1957 Woolton Garden Fête, was the fact that "that Allerton kid" could tune his own guitar, and hence, John's.[1365] *But tunin' a fuggin' 12-string,* John thought now, *is one of Dante's seven levels of hell!*[1366]

At what seemed like "long last," John was finally ready to give his song another try.

"'Help!' Take 7," Smith articulated, with hope in his voice, but the engineer's positive vibes lasted only up to the transition into the final verse, when John – who'd been working the rhythm with confidence and a bit of swing – felt his guitar slip out of tune again, and things, as a whole, fell apart.[1367]

Another band might have called for a break, a quick "cuppa," or a smoke. But not The Beatles. John assiduously set to tuning once more, and in mere minutes, the boys were ready to try again.

"This is it!" Paul was the cheerleader this time. "The swingin' set!"[1368]

But McCartney's positivity didn't work this go-round, and almost the moment it began, Take 8 faltered.[1369] "False start," Paul announced, and they fell silent.

Secretly, John believed in Take 9. It had been "his number" since he'd been born on the 9th and come home, a few days later, to 9 Newcastle Road. Nine had befriended him early on, and he felt it would serve him well now.[1370]

"'Help!' Take 9," was the announcement from above, and nodding, John took a deep breath. Standing with feet apart, chin uptilted, and chest expanded, he shouted "Help! I need somebody! Help!", and the singer-songwriter gave it all he had.[1371]

He sang the lyrics with the raw angst he'd intended to inject into the original, plaintive version. He sang with a stone in his heart, with "a sadness...that leaves me a spectator of my own stupidity," as he'd once said to his soulmate, Stu Sutcliffe.[1372] John sang his loneliness and isolation. He sang his thinly-veiled brittleness. He sang honestly. And just over two minutes later, John had the basis for the next hit record.[1373]

Of course, there was still work to be done. Take 9 was promptly rewound by Ken Scott and then reduced to three tracks on a new tape, leaving one free track for Harrison's unique lead guitar overdub.[1374] Whilst the boys waited for "a sign from above," they chatted and laughed about the live BBC interview they'd done earlier that afternoon from a cramped, parked "radio car" in Twickenham Studios' lot.[1375]

"*That* was a first!" George threw his eyes to the ceiling. "An interview from a car, no less! Now I've seen it all!"

"Well, I've done it all!" Ringo seconded.

"Yeah well, we got off lucky, if y'er askin' me." Paul was the official purveyor of good news. "I mean, I heard they wanted us to *come in* 'n tape a full-blown special for Easter Monday, didn't they?"[1376]

"I don't know." John looked down his nose. "Did they?"

"Yeah," Paul wouldn't be rattled, "they did. But Brian sorted it out, y' see, by offerin' the live interview...on set, as it were, durin' the regular work day 'n not at night...when we have a private life."

"We don't have a private life!" George scoffed. "We're public property now!"

Whilst they were batting the thing back and forth, George Martin trooped down the stairs for a quick word.

He explained that whilst working with Norman on the reductions, they'd "run across a few notions" about the opening of the song, and he wanted to make certain John was on board.

"You see," Martin gestured with both hands, cupping the idea protectively, "I'd like your introductory words to be completely unembellished…authentic, without ornamentation. No double-tracking, no effects."[1377]

As much as John despised the undoctored sound of his voice, he appreciated the producer's attempt to preserve the original song that John had presented to him. Poetic compromise was Martin's aim.

"Right," John nodded, his eyes saying everything. "That'll work."

"If you absolutely hate it when we listen to the playback, we can always…" Martin began.

"No, I can hear it in m' head. It's what's called for."

But minutes later, when the light shone for Take 11 (Take 10 being an unused reduction),[1378] Smith and Martin almost simultaneously realised that the double-tracking was still turned on. So, "Help!" was halted, and Take 12 was cued.[1379]

"Last time today…if we all, including me," Martin promised from the booth, "get it right. Let's give it a go."

And Take 12 was all it needed to be. "Most satisfactory!" Martin pronounced. "That's precisely what we needed."

"Track it!" John permitted.

Of course, it wasn't really "all" they needed it to be. George still had to record his clever, earworm riff, and Ringo had a bit of tambourine work left to commit to tape.[1380] But essentially, the song was "in the can." The hard part had been accomplished.

At the end of the evening, when the boys slogged upstairs to hear the rough mono mix,[1381] they were pleased with the early results. Even John.

It was, by no means, the soulful song he'd wanted to give to the world: a glimpse into the pain he managed day after day. It wasn't his broken-but-beautiful ballad anymore. But hidden inside the folds of this innocuous movie theme were "the slings and arrows of outrageous fortune."

The ditty held the bittersweet memories of Mimi's hard-skinned duty to a frightened child who craved love, of Uncle George's unanticipated (and unfair, John still thought) death, of Julia's life in 1 Blomfield Road — a scant one-and-a-half miles from the son who longed for her — and of Stu's cerebral hemorrhage that taken him from John, without a word of goodbye. Gone...just as Julia was gone. No warning, no reprieve.

John thought "Help!" the best song he'd ever written, and even sheathed in up-tempo, it was powerful. His wail was still there. His cry for survival...there.

There's still hope that they — whoever "they" are — might save me after all, John thought, *if only they'll listen.*[1382]

But even his closest friends seemed to hear nothing untoward in the lyrics. And as they packed for home at 11.15 p.m., the conversation turned to tomorrow's official announcement that United Artists was "replacing the former moniker of the upcoming comedy by the Fab Four, 'Eight Arms to Hold You,' with the revised title, 'Help!'."[1383]

"At least it isn't Shenson's 'The Day the Clowns Collapsed,'"[1384] George snickered.

"I don't know," Ringo yawned and stretched, "I'm fairly sure I'm at *that* stage o' the proceedin's right now."

The four had been up since 6.00 a.m. for the drive into "hair and make-up." Filming had begun promptly at 8.00 a.m., with the taping of their BBC *Pop Inn* interview squeezed into their late "lunch break."[1385] Since daylight, the boys had known nothing but industry, and they were withered.

John and Ringo were twenty-four ("Twenty-four-and-a-half!" they would've boasted, as boys.). Paul, twenty-two ("and three-quarters!"), and George, newly twenty-two. And yet, they were all working 'round the clock like wizened "Suits" — senior executives — with weighty matters in their hands.

And tomorrow, Paul reminded them, they were due in town bright and early, to film some sort of street scene in which they would roll up in a limo and merrily debark in front of a four-doored, communal Beatles flat.[1386]

"Ugh," John shook his head at the news. "I'm after an easy six."[1387]

"C'mon Johnny boy! We've got to give the people what they want!" George curled his lip.

"Isn't that what I've always done?" John said, almost to

himself. And as the lights dimmed in Studio Two, the Fab Four were off.

Notes!

It's ironic that just a few weeks after John wrote "Help!", Paul would write and record a song that he (and almost everyone else) would consider to be the best song that he ever composed, "Yesterday." Paul's classic ballad was, thankfully, permitted to exist in its intended form. However, John's emotional (and in its original form, elegant) song was completely transformed *for the film "Help!" Thus, both John and Paul's most exquisite ballad compositions were written in this very narrow time frame during April of 1965.*

*To hear the way John Lennon wanted "Help!" to sound, please first listen to **his rough original piano demo** at the end of this video: https://www.youtube.com/watch?v=bpBTSwF38Yg As you listen, keep in mind the words of Mark Lewisohn and Kevin Howlett in* In My Life: John Lennon Remembered, *"['Help!'] was a meaningful plea that was virtually overlooked." (p. 34)*

And John's own words from Norman's John Lennon: The Life *and from Hammack's* The Beatles Recording Reference Manual *state: "We did ['Help!'] too fast, to try to be commercial. I remember I got really emotional at the time, singing the lyrics. I really meant it. I don't mess around." (Norman, p. 398 and Hammack, p. 38)*

Then, please listen to this slower, piano-based, confessional version of "Help!" by Tina Turner, recorded as a tribute to John, after his death: https://www.youtube.com/watch?v=4cro7kZKG2c This cover song conveys the exact emotion that John had hoped to instill into the ballad.

*It is very possible that had John Lennon been permitted to record "Help!" in its original vein, "Help!" would have become his "Yesterday." Then, **both** brilliantly lovely ballads would have been created by the geniuses, Lennon and McCartney, within just weeks of one another.*

Sources:

Lewisohn, The Complete Beatles Chronicle, *189.*
Lewisohn, The Beatles Recording Sessions, *58.*
Lewisohn and Howlett, In My Life: John Lennon Remembered, *34.*
Winn, Way Beyond Compare, *314-315.*
Hammack, The Beatles Recording Reference Manual, *Vol. 2, 38-39.*
Harry, The Ultimate Beatles Encyclopedia, *303.*

Harry, The John Lennon Encyclopedia, *338-339 and 654-655.*
Martin, George, All You Need is Ears, *76, 141, and 169.*
Spizer, The Beatles for Sale on Parlophone Records, *50.*
Womack, Maximum Volume: The Life of Beatles Producer, George Martin, *257-259.*
Womack, Long and Winding Roads, The Evolving Artistry of The Beatles, *106-107.*
Everett, The Beatles as Musicians: The Quarry Men through *Rubber Soul, 296-297.*
Norman, John Lennon: The Life, *397-399.*
Hammack, Jerry, The Beatles Recording Reference Manual, Vol. 2, *39.*
Margotin and Guesdon, 220.
Mellers, Wilfrid, Twilight of the Gods: The Music of The Beatles, *52-54.*
MacDonald, 120-121.
Sheff, 149.
Turner, A Hard Day's Write, *74-75.*
Russell, 74.
Brown, 171.
Babiuk, 160-161.
Coleman, Lennon, *159.*
Spitz, 555.
Riley, Tell Me Why, *139-141.*
Miles, The Beatles' Diary, Vol. 1, *194.*
Hill, John, Paul, George & Ringo, *196.*
Robertson, "Help! The End of the Beginning," Trynka, The Beatles: Ten Years That Shook the World, *167.*
Bicknell, 40.
Friede, Titone, and Wiener, 36, and 177.
Carlin, 116-117.

https://tinyurl.com/yym2rrdk This website gives a history of the recording of the title track, "Help!"

https://www.beatlesbible.com/1965/04/13/recording-help/ This very reputable website, www.BeatlesBible.com, supplies a summary of the events of that day.

https://tinyurl.com/y2rgpau2 This website gives a good summary of the record's stats plus information about the promotional video for "Help!"

There is a good photo of the Framus Hootenanny 12-string guitar (being played by George) in Babiuk's Beatles Gear on p. 165. Babiuk describes the German-made instrument on p. 160.

https://tinyurl.com/y6nc8myw This is a good video of a musician using a Framus Hootenanny exactly like John's to play "Hide Your Love Away." You get a good look at the instrument.

https://www.youtube.com/watch?v=Fkedw92qOUs This video shows the scene from "Help!" with the four-doored Beatles dwelling that Paul references at the end of this chapter.

John Lennon (framus-vintage.de) This website discusses John's Framus acoustic and has a photograph from "Help!" of John with the instrument.

https://beatlesdaily.com/2021/02/24/14-john-lennons-guitars/amp/ This website shows photos of all 14 of John Lennon's guitars, including several of John with the Framus Hootenanny.

https://www.youtube.com/watch?v=bpBTSwF38Yg Here you may listen to John Lennon's rough piano demo of "Help!"

1336 Everett, *The Beatles as Musicians: The Quarry Men Through* Rubber Soul, 296 and https://www.youtube.com/watch?v=bpBTSwF38Yg At the end of this video, you can hear John sing his original piano demo for "Help!" What a treasure. For those who argue that "Help!" is not solely John's song, Everett states, *"When* 'Eight Arms to Hold You' was given to The Beatles as the name of the film, McCartney set to work on a title song and came up empty. When "Help!" was suggested, Lennon took up the challenge and was immediately rewarded."
1337 Womack, *Maximum Volume: The Life of Beatles Producer, George Martin,* 257.
1338 Womack, *Long and Winding Roads: The Evolving Artistry of The Beatles,* 107 and Miles, *The Beatles' Diary, Vol. 1,* 194. Womack points out that John's tender song was "intentionally sped up; after all, it was the title track for a zany comedy, and the up-tempo design made commercial sense." Miles adds, "George Martin thought the fans would prefer a faster number."
1339 John Lennon (framus-vintage.de) This website talks about John's Framus acoustic guitar and shows a photo from "Help!" of John with the guitar.
1340 Martin, George, *All You Need is Ears,* 169.
1341 Martin, George, *All You Need is Ears,* 76. Direct quote from George Martin.
1342 Martin, George, *All You Need is Ears,* 141. George Martin says, "For me, making a record is like painting a picture in sound."
1343 Womack, *Maximum Volume: The Life of Beatles Producer, George Martin,* 257 and Harry, *The John Lennon Encyclopedia,* 339,
1344 Womack, *Maximum Volume: The Life of Beatles Producer, George Martin,* 257, Harry, *The John Lennon Encyclopedia,* 339, Riley, *Tell Me Why,* 138,
1345 Turner, *A Hard Day's Write,* 75 and Robertson, "Help! The End of the Beginning," Trynka, *The Beatles: Ten Years That Shook the World,* 167. Turner and Robertson remind us that Maureen Cleave prompted John to write songs that were more sophisticated and personal. Another proponent of this was Kenneth Allsop, who asked John why he didn't write songs as personal as his prose and poetry.

[1346] Womack, *Long and Winding Roads*, 107 and Riley, *Tell Me Why*, 138-139. Womack and Riley both comment on the fact that although John was compelled to accept a faster tempo for "Help!", George Martin and John *used that mad pace* to convey what Riley calls "increasing delirium." (Riley, 139) Riley says that John sounds "panicked, trapped" (Riley, 139) and Womack says there is a sense of "growing desperation." (Womack, 107) If John couldn't have the slow, confessional song he'd planned, then this was the next best thing.

[1347] Margotin and Guesdon, 220.

[1348] The allusion is to "Stars and Stripes Forever," a 1952 20th Century Fox film starring Clifton Webb, Debra Paget, and Robert Wagner.

[1349] Winn, *Way Beyond Compare*, 314, Lewisohn, *The Beatles Recording Sessions,* 58, Womack, *Maximum Volume: The Life of Beatles Producer, George Martin,* 258-259, and Spizer, *The Beatles for Sale on Parlophone Records,* 50.

[1350] Winn, *Way Beyond Compare*, 315 and Hammack, Jerry, *The Beatles Recording Reference Manual, Vol. 2,* 39.

[1351] Hammack, 39.

[1352] Hammack, 39.

[1353] Winn, *Way Beyond Compare*, 315.

[1354] Winn, *Way Beyond Compare*, 315.

[1355] Winn, *Way Beyond Compare*, 315 and Hammack, 39.

[1356] Winn, *Way Beyond Compare*, 315.

[1357] Winn, *Way Beyond Compare*, 315 and Hammack, 39.

[1358] Hill, *John, Paul, George & Ringo,* 196. There is a very touching summary of John's feelings about the recording and the lyrics of "Help!" on this page. Well worth reading.

[1359] Riley, *Tell Me Why*, 139.

[1360] Womack, *Long and Winding Roads,* 107, and Riley, *Tell Me Why*, 139. Riley asserts, "Since Paul and George anticipate nearly every line Lennon sings in the verse, the effect is of voices inside the same head, prodding, goading. The call-and-answer device has been turned around…to chilling consequence."

[1361] Winn, *Way Beyond Compare*, 315 and Hammack, 39.

[1362] Winn, *Way Beyond Compare*, 315 and Hammack, 39.

[1363] Winn, *Way Beyond Compare*, 315 and Hammack, 39. As the song ends, Winn tells us that John immediately begins tuning his guitar, so he clearly heard the issue. But Hammack still finds Take 5 quite good. He calls Take 5 a "solid track" and says, "…it's hard to know what Martin felt was wrong with it. It is the producer's role to push his artists to give their all in a recording, though, and perhaps this was his approach in the session." (p. 39)

[1364] Miles, *The Beatles' Diary, Vol. 1*, 194. Miles says that on this day, "Paul bought a three-storey Regency house at 7 Cavendish Avenue in St. Johns Wood, London, for £40,000."

[1365] O'Donnell, Jim, *The Day John Met Paul,* 116 and Coleman, *Lennon,* 66. Coleman says that on the day that John and Paul met at the Woolton Garden Fete, "First, John was floored by the fact that Paul could actually tune his guitar, thus correcting the banjo tuning John had inherited from his mother."

[1366] Winn, *Way Beyond Compare*, 315. Winn says that a segment of the studio tape from this day, Segment G, shows "John's increasingly futile attempts to [tune up]...and when John is nearly weeping with frustration, the tape stops again."

[1367] Winn, *Way Beyond Compare*, 315, and Hammack, 39. Hammack says that John was "really working the rhythm" in Take 7 and "adding swing to the part."

[1368] Winn, *Way Beyond Compare*, 315. Direct quote from Paul McCartney.

[1369] Winn, *Way Beyond Compare*, 315, and Hammack, 39.

[1370] Harry, *The John Lennon Encyclopedia*, 654-655. Don't miss this very interesting discussion of John's lifelong link to the number nine.

[1371] Lewisohn, *The Beatles Recording Sessions*, 58. Lewisohn says, "Takes one to eight concentrated on the rhythm track, the first vocals being introduced at take nine."

[1372] Coleman, *Lennon,* 159. The full quote from John in a letter to Stu Sutcliffe is: "I can't remember anything without a sadness/ So deep that it hardly becomes known to me/ So deep that its tears leave me a spectator of my own stupidity."

[1373] Winn, *Way Beyond Compare*, 315, Hammack, 39, and Spizer, *The Beatles for Sale on Parlophone Records,* 50.

[1374] Winn, *Way Beyond Compare*, 315, Hammack, 39, and Spizer, *The Beatles for Sale on Parlophone Records,* 50.

[1375] Lewisohn, *The Complete Beatles Chronicle*, 189.

[1376] Lewisohn, *The Complete Beatles Chronicle*, 189, Miles, *The Beatles' Diary, Vol. 1,* 194, and Bicknell, 40. I like the way Alf Bicknell records this event: "They did another live interview...at Twickers, for yet another pop programme." The programme, according to Lewisohn and Miles, was *Pop Inn* on the BBC's Light Programme.

[1377] Hammack, 39. Hammack says, "...Martin chose to have the introduction vocals by Lennon single tracked, only adding the double-tracked lead vocal starting in the first verse."

[1378] Winn, *Way Beyond Compare*, 315. Winn says, "Take Ten is an unused reduction."

[1379] Winn, *Way Beyond Compare*, 315, Hammack, 39, and Spizer, *The Beatles for Sale on Parlophone Records,* 50.

[1380] Winn, *Way Beyond Compare*, 315, Hammack, 40, and Spizer, *The Beatles for Sale on Parlophone Records,* 50. As Spizer reminds us, "tambourine is heard on the stereo version, but not on the mono one." The mono version, used in the film, had the tambourine removed at a later date since no one was playing a tambourine in the introduction to the film where the song is played/sung. For a superb discussion of how this removal was accomplished, read Hammack, p. 40.

[1381] Winn, *Way Beyond Compare*, 315.

[1382] Carling, *McCartney*, 117. What is so clear to us now was really almost unobserved at the time that John sang, "Help!" One explanation is offered by Carling in his biography of Paul McCartney. He says that John "revealed his inner dissonance...cloaked in...double meanings."

[1383] Miles, *The Beatles' Diary, Vol. 1,* 194.

[1384] Miles, *The Beatles' Diary, Vol. 1*, 194.
[1385] Lewisohn, *The Complete Beatles Chronicle*, 189. Lewisohn tells us that the *Pop Inn* show was broadcast from 1.00 to 1.55 p.m. that day, and The Beatles came on live at 1.45 p.m. after the song "Ticket to Ride" was played.
[1386] Carr, Roy, *Beatles at the Movies*, Miles, *The Beatles' Diary, Vol. 1*, 194, and Lewisohn, *The Complete Beatles Chronicle*, 189. Also in this video, you can see the scene referenced: https://www.youtube.com/watch?v=Fkedw92qOUs
[1387] "An easy six" is a day at work with little or nothing to do.

Thursday, 15 April — Monday, 19 April 1965
The Easter "Break"
London

For The Beatles, Easter break was defined as "no work on the 'Help!' set from Thursday, 15 April to Tuesday morning, 19 April." But a void in their diaries? Never. Time apart from filming opened opportunities for public appearances. And Brian, who rarely ever ceased endeavoring on their behalfs, meant to utilize every precious moment.

To be fair, however, Brian was pushing the boys no harder than he was pushing himself. Constantly grinding his teeth,[1388] he rarely delegated tasks, preferring to do everything himself.[1389]

"If you've got the gift, you can delegate," Brian reluctantly admitted, "but you can't delegate and keep in personal touch."[1390] And with that, he dismissed the practice altogether. However, doing everything for everyone, whilst giving The Beatles an extra measure of devotion, was costing him.

Recently, Brian had been approached by Gerry Marsden. With the Pacemakers scoring a late 1964 hit in the States with Mitch Murray's "I Like It"[1391] and currently preparing an American release of "It's Gonna Be Alright,"[1392] Gerry had gathered the confidence to assert himself. He insisted that his group could no longer be marketed like The Beatles.[1393] He pressed for their own identity.

"Look Brian, we're sure to fail if y' carry on treatin' us like John, Paul, George, 'n Ringo," Gerry averred, his usually merry eyes now somber.[1394] "Our music, y' see, is entirely different. Y' know that! Our following's different, isn't it? *We're* different![1395] 'N we need *specific attention* paid to the Pacemakers as an individual act. We'll not succeed as a carbon copy of anyone else...not even copies of great friends 'n yes, superstars like The

Beatles."[1396]

But as much as Epstein would've loved to give the slim Scouser and his three amiable mates their own marketing plan, he was already stretched too thin. Brushing the back of his hand across his lips, Brian admitted as much. "Truthfully, Gerry, I...I simply cannot devote the same amount of time to The Beatles and yourselves...The Beatles have become the biggest property Britain has ever known, and at the moment, you come second."[1397]

It was a harsh truth, and Brian felt awful about admitting it. He genuinely liked Gerry and his brother, Fred. He liked Les Chadwick and Les Maguire.[1398] The Pacemakers were happy, uncomplicated musicians with a cheerful sound. They had relished the joyous Tin Pan Alley number "How Do You Do It" — the song that The Beatles had rejected, calling it embarrassingly sentimental. The Pacemakers had also loved Mitch Murray's "I Like It," and had smiled all the way to Number One on the Spring 1963 U.K. Singles Chart.[1399] In fact, Gerry and the lads rarely asked for anything, and Brian wished he could give them the time and direction they needed to succeed. But Brian was overloaded. He could do no more.

Brian was managing myriad futures. He guided the Kent-based instrumental group Sounds Incorporated — who had joined The Beatles on their 1964 North American Tour and was slated to rejoin them in 1965.[1400] And without much luck, Epstein was still seeking a spotlight for young vocalist Tommy Quickly. Unfortunately, in the four months since the freckle-faced boy had shared the boards with The Beatles at "Another 'Beatles' Christmas Show," little had changed for the better.[1401]

Despite excellent backing from the Remo Four (who had joined John, Paul, George, and Ringo on their 1964 U.K. Autumn Tour),[1402] the extravagant gift of Lennon and McCartney's original song "Tip of My Tongue,"[1403] and several overgenerous promotional tours later, the bowler-hatted, Peter-Noone-look-alike still floundered.[1404] All the right ingredients seemed to be present, but the boy hadn't an ounce of Beatles magic. Quickly's inexplicable failure kept Brian searching for an answer.

This short list of NEMS stars didn't even include Brian's beloved Cilla Black, who had been recommended to him by John Lennon.[1405] It didn't include the highly-respected and cabaret-inclined Fourmost,[1406] or the talented but challenging Billy J.

Kramer,[1407] who had initially rebuffed Brian's generous offer of "Do You Want to Know a Secret?" with a cross, "Don't you think we ought to find a *good song*?"[1408]

Brian was being questioned, second-guessed, and pressured from all angles. It was impossible to make so many people happy.

Discovering brief release in high-stakes gambling, Brian began frequenting London's most elegant clubs such as Mayfair's Curzon House. He began indulging in exotic foods and expensive wines at Crockford's and the Clermont.[1409] Losing himself in *chemin de fer, roulette,* and the thrill of the chase,[1410] Brian sought emancipation — however short-lived — from his many worries. But each morning, the familiar anxieties returned, and the only real remedy appeared to be working longer and harder than anyone thought possible.

Not surprisingly, Brian had become choleric.

"I am surrounded by *idiots*!" he often seethed, quite audibly and in public places.[1411] Though at heart, he still longed to be "Eppy" — the affable, gentle-natured manager — he was tending more and more these days towards the high-flown NEMporer.[1412] Brian rushed into rages and was known in Sutherland House as "*the boss*, and not a relaxed boss." His lovely brunette secretary, Joanne Newfield, was well aware that most people were frightened of him.[1413] And increasingly, business associates began describing Brian as "officious and rude, a pain in the ass."[1414]

Struggling under "too much work in too little time," Brian was losing his sense of boundaries. Ringing up associates to discuss business far too early in the morning and far too late at night, Brian briefly apologised for each intrusion with, "Are you sure I'm not interrupting?" or "Terribly sorry for ringing you at this time..." But despite these apologies, he kept right on calling, requesting, and working at odd hours.[1415] Brian was consumed.

Now, as the Easter holiday loomed before him, Epstein thumbed through his desktop diary, hoping to turn the long weekend into vast productivity. He planned to utilize these few "empty" days as a chance to accomplish "things left undone." He hoped to extricate himself from overdue promises and responsibilities.

Brian Esptein, 1965
Photograph from Wikimedia Commons

Most of all, Brian sought every opportunity to promote The Beatles' newly-released single. He believed, as he always said, that time was of the essence.

Friday, 16 April

Live Television appearance: The Beatles
Rediffusion
Studio One, Wembley Studios
Programme: "Ready, Steady Goes Live!" (formerly "Ready, Steady, Go!")
Host: Cathy McGowan
Other Guests: Adam Faith, Doris Troy, Herman's Hermits, The Kinks
Note: The new format (beginning 2 April) precludes pre-taping. Use two of the boys only...perhaps George...and definitely John, as his book release will be imminent.
Focus: Promote the new single, "Ticket to Ride"[1416]

Sunday, 18 April

The Beatles' mono and stereo mixes of "Help!" being completed at EMI
Beatles not required.[1417]

Possibility: Consultation w Martin about evolution of soundtrack.

Of interest: Release of the film, "Pop Gear." The Beatles' Pathé footage from 20 November 1963 will be included. Ascertain audience reaction.[1418]

Note: Ringo purchasing new bungalow for his parents. Speak to Wendy about a housewarming gift and note of congratulations.

Monday, 19 April

"Ticket to Ride" single to be released in America!![1419]

10-year anniversary of Elvis in music industry on 21st. Send congratulatory telegram.[1420]

Possibility: Bank holiday meeting with Dick Lester on film progress.

Even at a glance, Brian could see for himself that his diary was dominated by The Beatles. He didn't need the other NEMS acts to point out the imbalance.

Yes, yes, but, it's only natural, Brian reasoned. *The Beatles are international stars! They're wanted by everyone, everywhere, at every moment! And it's up to* me *to make them as universally available as possible.*

But it was more than that, and everyone knew it. The Beatles had Brian's heart.[1421] He traveled with them almost everywhere they went. He stood on the sidelines and watched them with a tender pride.[1422] He almost mouthed the very words as they sang. Terrified of loneliness, Brian thought of The Beatles as his family and more than once, confided to Wendy Hanson, "The boys always make an effort to involve me in what they're doing."[1423] It was his happiest boast. And repeatedly, Hanson had heard Brian profess to newsmen, "I hate to be called The Beatles' boss. I am their *friend*, and I happen to be their manager, too."[1424]

It was this intense affection that made Brian most vulnerable to the boys' displeasure. And today, he had irritated John.

The prospect of motoring to Rediffusion for a live BBC show on a holiday weekend — in the midst of "the official move" from the servants' quarters into Kenwood proper on the very same weekend that John's book revisions were due — had thrown Lennon into a swivet. Impulsively, the boy had rung Brian with a string of angry complaints.

Saying that he was overworked, unappreciated, and exhausted, John resented having to trek to Rediffusion at all. And sharing John's emotions about his own workload and esteem, Brian had hardly countered the accusations.[1425] Instead, he'd replied very quietly, "You *are* appreciated, John. Too much, I think. The whole world appreciates you. The whole world wants to hear from you. If you'd prefer not to appear on the programme tomorrow night, I can, of course, arrange that. But as I recall, you like Cathy McGowan, and if I'm not mistaken, you need to promote your new book...the book that you, and not me, decided that you would write. Furthermore, you composed 'Ticket to Ride.' It's your song. Who can speak to its unique nature better than you?"

For a moment, John was silent. As was Brian. Then, they both sighed, almost simultaneously.

"Right, then, Eppy," John spat reluctantly. "I'll be there."[1426]

"Thank you, John. That means a lot." And turning back to the mountain of work on his desk, Brian plowed on.

Notes!

Was Brian really working as hard as this chapter suggests?

Ray Coleman, the respected journalist who was considered a close friend of The Beatles and Brian, said this about the NEMS manager: "He was working seven days a week and into most nights, checking and telephoning, negotiating better fees, planning new records, and always keeping an eye open for further ways to expand."

Furthermore, in In My Life: The Brian Epstein Story, *Debbie Geller quotes Gerry Marsden as saying, "Brian was losing it. Brian didn't like to delegate. That was Brian's problem. He wanted to be there doing it, and he didn't want to feel as though he was letting you down. I think the whole thing was getting a little too much for Brian in those days, but he was still working very hard." (p. 132)*

Sources:

Lewisohn, The Complete Beatles Chronicle, *188.*
Lewisohn, The Beatles: Day by Day, *61.*
Harry, The Ultimate Beatles Encyclopedia, *166, 550, and 614-615.*
Harry, The Encyclopedia of Beatles People, *62-66, 134, 142-143, 185-186, and 263-264.*
Winn, Way Beyond Compare, *316.*
Norman, Shout!, *250-251.*
Howlett, The Beatles at the BBC, *67.*
Miles, The Beatles' Diary, Vol. 1, *194.*
Coleman, The Man Who Made The Beatles, *158-159, 162, 170, 182, 184-185, 188, 230, 238, 241, 246, 243, 270-272, and 320.*
Geller, Debbie, In My Life: The Brian Epstein Story, *113, 132, and 147.*
Schultheiss, 132.
Robertson, Lennon, *40.*

https://tinyurl.com/y3uc94pt This video reveals the charm that won Brian's heart; here is his Cilla Black singing "Liverpool Lullabye," a touching ballad to an errant Scouser:

https://www.allmusic.com/artist/gerry-the-pacemakers-mn0000541125/biography Mark Deming discusses Gerry and the Pacemakers here.

https://en.wikipedia.org/wiki/I_Like_It_(Gerry_and_the_Pacemakers_song) This website provides information on the hit song "I Like It" by Gerry and the Pacemakers.

https://www.billboard.com/music/gerry-and-the-pacemakers/chart-history The hits of Gerry and the Pacemakers are listed here, with information about each one.

Below is a modern-day photo of Sutherland House where NEMS was located. You can "Imagine" what it looked like in 1965, without the popular "Five Guys" burger establishment below.

Sutherland House, home of Brian Epstein's NEMS office, London
Photograph from Wikimedia Commons

[1388] Miles, *Many Years From Now*, 131. Paul McCartney states, "Brian would be, 'Ugggghhh, the pills!' The jaw would be grinding away!"
[1389] Harry, *The Encyclopedia of Beatles People,* 143. Harry says, "…since [Epstein] wouldn't delegate, this had a bad effect on the [NEMS] artists."
[1390] Coleman, *The Man Who Made The Beatles*, 238. Direct quote from Brian Epstein.
[1391]

https://en.wikipedia.org/wiki/I_Like_It_(Gerry_and_the_Pacemakers_song)

Like It" reached #17 in the American charts in 1964. It had hit #1 in the U.K. in 1963.

[1392] Harry, *The Ultimate Beatles Encyclopedia*, 266 and https://www.billboard.com/music/gerry-and-the-pacemakers/chart-history This website lists all of the hits of Gerry and the Pacemakers and dates of release.

[1393] Harry, *The Ultimate Beatles Encyclopedia*, 166.

[1394] Harry, *The Ultimate Beatles Encyclopedia*, 166.

[1395] Harry, *The Ultimate Beatles Encyclopedia*, 166 and Harry, *The Encyclopedia of Beatles People*, 143. Gerry Marsden is quoted saying, "The Beatles appealed to a different audience from us. They had more of a beatnik following."

[1396] Harry, *The Ultimate Beatles Encyclopedia*, 166 and Harry, *The Encyclopedia, of Beatles People*, 143. Harry says that Marsden kept telling Brian that his band "needed specific attention paid to their own individuality and style as an act," but with the vast amount of other responsibilities he was juggling, Brian simply did not have the time or energy to do that.

[1397] Coleman, *The Man Who Made The Beatles*, 188. Direct quote from Brian Epstein in response to Gerry Marsden.

[1398] https://www.allmusic.com/artist/gerry-the-pacemakers-mn0000541125/biography On this website, Mark Deming does a wonderful job of discussing each of the Merseybeat groups and their hits, including Gerry and the Pacemakers.

[1399] https://en.wikipedia.org/wiki/I_Like_It_(Gerry_and_the_Pacemakers_song) "I Like It" only made it to Number 17 on the U.S. Charts, however.

[1400] Harry, *The Ultimate Beatles Encyclopedia*, 614-615.

[1401] Coleman, *The Man Who Made The Beatles*, 183. Coleman tells us that "Brian felt he should continue to nurture Liverpool's music. Tom Quigley was a freckle-faced seventeen-year-old…He sang breezily, had an impish sense of humor and a cheerful presence. Brian noted that the girls in the audience liked him, and he believed there was 'something there to develop.'" But as the months passed, Quigley somehow never found success. Not even "The Man With the Midas Touch" could make it happen.

[1402] Harry, *The Ultimate Beatles Encyclopedia*, 550 and Harry, *The Encyclopedia of Beatles People,* 263.

[1403] Harry, *The Encyclopedia of Beatles People*, 263.

[1404] Coleman, *The Man Who Made The Beatles*, 184. Ray Coleman points out, "For the first time [Epstein's] commercial judgment had been rejected by the public, which would not be browbeaten into elevating all his acts to the hall of fame. Quickly's shows were popular, but the yardstick of real success was the record charts, which Quickly never entered."

[1405] Coleman, *The Man Who Made The Beatles,* 158-159. These two pages in Coleman give the history of Cilla's recruitment by NEMS. When Brian introduced himself to Cilla he said, "John Lennon has told me about you. He says if I'm looking for a girl singer to sign, it should be you." In this same charming history of her association with NEMS, Cilla states, "Actually, Brian really did think the sun shone out of my eyes."

[1406] Coleman, *The Man Who Made The Beatles,* 170.

[1407] Coleman, *The Man Who Made The Beatles*, 185.

[1408] Coleman, *The Man Who Made The Beatles*, 162.

[1409] Geller, Debbie, *In My Life: The Brian Epstein Story*, 113. Brian's friend, Geoffrey Elliss, is quoted as saying "At the time, [Brian] was very fond of gambling. He used to gamble quite heavily, and I accompanied him several times to Crockford's, to the Clearmont, where we would have an excellent dinner for which no bill was presented because he was a high roller..." Peter Brown says, "Brian and I started to go off looking for other places...more exlusive gambling clubs."

[1410] Coleman, *The Man Who Made The Beatles*, 241.

[1411] Coleman, *The Man Who Made The Beatles*, 268. Direct quote from Brian Epstein.

[1412] Coleman, *The Man Who Made The Beatles*, 238.

[1413] Coleman, *The Man Who Made The Beatles*, 268. The quote "the boss and not a relaxed boss" is verbatim from Brian's secretary, Joanne Newfield. She also said, "people were afraid of him."

[1414] Coleman, *The Man Who Made The Beatles*, 271-272. Direct quote from Al Brodax.

[1415] Coleman, *The Man Who Made The Beatles*, 270.

[1416] Lewisohn, *The Complete Beatles Chronicle*, 188, Winn, *Way Beyond Compare,* 316, and Miles, *The Beatles' Diary, Vol. 1,* 194.

[1417] Lewisohn, *The Complete Beatles Chronicle*, 188 and Winn, *Way Beyond Compare*, 316.

[1418] Miles, *The Beatles' Diary, Vol. 1*, 194.

[1419] Miles, *The Beatles' Diary, Vol. 1*, 194.

[1420] Miles, *The Beatles' Diary, Vol. 1*, 194.

[1421] Geller, 132-133, 147 and Norman, *Shout!,* 250-251. In Geller's book, Alistair Taylor is quoted saying, "...he adored [The Beatles] so much and they were the light of his life...He was almost tunnel visioned about The Beatles." (p. 132) And George Martin says, "[Brian] always thought The Beatles were the bee's knees." Gerry Marsden says of Brian's feelings towards The Beatles: "They were the boys he loved." (p. 147) Finally, Norman says, "The Beatles were not in Brian's head but in his heart." (p. 250-251)

[1422] Coleman, *The Man Who Made The Beatles,* 243.

[1423] Coleman, *The Man Who Made The Beatles,* 246. Direct quote from Brian Epstein.

[1424] Coleman, *The Man Who Made The Beatles,* 230. Direct quote from Brian Epstein.

[1425] Coleman, *The Man Who Made The Beatles*, 320. Coleman says: "Brian was constantly apologizing to John."

[1426] Coleman, *The Man Who Made The Beatles*, 320. Although John was known for "needling" Brian more than the others, Ray Coleman asserts that John's communication with Brian was "better than...any other Beatle." He says, "Lennon had the vision to see that the gold of Brian's dreams justified his methods." John knew that Brian always had John's best interests at heart.

Tuesday, 27 April 1965
Twickenham Film Studios
St. Margaret's
Twickenham

"Now I see why they gave us yesterday off!" George demonstratively lifted the folds of his houndstooth Sherlock Holmes-esque cape and let it drop, "To sweeten us up for wearin' *this* gear!"[1427]

"M' own auntie wouldn't recognize me in this!" John gingerly tugged at the wiry beard that flowed across his top coat. "It's like that limerick from Edward Lear:

"There was an Old Man with a beard,
Who said, 'It is just as I feared! —
Two Owls and a Hen, four Larks and a Wren,
Have all built their nests in my beard."[1428]

"Hey!" Paul had overheard John giving many a literary interview. "I thought you said you never read that Lear!"

"It was *King* Lear I was referrin' to, son." John deadpanned.

"Oh," Paul wiggled his itchy moustache.[1429]

"You look like that American baird on the 'Bewitched' programme, McCartney," Ringo pronounced, arching one eyebrow.

"She doesn't have a moustache!" Paul intentionally played the fool.

"Yeah, but that's her twitch!" Ringo chuckled.

The boys were idling time away at Twickenham's "Pan American counter," waiting for Lester's call for action. The airport terminal set was wonderfully authentic.[1430] No one could have guessed they were, once again, inside the film studio, as the four were rather routinely now.[1431]

But this morning, their garb was definitely out of the ordinary. The "film Beatles," dressed in hats, scarves, and heavy topcoats, (as called for in the script) were stealthily stealing away from England…and, they hoped, from Clang's henchmen.[1432] Attired, quite obviously, for frigid climes, Lester's Beatles were banking on the clever disguises to give their foes the slip, as they secretly winged their way to the Bahamas. That was the story line, anyway.

"I sort of like this get-up!" Ringo fingered the light-coloured, hooded, and waisted anorak with matching ski pants. His black, mid-calf, all-weather boots were sharp as well. And sporting a Fifties-era moustache and goatee, beneath a shaggy, centre-parted mane, Ringo looked every bit the eccentric, coffeehouse poet.

"…says Adrian Henri here," John thumbed towards Starr.

"*What*?! I'm no beatnik!"

"Nah, y'er generally off-beat, Nick. But check the mirror, son." John's eyes glinted fun through a pair of round, National Health glasses.[1433] "Y' look just like ole Adrian, don't you?" In truth, Ringo's disguise *did* bestow a certain resemblance to Liverpool's unofficial poet laureate. And to their credit, both quirky characters could carry the look off. They were similarly "hip."

Liverpool Beat Poet Adrian Henri
Photograph from Wikimedia Commons

Of the four Beatles, only Paul had been given a somewhat traditional disguise. He looked older and more distinguished, in a heavy, double-breasted overcoat, light-hued woolen scarf, and banded fedora. With an official "Press" pass in the band of his hat and a camera case slung round his neck, Paul was far from unconventional.[1434] In fact, he seemed completely incongruous with the band of bearded, long-tressed others.[1435]

"Look at the state of you!" Paul glanced at his comrades, wrinkling his nose in distaste. "Is this *really* how Lester 'n his cronies think we'll look twenty-five years from now?"[1436]

"I hope not..." George began.

"...because I'm in a fuggin' wheelchair!"[1437] John exploded.

"Y'er *all* bloody terrifyin'..." Paul snickered. "...well, except Ringo, y' know. He's quite chic altogether!"

"From the very start, bloke! 'N don't you forget it!" Ringo waggled his many-ringed fingers. "I was always the coolest kid in the sanitarium!"

Not a one of them doubted it.

Sources:

Lewisohn, The Complete Beatles Chronicle, *191.*
Harry, The Ultimate Beatles Encyclopedia, 300 and *671-672.*
Miles, The Beatles' Diary, Vol 1, *194.*
Yule, *105.*
The Beatles, The Beatles Anthology, *170.*
Lear, Edward, *"There Was an Old Man,"* Prelutsky, Jack, The Random House Book of Poetry for Children, *163.*
Buskin, *115. There is a superb photo of John in his disguise on this page.*

Adrian Henri | Poetry Foundation *This website supplies additional information for those interested in Liverpool's beat poet, Adrian Henri.*

Adrian Henri - Poetry Archive *This website supplies more information about Adrian Henri and lets you listen to several of his audio poems.*

[1427] Lewisohn, *The Complete Beatles Chronicle*, 191. There is an excellent photo of all four Beatles in their "airport disguises" on this page, and Lewisohn calls this uncanny costuming selection — prefiguring how The

Beatles would actually look in just a few years' time — as "one of the most remarkable scenes in 'Help!'"

[1428] Lear, Edward, "There Was An Old Man with A Beard," *A Book of Nonsense,* published in 1846.

[1429] Lewisohn, *The Complete Beatles Chronicle*, 191, Harry, *The Ultimate Beatles Encyclopedia*, 300, and The Beatles, *The Beatles Anthology*, 170. All descriptions in this part of the chapter come from the photos on these pages.

[1430] Lewisohn, *The Complete Beatles Chronicle*, 191, Harry, *The Ultimate Beatles Encyclopedia*, 300, and The Beatles, *The Beatles Anthology*, 170.

[1431] Lewisohn, *The Complete Beatles Chronicle,* 190. Lewisohn tells us that on 21 April, the boys were inside Twickenham filming a scene "in Scotland Yard" with Superintendent Gluck, and on 22 April, they had been again in Twickenham, supposedly in a TV studio performing "Help!" while Clang and his crew watched them on a movie screen. That afternoon, they shot a scene with a professor of dramatic art (comedian Frankie Howerd), which was not used in the film. This same scene was completed in Twickenham on 23 April. Only on Saturday, 24 April, do the boys get to leave the studio to do a scene in Chiswick where they walk down Post Office Alley out onto the Thames towpath — encountering Clang's evil hordes, disguised as bagpipers. For the most part, during late April, The Beatles were working inside Twickenham, with little view of the outside world.

[1432] Lewisohn, *The Complete Beatles Chronicle*, 191, Harry, *The Ultimate Beatles Encyclopedia*, 300, and The Beatles, *The Beatles Anthology*, 170. This is the photo used for all descriptions in this chapter.

[1433] Lewisohn, *The Complete Beatles Chronicle*, 191, Harry, *The Ultimate Beatles Encyclopedia*, 300, and The Beatles, *The Beatles Anthology*, 170.

[1434] Harry, *The Ultimate Beatles Encyclopedia*, 300. You can see a photo of Paul with his "Press" pass here. Several great shots of The Beatles in their disguises are on this page.

[1435] Lewisohn, *The Complete Beatles Chronicle*, 191, Harry, *The Ultimate Beatles Encyclopedia*, 300, and The Beatles, *The Beatles Anthology*, 170.

[1436] Yule, 105. Yule states, "When the group was made up in their various disguises in 'Help!" the idea was to make each of them look as they would in twenty-five years' time, complete with facial hair and Victorian glasses."

[1437] Lewisohn, *The Complete Beatles Chronicle*, 191, Freeman, 128, Harry, *The Ultimate Beatles Encyclopedia*, 300, The Beatles, *The Beatles Anthology*, 170, and Buskin, 115. There is a great photo of John in his costume on p. 128 of Bob Freeman's book and on p. 115 of Buskin's book.

May 1965

Chart Toppers

"Mrs. Brown, You've Got a Lovely Daughter" — Herman's Hermits
"Ticket to Ride" — The Beatles
"Help Me, Rhonda" — The Beach Boys

In The News

5 May: The first significant ground troop deployments from the U.S. arrive in Vietnam.

11 May: The second cyclone in less than a month hits India. Death total: 35,000. That day, a windstorm in Bangladesh kills 17,000.

12 May: The Rolling Stones record a new song, "Satisfaction."

16 May: The Cannes Film Festival opens, featuring "The Knack and How to Get It" by Director Richard Lester.

18 May: Ray Dolby founds Dolby Laboratories in London, England.

25 May: Muhammad Ali KO's Sonny Liston in Round 1 at Central Maine Civic Center.

Saturday, 1 May 19654
Kenwood
Weybridge, Surrey

Though many lyrics escaped him, John often recalled the words he'd written, ages ago, to open "With The Beatles": "Every night when everybody has fun, here am I, sittin' all on my own."[1438] The simple lines now appeared almost a prophecy. Tonight, and almost every night when he wasn't working too vigourously to notice it, John felt isolated — left out.

Even with a beautifully-renovated home, a wife who tried (too) hard to please him, a new record destined for Number One, and a second book off to the press, John felt devoid of joy.

Happiness, he thought, *is how you feel when you don't feel miserable.*[1439] But it had been a while since he'd experienced that sensation.

Few people, John mulled — wetting the kettle to brew his third cup of after-dinner Earl Grey — had ever understood him.[1440] Pete? *Yeah, Shotton still did.* On those weekends when Pete could trip down to Kenwood, "Shennon and Lotton" laughed together.[1441] They played Monopoly and Risk, listened to records, and watched TV.[1442] But those days were all too rare. Both men worked too often and too long.

Thel? A corner of John's lip curved, recalling his first Liverpool College of Art sweetheart, Thelma Pickles. *Yeah, she got me...well, at first...until m' darker side finally heaved her away.*[1443] Rummaging through Kenwood's very new-smelling modern, handle-less kitchen cabinets[1444] — in search of an errant biscuit tin — John made a comforting ruckus. He despised the silence of being alone.

And then, there's Cyn, he sighed. *She knows me...only too well.*

After six years together, Cynthia embraced the real John Winston Lennon. She knew that her husband wasn't infallible, wasn't invulnerable, and wasn't a tough man, after all. She knew every chink in his armour and loved him anyway. But John didn't want someone to love him "in spite of" or "although." John wanted complete acceptance, not understanding…and certainly not compassion.

The kind of love that Stu always…[1445] John started down that road, but the sudden lump in his throat warned him off. E*nough, "long lost John!"*[1446] he warned himself. *Just have yer fuggin' tea party 'n shirrup!*

And carefully balancing the long, royal blue tin of Cadbury Fingers, his teacup, a spoon, and the sugar bowl, John made space for himself at the massive white-tiled cook-island.[1447] He pilfered cream from the new state-of-the art refrigerator and carefully nudged a stool over with one bare foot.

Without ceremony, his beloved feline, Mimi, vaulted to the counter, nosing around the cream as if she'd been invited.[1448] "Who asked you up, Madam?" John ruffled behind her ears. "This is a private party, here." But no sooner were the words out of his mouth than Babaghi, the Lennons' newest tabby, joined them as well.[1449]

"One can't be dreary, surrounded by cats." Cynthia, in her robe and bare feet, padded into the kitchen. She reached for one of the small chocolate-covered cookie sticks that John loved, whilst parting her thick blonde fringe with a wave of her hand.

"Can't one?" John dunked a Cadbury into his tea.

"I believe those are the hard and fast rules," Cynthia smiled, stroking Babaghi's artfully striped coat.

But John had never been one to accept rules, and despite the fact that his kitchen contained *two* cats and a gorgeous blonde, he was glum. Tomorrow, he and the others were departing for the vast, open, largely abandoned chalk plateau in southwestern England known as Salisbury Plain.[1450] With over 300 miles of wild, undeveloped country at hand,[1451] it seemed the perfect place to film some of the "battle scenes" between Clang's troops and the beleaguered film-Beatles.[1452]

But something about the impending trek depressed John. He wasn't sure if it was the delayed spring this year…the unseasonably deep chill still hovering in the air.[1453] Or if lonely, magical haunts like this sweeping plain — the home of Stonehenge — filled him with dread. Either way, John wasn't eager to go.

But neither was he keen to stay. *There's no joy in sitting 'round, sayin' little 'n doin' less,* John thought.

He was in a doldrums that not even the muted May light in his beloved glassed-in sunroom could dispel.[1454] If he spent many successive days in Kenwood, John felt stymied. He felt like a doddering, old pensioner — puttering here, doing time there. John thrived on purpose.[1455]

For years, he'd been fixated on reaching "the toppermost of the poppermost." The obsession had kept him awake at night; it had energized him through countless days of upward climb and hard work. But now? Now, John had grasped that pinnacle, and standing at the top, he seemed to have lost all sense of direction.

John was still unbelievably busy, inhumanly tasked — constantly whisked from one mammoth project to the next. But he was unfulfilled. His over-arching purpose had been achieved. Yet John wanted something more.

No…he wanted *something else.* Craved it. But what that something else was, he couldn't say. He simply knew he didn't have it.[1456]

Sources:

Lewisohn, The Complete Beatles Chronicle, *192.*
Lewisohn, The Beatles: Day-by-Day, *61.*
Harry, The Ultimate Beatles Encyclopedia, *523 and 635-637.*
Harry, The John Lennon Encyclopedia, *809 and 873-897.*
Lennon, Cynthia, John, *151.*
Coleman, Lennon, *78-80.*
Norman, John Lennon: The Life, *387.*
Miles, The Beatles' Diary, Vol. 1, *195.*
Womack, John Lennon 1980, *186.*
Carr, Beatles at the Movies, *74-77.*
Shotton and Clayson, 100, 116.
Hertsgaard, 118.
Turner, A Hard Day's Write, *34.*
Robertson, John, The Music of John Lennon, *45.*
Schultheiss, 133.
Goldman, 194.
Robertson, Lennon, *40.*
Solt and Egan, 75.
Cleave, Maureen, "How Does a Beatle Live?" Egan, The Mammoth Book of The Beatles, *108.*

[1438] From "It Won't Be Long" by Lennon/McCartney, *With The Beatles*, 1963.
[1439] The Beatles, *The Beatles Anthology*, 171. Direct quote from John Lennon.
[1440] Robertson, John, *The Music of John Lennon*, 44. Robertson points out that although "John felt self-pity because no one understood him, it was clear that no woman would be offered the chance. As Lennon proudly announced in several Beatles interviews, 'Women were to be obscene and not heard.'" Cynthia was not remiss in trying to be there for John.
[1441] Shotton and Clayson, 100 and Norman, *John Lennon: The Life*, 387. Pete says, "I was to spend all of my free weekends with John…I must have been virtually the only person he knew (apart from his wife, which is another story altogether) with whom he could 'switch off' and feel free from any obligation to talk about music or business, 'act like a star' or submit to an unending Beatles Q and A."
[1442] Shotton and Clayson, 116, Norman, *John Lennon: The Life*, 387, and Harry, *The John Lennon Encyclopedia*, 809. Pete Shotton, in *John Lennon, In*

My Life, says that when he visited Kenwood, "John and I devoted many long nights to marathon sessions of Monopoly and a game of global conquest, Risk." He also talks about "watching TV and listening to records."

[1443] Turner, Steve, *A Hard Day's Write,* 34 and Harry, *The Ultimate Beatles Encyclopedia,* 523.

[1444] https://tinyurl.com/y6mamtov One can see the sleek white cabinets selected by designer Keith Partridge in this photo of the Kenwood kitchen. The photo is from several years hence when John is with Yoko, but the kitchen is the same.

[1445] Coleman, *Lennon,* 79-80 and Harry, *The John Lennon Encyclopedia,* 873-897. John is referring to his best friend at Liverpool College of Art, Stuart Sutcliffe. Stuart was the first bass player in The Beatles and was truly John's "brother" and soulmate. Coleman quotes Mimi as saying that Stu was John's "only friend." She says Stu was the only person John "really enjoyed being with for long periods of time." Futhermore, Bill Harry's *John Lennon Encyclopedia* (pp. 873-897) dispels many common myths about John and Stu. Stu's story is also found in Vols. 1 and 2 of **The John Lennon Series**, *Shoulda Been There* and *Shivering Inside.*

[1446] Womack, *John Lennon 1980,* 186. Womack says that this phrase (added as part the lyrics of "I'm Losing You") was John's reference to "Lost John" recorded in 1956 by Lonnie Donegan. Lonnie's character is introduced as Donegan's song commences as "long gone lost John." To listen to the song, go here: https://tinyurl.com/y4qrvgbt

[1447] https://tinyurl.com/y6mamtov This is an excellent photo of the white-tiled kitchen cook-island mentioned.

[1448] Lennon, Cynthia, *John,* 151 and Deezen, Eddie, "John Lennon Was a Crazy Cat Lady," found at https://www.mentalfloss.com/article/29696/john-lennon-was-crazy-cat-lady. This is a very thorough and correct list of John's cats, throughout his lifetime.

[1449] Lennon, Cynthia, *John,* 151 and Deezen, Eddie, "John Lennon Was a Crazy Cat Lady," found at https://www.mentalfloss.com/article/29696/john-lennon-was-crazy-cat-lady.

[1450] Lewisohn, *The Complete Beatles Chronicle,* 192, Robertson, *Lennon,* 40, Schultheiss, 133, and Miles, *The Beatles' Diary, Vol. 1,* 195.

[1451] https://www.britannica.com/place/Salisbury-Plain-England This website gives a good account of The Beatles' time spent on Salisbury Plain with colour photos.

[1452] Lewisohn, *The Complete Beatles Chronicle,* 192, Turner, *A Hard Day's Write,* 76 and 78, and Carr, *Beatles at the Movies,* 74-77.

[1453] https://www.tapatalk.com/groups/solobeatlesphotosforum/5-may-1965-uk-salisbury-plain-wiltshire-t6852.html This website states that the weather on Salisbury Plain, Wiltshire was "unseasonably cold and windy" during the week that The Beatles were there, and after three days, the boys looked "weather-beaten." Coming from Liverpool, where May can easily include quite chilly days, it must have been frigid on the open plain with nothing to break the wind.

[1454] https://tinyurl.com/y6zgkyjw This is a good photo of the sunroom overlooking the Kenwood gardens and pool. This was John's favourite room in the house.

[1455] Hertsgaard, 118. Hertsgaard quotes Paul as saying, "...the good thing about working with John is he didn't like to hang about too much. Didn't like to be bored..."

[1456] Cleave, Maureen, "How Does a Beatle Live?" in Egan, Sam, *The Mammoth Book of The Beatles*, 108 and Goldman, 194. John told reporter Maureen Cleave in her famous March 1966 interview: "You see, there's something else I'm going to do, something I must do — only I don't know what it is."

Sunday, 2 May — Wednesday, 5 May 1965
Salisbury Plain
England

Sunday Evening, 2 May
The Antrobus Arms, Amesbury, England
11.20 p.m.

After just over an hour's transport from London, the boys trekked into their new (though very temporary) home — the sedate, white-stuccoed Antrobus Arms, the local inn in the heart of quaint and historic Amesbury.[1457] Whilst Bicknell managed their scant luggage,[1458] The Beatles nosed around the high-ceilinged lobby, complete with massive, white dental moulding and wide baseboard mouldings edging an elegant grey-and-black tiled floor.[1459] At the rear of the room, a spectacular Palladian opened to a rose garden.[1460] Tonight, however, the boys could only themselves reflected in the polished glass.

"Reminds me a bit of Quarry Bank — this,"[1461] John mumbled, almost to himself. "The grand staircase, metal railings, hardwood banister."

"It's all sorta...quiet, isn't it?" Ringo's eyes grew wide. "Sorta eerie."

"Yeah, well, it's almost midnight in the oh-so-rural countryside," George reminded him.

"It's not *that*, y' see." John cut his eyes at Ringo. "It's the witchin' hour, son...right here, in the very shadow of very Stonehenge..."[1462]

"Bushwa!" Ringo tried to shrug it off. "I don't believe in that!"

"Right, don't listen to him, Rich." Neil tossed a glare John's way. "You've nothin' to worry about...from what I hear, this place used to be a vicarage.[1463] So, the only ghosts 'round here are holy ones."[1464]

"Besides," Paul said, "you're not roomin' alone, are you? We're all in a suite together."[1465]

"Oh, *not that again!*" George carped. He'd had enough of communal living. "Don't we make enough these days to have our own quarters, as it were?"

"Not to be tedious," Brian strode over and handed Neil the keys, "but there are only 20 rooms in this establishment, George.[1466] And as you well know, we've a host of stars to accommodate."

"Yeah, y' don't hear Eleanor Bron findin' fault, now do you, George?" John nudged him playfully as they trudged up the curved mahogany stairway.[1467] "Y' don't hear ole John Bluthal whingin'."[1468]

"Right," George shoved back, "but *they* aren't stuck with your late night bright-as-day readin' light...or Ringo's rampageous snorin'!"

"I never snore!" Ringo sputtered, "Or not anymore, anyway...I had me tonsils out!"[1469]

"Well, we'll see about that." George shook his head.

"And banterin' their way to the top," John employed his radio announcer's voice, "the lucky lads from Liddypool at last reached a whole new level!"

"Right," Paul sniffed. "The first floor."[1470]

But his yawning audience only groaned. They were, Paul assumed, too tired to appreciate true humour.

****

Monday, 3 May 1965
The Lounge-Bar,
The Antrobus Arms, Amesbury, England

8.00 p.m.

It had been a brutal day of filming. The temperatures were unkind, and the wind, severe and unrelenting. Though renowned Costume Mistress Julie Harris,[1471] had done her best to select serviceably warm (and yet, chic) attire for eight hours on an open

British plain, the boys' thick polos beneath warm pocketless suits had simply not been enough.[1472] Ringo's teeth had chattered most of the way back to the hotel, and George's hands had required a half-hour to thaw.

"'N *I* was the lucky one!" Ringo was camped in front of the large hardwood and black marble fireplace, warming his backside.[1473] "They gave me a cig, a cap, *and* a cape!"[1474]

"I had bad coffee from a paper cup," George muttered. "So did Paul."[1475]

"They tried wrappin' me in army-green corduroy," John confided, "but I was still forty below."

"Even with all the extra paddin', eh?" George snickered, taking the mickey out. John's few new pounds were fair game; with The Beatles, nothing was sacrosanct.

But when John returned the jab with an abrupt exit, George was sorry he'd said it.

"Ah, don't pay him a blind bit o' notice, Lennon!" Ringo called out to John's back. But there was no reply.

"What's with him?" Paul entered, frowning. He'd caught a glimpse of John's face in passing.

"Never mind. He'll sort it out." Ringo lit a cig and offered the packet 'round. "Just let boys be boys."

And preferring a different topic anyway, Paul turned to the day's comings and goings...the frigid morning hours spent miming "The Night Before" and "I Need You."[1476]

"Who ever thought *we'd* be the focus of an actual army exercise!" George grinned.

"It wasn't *the army*, y' know," Paul held up a finger and elucidated, "It was Her Majesty's Third Armoured Division, no less."[1477]

"Well," George smirked, "I'm glad it was *no more*...because we were *surrounded* by machine guns 'n gunners..."[1478]

"'N horse artillery!"[1479] Paul chimed in.

"*I* needed protection, as it were!"[1480] Ringo quoted from the script,

And as if on cue, Clang's lovely assistant, the exotic Ahme — Eleanor Bron — strolled towards the boys. "I brought *this one* back to the fold." She was tugging John by the shirt-sleeve. "He must've wandered off, willy-nilly."

Trying to make amends with his "older brother," George

jumped up and made room for the two newcomers in the tight circle beside the fire. "We were just talkin', Johnny," he smiled, "about the rather impressive array of artillery today." When John only offered a choking stare, George rambled nervously on. "'N the overwhelmin' array of photographers thisavvy."[1481]

"Right," Paul was still their official bearer of good news, "but from what I hear, *that* was the press's one 'n only chance to nab footage. We're supposed to be able work, uninterrupted, tomorrow 'n the day after."[1482]

"Yet never in peace!" Bron bantered, batting her long, dark eyelashes at Ringo in Ahme fashion. "For he who wears the ring… only three days to live!"[1483]

Ringo feigned shocked horror.

And laughing softly, the weary but now warm group of friends voted to send their youngest, George, up to order another round. It was a long-standing Beatles tradition, a fond remnant of their days in The Grapes.

"I'll stand y' a round when I'm carryin'!" John barked out his old pledge, and the boys shared a knowing smile. In "the good old days," John had rarely made good on the generous promise, but unlike their years in Liverpool, The Beatles now had all the money in the world.

****

Tuesday, 4 May 1965
Salisbury Plain, England

3.30 p.m.

With only one day left on location, Lester pressed the group to stay on task. The film crew worked to capture the crafty Clang's secret underground tunnel. Filled with green metal ammo boxes loaded with TNT (one box surreptitiously set by Clang himself, labeled "Equal To Exactly One Millionth Of All The High Explosive Exploded In One Week Of The Second World War"),[1484] the hideaway was supposedly situated right beneath the spot where The Beatles were to be performing their songs.

However, with the assistance of their secret fan, Ahme, the explosives had been planted well off-the-mark, and the famous British boys were, once again, thankfully spared.[1485]

"Now," Lester turned to The Beatles, "Let's discuss your soon to be famous 'escape-by-tank' scene. There's lots of running, jumping, and standing still..." he grinned, alluding to his famous Sellers and Milligan film,[1486] "so hopefully, it'll save you four from freezing half-to-death."

The boys listened, nodded, and doubted that any amount of exercise would solve the dilemma. A ragged wind swooped and lofted across the barren Salisbury plain. Noses were red, and fingers, numb. Everyone was miserable.

"At first," Lester set the stage for them, "you'll be running madly away from Clang's cannon fire, as it were...moving as fast as you possibly can, right in front of an oncoming tank. And I know that thus far in the film, the tanks have been on the side of good, on *your* side..."[1487]

"Have they?" John looked down his nose. None of them had a clue as to what was going on, big picture.

"They have," Lester was patient. "According to the script, The British Centurion tanks were summoned to *protect* you four as you supposedly gathered — in this secret, remote location — to record your songs."

"Go on, Director," John nodded.

"Anyway, as I said, up to now, tanks have equaled security for you. Yet, this particular one seems hell-bent on running you down...it mirrors your every step as you dart and weave."[1488]

"Nasty tank!" Paul winked.

"We're not much on physical sport, y' know, Lester," John repeated for at least the hundredth time.

"Which is precisely why," Lester chuckled, "you're slated to fall, John, right in the path of the oncoming vehicle. Now, you others," he swiveled to Paul, George, and Ringo, "will, of course, be fighting to save him, pleading with John to get up and try again."[1489]

"We do that quite often," Paul sniffed, to laughter.

"But he's all Mutt 'n Jeff — our John," Ringo deadpanned.

"...and it's only at the very last minute," Lester went on determinedly, despite the myriad interruptions, "that the tank lurches to a stop...inches from where John's malingering on the ground…"

"I haven't malingered since the summer of 1961," John objected.

"Right there and then," Lester ignored him, "you'll discover, to your surprise, that the Centurion tank is actually being operated by none other than your clandestine ally, Ahme…on hand to rescue you from disaster. You four'll pull yourselves together, scramble into the tank, and quickly move away — trying to escape, unscathed.[1490] Naturally, there's more to the scene, as it were, but for now, let's just shoot that bit and see how it goes."

So, for the next hour or so, the boys attempted the part over and over, working until — despite bitter temperatures — they were perspiring and parched.

Whilst the boys enjoyed a quick drink and a smoke, Lester glanced at the thin sunlight, swiftly waning as the afternoon slipped away. He hated to rush the boys along, but they had only one more day on location before returning to Twickenham for Paul's whimsical "Adventure on the Floor."

"Boys," he approached them with care, "no, no…don't get up. Just relax, and let's talk about what's next…"

And walking them through the "tank in the hayfield" episode, Lester set up the afternoon's final endeavour.

"If we can make good progress with this bit," the director held out a carrot, "we can return to the hotel for hot baths and fine Antrobus fare." The food at the inn had been, thus far, superb. The hotel staff had performed hand-flips to please them.

As the boys stood, stretched, and set their faces to film one more scene, they were already thinking of hot roast beef slathered with mushroom sauce and tiny, red, buttered potatoes.[1491]

Sources:

Lewisohn, The Complete Beatles Chronicle, *192.*
Lewisohn, The Beatles: Day by Day, *61-62.*
Harry, The Ultimate Beatles Encyclopedia, *523.*
Harry, The John Lennon Encyclopedia, *873-897.*
Winn, Way Beyond Compare, *317.*
The Beatles, The Beatles Anthology, *171-173.*
Shotton and Clayson, *100 and 116.*
Miles, The Beatles' Diary, Vol. 1, *178 and 195-196.*
Womack, John Lennon 1980, *186.*

Norman, Shout!, *248.*
Carr, 76-77.
Turner, A Hard Day's Write, *34 and 76.*
Margotin and Guesdon, 226-227 and 230-231.
Spizer, The Beatles for Sale on Parlophone Records, *189.*
Robertson, Lennon, 40.
Friede, Titone, and Wiener, 188.
Hill, John, Paul, George & Ringo, *198-199.*
Schultheiss, 133.
Solt and Egan, 75.
Bicknell, 42-43.

Deezen, Eddie, "John Lennon Was a Crazy Cat Lady," Mental Floss, *found at https://www.mentalfloss.com/article/29696/john-lennon-was-crazy-cat-lady.*

https://genius.com/The-beatles-help-film-script-annotated This website provides the entire script of "Help!" with annotations.

https://www.rollingstone.com/movies/movie-news/julie-harris-beatles-costume-designer-dead-at-94-44947/ This website provides information about Costume Mistress Julie Harris, who designed The Beatles' costumes for "A Hard Day's Night" and "Help!"

https://www2.bfi.org.uk/news-opinion/news-bfi/features/remembering-julie-harris-costume-designer-bond-hitchcock This is an interesting article on the career of Costume Mistress Julie Harris.

https://www.tapatalk.com/groups/solobeatlesphotosforum/5-may-1965-uk-salisbury-plain-wiltshire-t6852.html This website, covering The Beatles' time on Salisbury Plain, states that the weather was "windy and cold" and that after three days, the boys were "weather-beaten."

http://antrobushotel.co.uk/about-the-antrobus-hotel/facilities/accomodation/# This is the official website of The Antrobus Arms in downtown Amesbury. Excellent images are available of the rose garden, the lobby and stairs, and several of the rooms that remain almost unchanged since 1965.

https://www.beatlesbible.com/gallery/1965-photos/6505-beatles-help-salisbury-plain_01/ This website provides information about The Beatles' days in and around Amesbury.

https://www.imdb.com/title/tt0053231/ This website provides information about "The Running Jumping & Standing Still Film," which was directed by Richard Lester.

http://www.imfdb.org/wiki/Help!_(1965_film) *This amazing website lists every single weapon used in "Help!" and gives info about each.*

https://www.imdb.com/name/nm0089944/?ref_=ttfc_fc_cl_t6
This website provides information about John Bluthal.

https://tinyurl.com/y4qrvgbt This website permits you to listen to the 1956 hit "Long Lost John" by Lonnie Donegan, to which John alludes in the chapter.

There are excellent photos of the boys in their Salisbury Plain costumes, designed by Julie Harris in The Beatles Anthology, *p. 72-73. Also, see the classic Salisbury Plain photo of Ringo in Hill's* John, Paul, George & Ringo, *p. 198.*

Other photos mentioned in this chapter are cited in the footnotes.

The Antrobus Arms, Amesbury, where The Beatles lodged during the filming of scenes on Salisbury Plain for "Help!"
Photograph from Wikimedia Commons
Photographer Chris Talbot

[1457] Lewisohn, *The Complete Beatles Chronicle*, 192. Lewisohn says that The Beatles "arrived at their local hotel — the Antrobus Arms in Amesbury — at 11.20 p.m."

[1458] Bicknell, 42.

[1459] http://antrobushotel.co.uk/about-the-antrobus-hotel/facilities/accomodation/# All descriptions of the interior of the hotel will come from this website and from photos of The Beatles inside the Antrobus Arms in 1965.

[1460] https://tinyurl.com/y2y5f9oo In this photo, you can see the Palladian window by using a magnifying glass.

[1461] John is referring to his high school, Quarry Bank Grammar. See the photo at the end of this chapter.

[1462] http://antrobushotel.co.uk/about-the-antrobus-hotel/facilities/accomodation/# Stonehenge is two miles from the hotel.

[1463] http://antrobushotel.co.uk/about-the-antrobus-hotel/facilities/accomodation/#

[1464] http://antrobushotel.co.uk/about-the-antrobus-hotel/facilities/accomodation/#

[1465] http://antrobushotel.co.uk/about-the-antrobus-hotel/facilities/accomodation/# Guests of the Antrobus Arms today can stay in this same suite, now known, of course, as The Beatles Suite.

[1466] http://antrobushotel.co.uk/about-the-antrobus-hotel/facilities/accomodation/#

[1467] http://antrobushotel.co.uk/about-the-antrobus-hotel/facilities/accomodation/# You can see the hotel's lovely curved lobby stairway on this website.

[1468] https://www.imdb.com/name/nm0089944/?ref_=ttfc_fc_cl_t6 John Bluthal played the role of "Clang's" (Leo McKern's) second in command, Bhuta.

[1469] Miles, *The Beatles' Diary, Vol. 1*, 178. Ringo had had his tonsils removed five months prior, on 2 December 1964.

[1470] https://speakspeak.com/about-english/ground-floors-and-first-floors-in-british-and-american-english In England, the street level floor is called "the ground floor," and the second floor is called "the first floor." So, if you're American, the boys are on the second floor.

[1471] *The Beatles Anthology*, 172-173 and https://www.rollingstone.com/movies/movie-news/julie-harris-beatles-costume-designer-dead-at-94-44947/ This is an excellent article in *Rolling Stone* about the work Julie Harris did on both "A Hard Day's Night" and "Help!" There is a great photo of her with The Beatles on her birthday in 1964. You can see photos of The Beatles in the costumes Harris designed for the Salisbury Plain episodes on pp. 172-173 of *The Beatles Anthology*.

[1472] https://tinyurl.com/y5v79hay This is an excellent photo showing the costumes for the Salisbury Plain filming. Note that even though Ringo is wearing a heavy cape over his suit and polo, he is still freezing. And this is an excellent video of the making of "I Need You" on Salisbury Plain with Julie Christie's costumes front and centre: https://www.youtube.com/watch?v=FcEY7tCfSrg

[1473] http://antrobushotel.co.uk/about-the-antrobus-hotel/image-gallery/gallery/lounge-bar/ This is a current photo of the Lounge-Bar at the Antrobus Arms, but I've been assured that the fireplace is still the same as it was in 1965.

[1474] BBC - Memories of The Beatles on The Plain This photo of Ringo and George in between filming will clearly demonstrate how cold they were.

[1475] Lewisohn, *The Complete Beatles Chronicle*, 192. The photos of The Beatles on Salisbury Plain show George and Paul drinking hot beverages from paper cups.

[1476] Winn, *Way Beyond Compare*, 317.

[1477] Winn, *Way Beyond Compare*, 317, Lewisohn, *The Complete Beatles Chronicle,* 192, Miles, *The Beatles' Diary, Vol. 1*, 196, Turner, *A Hard Day's Write*, 76, and Spizer, *The Beatles for Sale on Parlophone Records*, 189.

[1478] Lewisohn, *The Complete Beatles Chronicle*, 192, Winn, *Way Beyond Compare*, 317, and Miles, *The Beatles' Diary, Vol. 1*, 196.

[1479] Lewisohn, *The Complete Beatles Chronicle*, 192, Winn, *Way Beyond Compare*, 317, and Miles, *The Beatles' Diary, Vol. 1*, 196.

[1480] https://genius.com/The-beatles-help-film-script-annotated Ringo is paraphrasing a line from the script of "Help!" which may be accessed at this website.

[1481] Winn, *Way Beyond Compare*, 317. Winn says that on Monday, 3 May, after miming "I Need You" and "The Night Before" for the film, "the press had been invited to take pictures and film…footage shot by ITV News (for broadcast that evening)." He says the Associated Press was there as well.

[1482] Winn, *Way Beyond Compare*, 317. Winn, who says that the "press were invited" that first day "to take pictures and film," seems to indicate that this was the one window of opportunity for publicity.

[1483] https://genius.com/The-beatles-help-film-script-annotated and https://www.imdb.com/title/tt0059260/characters/nm0111376?ref_=ttfc_fc_cl_t3 One of Ahme's famous lines from "Help!"

[1484] https://genius.com/The-beatles-help-film-script-annotated

[1485] https://genius.com/The-beatles-help-film-script-annotated

[1486] https://www.imdb.com/title/tt0053231/ "The Running Jumping & Standing Still Film" was directed by Lester, and he starred in it as well, with several members of The Goons (Peter Sellers and Spike Milligan). It was the primary reason Lester was selected to direct "A Hard Day's Night" and "Help!" The boys knew the film quite well, and certainly would have caught the joke. Watch a clip of it here: https://tinyurl.com/y4vhdzhc

[1487] http://www.imfdb.org/wiki/Help!_(1965_film) This amazing website lists every single weapon used in "Help!" and gives info about each. The cannons used to protect The Beatles were Centurion tanks, routinely driven by 3 Division in their usual war games on Salisbury Plain. They are the ones navigating the tanks in the film.

[1488] Carr, *The Beatles At The Movies*, 77 and https://genius.com/The-beatles-help-film-script-annotated. In Carr's book (p. 77) you can see two great photos of the filming of this particular scene.

[1489] https://genius.com/The-beatles-help-film-script-annotated

[1490] https://genius.com/The-beatles-help-film-script-annotated

[1491] https://tinyurl.com/y4regcaz This is a photo of John in the Antrobus Arms restaurant being served an excellent dinner. And here are the boys having dinner together at the Antrobus:
https://66.media.tumblr.com/d5bb069094d76d221ef0e5a14ca5ca39/tumblr_p800nm3JdF1urwo7uo8_400.jpg

Thursday, 6 May 1965
Kenwood
Weybridge, Surrey

8.00 p.m.
Mimi: Hello?
John: The next voice you hear[1492] will be one from the past.
Mimi: (Quoting Dickens rather than playing John's game)[1493] Long past?
John: (Responding in kind) No, your past!
Mimi: *Hmpf!* You've never been an advocate of Forster's "only connect," have you, John?[1494]
John: I thought that was *precisely* what I was about!
Mimi: Yes, well…at long last. I haven't heard a cry from you since… since that Fred Lennon was there.
John: Which was only a week or so ago.
Mimi: *Weeks ago!* Or so I sincerely hope.
John: Your dream is out, Mary Elizabeth…I haven't seen the man. In fact, I just came in from the cold[1495]…the brutal crosswinds of Salisbury Plain, as it were.
Mimi: Salisbury? Whatever for? You turn up in the strangest places, John.
John: For the fill-um, woman…the fill-um!
Mimi: Rock'n'roll on Salisbury Plain?
John: It's all part of the plot, so they tell me, though I can't make heads or tails of it.[1496] We filmed the last scene first, and the first scene, last.[1497] 'N whoever shall save his life must lose it.[1498]
Mimi: So, you *were* listening in Sunday School after all!
John: I never said I wasn't. In fact, I lately gave m' cloak to the poor.[1499]
Mimi: What *are* you on about, John?
John: M' clothes were kindly distributed to some needy fan or fans

who somehow or 'nother sussed out where our driver Alf Bicknell had parked the car in Amesbury. I'd left a change of cloak...er, clothes...lyin' about, 'n now, they're well 'n truly in the hands of someone else.[1500]

Mimi: Yes, they do that around here as well. If I merely leave the back door unlatched...[1501]

John: Which is why y' need a *new house*...as I've said before...

Mimi: Well, from what I hear you can afford the odd pilfer, here 'n there. The newspapers all claim you're a millionaire.

John: Do they? (John sniffed, proud of the fact that his aunt took notice of this, after years of telling him he was "destined to be a bum.")

Mimi: Yes, and I also have it on good authority that...

John: Look, Mim, I leave that all to George, y' see. He's the one mindin' the store, as it were. (John snickered.) George told this one reporter the other day, "I'm not really the 'most interested in money Beatle'...I'm just the only one interested in what's *happenin'* to it! I like to know where it's goin'!"[1502]

Mimi: Bully for George! I realise I never cared for him overmuch,[1503] but...well, you should *all* feel that way.

John: Now y'er soundin' like Eppy...he forces us to endure a bevy of assorted accountants who tell us about the two 'n a half per cent of this 'n the four 'n a half per cent of that.[1504] 'N suddenly, it's just like maths all over again. To nick a phrase from the last film..."it's a drag, a well-known drag." We're bored of it.

Mimi: Yes, well...I might be "bored of it" as well, had I enough ready cash to...well...(In a bruised voice)...to give Lillian Powell an allowance...equal to mine![1505]

John: Ah, Mim! She's Cyn's mum, just as you're...

Mimi: How *dare* she expect or even accept money from you?! What's *she* ever done to deserve *anything*?[1506]

John: Listen, Mim...

Mimi: I'm disgusted, John...I'm very, very annoyed![1507]

John: 'N I suppose you're equally disgusted that me 'n George bought Pete the supermarket, eh?[1508]

Mimi: George 'n *me*.

John: That's an untenable lie, 'n y' know it! (He tried to laugh her ire away.) I remember it well, and you weren't even there!

Mimi: *Hmpf!!!*

John: Which all goes to prove, Mary Elizabeth...that I'm clearly

wealthy enough to buy m' own auntie a new home…straightaway.
Mimi: Well, we shall see what we shall see, John. Don't badger me. It's unseemly.
John: Speakin' of expenditures…we're filmin' in London this week…a scene, they tell me, in Asprey's.[1509] What can I get for you whilst I'm there? Name it, woman. It's yours!
Mimi: (She sighed.) Don't be gaudy and crass, John. Life isn't about material things.
John: Something immaterial, then?
Mimi: (She sputtered a laugh, in spite of herself) Get a haircut. *That* would make me happy. I see you on telly and…yes, a haircut, John — *that's* what I want!
John: Right, well, who's y'er barber, then? I'll ring 'n make you an appointment.
Mimi: (Exasperated) John Winston!
John: Mary Elizabeth!
Mimi: (Silence…then…) Enjoy your filming this week, John. You're always *somewhere*, aren't you? The Bahamas and Austria and now, Salisbury Plain! Your wife must hardly know you these days.
John: She knows I'm the one takin' her to see Bob Dylan in the Royal Festival Hall this week.[1510] 'N she knows I'm escortin' her to the Cannes Film Festival in a coupla days.[1511]
Mimi: Good for her. Lucky girl.
John: I'll be 'round to see you soon, Mim. 'N we'll find you a new house, me 'n you.
Mimi: You know, John…you can't just decide things and expect everyone else to fall in line.[1512]
John: Look, you've told me over 'n over that y'er not happy in Liverpool…you've said you've no friends 'n that the fans 're doorsteppin' you, night 'n day…you've told me you wish you were anywhere but there! So, why not…[1513]
Mimi: Bournemouth, John. Let's search in Bournemouth.[1514]
John: (Stunned for a moment) Well, all right, then…I'll ask 'round.
Mimi: And remember, John, this was entirely *my* decision.
John: A Mimi mandate from on high.

Sources:
Lewisohn, The Complete Beatles Chronicle, *193.*

Lewisohn, The Beatles: Day by Day, *62.*
Harry, The Ultimate Beatles Encyclopedia, *607, 611.*
Harry, The Encyclopedia of Beatles People, *289.*
Harry, The John Lennon Encyclopedia, *809.*
The Beatles, The Beatles Anthology, *167.*
Lennon, Cynthia, John, *167, 174-175.*
Miles, The Beatles' Diary, Vol. 1, *195 and 196.*
Shotton and Clayson, 100-101.
Badman, 154.
Norman, Shout!, *242.*
Coleman, Lennon, *40, 42.*
Burrows, 69.
Schultheiss, 133.
Burns, 45 and 50.
Robertson, Lennon, *40.*
Wiener, 48.

Works Alluded to in this Chapter:

Holy Bible, *New King James Version.*
Forster, E.M., Howards End.
le Carré, John, The Spy Who Came in From the Cold.

To get a better sense of John's Aunt Mimi Smith, please watch this 9-minute YouTube video of Mimi talking about John, after his death. Watch using this link:
https://www.youtube.com/watch?v=LRqU2teFtw8
Or use the QRCode below:

[1492] John is alluding to the popular 1950 drama, "The Next Voice You Hear." For more information, go to: https://www.imdb.com/title/tt0042786/
[1493] Mimi and John are quoting an exchange between Ebenezer Scrooge and The Spirit of Christmas Past in Dickens's *A Christmas Carol.*
[1494] "Only connect" is the theme of E. M. Forster's 1910 classic, *Howards End.* The acclaimed novel focuses on the importance (and difficulty) of maintaining human connections. As self-confessed bookworms, both Mimi and John would know this reference.
[1495] John is alluding to the John le Carré novel *The Spy Who Came in From the Cold,* a 1963 best-seller that John read in 1964. Mimi, a voracious reader, would have also been quite familiar with the book as well.

1496 The Beatles, *The Beatles Anthology,*167.

1497 John is referencing a quote from the *Holy Bible*, Matthew 20:16.

1498 And here, John is paraphrasing Matthew 20:25.

1499 Here, the former Anglican altar boy is referencing Matthew 5:40 which states, "If a man wants to sue you and take away your tunic, let him have your cloak also." (*Holy Bible*, New King James Version)

1500 Bicknell, 42 and Schultheiss, 133. Schultheiss says the clothes "were stolen from John Lennon's car while he was filming on Salisbury Plain." Alf Bicknell says that he drove "the boys to the Antrobus Arms." Schultheiss is probably using the term "John Lennon's car" in the broad, general sense.

1501 Lennon, Cynthia, *John,* 175 and Coleman, *Lennon*, 42. Cynthia says Mimi was constantly complaining that she was "being pestered by fans…it was intolerable." And Coleman quotes Mimi as saying that if she "went upstairs, [she] had to lock the kitchen door. Otherwise, there wouldn't be a piece of crockery left in the kitchen by the time [she] came down." She said the fans were relentless.

1502 Badman, 154. Direct quote from George Harrison.

1503 Burns, 49 and Coleman, *Lennon*, 40.

1504 Badman, 154, Shotton and Clayson, 100-101, Harry, *The Ultimate Beatles Encyclopedia,* 607, Harry, *The Encyclopedia of Beatles People*, 289, and Harry, *The John Lennon Encyclopedia*, 809.

1505 Lennon, Cynthia, *John*, 175. Direct quote from Mimi Smith. Cynthia says that both Lillian and Mimi were getting £30 a week from John.

1506 Lennon, Cynthia, *John,* 175. Direct quote from Mimi Smith.

1507 Lennon, Cynthia, *John*, 175. Direct quote from Mimi Smith. This was said to Cynthia, not John. Mimi ended her diatribe with, "Tell John when you speak to him that I am very, very annoyed."

1508 Shotton and Clayson, 100-101 and Lennon, Cynthia, *John*, 175-176.

1509 Lewisohn, *The Complete Beatles Chronicle*, 193 and Norman, *Shout!*, 242.

1510 Lewisohn, *The Beatles: Day by Day,* 62, Robertson, *Lennon,* 40, Wiener, 48, and Miles, *The Beatles' Diary, Vol. 1,* 195.

1511 Miles, *The Beatles' Diary, Vol. 1,* 196.

1512 Lennon, Cynthia, *John,* 167. Cynthia says that John purchased cars for her without consulting her. He would sell one she liked and buy her another without asking her if she wanted to do this. She says, "Once he'd taken a decision, everyone and everything had to fall in line with it."

1513 Lennon, Cynthia, *John,* 174.

1514 Lennon, Cynthia, *John,* 174.

Sunday, 9 May 1965
Out and About In...
London

It had been the kind of day that seemed to spool out forever. In fact, there wasn't much The Beatles hadn't done.

Because London's thoroughfares were fairly serene on Sunday mornings, Lester had dog-eared the better part of the day for bits and pieces of outdoor filming. First, a scene in New Bond Street depicted the lads seeking professional "help!" with the removal of their drummer's ill-starred ring.[1515] In search of deliverers, The Beatles had strolled scrutinizingly past the Watches of Switzerland jewellers' shop.[1516] They had conferred, frowned convincingly, and considered options. But the moment Lester had cried, "Stop action!" the four had immediaterly fallen out of character and raced into Asprey's, located directly over the road.[1517]

They had only moments between takes, so whilst Paul and George were "merely browsing," John and Ringo were industriously selecting gifts, as fast as their eyes could scan.[1518] Entering the front door, the boys had swept through the famous silversmiths, pointing to this and that. In less than five minutes time, John had accumulated a choice selection of prezzies, valued somewhere between £600 and a great deal more.[1519] Laughing and exiting the back way, the boys had skittered over the road again and were waiting on set before Lester had really missed them.

"All right, next," the director had directed, "we're off to Blanford Street, to a restaurant ordinarily dubbed 'The Dolphin' but transformed this morning — through the magic of cinema — into the exotic 'Rajahama' Indian restaurant."[1520]

"Ah, the ideal place," Paul had winked, "to inquire about the consequences and import of bizarre Eastern rings."

"I know I wouldn't import them," John had muttered.

But puns aside, the group been hastily trundled off, in multiple cars and vans, to a prepared and waiting second location.

****

In The Dolphin, noted film, theater, and music critic as well as program host from WOR Radio Station in New York City, Sandy Lesberg, was patiently waiting.[1521] He had been promised a post-filming interview with The Fab Four, and he'd flown into London, fortified with pages of prepared queries.

But no one had prepared Sandy for the sheer temerity of the Liverpool boys. Work concluded for the day, and with the prospect of an evening's Dylan concert ahead, the four were even sprightlier than normal. With their producer, Walter Shenson, joining them for a drink and a chat with the American critic, the ingenue actors were laughing and firing private jokes at one another, whilst the tape was readied.

Cigs lit, ties loosened, jackets unbuttoned, and ice rattling in their glasses, the group found humour in almost everything. Lesberg cleared his throat and then initiated the session with a series of questions about the filming of "Help!"

Sandy Lesberg: Where were you…in Austria? Near Salzburg, Vienna, where?

Paul: A place called Obertaun [sic], near Salzburg, yeah.

John: (Rhythmically) Deutschland, Deutschland, Obertaun [sic], Obertaun [sic]. That's where we were!

Lesberg: When are you going to be at Shea Stadium in New York?

John: (Shrugs) I don't know.

George: (Glancing at Walter Shenson) Fifteenth of August, isn't it?

Ringo: (Leaning into the mic) Mr. Shenson is just gettin' his piece of paper out. He'll tell us!

Lesberg: You still call Mr. Shenson, "Mr. Shenson"?

John: (Deadpanning) Either that or "Soft Wally." Depends how we're feelin'.

(The others snicker.)

George: (Nodding as Shenson prompts him) Fifteenth of August — Shea Stadium.

Ringo: And *this picture* opens the first week of August in New York.

Paul: Are you goin' to go to it?

Lesberg: Oh, yeah. Are *you* going to be there? For the première?

Paul: For the film? (He glances at Shenson for answers as well.) I don't think so. But anyway, are *you* goin' to go to it?

Lesberg: (Laughing a little) Yes, of course.

Paul: (Big smile) I want a promise off ya that you're goin' to be there!

Lesberg: (Beginning to see how this interview is going to play out and getting into the spirit of things) I'll have a picture taken in front of the door.

Paul: (Cutting his eyes mischievously at the others) The thing is, y' see, if you'll be there — well, we *know* there'll be riots at the première, then! (Playfully narrowing his eyes) I've heard about your following, y' know.

Lesberg: (Laughing and shaking his head) Do you want to say something, Walter?

Walter Shenson: I think the boys ought to tell you (They all begin pointing at him, one after the other) — *I* ought to tell you — about the marvellous song they wrote called "Help!"...with an exclamation point.

Lesberg: (Jokingly) That was Walter Shenson, the producer of the picture, and that's enough now. What's this song that's...

(The boys make the "cut" sign to Walter and laugh.)

Lesberg: Oh Walter, I see you in New York all the time. Are *you* going to be there for the première of your picture?

Walter: Definitely, yes!

Lesberg: I'll say, then, there'll be riots!

Paul: (Nodding enthusiastically) Yeah.

Lesberg: *Are* there riots where Walter goes?

Paul: Yeah...with an exclamation point!

John: (Gutturally, in a stage aside) By the way, there's seven songs in the film.

Lesberg: Is your voice changing, John?

John: (Smiling innocently) No, no.

Paul: It's not that we're trying to plug this film, but it's seven songs, and it's a rollickin', rollickin', happy, smash! Uhm…what are other words do you say about films?

Lesberg: Let's get back to weekends…no kidding for a minute. When you were up in Austria, did you get the weekends off then?

John and Paul: (Almost simultaneously) *No!*

Ringo: (Shaking his head) No, we didn't.

Paul: We worked. But you've got to realize [sic]…

Lesberg: …*even on Sundays?!!*

Paul: Even on a Sunday.

John: (Using his cig for emphasis) What do you mean "even on Sundays"? *Especially* on Sundays!

Lesberg: Especially on Sundays, John?

John: To finish off making the mov… (He sees Shenson giving him the eye) Uh, nothing!! (Batting his eyelashes rapidly at the producer)

Paul: (Chuckles) Makin' the film, I think he was goin' to say.

Lesberg: Something like that, huh?

Paul: Somethin'…either that, or it was satirical.

John: (Sniffs sardonically, since he is constantly accused of being satirical) Satire is 'out,' Paul.

Lesberg: (Cutting his eyes to Lennon) What's 'in,' John?

John: I don't know. *Rabber!!* We're all very Rabber over in England these days.

Paul: Oh, yeah. I think he's trying to start a new craze, or somethin' or other.

John: Rabber. Rabber macs. Rabber boots.

Paul: Rabber Burns.

(Laughter all around)

Paul: You know Rabber Burns, don't you? (Sings) "Only A Rose!" That's Rabber Burns.

Lesberg: Would you like to do a little bit of that song that you wrote for the picture, Paul?

Paul: Uhm… (Laughs nervously and shakes his head) I'll tell you what, though. What we'll do is we'll promise to send you a copy just before it's released. Right? So, you've got the uhm… (When he sees Lesberg grimace) That's an *exclusive*, isn't it?! I mean. *That's* a favour!

Lesberg: (A bit offended) I'm *not* Hedda Hopper! I don't need…

Paul: (Cutting across Lesberg with a sniff) Right. You won't get it then…if you're goin' to be like that...

John: If we thought you *were* Hedda Hopper, we wouldn't have let you in here... Hedda Hopper was comin' in on her bike.

Lesberg: (Laughing, but stiffly now) Did *she* ever interview you?

Paul: She was at a party with a big hat. (Resuming his congenial, public relations mode) She's great. Good. Good girl, yeah. In Hollywood.

George: (His eyes glinting) She hopped past us.

Paul: Hopped past, yeah. Who's that other fella, though, that we *don't* like? Who's that fella? Walter Winchell?

Lesberg: (His ears perking up for a potential news story) What about it? Did *he* interview you?

Paul: Don't speak to me about him!

John: He's stupid.

Lesberg: *Why* is he stupid, John?

John: He's stupid because he just lies and writes a lot of trash!

Lesberg: (Ferreting out the story now) Have you ever met him, John?

John: No, but he keeps writin' things about Paul which are lies, so he must be off his head!

Paul: (Nodding vigourously) I've said many a time that he's just a bit off his head. I think he's, uhm…I don't know what's happened to him. Everyone said he used to be good. But he's…I tell ya, it's just *lies*! He says I'm married, y' see. 'N I'd like to say, "Mister Winchell…Walter sir, if you're listenin'…*I'm not!*" (Clicks his cheek) I told *him*, didn't I?!

Lesberg: (Still pressing to get the whole story) Is *that* the lie he's been telling about you?

Paul: (Nodding, his face solemn) Yeah! I mean y' know, that's pushin' it, isn't it?

John: But he goes on and on writin' it, y' know, as if he knows! He doesn't know *anything*, that old Winch!

Lesberg: (Smiling at the band of brothers defending one another, he leans closer to the recorder and says…) Goodbye, Walter! (Then, almost to himself) I'm taking inventory of the people I've lost as friends on this show!

John: (Leaning into the microphone as well) I like Hedda Hopper. She's nice.

Paul: Hedda's great, yeah. Everybody else is great! It's not that we've got anything against Walter...is it, Walter? No, of course it isn't.

George: (Smiling with one corner of his mouth) Walter Wimpy.

Lesberg: Is that what he says about *you*? I mean, he doesn't say anything really, more than...

Paul: (Shaking his head vigourously) No, it's not *bad*, y' know. But it's just that it's...*it's a lie!* That's all there is, y' know. Either that, or he's just got the wrong information.

Lesberg: (Eager to change the subject) How long...how much more...do you have to do on the picture?

Ringo: Two days actual filmin', but we have to do quite a bit of post-sync, which will take about two weeks, I believe. So they tell me.

Lesberg: Do you believe 'em when they tell you something?

Ringo: Oh, I always believe them.

Lesberg: (To Walter Shenson) Are you telling these boys straight?

Paul: (Striking an innocent pose) We're all very Gulliver.

Lesberg: You're very gullible?

Paul: We're very Gulliver, yeah.

Lesberg: And you travel a lot, too.

Paul: Travel a lot, yes, too. (Winks) You got that one!

Lesberg: (Laughs) Did you write the script, too, for this picture?

Paul: No, we had a good try, but it was obscene. Had to be banned.

Lesberg: (Laughs) Did you really write the score for this picture?

Paul: Score? I don't know what you mean by 'score.' We wrote seven songs, y' know. Uhm...if that's the score, well, we wrote it.

Lesberg: Called "Help!"?

Paul: "Help!" Yes, yes.

Lesberg: With an exclamation...

(All of The Beatles are nodding.)

Paul: With an exclamation mark.

Lesberg: ...mark, yeah.

George: You didn't say "No" then, did you?

Paul: You didn't nod your head then, did you? (Using an announcer's voice) I'm afraid you just lost the quiz! I'm afraid you just lost the major prize! Can you come back next week?

Lesberg: (Laughing) I can, but tell me what it is I just lost.

John: A life-size cardboard cut-out of Walter Winchell!

(The group falls out laughing.)

Lesberg: You mean, with darts coming out the back?
Ringo: No…in the front!
Lesberg: What Ringo? Say that again.
Ringo: Not me! I'm not saying anythin' bad... against *anybody*!
Paul: (To Lesberg) No, you've got it wrong! We like everyone!
Lesberg: (Raising an eyebrow) Do you, *really*?
Paul: Yeah, of course we do. We love 'em all!
Lesberg: How long are you gonna be in the States when you do that tour? Do you know?
John: Four weeks, isn't it?
Ringo: Two 'n a half weeks.
Lesberg: Stadiums mostly, huh?
Ringo: Shea Stadiums, mostly.
Paul: Yeah. We'll be doin' a coupla rounds of baseball before we go on, just to limber-up, y' know. Is that what you call it? "Rounds" of baseball? (He looks at the others, who are chuckling.) Maybe not.
Lesberg: (Smiling) No, it's close enough. If you can do a "round of baseball," then it will be very interesting.
Ringo: A square of baseball!
John: A round of bread…that's nice.
Ringo: A round the corner's not bad, either.
Paul: (Jokingly, to Ringo) Listen. What I want to know…how'd your wife fall for you? ...can't understand it!
Lesberg: When is the date when you first go to the States?
George: Shea Stadium.
(Laughter)
John: When are we...do y' know...does anybody know?
Walter Shenson: Thirteenth of August.
Paul: We're all a bit vague on dates 'n things. We always have been.
Lesberg: What are you going to do after you get through with this picture? Are you going to take a vacation?
Paul: (Nods) Probably, if we get a chance. Yeah.
John: We tour Europe. Before America, we go around Europe 'n see if *they're* still alive.
Lesberg: (Grins) Are they?
John: Yeah, I hope so. They just got the Cup, didn't they?
Ringo: Liverpool lost last night.

Lesberg: Liverpool lost; Milan won. That was really interesting. I think that's the one sport that could really make it in the States and could be the one universal sport. Soccer.

George: They don't have it there?

Lesberg: Very little. And if they have it, it's teams coming from over here, or they get the Irish League or something.

Paul: (Excitedly) I saw some mad game on TV in America. Irish game. What was it? Hooking, or something.

Ringo: (Jokingly) Hookey.

Paul: No, it wasn't hockey, I don't think. It was a MAD game that I'd never ever seen before.

John: 'N they were just smashin' about with old shillelaghs. Hittin' the ball with shillelaghs.

Paul: Yeah! Wild game, y' know.

John: It was direct from Ireland onto American TV...we were watchin' it.

George: (Jokingly) Bill Shillelagh.

John: (Chuckling) Bill Shillelagh...*I* get it, George! I get it. (He explains the pun to Lesberg.) "Rock Around the Clock." Got it?

Lesberg: (Laughing) Bill Shillelagh and his Comets! So anyway, do you want to briefly give me, no kidding now, some sort of schedule of where you are...where you're going to be in the States besides Shea Stadium?

Ringo: The only other place I know is Houston.

John: 'N California.

George: (Grinning mischievously) I think we're doing *Ted* Sullivan's show.

Lesberg: *Who?*

Ringo: (Smirking) Ted Sullivan's show.

John: 'N Los Angeles. We go there...I know that. Yeah, Hollywood!

George: Two shows in Chicago.

John: San Francisco...we go there.

Lesberg: How many are you going to do in Shea Stadium? Just one?

Ringo: I believe so. (He nods.) Just one.

Paul: Listen, though. As I said before, we're dead vague about things. 'N it would be better just to ask someone who knows about it.

Ringo and Paul: (Almost simultaneously) Like Walter.

Lesberg: You mean, Walter Winchell?

Paul: (Paul laughing and tossing a thumb at the producer.) No, Walter Shenson!

Lesberg: When you're not working on the picture, what do you do on weekends? Do you stay together on weekends? Do you split up?

Paul: We either go out for the day if the weather's good...go out for a drive or go to the pictures.

Lesberg: Are there any places you can go where you don't get mobbed? I just came in out of twenty more girls out in front, climbing the walls. Is there any place that you can go in the U.K.?

Paul: Millions of places where you don't get mobbed. (He bites his lip and then nods.) Yeah.

Ringo: (Sputters in disbelief) Name *one*!

Paul: Name one? Tunipia!!

John: (Sitting up) But *that's* not part of the U.K. is it, though, Paul, these days?

Paul: Europe, though! Isn't it in Europe? No...Africa.

Lesberg: Close enough.

Paul: (Shaking his head) Well, you damned fool, Paul.

Ringo: (Out of the side of his mouth, comically) You're vague about places.

Paul: (Pretending to hang his head in shame) I'm afraid I'm a fool...Listen, uhhh...around the Mediterranean there's a couple. For instance, Tunidia! Name one!

Lesberg: Tunisia?

Paul: (Hand to his ear) Pardon?

Lesberg: (Laughs)

Paul: Let's have a bit more of this play between, uhh...talk.

Lesberg: (Jokingly) Is this interview too formal?

Paul: Volley? What's it called — that talkin' back 'n forth?

Lesberg: Is there any place around London that you can get away without crowds, really?

John: Buckingham Palace. When She's out, it's quite quiet there.

Paul: There *are* places. I mean, we go to the...there's places where we can go in the U.A. — which is United Artists. (He sniffs, superiorly.) When you're in "the business," you get to call it the U.A.

Lesberg: (Grinning widely) Very hip, yeah.

Paul: Kinda informal, y' know. They run films for ya.

Lesberg: (Shaking his head) Paul, thank you.
Paul: Not at all.
Lesberg: Thank you, Ringo.
Ringo: Thanks a lot, pal.
Lesberg: (Laughs) Thanks, George.
George: Thank you, Walter Winchell!
Lesberg: (Looking to John) Do you want to say anything to Hedda Hopper? Thank you, John, very much.
John: (Into the mic) It's been a pleasure. If you want to get ahead-a, get a Hopper!
Lesberg: All right. The Beatles, in London! This is Sandy Lesberg...bedraggled.

When asked about the famous interview later, Lesberg only sighed, threw up his hands, and admitted, "They ran *roughshod* over me actually!"[1522]

After years of experience with New York celebrities and sophisticated stars, nothing had prepared the veteran reporter for the un-likes of John, Paul, George, and Ringo. Only Shenson's quiet, overawing presence had preserved some slight modicum of gravity. But the moment the tape was snapped off and the "thank you, goodbyes" were said, the boys were giddy.

"Well, we're off to see Dylan, lads!" George whooped. He was Zimmerman's biggest fan.

"Cyn comin' along, then?" Paul arched an eyebrow in John's direction.

"Yeah," John nodded, stretching. "Bicknell's after bringin' her."

"Hey," Paul suddenly remembered, "Alf said that over in Salisbury, you invited him along with us...on the North American Tour, that is."[1523]

"Yeah, that's right." Reminded that his wife was *en route*, John unwrapped a minty piece of chewing gum and mangled it. "What of it?"

"Well...you spoke with Brian, then?"

"Look Paul, Eppy works for us — for *me* — not the other way 'round." John smacked the gum with end-of-the-day disdain. "I'll invite in whomever I want."

"But...well...what if he's engaged some other driver, someone over in America, perhaps?"

"Then we'll have *two*, Paul." And sniffing once, John strode away before an incident could spoil his night.

For the next quarter hour, as the others chatted and said final goodbyes to Sandy Lesberg, John stood aloof, his eyes on the street. Moodily, he awaited the arrival of Mrs. L.

****

Royal Festival Hall
Kensington Gore
London

When George Harrison had purchased *The Freewheelin' Bob Dylan* in Paris, 1964, and The Beatles had played the L.P. over and over again in their *Hotel George Cinq* suite,[1524] John had never imagined sitting in privileged seats at an actual Dylan concert. And it wasn't something young John Lennon from Woolton would've ever envisioned either. But here they were, nonetheless, he and Cyn — lights low, audience quiet and rapt, people barely moving.

"...your sons and your daughters are beyond your command," the clear-skinned young singer with head bowed over his guitar delivered the line without showmanship or flair. Wrapped in a hint of echo and a world of sincerity, Dylan's "The Times They Are A-Changin'" filled the vast Royal Festival Hall. Only when the last note trailed away did applause respectfully rise, quite apart from the sound of music.[1525]

The second song, John didn't know as well.[1526] But the plaintive harmonica that buoyed Zimmerman's voice enticed the audience, drawing them closer. Turning an ear towards the stage, John scrabbled to sort out the words — lyrics about fooling oneself into believing that "you're better than no one, and no one is better than you." And when Dylan insisted that empty rhetoric leaves a soul with "nothing to win and nothing to lose,"[1527] John fought the urge to stand and applaud. Dylan understood.

Competition was central to everything John did...it coursed through his veins. But now that he had accomplished so much, fresh motivation was becoming harder to find. And without it, John felt hollow.[1528] But tonight, he felt a thrill, a challenge.

Dylan's third number, John thought, sounded largely like the one before, but it held the audience in thrall. No skin-tearing, banner-waving shriek-fest — this. In a ray of alabaster light, a poet chanted free verse. In this room, *mach schau* had no place.

Cynthia did tap her toe a bit to "If You Gotta Go, Go Now," and she smiled lightly as Dylan chanted just above the thin line of his suspended harmonica.[1529] When the bard bluntly encouraged an indecisive lover to leave, conveniently, before he doused the light and fell asleep, the Lennons sniggered quietly. And during a crest of applause, Cynthia coyly took her husband's hand.

John stored each moment in memory. Even in the semi-dark, the rows and rows of seats flanked by layers of staggered box-balconies was magnificent. Impressive. Dylan — standing with knees slightly bent, in front of a four-legged stool and armed only with his guitar and harmonica — embodied "folk hero." The spotlight silvered the ends of his soft, brown curls, and a choirboy face peered inquisitively into a dark audience.[1530]

John thought of himself on the boards — cursing the senseless frenzy, fighting against futility of speech, stamping madly in mockery of the frothing fans, and laughing, whilst secretly fearing the roaring hysteria. John watched Dylan jealously, yearning for the opportunity to sing his songs, just like this.

Instinctively, John glanced down the row to where George and Pattie sat, and almost instantly, George's eyes met his, filled with empathy. Over and over, George had expressed his own weariness with touring. But Brian was having none of it. "You are," Eppy always reminded them, "at the very height of popularity. The need now is to press on."

But as Bob Dylan strummed the first acoustic chords of "Mr. Tambourine Man" and laced them with his soulful harmonica and his raw, unsophisticated voice,"[1531] the two Beatles nodded to one another in unspoken covetousness. And even when their yearning eyes drifted back to the stage, they sighed…aching with the long-deferred need to be heard.

****

The Savoy Hotel
Strand
London

John was largely silent in the car.[1532] Everyone else was bubbling with critique, praise, and springboard ideas, but John blurred his eyes against the city lights and created collages that even Stu would have begrudged.

They'd all been invited to an after-party in Mr. Zimmerman's hotel suite. "That beat poet Allen Ginsberg'll be there,"[1533] Paul said. "And of course, our Alma."

Alma Cogan! Cynthia dug her teeth into her lower lip. She leaned forward to check her hair in the window glass and nervously fumbled in her evening bag for lipstick.[1534] She was glad that for once, she'd spent a bit of money on herself. Cyn had squandered almost her entire fifty-pound allowance from John[1535] on a sleek, new sheath and a professional coif.

I've done all I can do, she told herself. *So, just be confident. Or, at least, pretend to be.*

And she tried.

In fact, it was John who was most withdrawn this evening, sitting back on the hotel settee and watching as the various others pressed Dylan about this song or that lyric — wanting to know if "the lady in question is real" or if "you really said that, after all."

But despising the spotlight as much as John loved it, Dylan tried to shift the attention to someone else. "Ah, why not ask Lennon about *his* lyrics!" The bard's eyes danced. "The newspapers claim we're carbon copies, anyway!"

"*Pfft!*" John took a gulp of Scotch and Coke. "It wouldn't matter if I never sang! I could stand on the stage 'n make mouth movements — 'n, believe me, I do! Nobody fuggin' knows!"[1536]

"Yeah," George nodded. "It's not like tonight, y' know. When *we're* on stage, it's only a scream fest."

Alma tried to protest, but John cut across her. "I reckon we could send out four waxwork dummies of ourselves, 'n *that* would satisfy the fuggin' crowds! Beatles concerts are nothin' to do with makin' music anymore! They're just bloody tribal rites."[1537]

"Oh, I'm sure they'd sort us out if we used the waxwork dummies!" Paul winked, trying to make light of it all. He was always uneasy when John grumbled in public. "The dummies, or so I hear, haven't really mastered 'Long Tall Sally.'"

"Not yet, anyway," Ringo murmured.

And everyone, except John, laughed.

Cynthia knew that a drinking John was an angry John, but there was little she could do. Asking her husband to pace himself would only goad him on to more. So, she generously filled a plate of *hors d'oeuvres* for him and hoped the food would mitigate some of the damage.

"So, how's the film?" Dylan asked Paul, once again steering the focus away from himself.

"Great, good," Paul said.

"They filmed me postin' a letter today,"[1538] Ringo shrugged. "So, if it's seein' me post a letter y'er after, you'll want to get yer tickets early!"

"I know *I'm* in!" Long-haired, bespectacled Allen Ginsberg plopped down on the arm of the settee where John was already tucked in. Struggling to manage his drink and plate at once, the bard lost his balance and tumbled right into John's lap.[1539]

The room roared, especially the other Beatles. But Ginsberg, never at a loss for words, merely segued into an imaginary interview with the Literary Beatle. "Tell me, Mr. Lennon," he said, in a crisp, faux-London accent, "as author of an upcoming and quite anticipated book of poetry, how exactly do you feel about William Blake?"[1540]

"Never heard of him,"[1541] John snarled.

Seizing her one chance to alter her husband's injured mood, Cynthia's head snapped around. "Oh John!" she laughed his ire off breezily, "You *liar*! Of course, you have![1542] You love William Blake!"

And completely startled by his wife's extraordinary cheekiness, John snickered. Then, he too began to laugh. The room followed suit.[1543]

Seizing the cheery moment, Dylan quickly suggested they all go out clubbing, and within minutes, the group was grabbing coats and bags and ringing for cars.[1544]

It was well into the small hours before Alf Bicknell was summoned to retrieve his charges.[1545] Then, as he navigated here and there, dropping the riotous Beatles off at their various homes, he endured a loud, painfully off-key rendition of "Long Tall Sally"

— "performed just *like* the fuggin' dummies, Alf!" John informed him.

American Poet Allen Ginsberg
Photograph from Wikimedia Commons

"Ah, the dummies," Alf nodded, smiling patiently. "All right, then," And to himself, "Whatever that means."

And rallying once more, John sang on.

Motoring sleepily on towards Kenwood, Alf yawned and reminded himself that, despite the ungodly hour, almost no one had ever been fortunate enough to experience a private Lennon concert...without a single scream or the slightest interruption.[1546] It was, even when John was larkin' about, the biggest perk of the job.

Notes!

Was John truly as discontented in May of 1965 as this chapter portrays?

Journalist Ray Coleman, who was close friends with John and eventually wrote the biography, Lennon, says that in 1965, around the time that John "wrote 'Help!' something from deep within him gave vent to his insecurity, his feeling that all was not well, despite the millions of record sales, the adoration, the frustrating mansion in Weybridge which he described as 'like a bus stop, you wait until something comes along.'...[John] could not stand the inflated descriptions of what The Beatles were, or being constantly paraded, or the dukes and lords who regarded it as a social cachet to be photographed with a Beatle. To John, what had begun as rock'n'roll had become an industry..." (Lennon, 256-257)

Sources:

Lewisohn, The Complete Beatles Chronicle, *193.*
Lewisohn, The Beatles: Day by Day, *62.*
Harry, The Ultimate Beatles Encyclopedia, *211.*
Harry, The John Lennon Encyclopedia, *217-219.*
Harry, The Encyclopedia of Beatles People, *110-111.*
Lennon, Cynthia, John, *165-166.*
Miles, The Beatles' Diary, Vol. 1, *192.*
Norman, Shout!, *242.*
Coleman, Lennon, *214, 254, and 256-257.*
Spitz, *533.*
Badman, *155.*
Tremlett, The John Lennon Story, *60.*
Goldman, *181,*
Friede, Titone, and Wiener, *60.*
Robertson, *40.*
Trynka, *169.*
Hill, John, Paul, George & Ringo, *199.*

https://www.beatlesbible.com/1965/05/09/beatles-watch-bob-dylan-london/ *This website supplies information about The Beatles at the Dylan concert and at the after-party, including the Ginsberg incident.*

https://tinyurl.com/yxca4er5 This YouTube video supplies the entire concert audio of the 9 May 1965 Dylan at the Royal Festival Hall.

https://tinyurl.com/y28f9ney This is a photo of Dylan at the 1965 Royal Festival Hall concert with his harmonica on a neck stand.

https://tinyurl.com/yxaz9prf and https://tinyurl.com/yyu7hb24 These are two photos of Dylan on stage on 9 May 1965 at the Royal Festival Hall. There is some question amongst historians about whether or not Dylan used a folk acoustic guitar that evening or an electric guitar. There are reports that he was "booed" for using an electric guitar. However, all photos that I can find bear witness to the fact that at this point in 1965, he was still using a miked acoustic guitar...no leads, no cords on the floor.

https://www.bobdylan.com/date/1965-05-09-royal-albert-hall/ The official Bob Dylan website provides the set list for the 9 May 1965 Royal Festival Hall concert.

https://en.wikipedia.org/wiki/The_Freewheelin%27_Bob_Dylan If you're not familiar with Dylan's landmark LP, The Freewheelin' Bob Dylan, (popularly known as Freewheelin'), this website supplies basic information about the album

https://exhibitions.lib.udel.edu/beat-visions-and-the-counterculture/home/ginsberg/ This website supplies a biography and sample poetry of Allen Ginsberg.

https://www.beatlesinterviews.org This website supplies the interview between New York's Sandy Lesberg and The Beatles, conducted on 9 May 1965.

https://www.movie-locations.com/movies/h/Help-1965.php This website will enable you to see some of the places where The Beatles filmed "Help!" whilst "out and about in London" and to learn where they are, if you're planning a trip to London.
Or use this QR code:

[1515] Lewisohn, *The Complete Beatles Chronicle*, 192 and Norman, *Shout!*, 242.
[1516] Lewisohn, *The Complete Beatles Chronicle*, 192.
[1517] Lewisohn, *The Complete Beatles Chronicle*, 192 and Norman, *Shout!*, 242.

[1518] Norman, *Shout!*, 242 and Lennon, Cynthia, *John*, 166. Norman quotes Ringo as saying that "Asprey's was as good as Woolworth's." He said they had "everything spread out in the open so you could see it." Cynthia, in *John*, states, "John loved shopping even more than I did." She says he loved "scoop[ing] up goodies in [his] own version of a trolley dash."

[1519] Norman, *Shout!*, 242, Badman, 156, and Coleman, *Lennon*, 254. Norman says John spent £600. Badman quotes Director Richard Lester as saying, "In the few minutes that we filmed at Asprey's in New Bond Street, London, John spent £8000 pounds." And Coleman says, "Darting in and out of Asprey's, the exclusive and ultra-expensive store in Bond Street, John managed to spend about £80,000, within minutes." He quotes Richard Lester as well, saying, "God knows how he managed it. I think even John was amazed at how much he ordered from the place."

[1520] Lewisohn, *The Complete Beatles Chronicle*, 192.

[1521] https://www.beatlesinterviews.org Jay Spangler, the original owner of this website, meticulously transcribed the interview below and provided this background information.

[1522] https://www.beatlesinterviews.org Direct quote from Sandy Lesberg.

[1523] Bicknell, 43.

[1524] Harry, *The John Lennon Encyclopedia*, 217-218 and Spitz, 533. Spitz says it was Paul who discovered Dylan's music and brought it to the attention of the others. Bill Harry says it was George Harrison. Spitz does quote George (not Paul) as saying that listening to *Freewheelin'* was "one of the most memorable things on the [Paris 1964] trip."

[1525] To hear the entire concert from 9 May 1965 at the Royal Festival Hall, London, go to: https://tinyurl.com/yxca4er5 All details in this section of the chapter are taken from this live recording.

[1526] https://www.bobdylan.com/date/1965-05-09-royal-albert-hall/ According to the official Dylan website set list, the second song at the 9 May 1965 Royal Festival Hall Dylan concert was "To Ramona."

[1527] These are lines from "To Ramona," a folk waltz written by Bob Dylan and released 8 August 1964 on the Columbia label. For more information on this song, go to: https://en.wikipedia.org/wiki/To_Ramona

[1528] Tremlett, *The John Lennon Story*, 60 and Goldman, 181. Goldman aptly observes, "Like most men who hurl themselves at a goal, sacrificing everything to its attainment, Lennon had never given a thought to what he would do if he reached 'the toppermost of the poppermost.' Naively, he had assumed the payoff would be total fulfillment. Imagine his shock when one day he suddenly found…the view wasn't worth the climb."

[1529] https://tinyurl.com/y28f9ney This is a photo of Dylan at the 1965 Royal Festival Hall concert with his harmonica on a neck stand.

[1530] Robertson, *Lennon*, 40, https://tinyurl.com/yyu7hb24, and https://tinyurl.com/yxaz9prf The links provide two clear images of Dylan on stage at the Royal Festival Hall, 9 May 1965. **NOTE:** Again, you can clearly see that Dylan is using an acoustic guitar. There is a mic on the guitar to amplify the sound, but no electric leads or cords. Furthermore, Robertson, in *Lennon* (p. 40), specifically refers to the 9 May concert as "an acoustic concert."

[1531] https://www.bobdylan.com/date/1965-05-09-royal-albert-hall/ "Mr. Tambourine Man" was the seventh song on Dylan's playlist at the Royal Festival Hall, 9 May 1965.

[1532] Bicknell, 45. Alf Bicknell says he dropped them at the Royal Festival Hall for the concert, but then didn't pick them up again until the end of the evening after "another very late night at the clubs." I can't imagine The Beatles being able to travel by taxi to the party without being overrun by fans, but somehow they negotiated from The Royal Festival Hall to the Savoy Hotel.

[1533] Miles, *The Beatles' Diary, Vol. 1*, 195-196, https://www.beatlesbible.com/1965/05/09/beatles-watch-bob-dylan-london/, and https://exhibitions.lib.udel.edu/beat-visions-and-the-counterculture/home/ginsberg/. On the latter site, you can read the poem Ginsberg wrote in flight from Prague to London, the day before his meeting with Dylan and The Beatles.

[1534] Lennon, Cynthia, *John*, 162. Cynthia always felt "dowdy" when Alma was around, and she worried that John and Alma were having an affair.

[1535] Lennon, Cynthia, *John*, 165. Cynthia says John gave her an allowance of "fifty pounds a week, which in those days was a handsome sum."

[1536] Coleman, *Lennon*, 214. Direct quote from John Lennon.

[1537] Coleman, Lennon, 214. Direct quote from John Lennon.

[1538] Lewisohn, *The Complete Beatles Chronicle*, 193.

[1539] Miles, *The Beatles' Diary, Vol. 1*, 195.

[1540] Miles, *The Beatles' Diary, Vol. 1*, 195.

[1541] Miles, *The Beatles' Diary, Vol. 1*, 195.

[1542] Miles, *The Beatles' Diary, Vol. 1*, 195.

[1543] Miles, *The Beatles' Diary, Vol. 1*, 195.

[1544] Miles, *The Beatles' Diary, Vol. 1*, 195 and Bicknell, 45.

[1545] Bicknell, 45.

[1546] Bicknell, 45.

Tuesday, 11 May 1965
Kenwood
Weybridge, Surrey

There was a covey of striped shopping boxes huddled in the foyer. Cyn and Dot Jarlett had, no doubt, been off to Walton-on-Thames again.[1547] After living almost hand-to-mouth in a Liverpool bedsit during her art college years — with only one set of sheets that required washing, ironing, and re-bedding in a single day — Cynthia was passionate for linens.[1548] She was forever purchasing new ones as her "one small treat."

Well, sheets and shoes, that is,[1549] John thought.

He peered inside a box, lifted a shoulder, and then set it aside. He thumbed, absent-mindedly, through the mail on the library table. Kicked off his shoes.

"You're home early!" Cynthia scurried down the stairs, her eyes bright.

"Because it's over 'n done." John tried to smile back. "We've been 'Help!'ed all we can be."[1550]

"You mean…you finished the film?"

"Yeah, they've a coupla outdoor scenes tomorrow, but we're not part of it, so…"[1551]

"This calls for a celebration! Fancy a bacon butty and a mug of tea?"[1552]

"You must've read my mind."[1553] John's mouth quirked at the corner, thinking that fans would expect the Lennons to pop a cork or two, but the Liverpool twosome still preferred tea or milk…and a jam butty bedside the small fire in the sunroom.[1554]

"So, how was the final day, then?" His wife called from the kitchen. John headed in that direction.

"We had relay races."[1555] John yawned and stretched.

"*What?!* I thought you were in Cliveden House, filming the

so-called Buckingham Palace scenes."[1556]

"Right yeah, we were…but once out in the gardens, we were cruelly challenged by a team of carpenters, a team of cameramen, 'n a shockin' team of electricians…"[1557]

"Against the four of you?" Cynthia could see disaster written all over this scenario.

"Right, the foursome — happily augmented by Neil 'n Alf Bicknell."[1558]

"And?"

"Well, I'd say good money was on anyone but us." John removed his jacket and tie, tossing them on the kitchen counter. "In fact, I overheard someone or another callin' us 'unfit.'"[1559]

"How very dare they?!" Cynthia bit her bottom lip, suppressing a smile.

"Well, to be fair, they've never seen us sprint off stage with a furious horde in mad pursuit."

"And so?"

"'N so, we won."[1560] Her husband shrugged. "What fuggin' else? Did y' think Johnny Lennon would be bested?"

"No, to quote my favourite composer, 'I should have known better.'"

"Right." John rolled his "r" in good Scouse fashion. Though Mimi despised his lapses into the Merseyside lingo, John relished falling back on his familiar art college ways. It was home, in miniature.

"Victory cup?" Cyn handed John a steaming mug. Her new electric kettle was quick and efficient.

"*Slàinte mhath*, gerl!" John clacked her beaker.

"Cheers, luv. Congratulations! And here…I thought you might enjoy this bit…from the morning *Advertiser*."

John accepted the carefully folded newspaper and yawned again, to moisten his contacts. Then, he dramatized the article Cyn had circled:

Beatles
film at
Cliveden

WHILE Lord Astor rested in
his bedroom after an illness,
The Beatles filmed below his
window this week. The group
was at Cliveden on Monday and
Tuesday, filming scenes for their
new film - "Help!"
Lady Astor watched the filming from her bedroom window
on the second floor.[1561]

"I gave her a wave, y' know," John said. "It was the least I could do."

"Good of you," Cynthia smiled, nodding for him to follow her into the sun room. She managed the butties whilst John read:

. Outside the estate, carloads
of girls waited patiently for the
boys to leave.[1562]

"I waved to them as well," John muttered, falling into his chair.

"You're very polite." Cynthia proffered his plate.

In between filming, George
Harrison, wearing a corduroy
suit, played softball on the im-
maculately mown lawn, Ringo
Starr slept in a chair, Paul
Macartney sat on the balustrade
talking to the ADVERTISER,[1563]

"Now, *there's* a surprise," John threw his eyes to the ceiling. "Mac Art-Ney…talkin' to the press."

"He's well-mannered."

…and

**John Lennon stood quietly wait-
ing for his next scene.**[1564]

"Whereas I'm generally found to be very shy 'n retirin', y' know," he ducked his head, coyly.

"You're retiring?! Lovely! I've a lengthy list of odd jobs that need doing in your newfound spare time."

"Movin' on…"

**The film, the group's second
is in colour and is due to be
released on July 27.**[1565]

"Now *there's* a bit of news I can use," John whacked the paper with the back of his hand.

"You didn't know?"

"Well, we've no time for updates, have we? I mean, look, we were in studio Monday night 'til straight up twelve!"[1566]

Cynthia sat back in her chair, tucked her feet beneath her, and let her husband grouse. She knew, as well as he, that he'd probably been given the "Help!" release date a hundred times, but John was overwhelmed and thus, forgetful. Lately — in addition to long hours filming and sitting for miscellaneous interviews — he'd been hastily recording two of his favourite Larry Williams rockers, "Dizzy Miss Lizzy" and "Bad Boy," for an imminent new American LP on Capitol called *Beatles VI*.[1567]

He has more than enough to drive him 'round the bend! Cyn thought, nodding as he talked.

John sighed, leaned back, and read the rest of the article, wryly commenting on the observation, "also starring Patrick Cargill and Roy Kinnear" part.[1568] "*Starring?!*" John shook his head. "At best, Cargill's in a scene or two. Or ten."[1569]

"John, you're a Beatle. In fact, the Leader Beatle, as they always say. Why not let a professional actor enjoy a tossed laurel or two?"

"*Hmpf!* I will…but only because Cargill here says that 'actin' with The Beatles is marvellous.'"[1570]

"See? There you have it." Cynthia sipped her Earl Grey cautiously, blowing on the surface. The kettle, she thought, was a bit overzealous. "I just can't believe the film's truly finalized."

"Well, we've bits to overdub," John yawned as he talked. "Post-sync, they call it. Like…well, like in that scene in Obertauern, where we were on the sled, tearin' downhill. Now, we have to go back in 'n overdub us sorta chantin', 'Ho, ho, ho! Ho, ho, ho!' as we careen by."[1571]

"That shouldn't be difficult…or require rising early." Cynthia encouraged. "No hair and make-up needed for post-sync, I suppose."

"'N even if it were," John yawned a third time. "I couldn't find the 'get-up-n-go,' as the Americans all say. I'm all in, Powell. I could sleep straight through for a fuggin' week!"

"Well, let's get a head start, then." And rising to douse the lights, Cynthia waited for her husband to drag himself to his feet.

The Beatles had been shooting "Help!" since 23 February whilst wedging in awards ceremonies, television programmes, BBC performances, and recording sessions as well.[1572] As her mother constantly pointed out, John "was meeting himself coming and going." He desperately needed a break. His face, serious and careworn, made him appear much older than a youthful twenty-four. John needed time to breathe. He needed a holiday.

Notes!

Houston's Buddy McGregor was on hand in Cliveden House to interview The Beatles on their final day of filming "Help!" That interview, carefully transcribed by Jay Spangler, may be accessed here: http://beatlesinterviews.org/db1965.0510.beatles.html

Sources:

Lewisohn, The Complete Beatles Chronicle, *193-194.*
Lewisohn, The Beatles: Day by Day, *190-196.*
Lewisohn, The Beatles Recording Sessions, *58.*
Harry, The Ultimate Beatles Encyclopedia, *299.*
Harry, The John Lennon Encyclopedia, *966.*
Harry, The Encyclopedia of Beatles People, *336-337.*
Lennon, Cynthia, John, *165 and 168.*
Lennon, Cynthia, A Twist of Lennon, *133.*
Winn, *319.*
Miles, The Beatles' Diary, Vol. 1, *196.*

Margotin and Guesdon, 254-255.
Spizer, The Beatles' Story on Capitol Records, Vol. 2, *81.*
Riley, Tell Me Why, *26.*
Schultheiss, 130-132.
Carr, 85-88.
Hill, John, Paul, George & Ringo, *199.*
Friede, Titone, and Wiener, 227.
Badman, 155. Badman includes portions of the interview with
Houston's Buddy McGregor.
Robertson, Lennon, *40.*

https://www.rockarchive.com/prints/b/beatles-the-tb002whit
Photographer Robert Whitaker was at Cliveden House to capture stills
of The Beatles in the famous location. This is one of the shots from that
day.

https://www.beatlesbible.com/songs/dizzy-miss-lizzy/   This   website
provides additional information of The Beatles' recording of "Dizzy Miss
Lizzy" on 10 May 1965.

https://www.beatlesbible.com/songs/bad-boy/   This   website   provides
additional information on The Beatles' recording of "Bad Boy" on 10 May
1965.

https://www.beatlesbible.com/1965/05/11/filming-help-54/ This website
chronicles the events in the lives of The Beatles on 10-11 May 1965.

https://en.wikipedia.org/wiki/Patrick_Cargill   This   website   gives
information about professional actor Patrick Cargill, who played the
Scotland Yard Superintendent in "Help!"

https://www.imdb.com/name/nm0137092/ This is another website about
the acting career of Patrick Cargill.

[1547] Lennon, Cynthia, *John,* 165.
[1548] Lennon, Cynthia, *John,* 165 and Lennon, Cynthia, *A Twist of Lennon,* 133. Cynthia says she and Dot Jarlett would drive to Walton-on-Thames "and run amok" and that "high quality sheets, pillowcases, and bedcovers were high on my list."
[1549] Lennon, Cynthia, *John,* 165.
[1550] Lewisohn, *The Complete Beatles Chronicle,* 193 and Harry, *The Ultimate Beatles Encyclopedia,* 299.
[1551] Lewisohn, *The Complete Beatles Chronicle,* 193.
[1552] Lennon, Cynthia, *John,* 168. Direct quote from Cynthia Lennon.
[1553] Lennon, Cynthia, *John,* 168. Direct quote from John Lennon.
[1554] Lennon, Cynthia, *John,* 165. Cynthia says, "At home we lived simply. We drank little, usually preferring a glass of milk…to anything alcoholic."

[1555] Lewisohn, *The Complete Beatles Chronicle*, 193.

[1556] Lewisohn, *The Complete Beatles Chronicle*, 193, Miles, *The Beatles' Diary, Vol. 1,* 196, Winn, 318, and https://www.beatlesbible.com/1965/05/11/filming-help-54/ Lewisohn reminds us that "the outside view of Buckingham Palace was seen in 'Help!' (filmed on 12 May) but there was, of course, no way that permission could be obtained for The Beatles to film inside the real edifice."

[1557] Lewisohn, *The Complete Beatles Chronicle*, 193, Winn, 318, and https://www.beatlesbible.com/1965/05/11/filming-help-54/

[1558] Lewisohn, *The Complete Beatles Chronicle*, 193, Winn, 318, and https://www.beatlesbible.com/1965/05/11/filming-help-54/

[1559] Lewisohn, *The Complete Beatles Chronicle*, 193.

[1560] Lewisohn, *The Complete Beatles Chronicle*, 193.

[1561] "Beatles Film at Cliveden," London *Advertiser*, 12 May 1965, found in Lewisohn, *The Complete Beatles Chronicle*, 193.

[1562] "Beatles Film at Cliveden," London *Advertiser*, 12 May 1965, found in Lewisohn, *The Complete Beatles Chronicle*, 193.

[1563] "Beatles Film at Cliveden," London *Advertiser*, 12 May 1965, found in Lewisohn, *The Complete Beatles Chronicle*, 193.

[1564] "Beatles Film at Cliveden," London *Advertiser*, 12 May 1965, found in Lewisohn, *The Complete Beatles Chronicle*, 193.

[1565] "Beatles Film at Cliveden," London *Advertiser*, 12 May 1965, found in Lewisohn, *The Complete Beatles Chronicle*, 193.

[1566] Lewisohn, *The Complete Beatles Chronicle*, 193 and Miles, *The Beatles' Diary, Vol. 1,* 318.

[1567] Lewisohn, *The Complete Beatles Chronicle*, 193, Lewisohn, *The Beatles Recording Sessions*, 58, Spizer, *The Beatles on Capitol Records, Vol. 2*, 80, Margotin and Guesdon, 254-255, and Winn, 318. Lewisohn, Margotin and Guesdon, and Winn tell us that the two songs were recorded in EMI, Studio Two, between 8.00 to 11.30 p.m. and then mixed between 11.30 p.m. and 1.15 a.m. The Beatles probably did not stay for the mixing, but even if John had departed shy of midnight, it would have been 1 a.m. by the time Bicknell drove him home to Kenwood. Winn adds that John had done one of those miscellaneous interviews (to which Cynthia alludes) on this very day. The Beatles had given an interview to Houston, Texas journalist Buddy McGregor of KNUZ-AM. This interview was sold in Foley's department stores in Texas as "Buddy in Britain — A Chat with The Beatles."

[1568] Lewisohn, *The Complete Beatles Chronicle*, 193. From the London *Advertiser* article.

[1569] https://en.wikipedia.org/wiki/Patrick_Cargill and https://www.imdb.com/name/nm0137092/ Both websites provide information on the respected, extensive acting career of Patrick Cargill who "starred" in "Help!" as the Scotland Yard Superintendent.

[1570] "Beatles Film at Cliveden," London *Advertiser*, 12 May 1965, found in Lewisohn, *The Complete Beatles Chronicle*, 193.

[1571] Lewisohn, *The Complete Beatles Chronicle*, 194. The post-sync work was conducted on Tuesday, 18 May 1965 in Twickenham Studios.

[1572] Lewisohn, *The Complete Beatles Chronicle*, 184-194, Lewisohn, *The Beatles: Day by Day,* 58-62, Miles, *The Beatles' Diary, Vol. 1*, 190-196, Schultheiss, 130-132, Harry, *The Ultimate Beatles Encyclopedia*, 299, and Carr, 85-88.

Saturday, 22 May 1965[1573]
En Route To Cannes, France

Richard Lester had invited Walter Shenson,[1574] John, and Cynthia to accompany his wife, Deirdre, and him on a "long weekend" to the Cannes Film Festival,[1575] where his "Swinging Sixties" comedy "The Knack" was being unveiled.[1576] Based on a two-act play by Ann Jellicoe exploring the "sexual politics" of the era,[1577] Lester's incident-filled comedic film told the story of an introverted London schoolteacher, Colin — brilliantly played by Michael Crawford — who is "tutored" in the art of seduction by an experienced, calloused, and fast-moving drummer named Tolen.[1578]

"Lester hardly seems the type for such a...frolic," Cynthia shook her head, as they waited for Lester's car to drive them to London Airport.[1579]

"Well, y' know, still waters..." John raised his eyebrows rapidly, amusing his wife with the thought of Lester as a reckless cad.

"So they say!" Cynthia snickered, glancing in the foyer mirror to adjust the wide, black satin bow in her hair and her black button earrings. Cyn's thick blonde mane had finally grown past shoulder length, and these days, she was styling it identically to Pattie Boyd's.[1580] Knowing that the press would be on both tarmacs today, Cyn had splurged on white lace hose, black Baby-Doll heels, and a smart, textured spring suit with a sleek, white mock-turtleneck, whilst John had randomly thrown on a light-coloured suit, black shirt, black tie, and hat. The Lennons looked as if they'd carefully coordinated their outfits[1581] — an absurdity John would never have permitted, even if Cyn had entreated him to consider it.

"He doesn't think he has a chance, y' know — Lester." John

hoisted his small, plaid overnight bag. "I mean, not with Caine in 'The Ipcress File'[1582] and Connery in 'The Hill'[1583] as rivalry."[1584]

"Umm," Cynthia lifted a dubious eyebrow. "Rather stringent competition, I'd say."

"'N they're the *official* British entries, y' see. The festival committee asked 'The Knack' in, y' know, independently — on its own merit."

"Without proper British endorsement?" Cynthia hinted a smile.

"Right. It's the fuggin' dark horse, as it were."

"Well, *that* certainly says something, doesn't it? The fact that the committee's interested, regardless of who or what was formally nominated?" Cynthia heard the hired car rolling into the drive and located her purse.

"One never knows." John grabbed his overcoat. "We can only…"

"…keep our fingers crossed." Cynthia smiled and did exactly that.

And having already bid Julian goodbye before Dot lured the child off on a "butterfly expedition," John opened the front door, and the Lennons were off to the French Riviera.

****

Monday, 24 May 1965
An Undisclosed Café Near the Coast
Cannes, France

The weekend was Dick Lester's outing. He was "the man of the hour." But when they landed in France, Lester urged the Lennons to walk well ahead of Walter Shenson, Deirdre, and him — knowing that all cameras would be trained on the legendary couple. And, of course, they were.[1585] Swarming reporters crisscrossed the tarmac, capturing John and Cynthia from every angle. They smiled and nodded, graciously.

And somewhere in Cannes, gregarious, polished, young American television host and entertainer Merv Griffin was already waiting as well. He was keen to fill one of Lennon's "afternoons off" with an interview for his syndicated television programme, "The Merv Griffin Show."[1586]

Reluctant to spend time promoting "Help!" on a rare get-away,[1587] John had painfully relented when Brian had nudged, "In a half-hour's time, you could do The Beatles a *world of good* with this Griffin interview, John…on so many fronts! And it goes without saying, naturally, that you'd be free to promote your upcoming book as well. That is, if you'd like."

Thus, on Monday, 24 May, John found himself strolling with Richard Lester and Walter Shenson down to a quiet delicatessen café near the water.[1588] In Lenin cap, black polo, worn black kecks, and scuffed Cuban boots, John looked very much "a Beatle," circa 1961-1963. Laughing over one of his own barbs, he sauntered into the meeting in "full John mode" — brimming with mischief and quirky wit — and undeniably in charge.[1589]

Lennon, Lester, and Shenson shook hands with the casually sport-coated Griffin. They ginned up polite conversation and found seats around a small, linen-draped dining table. Griffin nodded to the tape recorder, already spooling along nicely.

Merv Griffin: (Lifting a comical eyebrow in John's direction) Captain Livingston, I presume?[1590]
John: Yes, that's me.
Griffin: It's a long way from Liverpool!
John: (Nodding) It's a long way from Liverpool.
Griffin: (Lifting his hand indicatively towards the Cannes coast) Do you speak French?
John: No, do you?
Griffin: (Smiling at the bold retort) No, not at all.
John: (Introducing Dick Lester) This is Dick.

(The two shook hands again, for the cameras.)

Griffin: Hello, Dick. (To the microphone) Dick Lester.
Lester: (Repeating the opening "theme") It's a long way from Liverpool!
Griffin: (Laughing) Yes!

John: (To himself, as if conducting the interview) Why don't you do more writing? (Then, shouting, as if from one of the few onlookers) *Write!*
(They all laugh.)
John: (Still shouting, as if from viewers) Why don't you do more?!

(Lester leans towards Merv Griffin and mutters something. In light of Griffin's response, Lester must have offered some droll comment such as: "You'll have to manage him...I find he's quite a problem on the set.)

Griffin: (To Lester) I'm trying, *I'm trying!* You're not the only one with a problem though!
John: Okay. Oh no! We gotta "write" problem, too.
Griffin: (Scrabbling to get control of the interview) Is this your vacation, John?
John: No, it's a weekend more than a vacation. Just four days, y' know. Four days.
Griffin: Of watching bathers and movie stars and –
John: (Sarcastically) That's it! I've come to have a look at a coupla people.
Griffin: What've you decided?
John: I've decided there's a lot of funny people 'round here.
Griffin: Have you written a poem?
John: No, not today. Have *you*?
Griffin: No, but I want to tell you, I fell out of my chair –
(Genuinely laughing as he thinks back, presumably about one of John's poems.)
John: Funny you should say that, 'cause we just finished the second film called "Help!" directed by Dick Lester here. Funny you should say that!
Griffin: (Smiling at John's blunt segue) I'm glad I said that! Did *you* think it was funny though, John?
John: Yeah. Oh, funny – I was laughin' – 'n it comes out... along with my new book – *that* comes out soon, folks!
Griffin: (To Lester) You directed their second picture, now.
Lester: (Nodding) Yes.
John: He directed the book, too.
Griffin: (Frowns towards Lester) Directed the *book*?

Lester: (Nods and smiles a bit) Yes.
Griffin: Is their second picture as exciting as the first?
Lester: (With a glint in his eye) I don't know. I haven't seen it yet.
Griffin: (Chuckling, to John) When is it coming out?
John: (Cutting his eyes at Dick) It's comin' out in...I don't know. When's it comin' out?
Lester: I think it'll come out the beginning of August for America.
John: (Smirking) Oh, my book just comes out *before that*! Funny you should say that!
Griffin: (Laughing and shaking his head)
John: (Leaning into the mic) *A Spaniard In the Works*...about 10 and 6...or equivalent money in America.
Griffin: (Grinning widely now) Mm-hmm. And what are you calling the new...This is not *Ben-Hur*...the new one?
John: (Thoroughly confused by the abrupt shift in the line of questioning) No...*what*?
Griffin: Your new movie.
John: Ohhhh, the new *movie* is called "Help!" H-e-l-p.
Griffin: H-a-l-p?
John: e-l-p.
Griffin: e-l-p...Help.
John: No, we're using the old spelling.
Griffin: (Smiling) Is this *also* another day in the life of The Beatles?
John: No, this is a day in the life of ...it's many days in the lives of many people.
Griffin: Is it a heavy drama?
Lester: (Wryly) Pretty heavy.
John: (In the background) Yeah.
Griffin: (To Dick Lester) Was it heavy to direct?
Lester: (His mouth quirking up at the corners) No, it was very light to direct, but heavy to watch.
Griffin: Ahh!

(The onlookers laugh, and John mutters something to Lester, which must have been about Phil Spector because Merv follows up with...)

Griffin: You *know* Phil Spector?

John: (Nodding) I met him on a plane once.

Griffin: (Surprised) You did?

John: (Deadpanning) He nearly crashed it. Good old Phil! All right, Phil.

Griffin: He didn't stay on for the whole flight, did he?

John: Oh, he was "on" for the whole flight, yeah. But – hmm…

Griffin: Now, you boys are leaving for America. I know…I know for a fact…my home is originally San Francisco, and people have been wiring me in New York to see if they can get tickets for your appearance in San Francisco.

John: You can't deal with 'em!

Griffin: No. (Laughing)

John: [Indiscernible]

Griffin: I'm sitting on the…wires. (Then…) Ah, (Clears his throat, broaching a new topic) The Beatles at the Cow Palace!

John: (Lifting an eyebrow) Yes, what about it?

Griffin: Well, it sounds like a condition of some kind.

John: (Opting for the serious high road in order to take the mickey out of Merv) No, it isn't. It's just a place. (John sniffs, mock-indignantly.) You oughta know that.

Griffin: (Chuckling) Right. And then, are you going to be at Forest Hills?

John: I don't think so. (Again, he looks to Dick Lester for answers. Lester shrugs. Tours are not his purview.) Some uh – (John gives up and openly admits) I don't know *where* we are, actually.

Unidentified Male:[1591] Isn't that a cemetery?

Griffin: No, no – *Forest Lawn* is the cemetery!

John: (Smiles) That's it!

(Audience laughs.)

Griffin: (To the unidentified man) Who are you?

Male: (Nodding towards John) I wear his hat.

Griffin: You're not a Beatle!

Male: No, no.

Lester: (To Griffin) You've noticed!

Griffin: (Laughing and shaking his head) Yeah!

Lester: (To Griffin) You've got a keen eye for detail, don't you?

Griffin: Very…yeah, very. (Turning back to Lennon) How long will you be here, John?

John: About 5 'til 11. (He Cheshire grins.) 'Til tomorrow.
Griffin: And where are the boys?
John: They're somewhere in merry olde England.
Griffin: Do they know you're away?
John: I think they'll have noticed.
(Onlookers laugh)
Griffin: (Feigning shock) Is that *allowed*?
John: (Nodding) It is allowed, yeah. It *is* allowed. Once a year, we're allowed to split up.
Griffin: Tell me about your book, which got extraordinary reviews in New York. Would you...would you do a poem for us?
John: Ah, no.
Griffin: (Sweeping his hand at the photographers around them and trying to persuade John to read the work for publicity value) This is the *paparazzi*!
John: (Irritated by the tactic) Well, here we are then. Well, we've gotta go now. You can stay here, though.
Griffin: I'm going to stay.
John: Okay, you stay here...
Griffin: ...and I'll discuss your interview.
John: I'm going to go.
Griffin: Thank you, John. Nice meeting you.
John: You do great work.
Griffin: (To Lester) Dick, thank you.
John: Plug the book.[1592]
(Griffin laughs and switches off the recorder.)

****

For Cynthia, it had been a most satisfactory weekend. When John was otherwise occupied, she'd strolled with Deirdre Lester and sometimes with "The Knack" star Rita Tushingham (when Rita wasn't being interviewed or photographed.)[1593] The three ambled the narrow city streets, sightseeing, taking snaps, and stopping off in this shop or that. And at the end of each afternoon, the three relaxed over plates of golden brown *socca*, the delectable, warm chickpea flatbread for which Nice and Cannes were famous.[1594] They smoked and talked over glasses of wine from the Riviera's sun-drenched Viognier or Grenache grapes.[1595]

"My husband," Deirdre confided to Cynthia, "thinks your John an utter genius."[1596]

"That's lovely," Cynthia smiled. She didn't want to confess that she agreed, though naturally, she did.

"Really," Deirdre went on, "he's always going on about John's 'innate intelligence' coupled with his no-nonsense ability to counter Dick's so-called 'flights of fancy.'"[1597]

"Is he?" Cynthia wrinkled her brow.

"Yes," Deirdre accepted the wedge of *socca* Rita offered her. "Dick admits that he, invariably, takes off on wild, creative binges — rabbiting on about some creative concept and getting further and further from reality. But then, John — who, of course, has been sitting and listening patiently, all the while — says but one sentence, and Dick sees he's been a fool. He swears John harbours 'a natural ability to see through to the centre of things.' And *that*, Dick loves about him."[1598]

Cynthia leaned back in her chair. "Well," she smiled, "sometimes at home, I'm afraid, it's just the opposite. John summons me up to his recording studio, to listen to all sorts of bizarre creations, and I'm the one counted on for rock solid practicality."[1599]

"Oh, but that's wives, you know — wives!" Deirdre dismissed Cyn's rebuttal with a wave of her hand. "We're the counterbalance for all those 'yes men' filling our husbands' lives...*and* for those hungry adversaries who routinely try to knock them down."

"Or we try to be," Rita chuckled. Even though the actress from Merseyside had captured the 1961 "Best Actress" award from Cannes for "A Taste of Honey," as well as "Most Promising Newcomer" from BAFTA and a Golden Globe, Rita too, was a wife and mother.[1600]

"Almost once a week," Deirdre confided, "Dick will come home and bury his head in his hands, mumbling, 'Pour me a drink,' as he begins to lament, 'It's the end of the world! It's the *end* of the world, I tell you!' He's a born pessimist — Dick! So, it's up to *me* to find a way to cheer him."[1601]

Rita and Cynthia nodded. The three, who shared much in common, were developing an easy camaraderie.

"Anyway, Cynthia," Deirdre went on, "I just want you to know how much Dick admires John, Beatle or no. He's told me so many times that John has 'few pretensions but considerable perception.'"[1602]

Cynthia nodded; her eyes, gentle. "Strange as it must seem coming from his wife — who sees both the good and the bad — I have to agree. John really *is* brilliant. Always has been."

"Well, forget that 'Beatle or no' business!" Rita snickered, leaning in, conspiratorially. "Do tell, Cynthia — what's it like, sleepin' with a Beatle, eh?"

Cynthia blushed, but her visage grew soft and full of memory. For a moment, sipping wine and searching for the ever-intangible *le mot juste*, she stared out over the harbour.

"Well," she finally began, "it's rather complex. Or perhaps, 'multi-faceted' might be a better term. Some night, yes…there's passion. Other nights — like the evening John wrote 'You're Going to Lose That Girl' — he unexpectedly bounced out of bed at 2 or 3 in the morning and then sat up 'til dawn, scribbling lyrics and playing the piece over and over. Sometimes, when that happens, I sit with him, dress-making or turning up a hem."[1603]

"And at *other times*?" Rita arched a meaningful eyebrow.

"Well," Cynthia smiled, "we do have a young son, you know…one who regularly rises early, full of vigour and vim. So, one of us has to rise as well and keep things quiet. If John hasn't a morning engagement, he'll lie in 'til well after lunch. So…I'm in charge…"[1604]

"Wives and mothers!" Deirdre commiserated. "We must be all things to all people."

"Yes, I wish…" Cynthia trailed off, watching the failing sun splay tangerines and midnight blues across the quay. "I wish the two roles didn't overlap. When John says, 'Dance with me, gerl!' I wish I could dance with him forever.[1605] And when he shouts down, 'Cyn, what are you doin'? Come listen to this!' I wish I had *nothing* to do but listen."[1606] Deirdre and Rita nodded, empathetically. "But unfortunately, I often do. We all do! And it's…well, as I said before, it's complex."

Beckoning the waiter over, Deirdre requested the check, and as final light frittered away, the three began gathering their belongings.

"Frustratin'…that's what it is," Rita observed, slipping into her slight Scouse accent.

"Right yes, frustrating." Deirdre agreed.

"But what I *should* have said much earlier, Deirdre," Cynthia went on, "is that John feels much the same about Dick. I mean, initially he and the other Beatles wanted to work with 'Mr. Lester' because they'd heard of his film with the Goons.[1607] And anyone who got on with Spike Milligan and Peter Sellers was de facto 'de gear,' as Scousers say."

"Garston here, y' know!"[1608] Rita confessed, raising a hand.

"Really?" Cynthia laughed. "I'm 'silver-spoon-Hoylake.'"

"Now *there's* a complete surprise!" Rita sputtered, throwing her eyes to the heavens. Cynthia's prim accent always gave her away.

"De Gear Dick Lester." Deirdre considered. "Hmmm, I like the sound of that!"

"Yes," Cynthia smiled widely, "the Goon connection was definitely a tremendous first impression on John. But after only a few days working with Dick on 'A Hard Day's Night,' John was genuinely impressed with…well, with everything about his new, celebrated director. He told me about Dick entering an American university at age fifteen and graduating in psychology at nineteen…"[1609]

"All true," Deirdre nodded.

"…but above all, John raved about Dick's ingenious, creative way of editing that John swore was *the making* of that first film…and will be with 'Help!' as well, I'm sure."[1610]

"Editing!" Deirdre forced swollen feet into her shoes and steadied herself on the table. She stood gingerly. "It's Dick's obsession! I'm not sure he's ever enjoyed being a director. Not really. But he absolutely *adores* editing! It's the one part of the job to which he looks forward."[1611]

"Well, according to John," Cynthia hoisted her bags and followed the others onto the busy walkway, "that obsession is the salvation of The Beatles. John says it's the only thing that makes them look as if they can act!"

"Oh, I'm not sure *that's* accurate…" Deirdre chuckled.

"No, no, wait!" Rita quickly agreed. "I second that for me as well! And it's *exactly* why I think 'The Knack' will take the *Palme d'Or* next week. Not because of me, although I'm not bad!" She fluttered the long eyelashes that framed her large, lovely eyes. "Not because of Donal Donnelly, either. Or Ray Brooks. Or even Michael Crawford![1612] It's the clever editing that'll win the day, y' know. It's 'all Dick,' as they say."

"Rita!"

"Dear girl!"

And giggling mischievously, the three wives and mothers linked arms and put their heads together. Whilst all across Cannes, countless lights were frizzing and sparking to life, the lovely trio made their way back to the hotel — and back to the much-debated and talented men they loved.

Dick Lester in 1966 on the set of "How I Won the War"
A Certain Cinema Gallery, Public Domain,
https://commons.wikimedia.org/w/index.php?curid=31388004

Notes!

"The Knack...and How to Get It" did, indeed, win the 1965 Cannes Film Festival Palme d'Or *the following week. And Lester's brilliant, unique form of editing — a precursor to the music video — went on to win him acclaim for "How I Won the War" (1966) with Michael Crawford, Roy Kinnear, and John Lennon. He also garnered high praise for "A Funny*

Thing Happened on the Way to the Forum" (1966) with Zero Mostel, Phil Silvers, Michael Crawford, Roy Kinnear, Buster Keaton, and many others. And in 1980, his "Superman II" with Christopher Reeve, Gene Hackman, and Margot Kidder was considered a work of cinematic art.

I highly recommend that you see "The Knack...and How to Get It." It's available on many streaming services online. The similarities to "A Hard Day's Night" and "Help!" (including shared actors and actresses Peter Copley, John Bluthal, Bruce Lacey, and others) will keep you engrossed. There's even a line about what "it takes to fill the Albert Hall." But most of all, pay attention to the unique editing style of Richard Lester.

In his book, How to Read a Film: Movies, Media, and Beyond, *author James Monaco aptly observes: "The lively 1960s films of Richard Lester — especially his musicals, 'A Hard Day's Night' (1964), 'Help!' (1965), and 'A Funny Thing Happened on the Way to the Forum' (1966) — popularized jump cuts, rapid and 'ungrammatical' cutting. Over time, his brash editorial style became a norm, now celebrated every night around the world, in hundreds of music videos on MTV and in countless commercials." (p. 543)*

Sources:

Lewisohn, The Complete Beatles Chronicle, *194.*
Harry, The Ultimate Beatles Encyclopedia, *388-389.*
Harry, The Encyclopedia of Beatles People, *197-198.*
Winn, Way Beyond Compare, *320.*
Yule, 27-28, 78-93, and 142.
Lennon, Cynthia, John, *166-170.*
Womack, The Beatles Encyclopedia, *Vol. 2, 535-536.*
Everett, The Beatles as Musicians: The Quarry Men Through Rubber Soul, *296.*
Miles, The Beatles' Diary, *Vol. 1, 196.*
Spitz, 555.
Hill, John, Paul, George & Ringo, *199 and 203.*
Hill, The Beatles: Unseen Archives, *149.*
Hill, Images of The Beatles, *110.*
Wells, Simon, The Beatles: 365 Days, *24 May 1965. (There are no page numbers in this book. The date suffices.)*
Robertson, Lennon, *40.*
Monaco, James, How to Read a Film: Movies, Media, and Beyond, *543.*

The transcription of the Griffin/Lennon/Lester interview was carefully completed by Suzie Duchateau (with additional Help! from Rande Kessler). Suzie is my partner in the compilation of the Beatles Interviews website: https://www.beatlesinterviews.org

https://tinyurl.com/y4thbwcv This is the official trailer for "The Knack...and How to Get It." You can see Rita Tushingham, Donal Donnelly, and Michael Crawford in it, as well as witnessing Richard Lester's cutting-edge style of editing for which he is so justly famous. To quote Walter Everett, "...it is acclaimed as one of Britain's funniest-ever films." (The Beatles as Musicians: The Quarry Men Through Rubber Soul, 296)

https://ifitshipitshere.blogspot.com/2009/05/cannes-film-festival-classic-cannes.html This website gives the history of the Cannes Film Festival with numerous photos of Palme d'Or winners. The photo of Merv Griffin and John Lennon is on this site.

https://www.beatlesbible.com/1965/05/25/john-lennon-interview-cannes/ This website gives information about John and Cynthia Lennon's trek to the Cannes Film Festival, 1965.

https://64.media.tumblr.com/0a4446caf625db8a45b16340ffe42562/tumblr_n5anvhmjwp1twx1pfo1_400.jpg This is a photo of John, Cynthia, and Dick Lester at the airport for the excursion to the Cannes Film Festival. It's interesting to note that John and Cynthia are clearly front and centre, whilst Lester lags behind, although he is the "star" of the event. NOTE: The photo in Wells's The Beatles: 365 Days shows both Walter Shenson and Dick Lester behind John and Cynthia. Acess that photo using the date.

https://www.imdb.com/title/tt2126123/ This is the IMDb synopsis of the 12 June 1965 "Merv Griffin Show," which was in syndication on Westinghouse in 1965. This episode features Griffin's interview with John Lennon.

https://www.imdb.com/title/tt2126123 This website gives all the data concerning John's appearance on "The Merv Griffin Show." It was broadcast on 1 June 1965.

https://www.collectorsweekly.com/stories/265052-john-lennon-on-merv-griffin-show-1965 This is an original 1965 advertisement promoting John on "The Merv Griffin Show." A photo of John and Merv together for the Cannes interview is also exhibited.

https://www.imdb.com/name/nm0504513/bio This website provides professional and biographical information about Richard Lester, whose real name is Richard Lester Liebman.

https://www.imdb.com/title/tt0059274/ This website supplies information on Sean Connery in "The Hill," one of the films in competition at the 1965

Cannes Film Festival.

https://en.wikipedia.org/wiki/A_Hard_Day%27s_Night_(film)#cite_note-59 This website addresses the directing and editing style of Richard Lester.

https://en.wikipedia.org/wiki/Rita_Tushingham This website supplies professional and biographical information about Rita Tushingham.

http://ritatushingham.com/ This website supplies professional and biographical information about Rita Tushingham.

https://www.tasteofhome.com/recipes/socca/ This website supplies the history and recipe for socca, the famed chickpea flatbread from the Nice and Cannes region.

https://tinyurl.com/yyy2hups/ This website supplies information about the grapes, wines, and wineries of the French Riviera.

https://www.youtube.com/watch?v=Xg9xdleZD-M This is a home-recording (audio only) of the interview that John gives Merv Griffin in Cannes on 24 May for a June broadcast on "The Merv Griffin Show." Or use this QR code:

https://www.youtube.com/watch?v=iw-97CkA5NE This is a video snippet of John being interviewed by Merv Griffin. Thanks to **Joe Johnson of Beatle Brunch** *for sending me this clip! Or use this QR code:*

[1573] Winn, 320.

[1574] Wells, May 24, 1965. On this page, you can see John and Cynthia at the airport in Cannes, with both Walter Shenson and Dick Lester behind them.

Wells identifies them both. I double-checked the photo, and indeed, Shenson was there.

[1575] Winn, 320.

[1576] Yule, 87 and https://en.wikipedia.org/wiki/The_Knack_...and_How_to_Get_It. Yules says, "Lester managed a quick visit to the festival, accompanied by John and Cynthia Lennon, a week before the results were announced."

[1577] Yule, 78.

[1578] https://en.wikipedia.org/wiki/The_Knack_...and_How_to_Get_It

[1579] In Alf Bicknell's book, there is no mention of Alf driving John and Cynthia to London airport.

[1580] https://64.media.tumblr.com/0a4446caf625db8a45b16340ffe42562/tumblr_n5anvhmjwp1twx1pfo1_400.jpg All descriptions of Cynthia's attire come from this photo from Tumblr.

[1581] https://64.media.tumblr.com/0a4446caf625db8a45b16340ffe42562/tumblr_n5anvhmjwp1twx1pfo1_400.jpg All descriptions of John's attire come from this photo from Tumblr.

[1582] https://www.imdb.com/title/tt0059319/ This website provides the stars and plot of "The Ipcress File" with Michael Caine that was in contention at the 1965 Cannes Film Festival.

[1583] https://www.imdb.com/title/tt0059274/ This website provides the plot and screen stars of "The Hill" with Sean Connery that was in contention at the 1965 Cannes Film Festival.

[1584] Yule, 87.

[1585] https://64.media.tumblr.com/0a4446caf625db8a45b16340ffe42562/tumblr_n5anvhmjwp1twx1pfo1_400.jpg You can see Dick Lester hanging back from the cameras as John and Cynthia exit the plane in Cannes.

[1586] Miles, *The Beatles' Diary, Vol. 1*, 195-196, Robertson, 40, Winn, 320 and https://www.imdb.com/title/tt2126123/. Several sources claim that American journalist Martin Agronsky flew to Cannes to conduct the interview for Griffin. However, there are photos (see the YouTube video below) that show Griffin interviewing John in Cannes in May 1965. Furthermore, Griffin's voice is heard on the audio tape. And Winn notes that "although the footage" of Griffin interviewing John "isn't circulating, a home-taped audio recording show what a playful mood the two were in." Here is a link to the YouTube audio recording: https://www.youtube.com/watch?v=Xg9xdIeZD-M

[1587] Spitz, 555. Spitz says that in May 1965, "Aside from a brief holiday abroad the last week in May, Brian filled all their 'spare time' with non-stop, frivolous radio and TV appearances, to 'plug' the latest single, 'Ticket to Ride' and to boost anticipation for the forthcoming film. Otherwise, there was precious little contact with the outside world."

[1588] https://www.beatlesbible.com/1965/05/25/john-lennon-interview-cannes/

[1589] https://www.youtube.com/watch?v=Xg9xdIeZD-M This YouTube "video" provides the photograph of Merv and John as well as the audio of Merv

Griffin's interview with John Lennon in Cannes, 24 May 1965. You can see the delicatessen-café in the background, and Dick Lester's presence is noted.
[1590] https://www.youtube.com/watch?v=Xg9xdIeZD-M This is the interview between Merv Griffin and John Lennon conducted on 24 May 1965. I am not going to endnote every sentence, but will endnote again at the end. Thank you to Suzie Duchateau and Rande Kessler for hours of work, transcribing this interview.
[1591] Who is the "Unidentified Man"? It might have been Walter Shenson, and the man *does* respond as if he's one of John's familiars. He's not a cameraman or any part of Griffin's crew because Griffin doesn't know him. However, if the man is Walter Shenson, why didn't John introduce him to Merv Griffin when he introduces Dick Lester? The same question arises if the man is Mal Evans or Neil Aspinall. Surely John would have introduced them. Very strange.
[1592] https://www.youtube.com/watch?v=Xg9xdIeZD-M This is the last line of the interview between Merv Griffin and John Lennon conducted on 24 May 1965. This last line is very garbled, and I can clearly hear, "…the book" but the first word of the sentence is unintelligible. I have guessed, in light of everything else that John has said, that he leaves Merv with the admonition, "Plug the book." That first word may be inaccurate.
[1593] Yule, 80-81. There is an excellent photo of Rita Tushingham, who stars as Nancy in "The Knack" and has accompanied the Lesters, the Lennons, and Walter Shenson on this weekend trip to Cannes.
[1594] https://www.tasteofhome.com/recipes/socca/ This website supplies the history and recipe for socca, the famed chickpea flatbread from the Nice and Cannes region.
[1595] https://tinyurl.com/yyy2hups This website gives detailed information about the wineries, grapes, and wines of the French Riviera.
[1596] Yule, 142.
[1597] Yule, 142. Direct quote from Dick Lester.
[1598] Yule, 142. Direct quote from Dick Lester.
[1599] Lennon, Cynthia, *John*, 167.
[1600] https://en.wikipedia.org/wiki/Rita_Tushingham Rita Tushingham married photographer Terry Bicknell in 1962, and they had two daughters.
[1601] Yule, 83. Direct quote from Dick Lester.
[1602] Yule, 142. Direct quote from Dick Lester.
[1603] Lennon, Cynthia, *John*, 168.
[1604] Lennon, Cynthia, *John*, 170.
[1605] Lennon, Cynthia, *John*, 166.
[1606] Lennon, Cynthia, *John*, 167.
[1607] Harry, *The Encyclopedia of Beatles People*, 197, Harry, *The Ultimate Beatles Encyclopedia*, 388, Womack, *The Beatles Encyclopedia, Vol. 2*, 535, and https://www.imdb.com/name/nm0504513/bio Cynthia is referring to "The Running Jumping & Standing Still Film" that Lester made with Sellers and Milligan in 1959.
[1608] https://en.wikipedia.org/wiki/Rita_Tushingham
[1609] Yule, 27-28, Harry, *The Encyclopedia of Beatles People*, 197, Womack, *The Beatles Encyclopedia, Vol. 2*, 535, and

https://www.imdb.com/name/nm0504513/bio Lester's university degree is in clinical psychology from the University of Pennsylvania.

[1610] https://www.imdb.com/name/nm0504513/bio This is one of the best biographies of Richard Lester. Lester's editing style for both "Help!" and "A Hard Day's Night" is credited as being the forerunner of what later became the music video.

[1611] https://www.imdb.com/name/nm0504513/bio Interviewed by Stephen Soderberg in 1999, for a book called *Getting Away with It*, Dick Lester admitted that he "had never actually enjoyed being a film director, although he did enjoy the editing process."

[1612] https://tinyurl.com/y4thbwcv This is the official trailer for "The Knack…and How to Get It." You can see Rita Tushingham, Donal Donnelly, Ray Brooks, and Michael Crawford in this 3:43 clip and glimpse Lester's brilliant editing at work.

Tuesday, 26 May 1965
NEMS Offices
Argyll Street
London

Brian suffered an uneasy dichotomy each time The Beatles lent weeks at a stretch to a United Artists film. He thrilled to the knowledge that his boys now were much-admired "stars of stage and screen." He welled up over "A Hard Day's Night" being dubbed "the Citizen Kane of jukebox musicals."[1613] Brian loved knowing that the film's popularity had required over 1,600 film prints simultaneously and that it had grossed over $20,000 at the box office, in the first week alone.[1614] But the dearth of The Beatles' live appearances during the eleven weeks[1615] of filming troubled him. Fans were fickle, and their memories, short-lived. Brian ached to propel John, Paul, George, and Ringo back into the public eye.

Granted, Sean O'Mahoney was doing an exceptional job with photos, news stories, and private glimpses of "The Fab Four" via his *Beatles Monthly* magazine. But the publication was strongly U.K.-based and had never truly influenced the U.S. market.[1616] *Datebook* had done its part to energize American teen-fans, but the publication failed to sway the young adult market. Thus, "Ticket to Ride" — one of The Beatles' strongest and most innovative musical offerings to date[1617] — had only topped the U.S. charts for one week.[1618]

One week! Brian sighed.

Now with Elvis Presley reclaiming his familiar Number One slot for "Crying in the Chapel," Brian's left eyelid had, annoyingly, begun to twitch again.

"Out of sight, out of mind," the thirty-year-old manager reprimanded himself. "It's imperative...I *must* get the boys back out there!"

So, on Wednesday, 26 May, Brian personally escorted The Beatles to London's Piccadilly Studios for their fifty-second and final BBC appearance.[1619] Having sung over 268 songs on various British Broadcasting Corporation programmes over the last few years,[1620] the boys had become fond, familiar fixtures. But truthfully, the long-running programmes that John, Paul, George, and Ringo popularized had now run their useful course. Even the name of today's *Light Programme* offering — "From Us to You" — was clearly outmoded.[1621] In fact, the boys had rigidly stipulated that the "Beeb"[1622] update the series moniker; tonight's recorded show would be now called "The Beatles (Invite You to Take a Ticket to Ride)."[1623]

Publicity guru Tony Barrow exhaled heavily, hopelessly pointing out that the new name was unpoetic, clumsy, and tedious. But John, who ordinarily cared about such things, only down-curled his mouth and lifted a shoulder in *ennui*. And the others agreed. The Beatles were consummately bored with repetitions of the past and would accept almost anything new and different in its place.[1624] 1965, they felt, was shaping up to be one long succession of things already seen, heard, tasted, and experienced.

Brian realised it. Because The Beatles were dear friends and not just clients,[1625] he could read their thoughts. Lately, their faces had been lined with malaise, dissatisfaction. And Brian feared that this evening's appearance would be no exception.

Performing "Ticket to Ride," "Everybody's Trying to Be My Baby," "I'm a Loser," "The Night Before," "Honey Don't," "Dizzy Miss Lizzy," and "She's A Woman"…promoting their single, the upcoming film, and the new Capitol release *Beatles VI*,[1626] the lads had a lot on the line. Yet Brian fretted that they would did so without relish — that they would treat this evening's performance off-handedly.

However, during The Beatles' opening number, "Everybody's Trying to Be My Baby," George fought a smirk. Cutting his eyes impishly at the camera, the boy brashly substituted "everydobby" for "everybody."[1627] And the game was on! John followed suit, purposely bungling the lyrics to "I'm A Loser" by singing, "Beneath this wig, I am wearing a tie."[1628] Then, Ringo extemporized with a whimsical "ba-bop-ba-ba-ba" scat in "Honey Don't."[1629]

Ringo Starr, 1965
Photograph from Wikimedia Commons

Even Paul flirted with a bit of illicit amusement by singing, "I know that she's no pheasant," in "She's A Woman."[1630] If there was no fun to be had on the sanctioned diary, well then, The Beatles reckoned, they would fashion their own!

Even their interview with Denny Piercy (the drummer for Bob Miller and his Miller Men, who was sitting in for long-time BBC host Brian Matthew) was slathered in Beatle banter.[1631]

Denny Piercy: One big question right now…the film.
Paul: (Arching an eyebrow) Yes?
John: (To Piercy) Yeah, that's not a question.[1632]

Then…

Piercy: What's the story behind the title?
Paul: Well, it's just they're tryin' to get Ringo's ring — the baddies, y' see…'n we're the goodies!
Piercy: Are you sort of a Double-O-Seven, Ringo?
Ringo: No, no. (Chuckling) I'm a sort of a *double entendre*![1633]
(The boys fell over in guffaws.)

    At first, the BBC affair was "Beatles as usual," chockfull of amusement. But as the long afternoon and evening wore on, the boys' giddy *joie de vivre* frittered away. Their faces grew stoic; their enthusiasm dulled. Watching from the wings and digging his nails into his palms, Brian tried not to panic.
    The all-important European Tour lay just ahead of them, and Brian prayed that in Paris or Genoa or Milan or Madrid or Rome, the boys who had once prized their time together on the boards would re-emerge. As one of their favourite former Cavern numbers had once advised, they needed a "shot of rhythm and blues."[1634] They needed the old *mach schau*. The Beatles had lost their tolerance for "grins at nothing."

Notes!

There is no extant video of this show. However, you can hear the performances of "Dizzy Miss Lizzy" and "Ticket to Ride" on the Live at the BBC *CD.*

Here are individual performances of the remaining five recorded songs (audio only) from that taping on 26 May 1965 in Piccadilly Studios, London. The audio signal level causes a bit of distortion in places, but you can clearly hear the lyric alterations mentioned in this chapter.

https://tinyurl.com/yx8sgz7r "Everybody's Trying to Be My Baby"

https://tinyurl.com/yyfju8cj "I'm a Loser"

https://tinyurl.com/y3wwvafd "The Night Before"

https://tinyurl.com/y67vhc5q "Honey Don't"
https://tinyurl.com/yxh5yz4r "She's a Woman"

Sources:

Lewisohn, The Complete Beatles Chronicle, *194.*
Lewisohn, The Beatles: Day by Day, *62.*
Epstein, A Cellarful of Noise, *115.*
Howlett, The Beatles at the BBC, *69.*
Miles, The Beatles' Diary, Vol. 1, *196.*
Winn, 320-321.
Coleman, The Man Who Made The Beatles, *322.*
Buskin, The Complete Idiot's Guide to The Beatles, *170-171.*
Bicknell, 48.
Wiener, 48-49.
Schultheiss, 130-133.
Robertson, Lennon, *40.*
Burrows, Terry, John Lennon: A Life in Pictures, *65.*

https://en.wikipedia.org/wiki/A_Hard_Day%27s_Night_(film)This website gives the reviews of "A Hard Day's Night" cited in this chapter.

https://tinyurl.com/y36pamrb This website gives a thorough history of "Ticket to Ride."

https://www.beatlesbible.com/1965/05/26/beatles-final-bbc-radio-session/ This website also gives a concise summary of the events of 26 May 1965.

[1613] https://en.wikipedia.org/wiki/A_Hard_Day%27s_Night_(film) This is a direct quote from the *Village Voice*, 1964.
[1614] https://en.wikipedia.org/wiki/A_Hard_Day%27s_Night_(film)
[1615] Lewisohn, *The Complete Beatles Chronicle*, 184-193, Lewisohn, *The Beatles: Day by Day,* 59-62, Miles, *The Beatles' Diary, Vol. 1*, 190-196, Schultheiss, 130-133, and Robertson, *Lennon*, 39-40. The first "real" day of filming for "Help!" was 24 February 1965 and filming (for The Beatles) concluded on 11 May 1965.
[1616] Coleman, *The Man Who Made The Beatles*, 322.
[1617] Burrows, Terry, *John Lennon: A Life in Pictures*, 65. Burrows quotes John, who called "Ticket to Ride" "one of the earliest heavy metal songs ever made." And Burrows concurs, adding "Among the lesser fare on the flip side sat Paul McCartney's 'Yesterday.'"
[1618] https://www.stereogum.com/2008159/the-number-ones-the-beatles-ticket-to-ride/franchises/columns/the-number-ones/ This website gives an excellent history and appraisal of "Ticket to Ride."
[1619] Lewisohn, *The Complete Beatles Chronicle*, 194, Lewisohn, *The Beatles: Day by Day*, 62, Howlett, *The Beatles at the BBC*, 69, Winn, 321, Miles, *The Beatles' Diary, Vol. 1*, 196, Buskin, *The Complete Idiot's Guide to The Beatles*, 171, and Bicknell, 48. Lewisohn says this is The Beatles' 52nd BBC appearance; Winn says it is the 51st; and Howlett says, 53rd.

[1620] Winn, 321 and Wiener, 48-49. Wiener interestingly points out that "This was the last BBC show with songs especially recorded by The Beatles, the last in their series of five holiday specials, and the only one without the 'From Us to You' title. Their first BBC appearance had been on 'Teenagers Turn,' recorded March 7, 1962 and aired the following day."

[1621] Lewisohn, *The Complete Beatles Chronicle*, 194, Lewisohn, *The Beatles: Day by Day*, 62, Howlett, *The Beatles at the BBC*, 69, Winn, 321, and Miles, *The Beatles' Diary, Vol. 1*, 196. As Lewisohn observes, The Beatles insisted upon the title change for the programme because they didn't feel that "From Us to You" was "respresentative of their current image." (*The Beatles: Day by Day*, 62)

[1622] Buskin, *The Complete Idiot's Guide to The Beatles*, 170. Buskin explains that "The Beeb is an affectionate nickname given to the BBC," the British Broadcasting Corporation.

[1623] Lewisohn, *The Complete Beatles Chronicle*, 194, Lewisohn, *The Beatles: Day by Day*, 62, Howlett, *The Beatles at the BBC*, 69, Winn, 321, Robertson, *Lennon*, 40, Buskin, 171, and Miles, *The Beatles' Diary, Vol. 1*, 196.

[1624] Lewisohn, *The Complete Beatles Chronicle*, 194. Lewisohn observes that the new programme title, "an unimaginative decision, indicate[d] the degree of importance [The Beatles] now attached to this type of engagement."

[1625] Epstein, *A Cellarful of Noise*, 115. Brian says, "I believe...I will always be with The Beatles...because they are my friends."

[1626] Lewisohn, *The Complete Beatles Chronicle*, 194, Lewisohn, *The Beatles: Day by Day*, 62, Howlett, *The Beatles at the BBC*, 69, Winn, 321, and Miles, *The Beatles' Diary, Vol. 1*, 196.

[1627] Winn, 321.

[1628] Winn, 321.

[1629] https://tinyurl.com/y67vhc5q This is Ringo singing "Honey Don't" on the 26 May recording of "The Beatles (Invite You to Take a Ticket to Ride)" for the BBC's Light Programme.

[1630] https://tinyurl.com/yxh5yz4r This is Paul singing "She's A Woman" on the 7 June 1965 airing of "The Beatles (Invite You to Take a Ticket to Ride) on the BBC's *Light Programme*. You can hear the "she's a pheasant" line. Paul also says, "My love, don't buy me presents" instead of "give me presents.'

[1631] Howlett, *The Beatles at the BBC*, 69 and https://tinyurl.com/y36pamrb.

[1632] Howlett, *The Beatles at the BBC*, 69. This three-line clip from the 26 May 1965 interview is found in Howlett's book.

[1633] Howlett, *The Beatles at the BBC*, 69. This four-line clip from the 26 May 1965 interview is found in Howlett's book.

[1634] https://en.wikipedia.org/wiki/A_Shot_of_Rhythm_and_Blues The Terry Thompson song "Shot of Rhythm and Blues" was a staple for The Beatles in The Cavern, with John performing extraordinary lead vocals. You can hear the boys deliver the number on *Live at the BBC* here: A Shot Of Rhythm And Blues (Live At The BBC For "Pop Go The Beatles" / 27th August, 1963) - Bing video

June 1965

Chart Toppers

"Crying in the Chapel" — Elvis Presley
"I Can't Help Myself (Sugar Pie, Honey Bunch)"
— The Four Tops
"Mr. Tambourine Man" — The Byrds

In The News

3-7 June: Gemini 4 is launched and safely returned to Cape Canaveral, Florida, causing NASA to predict "a moon shot by mid-1968." This historic flight included the first "space walk" by Ed White.

10 June: Pope Paul VI praises "the great mind" of Galileo Galilei, 350 years after the Catholic Church accused him of heresy for the concept of the earth orbiting around the sun.

11 June: Allen Ginsberg and Lawrence Ferlinghetti (amongst others) are selected to read to a crowd of 7,000 people in the Albert Hall's "Poets of The World, Poets of Our Time" exposition.

22 June: U.S. Secretary of Defense Robert McNamara announces that 22,000 additional soldiers will be deployed to join the 50,000 U.S. soldiers already fighting in Vietnam. On 26 June, General Westmoreland is given *carte blanche* to supply additional soldiers as needed.[1635]

Tuesday, 1 June 1965
Kenwood
Weybridge, Surrey

John sat up and squinted at the Smiths De Luxe folding alarm clock from Mendips[1636] with bleary eyes.

2.45 p.m.! Ugh! Feels like mid-mornin'! John collapsed back into the beckoning pillows and drew the blankets around his neck. *Five more minutes...that's all I ask.* He closed his eyes against the familiar ache of depression, clenched his jaw at the muted sounds of ordinary life going on downstairs.

With Paul and Jane off on holiday in Albufeira, Portugal,[1637] and Ringo and Maureen relishing marital bliss, he and Cyn had been taking in the London nightclubs with George and Pattie. And whereas it was "fanfuggin'tastic" being out as late as he wanted with the old friends he "rarely got to see anymore" — talking about books and ideas and music and politics — John was drained. As long as it lasted, pot was revitalizing, exhilarating. But when it fled, cannabis left John depleted.[1638]

He took a deep breath and held it, trying to find his equilibrium. If memory served, and John was afraid it did, he was also cross from a small hours quarrel with Cyn during the long ride home.[1639]

What they'd argued about, he wasn't sure, but John remembered the odd, shouted phrase, and none of it was good. Bickering, battling, snarling at one another — it was getting to be a way of life for them lately. Cyn blamed drugs for their growing discord. John blamed everything and everyone else, insisting that drugs alone upheld him.

Edging back the covers, he sat up cautiously, felt for his slippers, and patted the bedstand for his glasses.

"You simply *cannot* refuse, John!" he remembered Cyn

admonishing. "This time, I don't *care* what you want! You have to think of someone else besides yourself! Because you know, as well as I do, that the others'll follow your lead![1640] They always have, and they always will…I think."

And suddenly, John recalled the whole sordid debate — the controversy that had been driving him 'round the bend for the last few weeks.

To MBE or not to MBE. ***That*** *is the question!* he thought.

The invitation to accept Queen Elizabeth's honourary designation of The Beatles as Members of the Most Excellent Order of the British Empire had been a sticky wicket since Brian had learned of it, back in early May.[1641] The manager — hives blotching his neck and a fevered look to his aspect — had shown up quite unexpectedly one afternoon in Twickenham Studios.[1642]

"We must speak in the dressing room,"[1643] Epstein had uttered urgently to John. "As soon as possible."

"Right this way, then." John had cut his eyes questioningly at Paul, who had only shrugged and followed along. George and Ringo had lifted their eyebrows in response, as if to say, "Your guess is as good as mine." None of them had had an inkling.

Finally, after a long, dramatic pause, Brian had revealed the source of his mysterious ecstasy.[1644] "I've news for you," he'd smiled curiously, "the Prime Minister and the Queen have awarded you…an MBE!"[1645]

"MBE?" Ringo had repeated. "What's that? A sports car?"[1646]

"It's…it's a *very* significant honour…" Brian had sputtered, confounded by their unanimous looks of broad apathy.

"Does it involve a reduction of taxes?" Harrison had suggested, hopefully. "Or better yet, a complete exemption, as it were?"[1647]

"Surely you…*ugh*!" Brian had blinked, unbelievingly, and shook his head. "It's an award from the Crown for distinguished service to the country! Yours specifically, and I quote, is for 'great commercial advantage,' based upon the sale of 115 million records."[1648]

"Oh, the MBE! That ole thing!" John had laughed it off.

"It's the Most Excellent Order of the British Empire, right?" Paul had tried to minimize Brian's chagrin.

"Yes," Brian had desperately scanned the four faces in front of him for any hint of enthusiasm, "and it's one of only *five* honourary awards for distinguished service to Great Britain presented by the Queen…an honour bestowed only twice annually, once on the New Year and once again, on her birthday."[1649]

"'N whichever one have *we* landed, eh?" John had grinned toothily. Every son of England knew that Queen Elizabeth's birthday fell in June, only weeks away.

"I assure you; this is no laughing matter!" Brian had articulated precisely. "It would mean a great deal to us on a global platform,[1650] conferring prodigious dignity and credibility. Promoting sales. But most of all, elevating you from mere rock'n'rollers to the realm of respected musicians."

"Would it, now?" John had glanced at the others. "'N what if we don't *want* to be somethin' other than 'mere rock'n'rollers,' Eppy? What then? What if that's all we've ever wanted to be, from the very start, eh?"[1651]

That first afternoon's clash had instigated a month of fiery back-and-forth deliberations. Brian was anxious that the boys accept the offer; John was equally reluctant.[1652] He saw the royal nod as contradictory to everything he believed in.[1653]

"It's not us — this award," he'd continued to argue. "Look, I'm fuggin' embarrassed by it![1654] Rock'n'roll's the very *antithesis* of smug, comfortable, upper middle-class values!"[1655]

"Well, we *have* done a 'service to exports,' John,"[1656] Paul had pointed out, logically, "which is precisely why they're applaudin' us, right? I mean, we *are* a big part of why there's a Swingin' London, after all,[1657] 'n we've definitely furthered tourism and bolstered 'the economic upswing,' as they say. So…"

"I think a grateful government must've given us the MBE for all the taxes we've paid!"[1658] John had quipped.

"He's not far wrong about that." George had nodded.

"Our accountants can certainly vouch for it!" Ringo had said.

"Well, if y' ask me," George had offered, "it's good ole Harold Wilson we have to thank for all this! He likes us, does Harold! Up the Pool 'n all that, y' know!"[1659]

Prime Minister Wilson had, indeed, been M.P. from Liverpool in days not long past. And he'd never forgotten his roots.[1660] But Wilson's nomination of The Beatles to the Queen had much more to do with pounds than provincial pride.[1661] The Beatles had been short-listed for their very obvious contribution to England's burgeoning economy. Though Wilson admittedly owned an attraction to the music industry,[1662] to show business and theatre personalities,[1663] money was his bottom line.[1664]

"Well, what do y' think?" John had finally posed the inevitable question to the others towards the end of May. "Let's turn it down, eh? It's all daft."[1665]

"Yeah, I personally worry for the Queen's sanity when I think of it,"[1666] Ringo had grinned. "Me...with an MBE!"

"What's next?" George had droned, "*Sir* Richard Starkey?"

"Sir Paul MacArtrey!" John scoffed.

The boys had sniggered, bandying insults and taking the mickey out of one another. But still, they had no clear-cut answer to the tricky publicity nightmare that the award had promulgated. And with every passing day since, Brian had grown more annoyed and vexed at their hesitancy.

"We *must* send word that you're accepting the honour," the manager had hissed on the last day of filming. "There's no possible excuse for this ongoing delay. I *must* respond forthwith!"

Now, wrapping his terrycloth robe around him and opening the bedroom door, John gnawed the inside of his cheek nervously. He'd been asked by the others to ring Brian this afternoon with the group's acceptance of the proffered MBEs. But in his heart of hearts, John still felt it...insincere.

Just one more way of fuggin' "selling out" to be a Beatle,[1667] he sighed as he shuffled into the kitchen. But Cynthia had been absolutely correct last night. If he refused the honour, well then, Paul, George, and Ringo would do so as well. And the others were definitely pleased.[1668]

Who 'm I to speak for the group as a whole...or a hole? John heaved a sigh, rattling through cupboards to alert his wife that he was awake and hungry. *If they're all up for these fuggin' medals 'n mornin' suits, then I suppose I can go along as well.*

John resolved to ring Brian after breakfast and accept the Queen's unwarranted award...for the sake of public relations. But he still thought it hypocritical[1669] — and the absolute wrong decision.

****

Saturday, 12 June 1965
Twickenham Studios
St. Margarets
Twickenham

Brian was well aware of John's antipathy to the MBE, and he was grateful that John had seen past his personal reservations to do "the right thing." However, wary of John's mercurial nature, Brian had asked Paul to cut his Portuguese holiday short and return to England for the official press announcement of The Beatles' royal recognition. He needed Paul's vivacity and charisma.[1670]

The boys had gathered early in Twickenham Studios, under the guise of watching the first rough cut of "Help!" together.[1671] But they were, undeniably, kitted out for a press conference: Paul, in dark slacks, a brown tweed jacket, crisp, white shirt, and umber tie; Ringo, in a black wool suit with black turtleneck; George, in a similar black suit with an expensive, grey cashmere polo;[1672] and John? John was noticeably absent.

"I've rung him innumerable times!" Brian wrung his hands to Tony Barrow and Alf Bicknell. "He simply won't reply!"[1673]

"Surely...surely John's not going to object to this *publicly*!" Tony was anxious as well. "Not after he agreed to go along with it!"

"Oh, I assure you he is *not!*" Brian drew the back of his hand across his lips.

"Shall I..." Alf began solicitously.[1674]

"No! No, I'm driving out to Weybridge *myself*!"[1675] Brian hissed. "Keep ringing him, Tony, and if he answers, tell him to be dressed when I arrive! And whatever you do, keep the press at bay until we return."

****

In years to come, John would tell the story this way: "I set the alarm for eight o'clock, and then I just lay there. I thought, 'Well, if anyone wants me, they'll phone me.' The phone went lots of times, but that's the one I never answer. My own phone didn't go at all…so I just lay there."[1676]

****

2.40 p.m.[1677]

By the time John arrived in Twickenham, news cameras were everywhere. The Beatles' acceptance of the MBE was splashed abroad. Alf Bicknell was waiting to strongarm the frothing horde away from the Twickenham doorway. Cameras clicked above greedy shouts of inquiry. John, who was in no mood to be amenable, stared blankly at the throng and said nothing.

He wore a rumpled black suit and a grey shirt, unbuttoned at the neck — no tie. Despite an upbraiding from Brian, John's hair was unkempt.[1678] He looked exactly as if he had just tumbled out of bed.

"If you've decided to do this, *and you have*," Brian had lectured him on the way over, "then do it with graciousness and aplomb, John. The others are depending on you."

John had no reply. He set his mouth in a determined, thin line. Inwardly however, he had screamed, *Yeah? Well, what about* me*? What about what* I *want for a fuggin' change, Eppy?! What about the humiliation I've endured for years…the fuggin' Foyles Literary debaucle? The Washington Embassy where we were treated like caged primates? The signin's where I was told how to sign 'n what to sign, 'n where to sign 'n reminded that the soddin' buyers never imagined purchasin' somethin' like that from someone like me!? What about the inane fuggin' interviews, Brian? Or the days where I worked ('n still work!) from dawn to past fuggin' midnight? But who cares about that, right? As long as I'm a good boy 'n do what I'm told! Smile at the cameras, Johnny, and say what we tell y' to say…as long as* everyone else *gets what they want! Who fuggin' cares about* me*?*[1679]

But voicing none of this, John entered the studio that Tony Barrow had quickly assembled for the press conference.[1680] The Leader Beatle silently took his place next to George and nodded to the others. He spoke only to Alf, asking for a glass of water.[1681] And ignoring the look in John's eyes or the flush on his face, the press — about 150 reporters — began firing questions at The Beatles, one after another.[1682]

Reporter: How did you first learn you were getting the award?[1683]

George: Paul was looking through the pile of fan mail in our dressing room a few weeks back, and he came across this envelope that had "From the Prime Minister" written on it. It must have been there at least a coupla days. He opened it, and the letter said that he was bein' considered for an award and would he sign the enclosed form. We all said, "We wish we had one!" then dived through the rest of the mail and found we *did* have one — one each!

Paul: (Glancing coyly at the others) We thought MBE stood for Mr. Brian Epstein, because we always sign his contracts…because he's our manager.

Reporter: Why have you been honoured this way?

Ringo: (With a grin) Look at the dollars we've pulled in from America!

John: (With no grin) We've paid the government quite a bit in tax, don't you think?!

Second Reporter: Do you think you deserve the awards?

George: It's not up to us to say that. The Queen must've thought so, or she wouldn't't've given them to us, would she?

Third Reporter: What will you do with your medal?

George: Hang it on the wall.

Ringo: Tuck it around my neck.

Paul: Keep it in a safe place.

John: I think I'll have mine made into a bell push so that people have to press it when they come to the house…or I'll take it to an antique dealer and find out what it is.

Fourth Reporter: Do you think Cliff Richard should have got a medal, too?

George: Yes, a leather one with wooden strings.

Fifth Reporter: What do you think of Mr. Wilson?

George: We think of him what we always thought of him. He's a good lad![1684]

Throughout the afternoon, The Beatles were asked to give radio interviews[1685] for sources across the globe. Over and over, the boys answered the same questions, trying to state the limited facts of the matter in fresh, new ways.

Reporter: John, where do you plan to keep your MBE?
John: The smallest room in my house — m' study.
Reporter: And what do you think of receiving the honour?
John: I didn't know what an MBE *was* 'til I read it in the mornin' papers.[1686]

To another batch of newsmen, John responded, "I didn't think you could get it for this sort of thing. I thought you had to drive tanks 'n win wars 'n stuff."[1687]
Reporter: George, how do you feel about winning this great honour and being invited to walk in a State procession behind Peers of the Realm and hereditary knights?[1688]
George: (Ducking his head) I'm very honoured. I didn't think you could get this sort of thing for playin' rock'n'roll. Somebody told me I'm the youngest person ever to get the award!
Reporter: And what about you, Ringo?
Ringo: It's very nice 'n very unexpected. I'll keep the medal to wear when I'm old.[1689]
Reporter: Paul?
Paul: Oh, I think it's marvellous! What does that make my Dad?[1690]
(Laughter)
Reporter: And how about you, John? Did you know you could get an honour such as this for playing rock'n'roll?
John: (Exhaling smoke) I don't think we got our MBEs for rock'n'roll. On that basis, we'd have got OBEs. That is a higher award, 'n The Rolling Stones would have got MBEs. (Nervous chuckles from some of the press) I reckon we got them for exports...[1691]

After the wave of reporters had had their opportunity to pose questions and capture "snaps," the boys were surrounded by the various television news agencies for quick clips. First up was British Calendar News with host George Yateman[1692]:

George Yateman: Last month, seventy-five teenagers from Pennsylvania petitioned Her Majesty The Queen to have The Beatles knighted. This hasn't happened. But today, I'm pleased to say that they have been made members of the Most Honourable Order of the British Empire. Congratulations, John, George,

Ringo and Paul![1693]
Paul, George, and Ringo: Thanks!
John: (Very loudly) Thank you!
Yateman: (Turning to John) How did you all react to this?
John: Well, I went... (Gasp of surprise, his eyes wide) (Laughter)
Yateman: Which means, in "sound"?
John: (Without any expression) Whoopee.
Yateman: Well, done. George?
George: Well, I sort of went, "Wow! That's great!"
Paul: (Smiling and nodding) About the same.
Yateman: Ringo?
Ringo: Yes. (Looking to the others) I think we all felt pretty well the same.
Yateman: Now, last year in America, your records sold no less than ten million dollars' worth. Do you think your export sales have something to do with this?
Paul: Well, you know, somebody said it might have been that, but you never know. It *could* have been that...(He raises his left hand.) But it could have been...*that*! (He lifts his right hand.)
John: It might have been the tour in Australia!
George: (Giggles)
Yateman: Now, do you think you'll go back to the Commonwealth again? It was a sensational visit!
Paul: Yeah!
John: Well, y' know, we probably will. It's up to Mr. Epstein, our manager. (John flashes a Cheshire grin into the camera.) (The other Beatles chuckle.)
Yateman: What does this MBE mean to you all? How are you going to deck out to go to the palace? There's certain protocol to be observed. Are you going to dress up in morning dress?
John: Yes, well, I think you've got to, haven't you?
George: (Nodding) Yeah. We'll have to.
Yateman: What about the haircut, Ringo?
Ringo: (Looking concerned) Well, we're not gonna get it all cut off, y' know! Someone said we can carry the hats, so that'll be easier.
Paul: I think Her Majesty will understand, y' know.
Yateman: (Smiling) She may well do. (A slight pause) From obscurity in a cellar in Liverpool four years ago and now to

Buckingham Palace! Gentlemen, what do you think everybody on the other side of the Atlantic is going to say to this?

Paul: *Whoopee!!!* I hope.

(Laughter)

Paul: Y' never know. They might say "Boooo!" or...

John: They might say, uhm, "Hello, cobber."

Paul: (Giggles) Yeah.

Ringo: "Ullo dur, boys!"

Paul: (In his American accent) Or, "Howdy, Europe. Texas speakin'!"

Yateman: Now, two of you have gotten married, and you all live in good domestic splendor. Has this affected your writing, Paul and John?

Paul: (Shaking his head) No.

John: No, it's easier to write with cushions than on pieces of hard bench...

(Laughter)

John: Remember, we were on hard benches before we made it, in an unknown cellar in Liverpool, and it's much easier...on a nice cushion.

Yateman: What are your plans for tours for this year and next year?

Paul: We're going to Europe.

George: (Nodding) Next week.

Ringo: Next Sunday.

Paul: And then we come back, 'n then we go off to America!

Ringo: For two-and-a-half weeks.

Paul: ...and we do the telly.

Ringo: Oh! We do *Ed Sullivan*. Good old Ed!

Paul: Ed Sullivan. Hi, Ed! (Pointing into the camera) Look, he's watchin' — he's watchin' in this one. *Look! There he is!* All right, Ed.

(Giggling)

Paul: There's Mrs. Ed!

Ringo: (Peering into the camera) ...and Mister Ed!!

(The Beatles laugh at Ringo's allusion to the American sitcom about a talking horse.)

Yateman: Have you checked whether you'll be able to wear your MBEs on any of these other foreign television programmes?

John: Well, I suppose once they've given 'em to us, we can wear 'em.

Paul: (To John) Look a bit funny, though, goin' 'round with medals hanging off, wouldn't you?

John: (Shrugs) Well, we could wear 'em on stage.

Yateman: Anyway, it hasn't changed your life to any great extent?

John: No. (John sighs a bit.) We're just honoured. That's all.

Yateman: Well Beatles...we're all delighted. Congratulations again to the four of you![1694]

With only a minute's pause, ITV was given the opportunity to chat with The Beatles. John, who had spoken very infrequently during Yateman's interview, barely opened his mouth during this later chat with Richard Linley. He was bored of repeating the all-too-obvious facts. Bored.

Linley: Gentlemen, first of all, many congratulations on your MBE. The whole country seems very delighted indeed, but how do you feel about it, Paul?[1695]

Paul: (Nodding, his smile not quite as bright as earlier) Delighted indeed. You know, I'm glad everyone is delighted. I love it.

Linley: But I mean, (Watching the boys' faces) is it *fun* for you?

Paul: Yeah, of course. I mean, y' know. It'd be fun for you, wouldn't it, if you woke up one morning and they said, "Muh Buh Ehh!"?

(Laughter from the others)

Linley: Ringo, how did you first hear about it?

Ringo: Well, we heard about it six weeks ago when we got the forms to fill in. And then we knew that we were gonna get it two days ago, officially.

Linley: How did these forms come? Straight through the post, or in the fan mail, or what?

Ringo: Just in brown envelopes. They were delivered by somebody, y' know, by hand. I think one of Brian's secretaries...

George: (Cutting across Ringo) *I'll* tell you! They were sent from the Prime Minister at Downing Street to our manager's office, and they were delivered from there to Twickenham, where we were filmin', 'n then...

John: ...filmin' "Help!" our new film.

George: About a day later we just found them, 'n we thought we were bein' called up for the army...'n then we opened 'em, 'n we found out we weren't!

John: (To George) We already said that line.

George: (To John) I know, but this is ITV! *That* was the other one.

John: (Wearily) Oh, yeah. Ah, I see.

Linley: *Why* is the MBE awarded, though?

Paul: (Even Paul is fatigued at this point.) I don't know.

Ringo: (Shaking his head.) No idea.

Paul: In fact, I know nothin' about it...just that we've got it, 'n it's nice to have, 'n it doesn't make you "more respectable" or anythin', I don't think. Maybe other people think it does. It doesn't make *me* any more respectable. I'm still a scruff! (He grins mischievously.)

(A smattering of laughter from the others)

Linley: (Nodding) Well, I was wondering about that. Ringo, how do you feel about going to the palace in morning suit and all that?

Ringo: I don't mind, y' know. It's all right...when I buy one! (He smiles.)

Linley: (One eyebrow lifted) You haven't got one?

Ringo: No, not yet. I've got an evenin' suit, if that'll do.

Linley: (Smiles gently) I don't think it will.

Ringo: (Smiles back) Well, I'll just go in my pyjamas then![1696]
(They all chuckle)

After several intense hours of press conferences, interviews, appearances, and photos, The Beatles were finally excused for tea. Loosening ties and stretching, they pored over the folded newspaper that Tony Barrow handed them: "**SHE LOVES THEM! YEAH! YEAH! YEAH!**" the headlines proclaimed.[1697]

"Somehow," John stirred extra cream into his Earl Grey, "I doubt the Queen read through the 2,000 names that Mr. Wilson submitted to choose us!"[1698]

"Right," Paul took a cautious sip of the steaming brew, "but even if she didn't, I'm sure she realised, or was told, that we were included. After all, I would imagine it's a rather controversial move."

And so it was.

****

Monday, 14 June 1965
EMI Studios, Studio Two
St. John's Wood
London

Over the last few days, as indignant former MBE recipients had begun returning their awards to the Queen in upsurges of fury,[1699] The Beatles' nomination had erupted into front page news.

"Look, I understand!" George nodded, when they gathered in EMI on Monday for a recording session. "We're not a bit like that Coast Guard wack who was decorated for unusual bravery, are we?"[1700]

"Nor that war hero...that RAF Squadron Leader, Paul Pearson," Ringo sighed, "who says that if we get the honour, it makes the whole thing 'worthless.'"[1701]

"But that's *not true*, is it?!" Paul pointed out. "We have to remember that our award's for 'great commercial advantage in dollar earnings to this country.' And, when it comes right down to it, who's done more on that score then us, really? *Who*?!"

"Yeah, well, tell that to ole Donald Zec!" John spat, bitter. Zec, the *Mirror*'s entertainment reporter, was one of the few journalists John had always respected...and after their time together in the Bahamas, liked. But Zec's Sunday column had lashed out furiously at the Fab Four: "In the name of all that's sane, if not sacred, isn't pinning a royal medal onto four Beatles' jackets just too much? What about the Dave Clark Five, the Bachelors, the Animals, and the Rolling Stones?"[1702]

And from as far away as Canada, a member of Parliament, Hector Dupuis, had shipped back all twelve of his medals with a surly and highly-publicized note sniping, "English royalty places me on the same level as vulgar nincompoops!"[1703] John had never considered himself as "adorable" as Paul or as "approachable" as Ringo or as seemingly "enigmatic" as George, but he'd always viewed himself as brilliant. To be labeled a "vulgar nincompoop" was not without injury.

Every "Why us?" and "What for?" and "What have we done to deserve this?" that the others posed gigged John deeper. He'd asked himself the same thing for weeks.[1704] And the answer, he thought, was this: he hadn't wanted the ridiculous award, but he certainly deserved it. He was as smart, as talented, as hard-working, as industrious, and as capable as anyone else. He and The Beatles had earned this recognition. Every ounce of it.

But nothing hurt or terrified him as much as the highly-publicized letter from one 16-year-old American fan who returned her Beatles Fan Club membership card with a note that wept, "They've become *respectable*...and I don't want anything more to do with them!"[1705]

That pronouncement, for John, was a grim insult. And a dangerous trend.

Now, with eyes downcast and face impassive, he moved about Studio Two, prepping for a long afternoon of work. John focused, did this-and-that, answered questions, and tried to stay in the moment.

But time and again, he found himself back in the winter of 1961, sitting on the frozen cobblestones just outside The Grapes — refusing to join the extemporaneous party that The Beatles were throwing over the loose managerial arrangement they'd made with Brian Epstein. After some time, Paul had popped out into Mathew Street to locate John. And he'd sworn that Epstein wouldn't interfere, wouldn't alter The Beatles, wouldn't change who they were. Not really.

But even as the words had been spoken, John had known them to be false. John had realised that in order to succeed, The Beatles would *have* to transform, in ways big and small, in ways meaningless and life-changing. On that icy December night, John had known that he was selling out for the toppermost of the poppermost.[1706]

Now, he sighed, *the world knows it as well. It's all headline news. We've joined the ranks of the obedient and sanctioned. And in the process, we've lost our very souls.*

Notes!

Was John really afraid that he was selling out by accepting the MBE?

In a 1965 interview with Ray Coleman, John said that what "nagged away at him" was "the fear that The Beatles were no longer a rock'n'roll group" but were appealing to mothers and fathers. He stated, "...we seemed to be doing everything at once — getting older people interested in what we're doing as well as the young. But I don't like that." He went on to say, "It doesn't seem natural to see old people out there looking at us. They should be at home doing the knitting." (Lennon, 258)

In Lewisohn and Howlett's In My Life: John Lennon Remembered, *the two historians state, "[The MBE] was the ultimate seal of establishment approval for four smart-in-appearance yet scruffy-at-heart rock musicians from what had once been unfashionable Liverpool. The group — especially John — were somewhat embarrassed by the whole episode..." (p. 36)*

And in The Beatles Anthology, *John says very frankly, "We had to do a lot of selling out then. Taking the MBE was a sell-out for me." (p. 181)*

John must have been very *determined to turn the medal down because in* The Beatles Anthology, *John says that Brian admitted to him that if he rejected the honour, it would not be a tragedy. In fact, John quotes Brian as saying to him, "If you don't take it, nobody will ever know you refused." In making this grand concession, Brian must have been assuaging a* very *disturbed* John Lennon. *Brian was, in essence, giving John an "acceptable out" if John could not force himself to accept the award.*

Sources:

The Beatles, The Beatles Anthology, *181-183.*
Lewisohn, The Complete Beatles Chronicle, *180 and 194.*
Lewisohn and Howlett, *36.*
Lewisohn, The Beatles: Day by Day, *63.*
Harry, The Ultimate Beatles Encyclopedia, *444-445.*
Winn, *323.*
Lennon, Cynthia, John, *174.*
Davies, The Beatles, *207-208.*
Miles, The Beatles' Diary, Vol. 1, *197.*
Norman, Shout!, *246-247.*
Norman, John Lennon: The Life, *400.*
Badman, *158-159.*
Barrow, *147-148.*
Brown, Peter, *182.*
Brown, Craig, *272-275.*
Gould, *272-273.*
Frontani, The Beatles: Image and the Media, *84-85.*
Kenny, *171 and 174-177.*
Tremlett, *56-57.*

Connolly, 205.
Riley, Lennon, *278.*
Carlin, 116.
Robertson, Lennon, *40.*
Coleman, The Man Who Made The Beatles, *242-243.*
Coleman, Lennon, *258, 277-278, and 310.*
Bicknell, 49-50.
Hill, Images of The Beatles, *111. There is a photo of Paul returning*
from Portugal with the early MBE headlines already in the newspaper
that he holds in his hand.
Wells, June 12, 1965. (This book has no page numbers. Pages are
accessed by date.)
Wooton, Richard, John Lennon: An Illustrated Biography, *65-66.*

https://www.beatlesbible.com/1965/06/11/beatles-awarded-mbes/ This
website gives information about The Beatles' nomination to the MBE and
shows a photo of Paul returning from Portugal and holding the
newspaper announcing the honour.

https://www.beatlesbible.com/1965/06/12/press-conference-mbe-
announcement/ Here, the same website covers The Beatles' press
conference on 12 June 1965 concerning their upcoming MBE awards.

http://www.dmbeatles.com/interviews.php?interview=37 This website
supplies the television interviews from British Calendar News and ITV,
recorded on 12 June 1965.

https://www.youtube.com/watch?v=VfGapTHkLLs&t=47s This is the
YouTube video of The Beatles being interviewed by Richard Linley
regarding their MBE nomination on 12 June 1965.
Or use this QR code:

[1635] https://en.wikipedia.org/wiki/June_1965 This website details the events of
June 1965.
[1636]

https://www.retrowow.co.uk/retro_collectibles/clocks/smiths_travel_alarm_cl
ock.php The Smiths De Luxe folding alarm clock was sold in England in the
1950s and 60s. It had a nice leather travel case and was considered a "fine
timepiece." It was just the sort of thing Mimi would have thought John needed
when he entered Liverpool College of Art.

[1637] Lewisohn, *The Beatles: Day by Day*, 63.

[1638] Kenny, *The Making of John Lennon*, 176. Kenny wisely observes, "For John, the drug's mellowing effect provided the antidote to the unstoppable and rattling thoughts which caused his bouts of despondency and depression…" But Kenny recognizes that "the after effect of cannabis, besides bringing on fatigue, paranoia and anxiety, actually accentuated depression." (p. 178) Therefore, the use of the drug only intensified John's sadness.

[1639] We know that during this time, John and Cynthia were beginning to squabble. In fact, John is writing the very autobiographical song "It's Only Love," which he records in EMI on 18 June. ("Is it right that you and I should fight, every night?") One of the reasons that John always hated this song is that he found it embarrassing. It revealed the increasing struggles he was having in his marriage and unveiled his tender feelings towards Cynthia, despite their differences.

[1640] Kenny, 177. Kenny says that no matter how The Beatles insisted that there was no leader, "The other members could keep their heads down, if they chose, but John couldn't, or wouldn't. Despite Paul's allusions to group democracy, John was the one who was seen as the leader of the group."

[1641] Spitz, 556. Spitz gives a history of the honourary MBE designation and explains its significance. Very interesting reading. He also is clear that "in early May," 1965, Brian received a telephone call notifying him that The Beatles were going to receive the honour

[1642] The Beatles, *The Beatles Anthology*, 181 and Spitz, 556. Paul McCartney states that Brian arrived in Twickenham Studios behaving "secretively" and Spitz notes that "despite Brian's usual afffectations," the manager was still acting as if "something extraordinary was in the offing."

[1643] The Beatles, *The Beatles Anthology*, 181 and Spitz, 556. Direct quote from Brian Epstein.

[1644] The Beatles, *The Beatles Anthology*, 181 and Davies, *The Beatles*, 207. Davies says, "Brian was very much pleased about the honour."

[1645] The Beatles, *The Beatles Anthology*, 181, and Spitz, 556. Direct quote from Brian Epstein, according to Spitz.

[1646] Spitz, 556.

[1647] Spitz, 556.

[1648] Spitz, 556-557. This is a direct quote from the nomination letter.

[1649] Spitz, 556.

[1650] Kenny, 171.

[1651] Norman, *John Lennon: The Life*, 400 and Davies, *The Beatles*, 207. In both sources, John is quoted as saying that after weeks of deliberation, he finally decided to accept the MBE as part of "playing the game." He says, "We'd nothing to lose, except that part of you which said you didn't believe in it."

[1652] Miles, *The Beatles' Diary, Vol. 1*, 198. "[Brian] and a few other people persuaded me that it was in our best interests to take [the MBE] and it was hypocritical of me to accept it…"

[1653] Coleman, *Lennon*, 308 and Norman, *John Lennon: The Life*, 400.

[1654] The Beatles, *The Beatles Anthology*, 181 and Spitz, 557.

[1655] Coleman, *Lennon*, 307. Direct quote from John Lennon.

[1656] Robertson, *Lennon*, 40 and Coleman, *Lennon*, 308.

[1657] Norman, *Shout!*, 248. Norman states, "The [Beatles'] hair now sculpted and razored, their clothes one jump ahead of Carnaby Street, they were the model...of Swinging London."

[1658] Spitz, 556. Direct quote from John Lennon.

[1659] The Beatles, *The Beatles Anthology*, 181.

[1660] The Beatles, *The Beatles Anthology*, 181. George Harrison says, "Probably it was Harold Wilson that put us up for [the MBE]. He was Prime Minister and was from Liverpool, Huyton..."

[1661] Miles, *The Beatles' Diary, Vol. 1*, 197.

[1662] Coleman, *Lennon*, 310.

[1663] Norman, *John Lennon: The Life*, 399.

[1664] Norman, *Shout!*, 246, Coleman, *Lennon*, 278, and Connolly, 206. Connolly states, "The [MBE] honour wasn't for The Beatles' contribution to music, it was for their part in boosting the nation's exports."

[1665] Davies, *The Beatles*, 207, Norman, *John Lennon: The Life*, 400, and Spitz, 557.

[1666] Spitz, 557.

[1667] Miles, *The Beatles' Diary, Vol. 1*, 197 and Connolly, 246. Miles quotes John as saying, "We had to do a lot of selling out then. Taking the MBE was a sellout for me." Connolly says that when John finally agreed to accept the award, he "put aside his argument that they would be selling out even further."

[1668] The Beatles, *The Beatles Anthology*, 181, Connolly, 206, Coleman, *Lennon*, 278, and Badman, 159. In *The Beatles Anthology,* Ringo says, "We all thought [the MBE] was thrilling!" Paul, too, says he was pleased. But *every source* shows John as reluctant to accept the honour. Badman quotes John Lennon as saying, "So, instead of refusing, I accepted, and if I had refused, I would have stopped them getting theirs. They seemed to love the decoration." (p. 159)

[1669] The Beatles, *The Beatles Anthology*, 181. John says, "It was hypocritical of me to accept [the MBE]..." John says the only good thing about accepting it was that he could use it at a later date to protest Britain's support of the U.S. in Vietnam and Britain's involvement in the Nigeria-Biafra conflict.

[1670] Lewisohn, *The Beatles: Day by Day*, 63. Lewisohn says that Brian comes back from holiday in Albufeira, Portugal "a day earlier than scheduled" because "Brian wants Paul to be in the U.K. at midnight when the news embargo of The Beatles MBE announcement is lifted."

[1671] Lewisohn, *The Complete Beatles Chronicle*, 194, Lewisohn, *The Beatles: Day by Day*, 63, Bicknell, 49, and Badman, 159.

[1672] Lewisohn, *The Complete Beatles Chronicle*, 194. The description of The Beatles' attire is from the photo on this page.

[1673] Lewisohn, *The Beatles: Day by Day*, 63, Bicknell, 49, Miles, *The Beatles' Diary, Vol. 1*, 196, Barrow, 148, and Badman, 159.

[1674] Bicknell, 49. Alf says that "Brian was peeved at John because John wasn't on time." He goes on to add: "I don't think [John] really wanted to be there at all."

[1675] Lewisohn, *The Beatles: Day by Day*, 63, Wells, June 12, 1965, and Badman, 159. Lewisohn and Badman tell us that John had to be "fetched in his car by Brian Epstein." Wells states that "a frantic Brian Epstein personally retreiv[ed] the errant Beatle from his home."

[1676] Badman, 159 and Tremlett, 59.

[1677] Winn, 323. Winn says, "The press conference was arranged to begin at 1.30 p.m., but John decided to stay in bed...Brian Epstein finally persuaded John to show up, and the event began seventy minutes late." That would make the time that the conference began 2.40 p.m.

[1678] Lewisohn, *The Complete Beatles Chronicle*, 194, Lewisohn, *The Beatles: Day by Day*, 63, Schultheiss, 134, and Robertson, *Lennon*, 40. In the *Complete Beatles Chronicle*, Lewisohn includes a colour photo of The Beatles giving an interview about the MBE on 12 June 1965. John's attire and hair are taken from this photo.

[1679] Wells, June 12, 1965. Wells states, "John's evident embarrassment on receiving such an honour was typified by his absence at a press conference in Twickenham Studios, resulting in a frantic Brian Epstein personally retrieving the errant Beatle from his home."

[1680] Barrow, 148.

[1681] Lewisohn, *The Complete Beatles Chronicle*, 194. You can see the single stemmed glass of water on the coffee table in front of John in this photo.

[1682] Badman, 159.

[1683] This is the first line of a portion of the MBE press conference which took place in Twickenham Studios on Saturday, 12 June 1965. It can be found in Badman, pp. 159-160. I am not going to endnote each line, but will endnote again on the last line from this source.

[1684] This is the last line of a portion of the MBE press conference which took place in Twickenham Studios on Saturday, 12 June 1965. It can be found in Badman, pp. 159-160. Some portions of this interview may also be found in Brown, Craig, 273.

[1685] Lewisohn, *The Complete Beatles Chronicle*, 194. The photo in Lewisohn's book is of The Beatles talking about the MBE during a radio interview on 12 June 1965.

[1686] Tremlett, 57. Direct quotes from John Lennon.

[1687] Badman, 158 and Norman, *Shout!*, 246.

[1688] Norman, *Shout!*, 246.

[1689] Badman, 158-159 and Norman, *Shout!*, 246. Norman's quote from Ringo is "I'll keep it to dust when I'm old." These are direct quotes from Starr and Harrison.

[1690] Badman, 159 and Norman, *Shout!*, 246. Direct quotes from Paul. Badman quotes Paul as saying this in London Airport when he returned home from Portugal.

[1691] Badman, 158. Direct quote from John Lennon.

[1692] Winn, 323 and http://www.dmbeatles.com/interviews.php?interview=37 The DMBeatles website identifies the news sources as "British Calandar [sic] News" but Winn says that this interview was filmed "for U.S. public television." He adds that the completed interview shown in the U.S. "is prefaced by some footage from 'A Hard Day's Night' with an American voice-over, although the reporter, George Yateman, is British."

[1693] Winn, 323 and http://www.dmbeatles.com/interviews.php?interview=37 This is the first line of the British Calendar News interview conducted in EMI Studios on 12 June 1965 regarding The Beatles' nomination for the MBE. I am not going to endnote each line, but will endnote again at the end of the interview.

[1694] Winn, 323 and http://www.dmbeatles.com/interviews.php?interview=37 This is the last line of the British Calendar News interview conducted in EMI Studios on 12 June 1965 regarding The Beatles' nomination for the MBE. Winn says that the Yateman interview was included in the documentary *Imagine: John Lennon*, if you'd like to see it.

[1695] http://www.dmbeatles.com/interviews.php?interview=37 This is the first line of the ITV interview conducted in EMI Studios on 12 June 1965 regarding The Beatles' nomination for the MBE. I am not going to endnote each line, but will endnote again at the end of the interview. Also, you can watch this interview here: The Beatles interviewed by Richard Linley on being awarded the MBE - YouTube

[1696] http://www.dmbeatles.com/interviews.php?interview=37 This is the last line of the ITV interview conducted in EMI Studios on 12 June 1965 regarding The Beatles' nomination for the MBE.

[1697] Norman, *Shout!*, 246.

[1698] Spitz, 557.

[1699] Gould, 273. Gould points out that it was "the legitimization of The Beatles [to which] some people took offense."

[1700] Spitz, 557. George is referring to George Read, who sent a note to the Queen saying, "I am so disgusted with The Beatles being given this award that I am considering sending mine back!"

[1701] Harry, *The Ultimate Beatles Encyclopedia*, 444 and Spitz, 557.

[1702] Spitz, 557. Direct quote from Donald Zec in the London *Mirror*, 1965.

[1703] Frontani, 85, Harry, *The Ultimate Beatles Encyclopedia*, 444, and Spitz, 557. Direct quote from Hector Dupuis.

[1704] The Beatles, *The Beatles Anthology*, 181 and Davies, *The Beatles*, 207.

[1705] Frontani, 85. Direct quote from a fan. This may be found in Anthony Lewis's article for the *New York Times*, "Queen's Honors List Includes The Beatles," 12 June 1965, Late Edition.

[1706] To read more about this episode, go to the final chapter of Vol. 1 in **The John Lennon Series**, *Shoulda Been There*, pp. 722-725.

Tuesday, 15 June 1965
En route to EMI Studios
London

John hardly admitted it to himself: he felt left out.[1707] For the first time since he'd hand-selected The Quarry Men back in 1956 and '57, John suspected he was beginning to lose control of his band.[1708]

Last night, Paul had cut a track without him, without any of them, and without much ado. McCartney had simply taken up his Epiphone Texan acoustic in Two Studio and recorded the solo song he'd been nurturing for months. In only two takes, the ballad had been perfected.[1709]

Over the last year, Paul had been obsessed with the entrancing song that he'd heard one night in a dream. Immediately upon awakening — McCartney had repeated this story obsessively — he'd jumped up and played the tune over and over on the piano beside his bed,[1710] committing the melody to memory.[1711] But ever since then, Paul had fretted that the mysterious lilt was something he'd heard somewhere down the line…on a record, at a concert, in a film. And though Paul longed to believe that the haunting tune was his and his alone, he had a nagging feeling that he'd "nicked it."[1712]

"Have you heard this somewhere?" he'd asked John, George, Ringo, Mal, and Neil.[1713]

"Does this sound like anything you've ever heard before?" he'd queried, searching Alma Cogan's eyes[1714] and Lionel Bart's.[1715]

Paul had questioned George Martin about the enigmatic aire in the *Hôtel Georges Cinq*, in January of 1964.[1716] Even driver Alf Bicknell's opinion had been solicited, as recently as a few days ago.[1717] For months, McCartney had been near-frantic to locate the owner of the stray song that had wandered into his life to stay. But no one had stepped up to claim it.

Then, whilst on a leisurely holiday drive with Jane in Portugal, Paul had finally given himself permission to compose lyrics for the arcane melody, the long-simmering tune that Paul had fondly dubbed "Scrambled Eggs." The embryonic composition had finally evolved into "Yesterday."[1718]

John easily admitted Paul had written a great number. *It's like "And I Love Her," only better,*[1719] John thought. And he recognized — indeed, all of them recognized — that Paul needed to sing the song without a lot of embellishment.[1720]

"I can't really put drums on that."[1721] Ringo had shaken his head at the end of Paul's debut performance. "It wouldn't make sense."[1722]

"Well, I'm not sure I can put much on that either,"[1723] George had shrugged. "There's no point in havin' another guitar."[1724]

And just as John had reluctantly agreed to record "Help!" as an upbeat, powerhouse track to open the new film, so now, he concurred in the decision to leave "Yesterday" as McCartney's. "I can't think of anythin'," John had echoed the others, lifting an open palm. "I think you should just do it yourself. It's very much a solo thing."[1725]

"Yes, I agree," George Martin had nodded. "Why don't you just try it by yourself and see how it works?"[1726]

And strolling over to an empty chair to watch the recording unfold, John did as he'd always done — he brushed self aside for the good of the song, the group.[1727] Feelings be damned.[1728]

The official song rights, of course, would read: Lennon/McCartney.[1729] But on the record and over the airwaves, this was a first. It was the first fissure.

In May of 1960, young John had rejected an enticing, paid tour with star Billy Fury,[1730] if that grand opportunity came with a caveat that Stu Sutcliffe could not serve as The Silver Beatles' bass player. John had flatly refused to splinter his group.[1731] He'd always done what was best for the whole, so now, this whole "solo" affair niggled at him. It seemed a bend in the road, a divergence.[1732]

All the way into EMI, John kept his own counsel. Devoid of his usual patter, he stared out the window sullenly

"Paul, y' know," Alf now scrutinized Lennon in the car's rear-view mirror, "is a bit concerned about the rest of you boys not recordin' on his 'Yesterday.'"[1733]

"Is he now?" John sniffed. He ran his tongue over his top teeth and squinted his eyes, saying nothing.

And until they reached St. John's Wood, that was the only conversation. Then, leaning up, John ventured, "We're off to the clubs tonight, Alf.[1734] All of us, y' know. The whole entire group."

"I'll be ready when you lot are," the driver nodded, wondering if the reference to "the whole entire group" was some sort of covert statement. But John's tight jaw and almond eyes revealed nothing, and Alf was too abashed to ask. The two men parted in a tight silence, sharing only a curt wave in the EMI car park.

****

2.30 p.m.

It didn't help matters that John was recording "It's Only Love" this afternoon in Studio 2. He'd said quite openly that despised the number.[1735]

Increasingly in years to come, he would blame his revulsion on the song's lyrics, labeling them as "abysmal" or "abominable."[1736] But that was hardly the problem. And John knew it.

When he'd first wed Cynthia Powell back in August of 1962, John had confided to his young bride that "bein' married's like walkin' about with odd socks on!"[1737] She had blushed, giggled, and agreed.[1738]

Indeed, for a 21-year-old rock'n'roller, more accustomed to the dank grit of the Cavern Club or Hamburg's raunchy red-light district, being a "family man" felt off beam. One of John's early art school sketches had been a single line rendering of a grotesque and overbearing woman whom John had unkindly dubbed "The Wife."[1739] Marriage, John had thought, was...well, mortifying.

But in Liverpool of the 1940s, 50s, and early 60s, there was only one thing worse than the monotony of matrimony — and that was the calamity of having one's marriage fall apart. Broken homes were considered catastrophes in post-war England. A man could surrender his license, lose his job, and foolishly toss away a fortune, but floundering in his marriage was the supreme failure. Divorce was certainly nothing about which to compose a song.

But after one of his recent bouts with Cyn, John had torn off to his beloved sunroom to scratch out angry lyrics on the back of some letter from "someone or other." John found writing liberating. Once he'd rapidly spewed out his ire in print, he found relief. Scribbling his frustrations had always worked far better than trying to "talk things out," the way Cyn continually wanted to do. Writing a song or a poem brought catharsis.

John loved Cynthia. There was no denying it. He constantly told her so. And she loved him.

But in the last few months, they'd found themselves off kilter, always at odds. And so, he wasn't really stung when he flipped his make-shift "lyric sheet" over to find a heart-to-heart lament that Cyn had been composing to her art college friend, Phyllis McKenzie. Without meaning to pry, John's eyes swept the scrawled page. And there it was: The Bold Truth. Cyn's straightforward words spoke for them both:

"...*although my fears and premonitions are building up inside of me, I keep them very much to myself. And I'm afraid at times that I give a very boring, practical impression of an ordinary housewife...instead of a swinging, extrovert pop star's wife. Sigh! But I can't alter my nature, can I? I bend a little in order to try and understand...and fit into our new way of life. But...*

...don't get me wrong! I thoroughly enjoy the parties and functions we attend! I'm tickled pink to meet so many show business stars and celebrities!!!! Alma Cogan, Sybil Burton (wife of Richard Burton), Roman Polanski, Dickie Henderson — you name them! (Alma entertains in great style and with great humour!) And John and I've also spent many enjoyable evenings with

Peter Cook and his wife, dining superbly at their home in Hampstead with companions such as Dudley Moore and Patrick Campbell. It's all very stimulating and exciting, Phyl, but...[1740]

As John's eyes ran down the page, he caught an underscored abbreviation: "LSD." So, he read on:

"...and although he constantly works to lure me into the use of marijuana or LSD...which seems to be all right for him...I'm totally against it!! It's opened the floodgates of his mind and helped him escape from the imprisonment of fame. But though he recently tried to guide me through another LSD trip, I'm just not mentally receptive. I can't handle it, Phyl!! And this upsets John terribly!

So...suddenly, there's this new mental barrier between us...even bigger than the wall that was created by the old tensions and bad tempers..."[1741] *A drunken John, I've learned to cope with, but now with the drugs, he's gone deep within himself and won't even reply to me, if he doesn't want to.*[1742]

Our marriage is in trouble. We've lost communication. John's on another planet."[1743]

John had made himself put the letter down. Shaking his head and biting his bottom lip, he stood morosely watching a round of late-spring robins feeding in his garden. "Is it right that you and I should fight, every night?" he whispered the unpolished lyrics of the newborn song to his wife.

"*Ugh!* Fuggin' awful!" John spat, finding it hard to swallow, "but even worse is that we've come to this...after seven fuggin' years of bein' us...after stayin' together despite the world, the madness, the long fuggin' separations, 'n a million other obstacles. We were great, once, me 'n Cyn."

Cynthia had always been his "up-on-a-pedestal" Hoylake baird, the girl John felt he hadn't deserved — the obedient "A student" who ran with Michael Issacson and the egghead crowd…a proper girl in sweater sets and pearls, a lady who never swore in her posh accent or staggered home blind drunk. To John, Cynthia had always been "Miss Prim," the polished, polite lass with a silver spoon in her mouth,[1744] the coed whom everyone had whispered was "wasted on that no-good Lennon."

But Cynthia had never felt that way. From the moment she'd met John, she had been "totally under his spell."[1745] And try as she might, she'd never felt that she measured up to his standards — or his friends' standards, either.

When John had first introduced her to Paul and George, they'd made faces, cupped their hands, and muttered, "She's from over-the-water, isn't she?"[1746] and "Not a bit like Brigitte!"[1747]

His art school cronies — Geoff Mohammed, and Tony Carricker — had exchanged surreptitious glances and whispered to one another, "She's not a bit funny!" and "What does John *see* in her?"[1748] Back then, Cynthia had tried to ignore their muffled bets that the bizarre relationship would never last, because she'd desperately, *desperately* wanted it to last…and she still did.

Cynthia had done all she could to win over her irreverent Teddy Boy. She had dyed her dowdy brown hair a chic Hiltone blonde. She'd exchanged sweater seats for short skirts, black tights, and Winklepicker shoes.[1749] She'd charcoaled her eyes and adopted a thickly-teased flip with a blunt, heavy fringe. But most of all, Cynthia had learned to dismiss John's startling emotional outbursts in hopes of breaking through his shell and conditioning him to trust her.[1750]

"If John could just believe in *one person* — me," she'd stumblingly explained to Phyllis years ago, "then he'd be well on the way to calming his troubled spirit…and I want him to be at peace with himself…and with the world."[1751]

So, when John had accused her of flirting with his friends, Cyn had been patient, assuaging his fears. When he'd raged that she was "lookin' at someone else," she'd been serene and loved him even more.[1752] For years, Cynthia's dedication to making John happy had worked its singular magic. But now, it seemed, nothing could scotch his pain.

"It's only love and that is all," John had written. "*Why* should I feel the way I do? It's only love and that is all…but it's so hard loving you."

This song's fuggin' terrible, John frowned.[1753] The stumbling admission of his mad devotion paired with his confession of failure was, John thought, more than he should ever reveal.[1754] He was exposing himself to his mates, the fans, and the world at large as some hapless sap who'd let a woman get the better of him. John was admitting to all and sundry that he'd allowed "some baird from Hoylake" to affect him that intensely.[1755]

Mere days ago, he'd played the song offhandedly for Paul in Kenwood, and unwilling to call attention to it, John had brushed the number aside a "just an album filler." Paul had nodded politely and tried tactfully pointing out that the lyrics were "a tad bland, y' know" and "in need of a bit of a tweak, here 'n there."[1756] But John had irritably growled that the song wasn't worth their time. He'd insisted they move on.[1757]

So now, twenty-four hours after the "miraculous" recording of "Yesterday," John clenched his jaw and prepared to stride up to Two Studio's microphone for a full confession of his shortcomings. He steeled himself to admit — in front of God and all — that he was losing one of the few wonderful things that life had ever given him. He was losing Cyn, or she was losing him. They were losing each other.

"It's Only Love, Take One," Norman Smith announced from the booth overhead.

"Right," John muttered to himself. He took a deep breath, closed his eyes, and paused. Then he exhaled the melancholy story of a failed romance.

Notes!

1. Did John actually feel minimized by Paul's creation of a solo song on which none of the other Beatles performed?

Rod Pont, a Liverpool musician who was there for The Beatles' early days, clearly acknowledged, "There's no doubt about it: John Lennon was the leader, the boss man of The Beatles." Pont said that in the early years, "Paul would fall in line." Now, in 1965, the balance of power was beginning to shift. (Coleman, The Man Who Made The Beatles, *p. 101)*

Indeed, Alan Clayson asserts in his biography, Paul McCartney, *that as the years passed, "George [Harrison] and the others (not always affectionately) nicknamed Paul 'The Star,' partly because he seemed to have the most highly developed instinct — and desire — for riding the waves of showbusiness protocol, whilst gilding the image of loveable and slightly naïve..." (p. 97) Clayson goes on to say that Paul was revealing "a skill for combining necessary ruthlessness with keeping his popularity intact." (p. 97)*

According to both Clayson in Paul McCartney *and* Carlin in Paul McCartney: A Life, *this tendency led George Harrison — who was tasked with introducing Paul's 'Yesterday' on the taping of ABC's* Blackpool's Night Out *— to quite tellingly say to the audience, "For Paul McCartney of Liverpool, opportunity knocks!" (Clayson, p. 97 and Carlin, p. 120) None of The Beatles were oblivious to the considerable ramifications of this powerful McCartney solo number.*

But the recording was even more problematic for John Lennon. As Riley states in Lennon, *"['Yesterday'] created new tension in the partnership. Lennon could not help admiring it or enjoying the profits he would share in its extraordinary publishing returns. But...there was no place for him to so much as harmonize alongside his songwriting partner." (p. 279) It was a first.*

Finally, revered Beatles historians Lewisohn and Howlett state that one crucial element of The Beatles' success was "the competition between [John and Paul]. As Paul recalls, 'If [John] had a great idea, I wanted to have a great idea.'" Lewisohn and Howlett say "...each would try to impress the other or compete for the A-side of the next single." Both were highly competitive and always knew exactly how many tracks each of them had written on an LP. John would not *have been oblivious to the significance of Paul's composing and recording the group's first solo song.*

2. Were the other Beatles present when Paul recorded "Yesterday"?

Beatles Guru Mark Lewisohn was the first to alert us that in fact, contrary to popular rumour, the other Beatles were *in studio when "Yesterday" was being recorded. In his 1988 classic work* The Beatles Recording Sessions, *Lewisohn wrote: "Newspapers of the time made a big fuss of the fact that none of the other Beatles played on the recording, and that they were not even in the studio. This myth has persisted for more than 20 years, but while none of the others did play on "Yesterday," George Harrison, if not John and Ringo, was certainly present, his voice coming across loud and clear at one point on the original session tape." (p. 59)*

In The Beatles for Sale on Parlophone Records, *Beatles music expert Bruce Spizer also stated, "Although Paul was the only Beatle to play or sing on the song, George (and possibly John and Ringo) were present in the studio. In fact, Paul tells George what key the song is in, but George never actually plays his guitar on the track." (p. 191)*

Then in 2000, when The Beatles Anthology *book was released, we were told definitively by Paul himself that **all of The Beatles** were present for the initial recording of "Yesterday." He said, "I brought the song into the studio for the first time and played it on the guitar, but soon Ringo said, 'I can't really put any drums on — it wouldn't make sense.' And John and George said, 'There's no point in having another guitar.' So George Martin suggested, 'Why don't you just try it by yourself and see how it works?' I looked at all the others: 'Oops. You mean a solo record?' They said, 'Yeah, it doesn't matter; there's nothing we can add to it — do it.'"*
(p. 175)

Thus, in his 2009 biography, Paul McCartney: The Life, *Peter Ames Carlin confidently asserts that, "The band broke for dinner at five thirty, and when they returned at 7 p.m., Paul propped his acoustic guitar on his knee and played through an elegiac acoustic ballad he was now calling 'Yesterday.' John, George, and Ringo were in the studio, too, sitting on stools and listening as Paul sang the song..." Later, Carlin states that Paul "unveiled the finished song to his producer and bandmates that June evening." (p. 119)*

In Maximum Volume: The Life of Beatles Producer, George Martin, *author Kenneth Womack writes, "...the evening session progressed fairly awkwardly given the uncertainty about what the other bandmates would contribute ..." Womack faithfully recounts Paul's conversation with the other Beatles and Martin, and then adds, "And with that, Paul 'sat on a high stool' in Studio 2, with his Epiphone Texan and sang 'Yesterday.'"*
(pp. 261-262)

Additionally, Barry Miles in Many Years From Now, *says that after Ringo made the comment about the drums, George Harrison commented, "Well, I'm not sure I can put much on that either." Then John said, "I can't think of anything; I think you should just do it yourself. It's very much a solo thing." (p. 205) Miles, too, has Paul recording the song in front of the other Beatles.*

Finally, in his Beatles Diary, *Beatles driver Alf Bicknell states that the other Beatles were present during the recording, as was he. He says, "...most of the day was spent out of the way in Number Two studio. Later on this evening, Paul was doing his 'Yesterday' song...The rest of the boys just hung around while Paul got on with it. After the session, I took Paul and Jane to the Cromwellian Club. Paul was very concerned about not using the rest of the boys on the recording of 'Yesterday.'" (p. 49-50)*

3. What happened in studio as John recorded "It's Only Love"?

As Mark Lewisohn observes in The Beatles Recording Sessions, *the 2.30-5.30 p.m. session in Studio 2, EMI was uneventful, and the song's recording "was a straightforward taping." In the booth were Producer*

George Martin; Engineer Norman Smith; and Second Engineer Phil McDonald. (p. 60)

In The Beatles Recording Reference Manual, *Hammack explains the multiple number of guitars used on this song: "The backing track featured Lennon on the 1965 Framus Hootenanny 5/025 (12-string) acoustic guitar, Paul McCartney on his 1962-9163 Höfner 550/1 bass, Harrison on his 1962-Gibson J-160E acoustic guitar…"*

Hammack tells us that during the first few takes, John's vocal was a bit harsh, and George Martin objected to "the aggressive nature of his 12-string acoustic part." But Hammack says that by Take 6, Lennon's vocals were "no longer present" and in later superimpositions, a "softer [Lennon] lead vocal (double-tracked at the choruses)" was added. Furthermore, John is heard playing a "chopping rhythm guitar part on his 1964 Rickenbacker 325 Capri." In these superimpositions, Hammack explains, Harrison added "12-string electric lead accents (played with an extreme tremolo setting on the amplifier)." (p. 53)

John's trilled "r" on the word "bright" is addressed by Spignesi and Lewis. They suggest that John's intense embarrassment in singing this song may have been cloaked by a bit of "goofing around." They point out that in the Take 2 offering of "It's Only Love" on Anthology 2, *John "sings the bright straight on." Perhaps, they suggest, as John had to repeat his soul-baring confessional over and over, he began to act silly and make light of it. (p. 233)*

Final Note:

"It's Only Love" is far from an abysmal song. In truth, it is one of John Lennon's most moving works.

Hammack, in The Beatles Recording Reference, *calls it "a masterful number, its off-beat verses adding a subtle complexity that makes the transition to the chorus much more powerful." (p. 53)*

Spignesi states, "This is one of those songs that, once you hear it, you can't get it out of your head…Every little bit of 'It's Only Love' is a legitimate hook from the opening four-note ostinato (which reprises discreetly throughout the song) to the melody of the instantly-rememberable three-note chorus…For all its pop sensibility, the melody and construction have a 'classicalesque' quality." (p. 233)

Without stating this verbally, George Martin certainly seconds Spignesi's observation. He chose to record "It's Only Love" instrumentally for release on his orchestral version of "Help!" (Russell, 73)

In Way Beyond Compare, *Winn says that John's comment that he hated the song, "does a disservice to the lovely melody and great singing." (p.*

325)

And Hertsgaard in A Day in the Life *states, "Lennon said he always hated 'It's Only Love' because of its abysmal lyrics, a harsh judgement that does injustice to the song's lovely lilting melody."*

John always downplayed the track, not because it wasn't an enchanting melody but because the words "uncovered" him in front of the world. As Turner observed in A Hard Day's Write: *"All of the songs John regretted having written were condemned on the basis of lyrics rather than their melodies." (p. 82) John deeply regretted revealing so much personal information to gawking fans.*

As Beatles photographer and friend Robert Freeman accurately observed in The Beatles: A Private View: *"John was a powerful performer with a vulnerable intensity. In his songs, there was often a yearning for love and tenderness which he expressed through the raw, emotional quality of his voice. John drew on the conflicts in his life for his music and in singing his songs, he tried to exorcise the confused feelings raised by his relationships with women." (p. 146) Nowhere is this practice more evident than in 1965's "It's Only Love."*

The proof on the flat-out honesty of John's lyrics is illustrated best in a verse that was omitted from the final version of "It's Only Love." John had written:

Can't explain or name...I think it's pain,
I'm ashamed the flame of love is maimed.
Now and then I'll complain in vain...
And I'll still love you.

(Spignesi and Lewis, 233)

I'm sure that this poignant ballad of longing must have touched Cynthia's heart. As Margotin and Guesdon fittingly state, "'It's Only Love' has an undeniable charm."

Sources:

Lewisohn, The Complete Beatles Chronicle, *195.*
Lewisohn, The Beatles Recording Sessions, *59.*
Lewisohn and Howlett, John Lennon: In My Life, *63-64.*
Harry, The Ultimate Beatles Encyclopedia, *331 and 713-714.*
Harry, The John Lennon Encyclopedia, *404.*
Winn, 325.
The Beatles, The Beatles Anthology, *175.*
Martin, 166-167.

Hammack, 51 and 53.
Badman, 22 and 165-166.
Clayson, Paul McCartney, *96-97.*
Clayson, Alan and Leigh, Spencer, The Walrus Was Ringo, *110-111.*
Spitz, 559-561.
Connolly, 198-199.
Brown, Peter, 171.
Norman, John Lennon: The Life, *398-399.*
Norman, Shout!, *258.*
Womack, Maximum Volume: The Life of Beatles Producer, George Martin, *261-262 and 265.*
Womack, The Beatles Encyclopedia, Vol. 1, *479.*
Womack, Long and Winding Roads, The Evolving Artistry of The Beatles, *110-11 and 112-113.*
Miles, Paul McCartney: Many Years From Now, 100 and *202-205.*
Miles, The Beatles' Diary, Vol. 1, *198 and 205.*
Coleman, The Man Who Made The Beatles, *101.*
Spignesi and Lewis, 23 and 232-233.
Hertsgaard, 127 and *131-132.*
Turner, 82-83.
Hammack, 53.
Carlin, Paul McCartney: A Life, *118-120.*
Everett, 303-304.
MacDonald, 124-125.
Russell, 73.
Margotin and Guesdon, 242 and 250.
Yule, 103.
Riley, Tell Me Why, *149.*
Riley, Lennon, *278-279.*
Spizer, The Beatles for Sale on Parlophone Records, *190-191.*
Gould, 277 and 279.
Egan, The Mammoth Book of The Beatles, *92.*
Noden, Merrell, "A Dream of a Song," Trynka, The Beatles: Ten Years That Shook the World, *170.*
Bicknell, 49-50.
Hill, John, Paul, George & Ringo, *205.*
Schultheiss, 133.
Robertson, Lennon, *40-41.*
Friede, Titone, and Wiener, 234.

It's Only Love - Wikipedia This website contains additional recording information about the song.

https://www.beatlesbible.com/songs/its-only-love/ This website supplies solid factual information about "It's Only Love."

*http://www.beatlesebooks.com/yesterday   This   website   supplies
extensive information about the writing and recording of "Yesterday."*

*"It's Only Love" by The Beatles. The in-depth story behind the songs of
the Beatles. Recording History. Songwriting History. Song Structure and
Style. (beatlesebooks.com) This website supplies extensive information
about the recording of "It's Only Love."*

*https://www.youtube.com/watch?v=60iDv3AcrJA To hear the studio
version of "Yesterday" from 14 June 1965, go to the Anthology 2 DVD
or listen via the above link.*
Or use this QR code:

[1707] Connolly, 199. Connolly says, "It was the first time any of The Beatles had
sung on records without the others providing the backing, and the first time
that John had found himself left out."

[1708] Robertson, *Lennon*, 40. Robertson says that Paul "seize[d] the reins of the
group's career from Lennon — who is absent as his partner tapes
'Yesterday.'"

[1709] Lewisohn, *The Beatles Recording Sessions*, 59, Hammack, 51, Winn, 325,
Margotin and Guesdon, 250-251, and Spignesi and Lewis, 25.

[1710] Yule, 103. Yule says Paul also played the piano on the film set constantly,
running the tune of "Yesterday" over and over. Finally, Richard Lester
jokingly exploded, "If I hear that once more, I'll have the bloody piano taken
away!"

[1711] Clayson, *Paul McCartney*, 96, Spitz, 559, Connolly, 198-199, Brown, 171,
Norman, *John Lennon: The Life*, 398-399, Noden, Merrell, "A Dream of a
Song," Trynka, *The Beatles: Ten Years That Shook the World*, 170, Womack,
Maximum Volume: The Life of Beatles Producer, George Martin, 261, Miles,
The Beatles' Diary, Vol. 1, 205, Badman, 165-166, Spignesi, Stephen and
Michael Lewis, *100 Best Beatles Songs*, 23, Turner, 83, Carlin, *Paul
McCartney: A Life,* 118, Margotin and Guesdon, 250, Miles, *Paul McCartney:
Many Years From Now*, 203-204, Riley, *Tell Me Why*, 149, and Spizer, *The
Beatles for Sale on Parlophone Records*, 191.

[1712] Carlin, 118, Spizer, *The Beatles for Sale on Parlophone Records*, 191,
Noden, Merrell, "A Dream of a Song," Trynka, *The Beatles: Ten Years That
Shook the World*, 170, Badman, 165, Miles, *The Beatles' Diary, Vol. 1*, 205,
Connolly, 199, Spitz, 559, Margotin and Guesdon, 250, and Turner, 83.

[1713] Womack, *Maximum Volume: The Life of Beatles Producer, George Martin*, 261 and Clayson and Leigh, *The Walrus was Ringo*, 101-102.

[1714] The Beatles, *The Beatles Anthology*, 175, Womack, *Maximum Volume: The Life of Beatles Producer, George Martin*, 261 and Clayson and Leigh, *The Walrus was Ringo*, 101-102.

[1715] Riley, *Lennon*, 278-279 and Hill, *John, Paul, George & Ringo*, 205. Hills says Paul ran the song "by a host of show-biz luminaries, including Lionel Bart, who assured him it was an original — and marvellous."

[1716] Womack, *Maximum Volume: The Life of Beatles Producer, George Martin*, 261.

[1717] Bicknell, 50.

[1718] Carlin, 119, Hill, *John, Paul, George & Ringo*, 205, Womack, *Maximum Volume: The Life of Beatles Producer, George Martin*, 216, and Margotin and Guesdon, 250.

[1719] Spignesi and Lewis, 155. John is quoted as saying: "'And I Love Her' was Paul's first 'Yesterday.'"

[1720] Margotin and Guesdon, 138 and Spignesi and Lewis, 155. You can hear the early version of "And I Love Her" with electric guitars and Ringo on drums rather than playing claves and bongos on *Anthology 1*. The Beatles learned in making this first McCartney ballad that the softer acoustic approach was much more suited to the tone and air of the song.

[1721] The Beatles, *The Beatles Anthology*, 175. Direct quote from Ringo Starr.

[1722] The Beatles, *The Beatles Anthology*, 175. Direct quote from Ringo Starr.

[1723] Miles, *Many Years From Now*, 204. Direct quote from George Harrison.

[1724] The Beatles, *The Beatles Anthology*, 175. Direct quote from George Harrison.

[1725] Miles, *Many Years From Now*, 204. Direct quote from John Lennon.

[1726] The Beatles, *The Beatles Anthology*, 175. Direct quote from George Martin.

[1727] Hammack, 13. Hammack states, "The most evolutionary change for the band came with their willingness to allow 'Yesterday' to be essentially a solo number. The decision represented an openness to do whatever was best for the song, even if it meant putting ego aside."

[1728] Connolly, 199. Connolly says that "no matter how much [John] admired the shape and lyrics of ['Yesterday'], and he did, that familiar little itch of jealousy couldn't help but nag at him, as over the years and everywhere in the world he would hear it…and know he'd had nothing to do with it."

[1729] Connolly, 199, Coleman, *Lennon*, 277, Norman, *John Lennon: The Life*, 398-399, and Hill, *John, Paul, George & Ringo*, 206. It's interesting to note that according to Ray Connolly, "John suggested that Paul…hang on to all of the royalties for ['Yesterday'] instead of sharing them. Paul thanked him for the thought and refused. That would have been against the spirit of the songwriting relationship they'd always had." A very interesting side note supplied by Tim Hill is that after John's death, "Yesterday" was spotlighted in a Beatles compilation, and Paul approached Yoko, asking if for this compilation, "the song could carry a McCartney/Lennon credit." As Hill concisely says, "Yoko refused." (p. 206)

[1730] Badman, 22 and Lennon, Cynthia, *A Twist of Lennon*, 44.

[1731] Gentle, Johnny and Ian Forsyth, *Johnny Gentle & The Beatles: First Ever Tour, Scotland 1960*, 24-32, Lennon, Cynthia, *A Twist of Lennon*, 44, and Williams, Allan, *The Man Who Gave The Beatles Away*, 44-48. Cynthia states that when Larry Parnes offered to hire all of The Silver Beatles except Stuart Sutcliffe to tour with Billy Fury, John responded with, "If Stuart isn't with us, then they can forget it." John was always adamant about keeping "the group" together.

[1732] Hammack, 13.

[1733] Bicknell, 50. Direct quote from Alf Bicknell.

[1734] Bicknell, 50.

[1735] Badman, 165, Spizer, *The Beatles for Sale on Parlophone Records*, 190, Winn, 325, Margotin and Guesdon, 242, Spignesi and Lewis, 232, and Turner, 82.

[1736] Badman, 165, Spizer, *The Beatles for Sale on Parlophone Records*, 190, Winn, 325, Margotin and Guesdon, 242, Spignesi and Lewis, 232, and Turner, 82. John is quoted in every source as hating the song because the lyrics were variously "abysmal" or "abominable."

[1737] Lennon, Cynthia, *John*, 97 and Stark, 120. Direct quote from Cynthia Lennon, repeating John's words to her.

[1738] Lennon, Cynthia, *John*, 97.

[1739] Coleman, *Lennon*, 158.

[1740] Lennon, Cynthia, *A Twist of Lennon*, 144. The first two paragraphs of this letter are verbatim from Cynthia, with only verb tense changes. These are her words.

[1741] Coleman, *Lennon*, 290. These are Cynthia Lennon's direct words. The quotes are found in various paragraphs on this page, but all are there.

[1742] Coleman, *Lennon*, 291. The last sentence is a paraphrase of Cynthia's words to Ray Coleman.

[1743] Coleman, *Lennon*, 291. This paragraph is a direct quote from Cynthia Lennon.

[1744] Lennon, Cynthia, *John*, 18.

[1745] Lennon, Cynthia, *A Twist of Lennon*, 26. Direct quote from Cynthia Lennon.

[1746] Lennon, Cynthia, *John*, 16. Direct quote from Cynthia Lennon. "Over the water" is a Scouse term for people who come from the Hoylake Peninsula across the Mersey River from Liverpool.

[1747] Lennon, Cynthia, *A Twist of Lennon*, 23 and Lennon, Cynthia, *John,* 16. Direct quote. This is word for word what Cynthia says they said about her.

[1748] Lennon, Cynthia, *A Twist of Lennon*, 23. Direct quote from Cynthia Lennon regarding what John's friends said of her.

[1749] Lennon, Cynthia, *John*, 21.

[1750] Lennon, Cynthia, *A Twist of Lennon,* 25-26.

[1751] Lennon, Cynthia, *A Twist of Lennon*, 26. This is a direct quote from Cynthia Lennon.

[1752] Lennon, Cynthia, *A Twist of Lennon*, 25-26.

[1753] Miles, *Many Years From Now*, 200. John Lennon is quoted as saying, "That's one song I really hate of mine. It's terrible."

[1754] Margotin and Guesdon, 233. The authors say, "…the singer repeatedly reassures himself that 'it's only love,' trying to convince himself that he should not make as big a deal of the relationship as he obviously feels compelled to do."

[1755] Margotin and Guesdon, 234.

[1756] The Beatles, *The Beatles Anthology*, 175.

[1757] Miles, *Many Years From Now*, 200.

Tuesday, 16 June 1965
NEMS Enterprises
Sutherland House, Argyll Street
London

In eight days, John's second book of prose and poetry, *A Spaniard in the Works*, would hit the market, and the timing, Brian thought, was "incredibly fortuitous."

"John could use a bit of centre-stage, this week," he confided to his perceptive, blonde assistant, Wendy Hanson. "There's a good bit of 'Yesterday' chatter about, you see."[1758]

"Yes," Wendy nodded. "I've heard. Quite the buzz!"

"And well-deserved, of course. Extremely well-deserved. But for John…" Brian sank down into his chair. "Well…" He lifted a shoulder and let it fall.

"He could use a packet of candy, as they say."

"Right." Brian nodded.

So, Epstein had arranged several interviews for John this evening in the NEMS office. The first — from 8.00 p.m. to 8.30 p.m. — was with Wilfrid De'Ath, host of BBC's Home Service programme "The World of Books" and the second, with BBC contributor Tim Matthews for the popular Home Service programme *Today*.[1759] Though John generally (almost obligatorily) grumbled about the "toil and trouble" of nighttime engagements, Brian knew that, in point of fact, John welcomed these literary forays. John relished the opportunity to read and discuss his work.

John had always been fond of intelligent people. He liked the sharing of ideas, the mental isometrics. He continuously wanted to learn more. The only aspect of book promotion that John dreaded was being insincerely complimented or credited with more than he thought he deserved. John craved honesty.

Having worked as a producer for the BBC since 1960, Wilfrid De'Ath was good at that. He had interviewed scores of bright ones, including respected actress Judi Dench, author Daphne du Maurier, and Evelyn Waugh's journalist son, Bron Waugh.[1760] Known for "cutting to the chase," De'Ath posed swift, direct questions and expected equally direct answers. And Brian knew that in such rarefied air, John would thrive.

Wilfrid De'Ath: Let me ask you first of all: How do you write? Do you write in a disciplined way, or do you write when it comes into your head?"[1761]

John: Um, it's more disciplined. The second book was more disciplined because it was startin' from scratch. They sort of say, "You've got so many months to write a book." The first book, a lot of it, I'd written at odd times durin' m' life.

De'Ath: Do you set aside certain hours in the day to write? Or do you...

John: No, none of that. I haven't...I haven't written enough. It's not...it's not a job, y' see.

De'Ath: Would you like to discipline yourself? Do you feel a need to discipline yourself as a writer?

John: No, I'm not very keen on bein' disciplined. It seems odd, bein' a Beatle, because we're disciplined, but we don't *feel* as though we're disciplined. I don't mind bein' disciplined 'n not realizin' it.

De'Ath: You know, these little pieces in the book — they give an appearance of great finish — of perfection. Do you revise them?

John: (Slight laugh of amusement) Do they?

De'Ath: Yes. Now I mean, they're not...they don't look all that spontaneous. They look as though they've been worked over. Do you work them over?

John: (Rather shocked, John laughs a bit.) They're not at all! I never...nobody's ever said that to me. (Flattered laugh) Wonderful! They're spontaneous, and I hardly ever alter anythin' because I'm selfish about what I write...or big-headed about it. Once I've written it, I like it! And the publisher sometimes says, y' know, "Should we leave this out, or change that?" 'n I fight like mad. 'Cause once I've done it, I like to keep it. But I always write it straight off. I might add things when I go over it before it's published, but I seldom take anythin' out. So, it *is* spontaneous.

De'Ath: Now the puns, and all the other technical things. The puns, the onomatopoeia, the changing...

John: (Overtalking De'Ath) The what? *What?*

De'Ath: That's a long word. I'll tell you...onomatopoeia is...

John: (Obviously having fun) That's *three words* I've learned today!

De'Ath: ...you know, when I say a word like "buzz." "Buzz" is an onomatopoeia, because it's...in the word is captured the noise of the bee. That's onomatopoeia, and you, probably without realizing it, your book is full of them. Do you know what I mean?

John: *Is it?* Well, I'm glad to know that. (Chuckles) Lot of onomatopoeias!

De'Ath: Well, you've rather answered my question because I was going to ask you whether these were contrived,[1762] whether they came natural.

John: No. I just haven't got a clue what you're talkin' about really. "Automatic Pier" sounds like to me. (Laughs a bit) That's probably why I change words — 'cause I haven't a clue what words mean half the time![1763]

De'Ath: Do the other boys give you ideas? Do they throw you ideas?

John: Uh, yes, some. Uh, we were on holiday in Tahiti with George...I went with George, 'n I was writin' "The Singularge Experience of Miss Anne Duffield," 'n it was the longest one I've ever done. That was like a discipline. I was seein' how far it could go 'cause I always get fed up or bored...

De'Ath: That's the...that's the Sherlock Holmes take on...

John: Sherlock Holmes, yeah...'n I wanted to see if I could carry on and on. I would've gone on 'n on 'n made a whole book out of it if I could, but I couldn't. I'd get a sentence 'n it just didn't work somehow, so I'd say to George, "Have you got...what...what...what's another word for...for, I dunno, "fly," 'n he'd suggest somethin'.

De'Ath: That little piece, to me anyway, showed quite a...

John: (Smiling) That's m' *big piece*!

De'Ath: (Also grinning) That's your big piece! I beg your pardon. (De'Ath laughs.) That *big piece* shows close acquaintanceship with the work of Conan Doyle. Do you read his books?

John: I'd read one of two when I was younger, but on this boat that we'd hired there was a set of books...half of them were in French 'n half of them were in English. Well, just lyin' about in the sun gets a bit borin'. Well, it does for...well, I'm sorry about those people who don't lie about in the sun...So, I just read every book that was in English whether I liked it or not, just...just through boredom really. 'N there just happened to be a big volume of Sherlock Holmes. I'm not mad on it because they're all pretty similar. That's what I was doin'...really writin' all of them into one.

De'Ath: I know you hate this question, but what are the other influences? Obviously, Conan Doyle in that case...all the names that people toss out when they read your things...

John: Well, they...

De'Ath: Nursery rhymes, Lewis Carroll, Edward Lear. You'd deny all this, would you?

John: I deny it because I'm ignorant! I was ignorant of the fact...of Lear! I'd never...I'd heard the name obviously, y' know, somewhere. But we didn't do him at school, and the only sort of classic kind of old, very highbrow or anythin' kind of things I'd read were at school. Or that I knew of! And, what is it...Joyce and Chaucer? I might have read a bit of Chaucer at school, 'cause I think they do that. So, I bought all the books that they said it was like. I bought one book on Edward Lear, I bought *Finnegan's Wake*. Chaucer's...a big book on Chaucer. And I couldn't see *any resemblance* to any of them![1764] A little bit of *Finnegan's Wake*, but *Finnegan's Wake* was so way out 'n so different! Just a few word changes, but anybody who changes words is gonna be... has got to be compared. His stuff is just somethin' else!

De'Ath: Can I...can I ask you about Lewis Carroll?

John: Oh, Lewis Carroll! Yeah, I always admit to that because I love *Alice In Wonderland* and *Alice Through The Looking-Glass*. But I didn't even know he'd written anythin' else. I was that ignorant. I just happened to get those for birthday presents as a child, and liked them. And I usually read those two about once a year, because I still like them!

De'Ath: A lot of people say your pieces are "sick." What do you say to them?

John: (Not at all resentful) If it makes people sick, they're sick. But I can read it without...it doesn't appear "sick" to me.

De'Ath: That marvellous cartoon...you know, "I am blind." This is my favourite thing in the whole book!

John: (Pleased smile) Oh.

De'Ath: The other one...the street musician. "I am blind" and the other one: "I can see perfectly well." Is this typical of your kind of humour? Is this the way your mind works?

John: In certain moods. (He shrugs.) We used to do a lot of gags like that at school. I was just drawin', 'n I just happened to make him blind — the fella — 'n gave him a dog. 'N then, I just drew another one next to him who wasn't. 'N then, I didn't think of the joke, 'n then put it down, because at school we used to draw a lot 'n pass it 'round. I remember we had blind dogs with sunglasses on...leadin' ordinary people, or y' know, just all variations on the theme. 'N I just found m' self drawin' somethin' that I'd done at school, but without the tagline.

De'Ath: Let me ask you...the difference I noticed between the first book and the second...the thing that struck me most, possibly, was there's an awful lot of pompous expression. There's more social conscience somehow in this second book, more awareness of what's going on. What about this preoccupation with: "We must not forget! We must not forget! We must not forget!" There's almost a kind of message here, a kind of purpose. You know, in spite of yourself, this almost...I'd call it "social conscience" emerges.

John: Ah, well. I'm not a "do goode" about things. I won't go 'round marchin' or...I'm not *that* type. It just so happens that my feelings about coloured people or religion or anythin' like that, do happen to work with the way I write. I make fun of coloured people in the book, 'n Christians 'n Jews, but really, I'm not *against* them!

De'Ath: I think you keep...

John: ...but I use them to get laughs.

De'Ath: I think you keep very abreast of what's going on, actually. You must do! It comes in all the time.

John: Well, obviously, I read most newspapers all the time, y' know. 'Cause we're often in newspapers, 'n it's still nice to read about yourself. (Quick smile) 'N then, after I've looked 'n seen we're not in it, then I go through the rest of it. 'N then, I finally

end up readin' the political bit, when I've read everythin' else.
So, I'm...y' know, I can't help bein' up with the times, because
(Adopting a geriatric voice) I'm *part of the times* through what
we've been up with, really.

De'Ath: Let me ask you. This piece is very short, and the books
are very short. Do you envision writing anything longer, ever?

John: Well, with the second book, most of it is longer than all
the bits in the first book, I think.

De'Ath: But they're still "mini-pieces," really.

John: (Chuckles) *To you*, they're mini-pieces! To me, they're
marathons! That Sherlock Holmes, as I said, I was seein' how far
it could go 'n how long. I just can't...my mind won't stay on the
same...I have to keep lookin' back...I forget who I've brought
in! By the...after I've written about four — well, it's twenty
pages long 'n some other stuff, 'n I forget which characters have
come in. I get lost, 'n I get fed up 'n bored. That's why I usually
kill...I killed the lot off in the first of the book, but I tried not to
kill everybody off when I got bored 'n tried to progress 'n see
how far the people would go. I just can't think...

De'Ath: Who do you most admire among famous and great
writers?

John: (Frowns) I...I...none of them...y' know.

De'Ath: (Rushing to mitigate John's frustration) No, I'm not
asking for influences, I'm...

John: (Talking simultaneously) No, no I...

De'Ath: Who do you like? Dickens?

John: Dickens I don't like much. I like...I've got to be in a
certain mood...I've never read it...it's too "schooly." I'm still so
young. I'm still too near school to read Dickens or Shakespeare. I
hate Shakespeare! And, y' know, I don't care whether you should
like him or not, because, I don't know whether it's because of
school or just because it doesn't mean anythin' to me. No, I like
Lewis Carroll. I've just been readin' *Winne the Pooh*, which I
never read as a child. It's the sort of only...sort of classic
child...I never seem to get *Winnie the Pooh*, 'n I just discovered
him about a year ago...(Coming full circle to De'Ath's original
question, John shrugs.) Yeah, I dunno.

De'Ath: One or two questions to wind up: What about the other
boys? How do they look upon your writing? What do they think
about it?

John: Um, well Ringo hasn't read anythin' I've ever written. Ah, Paul 'n George have. Yeah, obviously, Paul was because at the time, people were beginnin' to say, "Well, is that all they do?" Y' know. 'N Paul was dead keen…he was that keen to write the Intro, even.

De'Ath: And Paul you're particularly close to anyway, in this verbal punning thing, aren't you?

John: (Pause) Uhm, no more than the others, y' know. The…the…the verbal punnin' goes on between all of us, y' know…just all the time. It's not more…more with Paul than anybody. We're never more with one than the other.

De'Ath: Do you think they envy you this extra dimension that you have?

John: (Shakes his head) No, I don't think so. It's nothin' to stop them from doin' somethin'. I've always done it…I was doin' this kind of thing before I was "Beatling." When they met me, I was already doin' it…sort of after the first couple of weeks, I probably brought out things…I'd read this, so this came before the other…you get my meanin'.

De'Ath: What about the drawings? Let me ask you about those. Did you draw like that from when you were tiny, or have you developed?

John: Um, for a long time, yes. But not with so fine a line. I used to draw with almost anythin' — usually black pen, or just an ordinary fountain pen with black ink in it. 'N then, when it came to doin' the book, I said, "Well, I draw as well," y' know. 'Cause they've mainly got all the writin', 'n the drawin's are very scrappy, 'cause I'm heavy-handed.

De'Ath: Does the drawing spring out of the story, or does the story come from the drawing? Or is it…

John: Sometimes, but hardly ever. Because I draw like I write — I just start 'n draw, 'n if it looks like something vaguely to do with a story, I do it!

De'Ath: John, read something for us, will you?

John: Right. I'll read a bit of "The Fat Budgie."

(John reads, stiffly at first, but develops animation as he goes along.)

"I have a little budgie
He is my very pal
I take him walks in Britain
I hope I always shall.

I call my budgie Jeffrey
My grandads name's the same
I call him after grandad
Who had a feathered brain."[1765]

John: Is that enough?[1766]

He flashed a Cheshire grin at De'Ath, who nodded, "It's a print!" And the recording ceased.

"Y' did all right, De'Ath!" John flashed a relieved toothy smile. "It appears you should take this up as a livin'!"

"Oh, well," De'Ath smirked and stood to shake John's hand, "I'll take that under advisement, then. Note to self!"

And from a disregarded corner of the room, Brian smiled as well.

****

The follow-on interview with Tim Matthews was not as insightful. In fact, much of it was tedious repetition: a discussion of John's inspirations and influences, his method of composition, and yet another sampling from the second Lennon literary release.

This time, John selected a bit from "The National Health Cow."[1767] Articulating in a clipped, precise dialect that Mimi would endorse — instead of his fan-approved, back-of-the-throat Scouse — John imagined his aunt nodding favourably. He further insured her sanction by reading only the innocuous portion of his unexpectedly disquieting verse.

As John had openly admitted earlier, when he tired of his imaginary characters or had nowhere to go with them, he simply "killed them off." And *that*, of course, was the fate of the unusual "National" bovine in the poem. John, however, had quite wisely decided to circumvent the selection's shocking conclusion.

"I strolled into a farmyard
When no-one was about
Treading past the troubles
I raised my head to shout.

'Come out the Cow with glasses,'
I called and rolled my eye.
It ambled up toward me,
I milked it with a sigh."[1768]

John trailed off. He lifted his eyes at Matthews and flourished a roguish smile. But no amount of charisma, he realised, would camouflage the poem, once released.

The fans'll have a difficult time, John thought, *aligning "Beatle John" with the bard of "The National Health Cow." It'll rattle their cages — this one. Eck, eck!*

Already, he anticipated shock waves that poems such as "Last Will and Testicle" and "Our Dad" would provoke. *A Spaniard in the Works* was no collection of light, bright, Fab Four humour. Instead, the slim volume unearthed observations from a long-neglected and cobwebbed gloom. And at unguarded moments, John feared that the book — much like his latest song, "It's Only Love" — would, perhaps, reveal a bit too much.

****

Thursday, 17 June 1965
EMI Studios
3 Abbey Road, St. John's Wood
London

The next seven days were a blur. With The Beatles' second "World Tour" — this year, pared down to a mere "European Tour" — looming just ahead, the boys converged in EMI to concentrate on the completion of the film's soundtrack.

Earlier this afternoon, at George Martin's recommendation, a string quartet had assembled in Studio Two to artfully fill Paul's "Yesterday" with the elegant score that Martin and McCartney had created.[1769] The stark and chilly room had been astir with introductions, instructions, direction, and the rustle of sheet music. Guidance had been given; suggestions, taken. Then, Martin had retreated to the booth to supervise.[1770]

For a few minutes, the four London Symphony musicians — Tony Gilbert on first violin, Sidney Sax on second violin, Francisco Gabarrow on cello, and Kenneth Essex on viola — had taken their places and chatted amiably.[1771] But then, as the red light flashed, they were all business. In less than two hours time, Paul — as George Martin phrased it — "had another go at the vocal," and then the perfected, overdubbed, poignant string arrangement had been added to Paul's 14 June Take Two of the solo song. "Yesterday" had been beautifully completed.[1772]

Following on, Ringo, who had initially planned to use his 18 February recording of "If You've Got Trouble" for the *Help!* LP,[1773] had politely requested a slice of studio time to record an alternate number.[1774] Lennon and McCartney's raucous West Coast/Jan and Dean spin-off[1775] had never been successful, and all of them saw it. So, the drummer had been practicing one of his favourite tunes — Buck Owens's gigantic hit, "Act Naturally." Ringo heartily endorsed it as "the perfect number, y' know, for a film soundtrack."[1776]

So, between 4.00 p.m. and 5.30 p.m., Starkey had droned out the country and western musical saga of his newfound stardom whilst Paul had supplied harmony, and George had banged out the rhythm line on his Framus Hootenanny acoustic.[1777] It was all great fun, except…

"Where's John?" Ringo frowned, somewhere in the 13 takes required to perfect Side Two's light-hearted opening number.

"I dunno," Paul glanced at the booth, as if an answer might drift down from on high.

"Doubtless at some book promotion or another, folks,"[1778] George suggested, his hands atop his guitar. "He *has* to be here tonight, though. We *have* to finish up."

"Yeah right. 'N the last song's half his." Paul took a quick drag on a dwindled cig. "'Wait.'"

"*What?*" Ringo feigned confusion, playing the perfect straight man. "I'm not goin' anywhere!"

"No, no...'Wait.' That's the *song*," Paul fell for the old comedy gag. "John shares lead vocal, as it were."[1779]

"He gets it, Paul." George shook his head.

"It's a joke, son!" John's nasal voice sounded from the doorway.

"Where've *you* been?" George relaxed. When John wasn't around, everything skewed.

"Where d' ya think?"

"I dunno. That's why I'm askin'." George quirked the corner of his mouth. "Skivin' off, eh?"

"What're you?" John crossed the room and hoisted his guitar. "Teacher's best boy? Never y' mind where I was. I'm back now."

"And not a moment too soon, actually." Paul nodded towards the wall clock. "We've work to do."

"Shall we, then?" John proposed, as always.

"We shall!"

****

7.00 p.m.[1780]

In most cases, the Lennon/McCartney partnership was a matter of unilateral composition and joint renovation. John wrote a song that Paul neatly tweaked. Or Paul wrote a song to which John contributed a word, a well-coined phrase, or a concept here and there.[1781] It was only infrequently that they created a track with equal input. "Wait" was such a one. [1782]

John had knocked out the verses,[1783] lyrically reminiscent of

"When I Get Home," "Every Little Thing," "Any Time at All," and even "A Hard Day's Night." The all-too-familiar and very personal theme of separation from his "gerl" coupled with the joys of homecoming came naturally to him.

Paul had rendered the confessional middle eight[1784] with a shy eye towards Jane Asher. Admitting that he'd endeavoured to "be good" in the days they'd spent apart, Paul had neatly qualified his behaviour with the codicil "good...as good as I can be." Naturally, not a fan could fault him.

But despite the song's lyrics, The Beatles realised that "Wait" was "not particularly strong."[1785] It was no lambent "Yesterday," no emotional "You've Got to Hide Your Love Away." It was merely a standard LP placeholder.

But what were they to do? With John's book promotional interviews filling most of Friday, the group's pre-European tour interviews with BBC's Italian language service occupying Saturday afternoon, and John's live television appearance on *Tonight* with Kenneth Allsop slated for Saturday evening, the boys had to complete the "Help!" soundtrack tonight.[1786] The Beatles needed to record one last song.

"Wait, Take One," Norman Smith intoned blandly from the booth.

"All well, Norman?" Martin frowned, scrutinizing the First Engineer. The producer knew the events of the last few days, and he sympathized. Smith had very nearly talked the boys into accepting one of his original songs for the new soundtrack. In fact, he had missed a life-changing opportunity only by a margin.

"Ah...well..." Norman grimaced and shrugged, "'For of all sad words of tongue or pen...'"[1787]

"'...the saddest are these," Martin finished John Greenleaf Whittier's famous line from "Maud Muller." "'It might have been!'"[1788]

And really, Norman's story *was* disappointing. Several sessions ago, Norman had shyly approached George Martin about "a prospect...for all of us."

"And what's that?" Martin had arched an eyebrow.

"I know the boys heard this before," Norman had begun, "but...I happen to have a song in my pocket."[1789]

"Get on the talkback and tell them."[1790] Martin had wasted no time.

"Uh…it wouldn't do to…" Norman had been reticent to impose himself on the boys.

So, George Martin had surveyed the activity below, flipped on the 1MC, and asked, "Paul, can you come up? Norman's got a song for you."[1791]

"*Really,* Normal?"[1792] Paul's eyes had enlarged.

Smith had wagged his head at the fond moniker that John had coined for him ages ago.[1793] "Yes. Yes, really."[1794]

So, with John otherwise occupied, Norman, Paul, and George Martin had quickly trekked over to Studio Three for a listen. Norman had settled himself at the battered, brown, upright piano and biting his lower lip, he'd nervously "bashed the song out."[1795] Paul had been interested; then, impressed.

"Uh…that's *really* good,"[1796] Paul had stared with disbelieving eyes. But Norman had assured him the song was completely original — written expressly with The Beatles in mind. "Well…all right then." Paul had clicked his cheek, "I can hear John singin' that!"[1797]

And moments later, John himself had been summoned, to hear the ingenue Norman Smith song.

Narrowing his eyes and listening intently, John had folded his arms — hardly moved. Then, turning his head to view "Normal" with new eyes, John had wasted no time in claiming the property. "That's great!" he'd grinned widely. "We'll do it!"[1798]

"But," Paul had raised a cautionary finger, "first, we'll need a demo version, 'n naturally, y' know, we'll have to make it our own."[1799]

"Oh, yeah, of course," Smith had nodded, smiling widely. "That goes without saying." And all had seemed right with the world.

But twenty-four hours later, a hangdog Lennon and McCartney had approached the First Engineer with sideways glances.[1800]

"Ach! You don't want the song after all!" Norman had seen it immediately.

"Look, we definitely liked your song…"[1801] John had begun.

"…but we've realised," Paul quickly went on, "that Ringo hasn't got a vocal on the LP, and he's *got* to have one. We'll do yours another time, eh?"[1802]

"Sure, all right." The crestfallen Smith had been typically

amenable. But the engineer knew that a dream deferred is rarely realised. And in light of the fact that Beatles music publisher Dick James had generously offered him £15,000 to secure the rights for his upcoming Beatles song, Norman's loss was significant.[1803] However, saying nothing to John or Paul about this, Norman had merely shrugged and hoped for another opportunity.

Now tonight, as the commonplace "Wait" imprinted itself on the reel-to-reel tape in only four takes, Norman smiled sadly at George Martin and muttered four woeful words, "Gone in a flash."[1804]

Notes!

1. What happened to Norman Smith and his songwriting talents?

Lest you feel awful for Norman Smith, he did, indeed, finally get a hit song. In fact, he not only wrote the song; he sang it! In 1972, he recorded "Oh Babe, What Would You Say," as Hurricane Smith, and it went all the way to Number One on Cashbox *and Number Three on* Billboard. *If you'd like to hear Smith's Seventies dance song once again, please listen here: https://www.youtube.com/watch?v=ZMlPsTrLn1l*

It is interesting to note that when George Martin did the stereo mixes for the Help! *soundtrack, he decided to hold "Wait" in abeyance. The song finally ended up, months later, on the* Rubber Soul *LP. Who knows what might have happened if Smith had been afforded the chance to have his song recorded by The Beatles instead?*

2. Why didn't John come into the studio on the morning of Thursday, 17 June?

We don't know. George Harrison conjectured that John was promoting his new book, A Spaniard in the Works. *And indeed, as Allen Wiener points out in* The Ultimate Recording Guide, *John had two such interviews on the previous evening and one on Friday, 18 June with Kenneth Allsop.(p. 49) But nothing was in John's diary on Thursday morning, 17 June.*

It is possible that his absence was a reaction to the solo recording of "Yesterday." He may have been saying, in his own Lennonesque fashion, "Well, if y' don't need me, then…" Indeed, Spitz tells us that George Martin was very concerned that EMI might release "Yesterday" as a McCartney single and "…That wouldn't sit well at all with John…whose ego was in fragile enough shape without shifting more attention toward Paul." (p. 563)

Was John absent because his feelings were hurt? There is no documentation to prove this, and we'll never know for sure.

Sources:

Lewisohn, The Complete Beatles Chronicle, *195-196.*
Lewisohn, The Beatles Recording Sessions, *60.*
Lewisohn, The Beatles: Day by Day, *63,*
Harry, The Ultimate Beatles Encyclopedia, *611 and 683.*
Harry, The Encyclopedia of Beatles People, *164-165.*
Harry, The John Lennon Encyclopedia, *833.*
The Beatles, The Beatles Anthology, *173.*
Lennon, A Spaniard in the Works, *18 and 62-63.*
Miles, The Beatles' Diary, Vol. 1, *198.*
Miles, Many Years From Now, *206.*
Winn, 326-327.
Howlett, The Beatles at the BBC: The Radio Years, 1962-70, *73.*
Womack, Maximum Volume: The Life of Beatles Producer, George Martin, *262-263 and 265-266.*
Womack, The Beatles Encyclopedia, Vol. 2, *969.*
Womack, Long and Winding Roads: The Evolving Artistry of The Beatles, *110.*
Coleman, Lennon, *242-243.*
Spitz, 562-563.
Hill, John, Paul, George & Ringo, *202 and 205.*
Everett, The Beatles as Musicians: The Quarry Men Through Rubber Soul, *296.*
Riley, Tell Me Why, *168.*
Hertsgaard, 129.
Lewis and Spignesi, 25.
Hammack, 51, 55, and 57.
Spizer, Beatles for Sale on Parlophone Records, *190-191 and 203.*
MacDonald, 127.
Margotin and Guesdon, 152 and 240.
Mellers, 64-65.
Turner, 98.
Cain and McCusker, 178.
Tremlett, 64.
Burrows, 67.
Robertson, 41.
Wiener, 49.
Bicknell, 51.

Works Alluded to in this Chapter:

Whittier, John Greenleaf, "Maud Muller," 1856.

http://beatlesinterviews.org/db1965.0616.beatles.html This transcription of the interview between Wilfrid De'Ath and John Lennon for "The World of Books" was initially very carefully completed by Jay Spangler. When Suzie Duchateau and I purchased BeatlesInterviews.net in 2019, we updated some of the interviews on the site. This one has undergone a few edits from the original transcription. Thanks to Jay for his hard work and to Suzie for the updates!

"Wait" by The Beatles. The in-depth story behind the songs of the Beatles. Recording History. Songwriting History. Song Structure and Style. (beatlesebooks.com) This website provides in-depth information about the songs on "Help!," including "Wait."

http://www.beatlesebooks.com/act-naturally Similarly, this same website provides in-depth information about "Act Naturally."

https://www.beatlesbible.com/1965/06/17/recording-yesterday-act-naturally-wait/ This website gives a brief but accurate summary of the events of Thursday, 17 June 1965.

https://pastdaily.com/2020/10/09/john-lennon-in-a-few-words-1965-past-daily-pop-chronicles/ Listen here to almost nine minutes of the interview between Wilfrid De'Ath and John Lennon, found in its complete version in this chapter.
Or use this QR code:

[1758] Spitz, 563.
[1759] Lewisohn, *The Complete Beatles Chronicle*, 195-196 and Miles, *The Beatles' Diary, Vol. 1,* 198.
[1760] https://en.wikipedia.org/wiki/Wilfrid_De%27ath This website supplies biographical information about Wilfrid De'Ath who interviewed John Lennon on 16 June 1965.
[1761] This is the first line from the recorded interview which took place between Wilfrid De'Ath and John Lennon, 16 June 1965, at the NEMS Offices, London. I am not going to endnote each line of the interview but will endnote again at the end. You may hear the interview at: John Lennon - In A Few Words - 1965 - Past Daily Pop Chronicles - Past Daily: News, History, Music And An Enormous Sound Archive. Additionally, you may read a good portion of the interview in Howlett, *The Beatles at the BBC*, 73 and in Coleman's *Lennon*, you can read a summary of the interview on pp. 242-243.

[1762] The end of this sentence is not found in Howlett's account of the interview in *The Beatles at the BBC*, p. 73. However, it *is* in the audio version.

[1763] This is the end of the segment from John's interview with Wilfrid De'Ath found in Howlett's *The Beatles at the BBC*, 73. The rest of the interview may be heard at: John Lennon - In A Few Words - 1965 - Past Daily Pop Chronicles - Past Daily: News, History, Music And An Enormous Sound Archive.

[1764] Harry, *The John Lennon Encyclopedia*, 835. This paragraph of John's can also be found in Harry's book.

[1765] Lennon, John, *A Spaniard in the Works*, 18.

[1766] This is the last line from the recorded interview that took place between Wifrid De'Ath and John Lennon, 16 June 1965, at the NEMS Offices, London. found at: John Lennon - In A Few Words - 1965 - Past Daily Pop Chronicles - Past Daily: News, History, Music And An Enormous Sound Archive.

[1767] Winn, 326 and Lewisohn, *The Compete Beatles Chronicle*, 195-196. Winn says that one can hear the excerpt of John reading "The National Health Cow" on a bootleg CD entitled *The Beatles Broadcast, Trailer 2*.

[1768] Lewisohn, *The Complete Beatles Chronicle*, 196. Lewisohn tells us that in the Matthews interview, John read aloud "two verses of 'The National Health Cow'."

[1769] Womack, *Maximum Volume: The Life of Beatles Producer, George Martin*, 262, Lewis and Spignesi, 25, and Hammack, 51. All accounts of the creation of the string arrangement for "Yesterday" state that it was Martin's idea, and that he created the score with Paul's input. Womack quotes Paul talking about his work on the "Yesterday" score. He says, "The thing people don't generally know is that me or John or whoever was involved in the orchestral angle would go 'round to George's house or he would come 'round to ours, and we would sit with him, and I did on this. I went 'round to George's house, and we had a pleasant couple of hours." (p. 262) Then, Womack quotes George Martin as saying, "Paul worked with me on the score, putting the cello here and the violin there." (p. 262) Martin goes on to point out Paul's various contributions to the score.

[1770] Womack, *Maximum Volume: The Life of Beatles Producer, George Martin*, 263. Womack says, "After walking the musicians through their parts, Martin headed for the control room…"

[1771] Lewisohn, *The Complete Beatles Chronicle*, 196, Winn, 326-327, Lewsiohn, *The Beatles Recording Sessions*, 59, Hammack, 51, Margotin and Guesdon, 152, Lewis and Spignesi, 25, Spizer, *The Beatles for Sale on Parlophone Records*, 191, Miles, *Many Years From Now*, 206, and Womack, *Maximum Volume: The Life of Beatles Producer, George Martin*, 262-263.

[1772] Lewisohn, *The Complete Beatles Chronicle*, 196, Winn, 326-327, Lewsiohn, *The Beatles Recording Sessions*, 59, Hammack, 51, Margotin and Guesdon, 152, Lewis and Spignesi, 25, Spizer, *The Beatles for Sale on Parlophone Records*, 191, Miles, *Many Years From Now*, 206, and Womack, *Maximum Volume: The Life of Beatles Producer, George Martin*, 262-263. The string quartet was not a long-standing group, but they were well acquainted professionally. Womack says they were "four session players from the Top of the Pops." (p. 262-263) Spizer and Miles specify that they were "four musicians from the London Symphony Orchestra." (Spizer, 191 and Miles, 206).

[1773] Lewisohn, *The Complete Beatles Chronicle*, 196, Lewisohn, *The Beatles Recording Sessions*, 60, Womack, *Long and Winding Roads*, 110, MacDonald, 127, Hertsgaard, *A Day in the Life: The Music and Artistry of The Beatles*, 129, and Hammack, 55.

[1774] The Beatles, *The Beatles Anthology*, 173. In *The Beatles Anthology*, Ringo says, "I recorded a song for the *Help!* album that was never released — "If You've Got Trouble." And George replies, "We've just come across that, and it's the most weird song. I've no recollections of ever recording it. It's got stupid words and is the naffest song. No wonder it didn't make it onto anything."

[1775] To hear the similarities between "If You've Got Trouble" and Jan and Dean's music, listen to their hit song "Linda," found here: https://www.youtube.com/watch?v=ZWOq2S7Hwj8

[1776] Spizer, *The Beatles for Sale on Parlophone Records*, 190, Womack, *Long and Winding Roads*, 110, Margotin and Guesdon, 240, MacDonald, 127, and http://www.beatlesebooks.com/act-naturally. Though some sources credit George Martin with choosing this cover song for Ringo, Spizer tells us that "Act Naturally" is "a charming country and western tune **selected by Ringo** as his vocal spotlight on the album." (p. 190) And Margotin and Guesdon agree that it was the drummer who chose the song. They quote Ringo as saying, "I sang 'Act Naturally' in "Help!" I found it on a Buck Owens record, and I said, 'This is the one I'm goin' to be doin',' and they said 'OK.'" (p. 240)

[1777] Lewisohn, *The Complete Beatles Chronicle*, 196, Lewisohn, *The Beatles Recording Sessions,* 60, Winn, 327, Hammack, 51, Womack, *Maximum Volume: The Life of Beatles Producer, George Martin,* 266, Margotin and Guesdon, 240, Miles, *The Beatles' Diary, Vol. 1*, 204, and Spizer, *The Beatles for Sale on Parlophone Records,* 190.

[1778] Womack, *Maximum Volume: The Life of Beatles Producer, George Martin*, 265-266. Womack notes that John was "noticeably absent from [this afternoon's proceedings] because "*A Spaniard in the Works* was scheduled for release on 24 June," and with the European Tour so imminent, John was taking advantage of "some much needed PR time to publicize his second book."

[1779] Lewisohn, *The Complete Beatles Chronicle*, 196, Lewisohn, *The Beatles Recording Sessions*, 60, Winn, 327, Margotin and Guesdon, 304, Spizer, *The Beatles for Sale on Parlophone Records*, 203, Harry, *The Ultimate Beatles Encyclopedia*, 683, Hammack, 57, and Turner, 98.

[1780] Lewisohn, *The Complete Beatles Chronicles*, 196, Margotin and Guesdon, 304. Margotin and Guesdon refer to "Wait" as "more of a filler than a masterpiece."

[1781] Tremlett, George, *The John Lennon Story*, 64. Tremlett quotes John as saying, "Even in the early days, we used to write things separately because Paul was always more advanced than I was." John goes on to say, "…usually, one of us wrote most of the song, and the other just helped to finish it off, adding a bit of a tune or a bit of a lyric."

[1782] Lewisohn, *The Complete Beatles Chronicles*, 196, Hammack, 57, Womack, *Maximum Volume: The Life of Beatles Producer, George Martin*, 267, Riley, *Tell Me Why*, 168, and Turner, 98. There is some debate about who wrote this song. Some sources attribute the song solely to Paul, but Hammack states, "John Lennon and Paul McCartney's 'Wait' was as clear a demonstration of the duo's songwriting partnership as one could ask for — the verses clearly Lennon's while the middle eight clearly McCartney's." Turner also says that "Wait" was "written by both John and Paul, it's an all-purpose song…" And Womack calls "Wait" "the most recent Lennon and McCartney composition."

[1783] Hammack, 57 and Riley, *Tell Me Why*, 168. In later years, Paul claimed full authorship for this song, but all early sources attribute the song to both Beatles and dub it one of the few true collaborations.

[1784] Hammack, 57 and Riley, *Tell Me Why*, 168.

[1785] Hammack, 57 and Riley, *Tell Me Why*, 168.

[1786] Lewisohn, *The Complete Beatles Chronicle*, 196, Miles, *The Beatles' Diary, Vol. 1*, 198, and Robertson, *Lennon*, 41.

[1787] Whittier, John Greenleaf, "Maud Muller," 1856.

[1788] Whittier, John Greenleaf, "Maud Muller," 1856.

[1789] Lewisohn, *The Beatles Recording Sessions*, 60 and Womack, *Maximum Volume: The Life of Beatles Producer, George Martin*, 266. Direct quote from Norman Smith.

[1790] Lewisohn, *The Beatles Recording Sessions*, 60 and Womack, *Maximum Volume: The Life of Beatles Producer, George Martin*, 266. Direct quote from George Martin, according to Norman Smith.

[1791] Lewisohn, *The Beatles Recording Sessions*, 60 and Womack, *Maximum Volume: The Life of Beatles Producer, George Martin*, 266. Direct quote from George Martin, according to Norman Smith.

[1792] Lewisohn, *The Beatles Recording Sessions*, 60 and Womack, *Maximum Volume: The Life of Beatles Producer, George Martin*, 266. Direct quote from Paul McCartney, according to Norman Smith.

[1793] Harry, *The Ultimate Beatles Encyclopedia*, 611 and personal interview with Richard Langham, Second Engineer at EMI in 1962-64. Both Langham and Harry vow that John is the one who came up with the nickname "Normal." Harry states, "John used to call him 'Normal Smith,' and Paul's pet name for him was 'Two D-C's Smith,' referring to the time Norman told him to turn his amplifier down by a couple of decibels."

[1794] Lewisohn, *The Beatles Recording Sessions*, 60 and Womack, *Maximum Volume: The Life of Beatles Producer, George Martin*, 266. Direct quote from Norman Smith.

[1795] Lewisohn, *The Beatles Recording Sessions*, 60 and Womack, *Maximum Volume: The Life of Beatles Producer, George Martin*, 266. "Bashed the song out" is a direct quote from Norman Smith.

[1796] Lewisohn, *The Beatles Recording Sessions*, 60 and Womack, *Maximum Volume: The Life of Beatles Producer, George Martin*, 266. Direct quote from Paul McCartney, according to Norman Smith.

[1797] Lewisohn, *The Beatles Recording Sessions*, 60 and Womack, *Maximum Volume: The Life of Beatles Producer, George Martin*, 266. Direct quote from Paul McCartney, according to Norman Smith.

[1798] Lewisohn, *The Beatles Recording Sessions*, 60 and Womack, *Maximum Volume: The Life of Beatles Producer, George Martin*, 266. Direct quote from John Lennon, according to Norman Smith.

[1799] Lewisohn, *The Beatles Recording Sessions*, 60 and Womack, *Maximum Volume: The Life of Beatles Producer, George Martin*, 266. Direct quote from Paul McCartney, according to Norman Smith.

[1800] Lewisohn, *The Beatles Recording Sessions*, 60 and Womack, *Maximum Volume: The Life of Beatles Producer, George Martin*, 266. Mark Lewisohn described them as having "sheepish, long faces."

[1801] Lewisohn, *The Beatles Recording Sessions*, 60 and Womack, *Maximum Volume: The Life of Beatles Producer, George Martin*, 266. Direct quote from either Paul or John, according to Norman Smith. I chose John for this one and Paul for the next one.

[1802] Lewisohn, *The Beatles Recording Sessions*, 60 and Womack, *Maximum Volume: The Life of Beatles Producer, George Martin*, 266. Direct quote from either John or Paul, according to Norman Smith.

[1803] Lewisohn, *The Beatles Recording Sessions*, 60 and Hill, *John, Paul, George & Ringo*, 202.

[1804] Lewisohn, *The Beatles Recording Sessions*, 60 and Womack, *Maximum Volume: The Life of Beatles Producer, George Martin*, 266. Direct quote from Norman Smith. The full quote, is "That was my £15,000, gone in a flash."

Friday, 18 June 1965
Kenwood
Weybridge, Surrey

The following morning was chaotic, as The Beatles' European Tour drew closer. For days, Alf Bicknell had been nudging John to have his baggage ready for transport by Friday.[1805] The chauffeur had planned to collect Lennon's belongings when picking up the boy for a tour-related interview in NEMS and a televised evening book promotion in BBC studios.[1806] Bicknell feared that if he didn't begin gathering the boys' belongings today, they'd never be prepared for the early flight into Paris, Sunday morning.[1807] The four — for all their importance and fame — were still university-aged boys. Packing wasn't their forté.

"But I wasn't even *home* 'til midnight, just!" John raged, as Cynthia packed for him, only asking her husband to select "this shirt or that," or "these pyjamas or those." John was tired, irritable, and unwilling to make decisions under "command performance." And, in a way, he was justified.

The Beatles hadn't left EMI on Thursday evening until well after 9.30 p.m.,[1808] and then, John had endured the monotonous hour's trek back to "the God-forsaken stockbroker's belt!" Dragging in the front door, close on 11.00 p.m., John had been "knackered, to be honest" and completely unwilling to begin "rummagin' through the wardrobe at this hour!" Unfortunately, he was just as annoyed by the process now.

Hunched over the breakfast table, John morosely shoveled in Corn Flakes with one of Julian's stainless steel Peter Rabbit spoons. Julian sat beside him, imitating his father's every move. John made a face; Julian made a face. John let milk dribble from his chin; Julian followed suit. Then unexpectedly, the toddler dropped a large plop of Corn Flakes and milk on the table beside his bowl, and fearfully, his eyes darted to his father. Would they laugh? Was he in trouble? Would…

"*Shite!*" John jumped up, not knowing whether to scoop up the food with his bare hands or scarper to the sink for a damp tea towel. "*Fuggin'ell!*" He bellowed irritably, as Julian burst into tears.[1809]

"What's the kerfuffle in here?" Cynthia rushed into the room, assessing the situation with a glance. She grabbed a paper napkin and quickly bundled the gooey glob, drying the table with the other side of the crumpled paper.

"Christ, Julian!" John was still fuming. "Can't you even once…"

"*Stop!*" Cynthia picked her son up and cradled his head against her shoulder. "*Stop it right now!*" Her eyes — trained on her husband — were narrow slits of indignation.[1810]

Stunned, John drew back. In five years, Cynthia had never crossed him. Not ever. He wasn't sure how to react.

"If you were here more often," Cynthia spat, angrily, "you'd realise that *this* is how little boys of three eat!"[1811] She moved towards the door with her child. "*Now leave him alone!*"[1812]

And hurrying upstairs, Cynthia left a stunned John gaping, his mouth ajar.[1813]

In the nursery, Cyn knelt on the braided rug and patted her son's heaving back. "It's not you, Jules," she mumured, softly. "Daddy's not angry with you. He's riled at someone else…a lot of someone elses, actually. Daddy loves you very, very much. He's just in a terrible tear."

The boy's wails subsided slowly to a ragged, shivery breath, but he clung to his mother. He buried his face in her hair. Julian curled a tendril of the golden flax around and around his chubby hand and nestled his head against her shoulder.

"Daddy's had an awfully pear-shaped week, you see." Cynthia's voice assumed a warm, storybook tone. "And he's frightened, just the way you are, sometimes, in the dark…because he has a new book of his stories that's going out to a lot of big stores for people to read…and, truth told, he's afraid no one will like them."

Julian sniffled, listening.

"A few days ago," Cynthia carried on, "one of his friends rather hurt Daddy's feelings, but Daddy can't say anything or do anything to make it better." Julian nodded, and his mother continued the story. "On Sunday, Jules, your daddy's going on another long trip that will mean a *lot* of fuss and bother...in a strange place with strange people all around him. He has lots of worries — your daddy. But he's not angry with *you* at all."

Julian peeked at his mum and nodded silently.

"This afternoon," Cynthia smiled, "Daddy has to appear on an important radio show with Paul and George and Ringo, and he's always afraid he'll say or do something amiss, you see. And tonight, he's on telly, all by himself, with a smart man who'll ask him lots and lots of hard questions about his books. So, he's frantic about that as well.[1814] Your Daddy's stroppy about a lot of things, Julian. But not you. Never you."

As his mother talked and rocked him gently, Julian's world gradually returned to normal. Yet, when the driver came to take his daddy away, Julian and his mum lingered in their quiet place, and neither of them ventured downstairs to bid him, "Goodbye."[1815]

****

BBC's Lime Grove Studios
London

7.00 p.m.

In reality, John hadn't been overly concerned about the afternoon's Italian-language interview in NEMS.[1816] It was standard fare: the same uninspired questions from the same unimaginative press.

But the *Tonight Show* interview with Kenneth Allsop was something entirely different. The man was brilliant, and he thought John brilliant as well. In fact, when last they'd met, in BBC's Lime Grove Studios in 1964,[1817] Allsop had challenged John to "up his game," to become a stronger musical lyricist.[1818] He'd urged John to draw upon his life's rich experiences to create songs as well-considered and well-constructed as his poetry and prose.[1819]

Allsop never asked ordinary questions, and he didn't expect

insipid answers. The respected author — a reporter for the *Daily Mail* and the Rector of Edinburgh University — set a high conversational bar.[1820] John knew that.

Recently, in fact, John had read Allsop's brilliant analysis of 1950's literature, *The Angry Decade*, and he'd marvelled. It embarrassed John that his paltry collection of poetry and prose should be examined by the very man who had penned, "In this technologically triumphant age, when the rockets begin to scream up towards the moon but the human mind seems at an even greater distance, anger has a limited use. Love has a wider application, and it is that which needs describing wherever it can be found so that we may all recognise it and learn its use."[1821] John thought these important words, and he longed to write something with the same potency and truth.

Kenneth Allsop, author, reporter,
and Rector of Edinburgh University,
who interviewed John about his books in 1964-65
Photograph from Wikimedia Commons

Furthermore, John thought Allsop a true hero. Flying for the R.A.F. in World War II, the reporter had lost his leg. But Allsop had never let the loss slow him one iota. Sometimes, when John grumbled about nights with scant sleep or diaries brimming with meaningless events, he thought of Allsop and how the man forged ahead seamlessly, as if nothing had happened to him.

John favoured few people, but he genuinely liked Allsop. Respected him. And tonight, John wanted very much to impress him. There would be no silly faces, no sharp, smart remarks, no "shilly-shally."

The interview was to be preceeded by the author's own interpretation of his poetry.[1822] John had been asked to read a selection (or two) from *A Spaniard in the Works,* and thus, two it was.

First, the "Literary Beatle" straight-faced a whimsical bit from the politically-inspired "We must not forget the General Erection,"[1823] and then John indulged himself in one of his favourites, "The Wumberlog (or The Magic Dog),"[1824] a fond homage to Lewis Carroll's "The Hunting of the Snark."[1825]

Swathed in memories of his "good ol' Uncle Ge'rge," John's poem traced the bizarre adventures that once unfolded when "crept a little boy from bed," striking out in the world, alone. Seeking his uncle, the child discovered "the Wumberlog, the highly feathered crow," and…

"He met him friendly magic dog,
All black and curlew too,
Wot flew him fast in second class
To do wot he must do."[1826]

And there, John left the audience wanting more. Being rapidly directed to the *Tonight* show's interview set for a "sit-down" with Allsop, John rubbed moist palms against his trousers, greeted the reporter warmly, and sat perched, anxious about the first question.

Kenneth Allsop: Mr. Lennon, your first book is a bestseller, and I shouldn't see any doubt this one's going to be, too. Do you think that you'd be published were you not a Beatle?[1827]
John: I could probably get published but, y' know, I wouldn't sell as many. I mean, they publish a lot of rubbish, anyway. But, uhh, I wouldn't *sell*.

Allsop: Do you think you've got a built-in advantage in being a Beatle? I mean, are you glad about this, or would you rather have found a reputation as a writer in your own right?

John: No, I mean, I never thought of it. If I hadn't been a Beatle, I just wouldn't have thought of havin' the stuff published 'cause I would've been crawlin' around broke, 'n just writin' it, 'n throwin' it away. (Slight pause) I might've been a Beat poet.

Allsop: How did it come about that you *weren't* a Beat poet and that your first book was published?

John: Well, some American, who shall remain nameless, who's called Michael Brown[1828] — I showed him the stuff, 'n he took it to the publisher, 'n they published it. That was it.

Allsop: Did you ever think of publishing it under a pseudonym — not as John Lennon?

John: (Nods) I thought about it, but what's the use, y' know? (He shrugs.) Because *he* took it to the publisher first…without tellin' them who he was, just to see if they would've published it. That answers your first question as well.

Allsop: It does indeed, yes. (Short pause) Living in the butterfly world of "pop" as a Beatle, do you think that this undermines people's serious acceptance of you as a writer?

John: (Nodding) Uhh, it does. But I didn't really expect them to take me seriously, so, y' know — there's nothin' to say about that. They *do* take it more seriously than I thought, so that's good enough for me.

Allsop: (Smiles a bit) Indeed. I mean, the first book was reviewed in the posh *Sundays*, and on the other side of the fence, your music is recorded by people like Ella Fitzgerald. Now, this is *serious recognition* in both areas. Which do you find more satisfying?

John: Well, uhh…the book, really. It means more to other people that Ella Fitzgerald recorded one of our tunes than it does to us, because the tune is still somethin' that Paul 'n I have written, so we still have the same faith in it. It just gives *other people* more "faith" in the tunes.

Allsop: This book is very similar to the first, in being bits and pieces of poems and bits of prose. Do you think you'd ever want to do anything longer? A novel, for example?

John: Well, I tried writin'… (Short pause) The longest thing I've written is in this book. It's one about Sherlock Holmes, 'n it seemed like a novel to me, but it turned out to be six pages. (Laughs a bit) But I don't think I could...I couldn't do it, y' know. I get fed-up. And I wrote so many characters in it, I forgot who they were!

Allsop: (Nods) This happens to other writers, too.

John: (Smiles) Hmmm. Other writers! Good.

Allsop: The "pop" business is a young man's world. It seems to have an ever-increasingly young audience. Do you think that perhaps writing a book like this, and writing at all, perhaps, might be an unconscious attempt to win recognition in the adult world?

John: (Shaking his head strongly) No, because I started all this writin' long before I was a "pop" artist, or even a Beatle, or before I had a guitar. So it's nothin' to do with that. The guitars came second.

Allsop: And which comes first?

John: Well, *now* the guitars come first...'cause this (Gesturing towards a copy of his book on the table in front of them) is still a hobby, which it always has been.

Allsop: (Kind smile) You're going on doing it, are you?

John: (Lifting his chin) I'll go on doin' it.

Allsop: Have you written anything else? Is anything else coming off of this?

John: Well, uhh, I don't get much time. (Slight chuckle) If I had more time, I'd probably write more. The publisher rang-up 'n said, "Have y' written anything yet?" and I said, "No, I've been writin' songs...because I can't do *both* at once!" Y' know, I've got to concentrate on the book or the songs. So I haven't written anythin' since then.

Allsop: (Smiles) We'll look for it nevertheless, John. Thank you very much, indeed.

John: (In a comically exaggerated voice) Thank YOU![1829]

When the red camera light flicked to black, John blew relief through his lips. He smiled.

"I've been takin' your advice, y' know," he informed Allsop as they stood and sauntered off set.

"How's that?" Allsop raised a bushy eyebrow.

"Well, y' haven't been listenin' to the radio, have ya?" John took the mickey out. "'I'm a Loser' for example.[1830] It was on our last LP 'n...well, I've been doin' what y' told me to do last year y' know…about makin' m' songs more like m' books. More about *me*, as it were.[1831] The real me, anyway.[1832] 'N there's lots more 'real' to come…in the new soundtrack."

"Really?" Allsop stopped and smiled. *"You don't say?* Few people heed me, actually. I'm quite honoured." Allsop beamed. He knew that John Lennon let his songs speak for him. They were his ambassadors to the world.[1833] And if John had imbued his Beatles hits with greater honesty due to something Kenneth had said…well, Allsop was astounded.

"Well…" John flushed, speechless for once, "Ta."

And instead of rabbiting on, John merely stuck out his hand and shook Allsop's — two "off-the-beaten-path" authors exchanging confidences and an abundance mutual respect.

Notes!

How accurate is the statement that John respected reporter, author, and BBC programme host Kenneth Allsop, and that John took his autobiographical lyric writing to a deeper level at Allsop's suggestion?

Although many biographers give Bob Dylan and his The Freewheelin' Bob Dylan *LP credit for influencing John's long-standing autobiographical bent in song-writing, Kenneth Allsop also played a significant role in encouraging John's tendency to sing his life's story.*

Indeed, in his book, A Hard Day's Write, *Stephen Turner observes: "The second event to affect John in a big way was meeting journalist Kenneth Allsop, a writer for the* Daily Mail *and a regular interviewer on* Tonight, *BBC Television's news magazine programme. John first met him on March 23, when he was interviewed for four minutes on* Tonight *about his book* In His Own Write, *and then again at a Foyles Literary Luncheon at the Dorchester Hotel in London's Park Lane. Allsop was 44 years old…at the time…and had been in journalism since 1938, with a brief interruption caused by the war…*

"It was in the 'green room,' the hospitality suite, at the BBC's Lime Grove Studios on March 23 that Allsop first spoke to John about his song-writing, encouraging him not to hide his true feelings behind the usual banalities of the pop song. It was obvious to Allsop from reading In His Own Write *that John had much more to give if he was prepared to open up to his deeper feelings.*

"Years later, John told his confidant Elliot Mintz that this meeting marked a significant turning point in his songwriting. 'He told me that he was very nervous that day and, because of this, became very talkative and engaged Allsop in conversation,' says Mintz. 'Allsop had in essence said to him that he wasn't terribly enamoured with Beatles' songs because they all tended to be 'she loves him,' 'he loves her,' 'they love her,' and 'I love her.' He suggested to John that he try to write something more autobiographical, based on personal experience rather than these abstract images. That struck a chord with him.'" (Turner, 64)

Similarly, in Way Beyond Compare, *Winn states, "...Kenneth Allsop had encouraged John to employ some of the imagination he used in writing poems when writing song lyrics. Thus, [in June 1965] John was more than happy to chat with Allsop once again, having composed weightier songs such as 'I'm a Loser,' 'You've Got to Hide Your Love Away,' and 'Help!' in the interim."* (327-328)

John's friend, Bill Harry, also confirms Allsop's influence in his John Lennon Encyclopedia *(p. 18-19), as does Norman in* John Lennon: The Life. *(p. 422-423)*

And finally, Ian MacDonald in Revolution in the Head *agrees, saying that, "...the eminent journalist, Kenneth Allsop, whom Lennon admired, challenged him as to why his songs didn't employ the same acerbic word-play of his books,* In His Own Write *and* A Spaniard in the Works.*" MacDonald asserts that Allsop's challenge led John to, later in 1965, pen the autobiographical work "In My Life." (p. 136)*

Sources:

Lewisohn, The Complete Beatles Chronicles, *196.*
Lewisohn, The Beatles: Day by Day, *63.*
Harry, The John Lennon Encyclopedia, *18-19.*
Harry, The Encyclopedia of Beatles People, *26-27.*
Miles, The Beatles' Diary, Vol. 1, *198.*
Wiener, 49.
Lennon, Cynthia, John, *171.*
Norman, John Lennon: The Life, *417 and 422-423.*
Bedford, The Country of Liverpool, *74.*
Turner, 64.
Winn, 326-328.
MacDonald, 136.
Schultheiss, 135.
Lennon, John, "The Wumberlog (or The Magic Dog)," A Spaniard in the Works, *44.*
Tremlett, 62 and 125.
Bicknell, 51.

Hill, John, Paul, George & Ringo, *206.*
Robertson, Lennon, *41.*

https://www.youtube.com/watch?v=qiLQzON6XsE This video shows John on the 18 June "Tonight Show" reading "We must not forget the General Erection." (his capitalizations)

I'm A Loser – The Beatles Bible This website discusses the influence of Kenneth Allsop on John's later autobiographical songs.

https://faroutmagazine.co.uk/beatles-song-john-lennon-inspired-bob-dylan-im-a-loser/ This article also discusses the impact of Kenneth Allsop on John Lennon's lyrics.

Kenneth Allsop - Biography - IMDb This website provides biographical information about Kenneth Allsop.

Kenneth Allsop - Wikipedia This website also provides biographical information about Kenneth Allsop.

http://beatlesinterviews.org/db1965.0618.beatles.html The transcribed interview between John Lennon and Kenneth Allsop may be found here. The transcription was completed primarily by Jay Spangler and augmented by the author in 2020.

[1805] Bicknell, 51.

[1806] Lewisohn, *The Complete Beatles Chronicles*, 196, Lewisohn, *The Beatles: Day by Day,* 63, Miles, *The Beatles' Diary, Vol. 1,* 198, Robertson, *Lennon,* 41, Wiener, *The Beatles Ultimate Recording Guide*, 49, and Schultheiss, 135.

[1807] Bicknell, 51.

[1808] Lewisohn, *The Complete Beatles Chronicles*, 196. Contrary to other sources who state that the recording session at EMI ended at 5.30 p.m. on 17 June, Lewisohn states, "From 7.00 until 9.30 p.m. (ending the session 30 minutes early), The Beatles recorded a new Lennon-McCartney song called 'Wait.'"

[1809] Lennon, Cynthia, *John,* 171. Cynthia says, "[John's] moods could be unpredictable and at times, he was intolerant and impatient with Julian. On one occasion, I remember him shouting at the dinner table because Julian was eating messily."

[1810] Lennon, Cynthia, *John,* 171. Cynthia says, "I was livid and stormed [at John]."

[1811] Lennon, Cynthia, *John,* 171. Direct quote from Cynthia Lennon.

[1812] Lennon, Cynthia, *John,* 171. Direct quote from Cynthia Lennon.

[1813] Lennon, Cynthia, *John,* 171. Cynthia says, "I rushed upstairs in tears…"

[1814] Bicknell, 51. Alf Bicknell backs up what Cynthia is telling Julian. That night, he drove John to his TV interview with Kenneth Allsop, and he states,

"I drove John to the BBC…to plug his new book on the *Tonight* programme. He was so nervous in the car."
[1815] Lennon, Cynthia, *John,* 171 and Absolute Elsewhere: The Spirit of John Lennon | Articles: My Friend John. Cynthia, in her book *John*, said, "…the shock on Julian's face when John had erupted at him had really upset me…I'd learned to keep away from John if he was edgy, and Julian had, too." And Pete Shotton, who spent many weekends at Kenwood in 1965, commented to Beatles biographer Hunter Davies, "John didn't do much with Julian, their son. He spoiled him with expensive toys, but [John] had a low tolerance level. He'd put Julian out of the room…"
[1816] Lewisohn, *The Complete Beatles Chronicles*, 196, Lewisohn, *The Beatles: Day by Day*, 63, Miles, *The Beatles' Diary, Vol. 1*, 198, Robertson, *Lennon,* 41, Wiener, *The Beatles Ultimate Recording Guide*, 49, and Schultheiss, 135.
[1817] Lewisohn, *The Complete Beatles Chronicle*, 152, Lewisohn, *The Beatles: Day by Day*, 63, Harry, *The Encyclopedia of Beatles People*, 26, Harry, *The John Lennon Encyclopedia,* 18-19, and "In My Life" by The Beatles. The in-depth story behind the songs of the Beatles. Recording History. Songwriting History. Song Structure and Style. (beatlesebooks.com)
[1818] Harry, *The Encyclopedia of Beatles People*, 26-27, Harry, *The John Lennon Encyclopedia*, 18-19, Norman, *John Lennon: The Life*, 417, https://faroutmagazine.co.uk/beatles-song-john-lennon-inspired-bob-dylan-im-a-loser/, and "In My Life" by The Beatles. The in-depth story behind the songs of the Beatles. Recording History. Songwriting History. Song Structure and Style. (beatlesebooks.com) These two websites discuss the influence of Kenneth Allsop on John's biographical song-writing.
[1819] Norman, *John Lennon: The Life*, 417, Harry, *The John Lennon Encyclopedia*, 18-19, and https://faroutmagazine.co.uk/beatles-song-john-lennon-inspired-bob-dylan-im-a-loser/.
[1820] Turner, 64 and Kenneth Allsop - Biography - IMDb and Kenneth Allsop - Wikipedia Both websites give biographical information about Kenneth Allsop. Turner also furnished an excellent bio of Allsop and discusses his influence on John's lyrics.
[1821] Kenneth Allsop - Wikipedia
[1822] Winn, 327-328. Winn states that John performed the two poetry readings prior to his interview with Kenneth Allsop.
[1823] https://www.youtube.com/watch?v=qiLQzON6XsE This is a video of John reading "We must not forget the General Erection" (capitalized as such by John himself!) from *A Spaniard in the Works*.
[1824] Lewisohn, *The Complete Beatles Chronicle*, 196 and Winn, 326-327.
[1825] Norman, *John Lennon: The Life*, 401.
[1826] Lennon, John, "The Wumberlog (Or the Magic Dog)," *A Spaniard in the Works*, 44.
[1827] http://beatlesinterviews.org/db1965.0618.beatles.html This is the first line of the interview, transcribed by Jay Spangler, between John Lennon and Kenneth Allsop on the BBC *Tonight* show, 18 June 1965. I am not going to endnote every line, but will endnote again at the conclusion of the interview.

[1828] Winn, 327-328. Winn explains that John is naming Michael Braun, who traveled with The Beatles and wrote *Love Me Do: The Beatles' Progress,* as the person who showed his work to a publisher.

[1829] http://beatlesinterviews.org/db1965.0618.beatles.html This is the last line of the interview with John Lennon and Kenneth Allsop on the BBC *Tonight* show, 18 June 1965.

[1830] Winn, 327-328, Harry, *The John Lennon Encyclopedia,* 17-18, Bedford, *The Country of Liverpool,* 75, and Turner, 64-65.

[1831] Turner, 64-65 and Harry, *The John Lennon Encyclopedia,* 17-18.

[1832] Winn, 327-328.

[1833] Tremlett, 62. Tremlett states, "John made his songs talk. For him, they were a testament, a vehicle for ideas, a means of expressing himself far more pointedly and to a much larger audience than he could have ever done by writing a poem or a short story, by appearing on radio or television, or giving an interview..."

Act 2:

A Million Eyes

The Beatles on The European Tour, 1965
Photograph from Wikimedia Commons

Sunday, 20 June 1965
Kenwood
Weybridge, Surrey

9.00 a.m.

Five minutes after opening his eyes, John could predict exactly how the day would unfold. It had just gone 5.30 a.m. when the jarring alarm clanged. *That* was grim enough. Then, trying to shut "the bleedin' thing off," John whacked his glasses into the plush carpet and spent minutes hanging off the bed — blood rushing to his head — patting for the "specs" in the dark.

"You can switch on the light," Cyn croaked, half-awake. But still cross from Friday, she rolled away and said nothing else.

John showered as quickly as the slow-heating water in Kenwood would allow; then, grumbling, he donned the travel suit, shirt, and the tie that Cyn had laid out for him last night. Ordinarily, she'd have been in and out of the master closet with hot, sugared tea and bright conversation. But this morning, his wife feigned sleep and hardly moved.

Quietly — with shoes in hand — John slipped down to the kitchen. His socks had holes at the heel, and he shivered as bare feet met quartz tile.

Mimi had taught him, of course, to prepare tea and toast, to pour his own cereal; it wasn't out of his realm. But John preferred — and expected — to be served.[1834] And as he gruffly plunged bread slices into the magnificent toaster that architect Ken Partridge had requisitioned, he muttered sardonically, "This is lovely, so it is." John was miserable.

By the time Alf Bicknell rolled into the driveway, at precisely half-six, John was lingering sullenly outside the arched front door and scowling at invisible birds offering cheery anthems to the sun.

"'Ullo dur," he spat, unhappily.

"Mr. Lennon, sir!" Alf snapped into a mock-salute.

"Hmpf!" John ducked into the car, turning back once more to glance at the silent house. "If things proceed as they have thus far, Alf, we're fated to hit a quantum snag *en route* 'n reach the tarmac well past wheels-up."

"Don't even say it!" The driver hurriedly sought a bit of wood on which to knock. "Today's *not* the day for complications! You've two concerts within the next few hours.[1835] And your Mr. Epstein's made it clear: we have to hit our marks."

"Drive on," John sighed.

And furtively parting her Irish lace bedroom sheers, Cynthia peeked from the window as the famous Beatle and his chauffeur motored away.

****

London Airport
Heathrow

No one wanted to take responsibility for the fiasco. But someone, somewhere, had given the word that fans were not permitted in Heathrow's London airport. They were barred — banned from bidding The Beatles goodbye. Stern airport authorities had firmly turned "the loyal" away in droves.[1836] Carload after carload was ordered to "circle 'round and go home." And even worse, the brokenhearted devotees were informed that this directive came "straight from the boys themselves."[1837]

"*What? Us?*" Ringo was agog. His eyes swept for answers.

"We've said *no such thing!*" George glowered.

"What would be the point of that?" John snarled at a reporter trying to "scoop" the story. "Y' don't want to believe such griff!"

"Right, yeah," Paul nodded vigourously, "Whoever told y' that can't be a particle of serious…we would *never…*"

Brian raised a hand to hush the discussion and then purposely spaced each word. "This - is - absolutely - untenable." He paused dramatically. "I gave *no such order*. The Beatles gave no such order."[1838]

"Well, see here," the reporter insisted, "someone…"

"We love the fans!" John barked, cutting across the man. "It's depressin' goin' off without a proper farewell. It's uninspirin'." He thought of Cynthia and Jules. "Write *that* in yer paper, why don't you?!"

"Yeah, put *that* down!" Ringo waggled a finger in the reporter's face.

"What's the time?" Brian wanted no additional harm in this already upending morning.

"Just past quarter after. Time to board," was Aspinall's sharp retort. "Wheels up at 9.55."[1839]

"C'mon, let's go, then." John led the way.

And without discovering who had pilfered their faithful fans, the Fab Four were swiftly on the plane and soon, off to Paris.

****

Hôtel Georges Cinq
31 Avenue George V
Paris

10.30 a.m.

"Maybe they turned away the fans here, as well," Ringo whinged as the car halted before the three elegantly-arched entrance doors of Paris's most splendid art deco hotel.[1840] At most, fifty girls had gathered in front of the *Georges Cinq* — hardly a rousing horde to greet *Les Beatles*.[1841]

"Not to state the obvious," Brian worked to hide his own discontent, "but I would imagine the bulk of our fans are already well-queued outside *Palais des Sports*. The concert's in four-and-a-half hours, you understand. Only those unable to acquire tickets would be loitering here at this hour."

The first show was, indeed, slated for 3.00 p.m., and the second, at 9.00 this evening.[1842] The boys would have to scramble to arrive on time. They needed to check in, freshen up, and make for the theatre, straight away.

"Ah, the good ole George V!" John lifted wistful eyes. He had spent his belated honeymoon here in mid-September 1963,[1843] and then, in January 1964, he and the others had been in a room just above when they'd received the miraculous news that "I Want to Hold Your Hand" had captured Number One in America.[1844]

Good memories, all. He curled the edge of his mouth. *Me 'n Paul wrote most of the songs for* A Hard Day's Night *right here in this hotel. 'N me 'n Cyn...well...*

Trudging into the familiar lobby, John pledged to sit down and write his wife tonight...to make things up to her, to explain. "Hmpf! To intellectualize it away!" Mimi would have hissed. Or at least that was his aunt's patent response to his lifelong apologies. "You always find *some* silly, threadbare excuse, John Winston!" his aunt would say. And John supposed "the mighty Mary Elizabeth" was right.

John knew he'd been unfriendly over the last few days. All right, unendurable. It was that old line his mother had bandied about so often. "Unendurable and inescapable," she'd repeated. "Unendurable and inescapable: the very definition of 'tragedy,' John." And *that*, John thought, was a fairly accurate description of how he'd behaved of late.

But one thing I know about ole' Cynthia Powell, he took a deep breath as the boys filed towards the lift. *You can always make the gerl understand. And this evenin',* John swore, *once the concert's done 'n dusted, I'm goin' to sit down 'n give it a go.*

****

But he couldn't wait a moment longer. The instant the bedroom door snapped behind him, John began to plunder the bedside table for hotel stationery. Mimi's haunting caution about the "unsanitary conditions" of hotel furnishings never left him, so John always carried his own writing pen. But resigning himself to the exotic germs inhabiting *Hôtel Georges Cinq's* ivory-hued, textured writing paper, John began to scrawl:

Dear Cyn,[1845]

I really miss Jules[1846] as a person now — do you

know what I mean — he's not so much "the baby" or "my baby" anymore he's a real living part of me now — you know he's Julian and everything and I can't wait to see him. I miss him more than I've ever done before — I think it's been a slow process my feeling like a real father! I spend hours in dressing rooms and things thinking about the times I've wasted not being with him — and playing with him — you know I keep thinking of those stupid bastard times when I keep reading bloody newspapers and other shit whilst he's in the room with me and I've decided it's ALL WRONG! He doesn't see enough of me as it is and I really want him to know and love me, and miss me like I seem to be missing both of you so much.

I'll go now cause I'm bringing myself down thinking what a thoughtless bastard I seem to be — and it's only sort of three o'clock in the afternoon and it seems the wrong time of day to feel so emotional — I really feel like crying — it's stupid — and I'm choking up now as I'm writing — I don't know what's the matter with me — it's not the tour that's so different from other tours — I mean I'm having lots of laughs (you know the type he! he!) but in between the laughs there's such a drop — I mean there seems no in between feelings.

Anyway, I'm going now so that this letter doesn't get too draggy. I love you very much.

To Cyn from John [1847]

Re-reading the missive quickly, John rapidly folded the letter, and discovered a matching envelope. He squeamishly licked the seal to secure the missive inside, and placed it by the door. *I'll post it at the front desk before trekkin' to the gig,* he swore. *I have to get this off m' fuggin' mind before it ruins another day!!* John needed to confess, to make reparations.

John was always desperately sorry for the things he said and did in a moment's anger. And in his songs, he frequently apologised.[1848]

Given a second time, John always promised to "be a good boy."[1849] And truthfully, he had every intention of doing so now.

Somehow though, John simply got away from himself. Like his childhood hero, Richmal Crompton's *Just William*, John considered himself brilliant...but completely and totally incorrigible. He lacked self-control.

****

For the next fourteen days, the playlist would remain the same: an abbreviated version of "Twist and Shout," "She's a Woman," "I'm a Loser," "Can't Buy Me Love," "Baby's in Black," "I Wanna Be Your Man," "A Hard Day's Night," "Everybody's Trying to Be My Baby," "Rock and Roll Music," "I Feel Fine," "Ticket to Ride," and the traditional closer, "Long Tall Sally."[1850] Each of The Beatles was afforded a moment to shine, and as always, the boys left the crowd on their feet.

Last year, the Parisian audiences — predominantly male — were lukewarm at best. But this year, the six thousand in each house were decidedly female, and their screams rent the roof asunder.[1851] Beneath the hubbub, the boys tuned up as John tested the mic. "Hello, hello?"

Dressed in matching black Chesterfield-style suits[1852] and cleverly navigating an elaborate tangle of electrical cords in front of Ringo's podium, the boys seized the chance to *mach schau* once again. It had been ages since they'd amused a frenzied crowd, eye-to-eye, and the four laughed and winked and mugged for the French fans.

"Twist and Shout" fed directly into "She's A Woman," but

then, the tricky navigation of a French introduction was demanded, and Paul did his best.

"Thank you! *Merci beaucoup...eh, eh...maintenant...une chanson...chanson...qui s'appelle 'I'm A Loser'!"* McCartney stuttered.[1853] It was a brave attempt and though John cackled, he was impressed.

The Beatles in Paris, 1965
Photograph used by kind permission of Sara Schmidt

Still chuckling, John launched — a bit off key — into "I'm A Loser," and though he worked to sustain the lines melodically, (even employing a hint of vibrato) and worked to complete the second harmonica solo, the song fairly escaped him. When, after the second chorus, the song fell apart, the boys stopped playing and grinned at one another, chuckling as they bowed. But there was no censure — only a rolling wave of squeals and adoration.[1854]

"Merci!" Paul winked and twitched his quick, sideways nod, *"Merci beaucoup,* everybody! This song," he spoke very slowly, as if the crowd could understand him better in slow motion, "This…a song…*chanson*…is called 'Can't Buy Me Love!'"[1855]

The mere title was all the girls needed to hear. The song's rollicking opening chorus was superseded by the sounds of *amour.* The Beatles grinned.

Paul was in no better cry tonight than John. Slightly flat throughout the number, he pushed the sound towards *les belle jeune filles* and their chaperoning *Peres.* Bending his knees and cupping his body around the mic, Paul employed a rock'n'roll stage growl to carry the melody.[1856] Then, calling upon his Hamburg nights, he pointed to the audience, enlisting them in the performance. "Can't buy me love…" he began.

"Ohhhh!" the crowd sang back.

"Love…" he tried it again.

"Ohhhh!"

"Can't buy me love…"

And they all sang it together: "Oh, oh, *ohhhhhh!*"[1857]

In practiced unison, The Beatles bowed to an audience elated and on its feet. For a moment, the boys lingered, relishing the sound. Then…

"Merci beau-coup!!!" John shouted, in an unvarnished, deeply Scouse version of *Francais.* "Uh…the next song we'd like to sing ('n we're doin' it here) is a slow number…a waltz…from our last LP…*Beatles '65!"* John laughed a little and then said, "And it's called 'Baby's in Black.'" Then, rather bluntly, the band strummed into their fifth offering.[1858]

Singing together, in close harmony, the boys were far better than they were alone. The shared melody was "dead on" and strong.[1859] John and Paul cut eyes at one another and smirked.[1860]

This one, John thought, *we've finally got right.*

As the song neared its end, the crowd felt it, too. They joined the boys in the final verse, swaying with arms linked.[1861] Never a hit on the charts (never even a single!), "Baby's in Black" was the all-out winner tonight. In Paris, it garnered a standing ovation.

"Merci, merci beaucoup, merci!" Paul was more confident now. *"Maintenant, une chanson…une chanson…"* The female fans swooned over his idiomatic pronunciation, and Paul took it to

the bank. *"Une chanson?"* he intoned sweetly, with a coy grin. The girls swooned. *"Une chanson, ah um...un homme* The Beatles...singin' a song called 'I Wanna Be Your Man'...*Ringo*!!!" Paul swept a dramatic arm in the drummer's direction and instantaneously, Ringo's rugged solo number exploded into sound.[1862]

Singing far faster than he'd done on the recorded version, Ringo tore through the Lennon/McCartney lyrics. And as Paul and John had done before him, the boy from the Dingle missed the tune almost entirely, letting gusto and a wide smile compensate for his blunders.[1863] The wailing crowd now made it impossible to hear anything at all, so Ringo simply opened his mouth and sang for all he was worth.

"Wanna be your man! Wanna be your man!" He surrendered the "I" in his enthusiasm. And inspired by Paul's earlier inclusion, the audience joined in. They sang heartily along.

It wasn't Beatles music the crowd had come to hear; it was "The Beatles Experience" they'd paid to see. George Harrison's guitar solos, though powerful tonight,[1864] weren't as crucial as his crooked smile and three-step shuffle. Almost on command, John jammed his tongue behind his lower lip and then, pulled his "Eccles" face. And Paul delightfully — and predictably — wagged his head. The performance was what the fans had queued to behold. Pure ecstasy.

"Thank you!" Ringo shouted. "Thank you!"[1865]

"Ringo, shut up!" John barked, laughing.

"Merci, merci!" Paul waved as another swell enveloped the hall.[1866] The boys were halfway through the concert and perspiring heavily. But they were smiling. Invigourated.

Standing in the wings — transfixed and utterly delighted — Brian never took his eyes from his lads.[1867] The miracle had happened, just as Brian had prayed it would. The Beatles were back again.

"The next song we'd like to do is from a film we made," John spat with authority and a twinge of sarcasm, "Only four of you sawr it, but for the four who sawr it..." He taunted them with French-sounding gibberish, "...a song that's called 'A Hard Day's Night'!"[1868]

This time, John's delivery of the verses was well-managed. His voice was clear, melodic even. His articulation — especially the "t" in "night" — was crisp. And for once, the crowd listened, letting him perform.[1869]

When Paul attempted the bridge, he was shaky, stretching above his range. But showman that he was, McCartney persevered, funneling every bit of charisma into the notes and shouting when he couldn't actually hit a tone or two.[1870]

Then, Lennon and McCartney joined in harmony, and the crowd roared. If only four French fans had actually seen the boys' last film, they were certainly discovering the title song now. And without reservation, they embraced it.

"*Merci, merci!*" Paul grinned widely and winked. "Uh...*maintenant une chanson...de* George..."[1871] That was all Paul had to say to unleash another epidemic of screams from the audience. George blushed, ducking his head, and the screams intensified. When Paul finally announced "Everybody's Trying to Be My Baby!", the fans fell out. Pandemonium! Harrison, as they'd always said in Liverpool, "had got their hearts."

Swathed in thick, back-of-the-throat Scouse, George served up Merseyside's own unique form of country and western. He prepended an "a" to almost everything: "a-dressed it up," "a-didn't stay a-late," "a-nineteen dates" — it was George's exclusive hillbilly jargon. And on a Parisian June night at the *Palais des Sports*, it worked. The fans were fascinated.[1872]

Unfortunately, it was George's turn to introduce the upcoming number, and as he'd told Brian, "It's hard enough managin' the Queen's English, let alone *foreign verbiage*. I don't even have a shadow of French, do I?" So, the lead guitarist opted to speak very slowly and very loudly in his native tongue.

"Uhm, *merci beaucoup!* The - next - song - is - from - our - latest - long-playin' record, - and - it - is - called - 'A-Rock'n'Roll Music'!" Perhaps it was Harrison's winsome grin or his gratuitously-prepended "a" to the song title, but somehow, the boy conjured magic, and the crowd squealed with delight.[1873]

John barely let the introduction settle before leaping into Chuck Berry's "Rock'n'Roll Music," full-throttle. He set a furious pace, and the others tried to keep pace, John spitting out words as rapidly as possible and struggling with his breathing in the process.[1874]

The Beatles were swept up in a moment of their own making. Perspiring, shaking their heads, moving across the stage, and smiling over the vast expanse of frenzied fans, the Liverpool lads ruled Paris. John laughed, shook sweat off his hair, and shouted the final verse. And when fans reached out, extending their arms towards the stage, John threw himself at the song. Tonight, he wanted them as much as they wanted him. A tacit agreement.

Paul delayed speaking until the turmoil had dissipated. Then, he announced the next number. "*Merci beaucoup,* John, *merci!*" He rested his hands atop his Höfner bass, waiting a second longer. "*Ehhhh, maintenant...again, une chanson...qui...une chanson...*"

Distracted by John's attempt to create his signature feedback for the beginning of "I Feel Fine," Paul paused and watched. But when all efforts to reproduce the sound only created a shrill high-pitched squeal, Paul said, "...*qui s'appelle* 'I Feel Fine.'" The boys snickered, shrugged, and flew right into the opening line.[1875]

George's lead set the tempo, with John's vocal tagging along, worn from Chuck Berry's gymnastic "Rock'n'Roll Music." At first, John's voice lacked power, but purposely sustaining his notes and pushing the air from his lungs, he managed to gain foothold.[1876]

Only two fuggin' songs left! he encouraged himself. *You can do it!*

As the boys commenced their final refrain, John sang, "She's in love with me, and I feel fine," twice, intending to cut the lyrics there. But Paul volunteered his high harmony for a third go-round, and sputtering laughter, John joined him just in time to declare, "I feel fine" as well.[1877] And he did.

When the echoes of appreciative shrieks and yelps subsided, the boys looked at one another and nodded. "I think I'm gonna be sad..." John began singing without ado, and "Ticket to Ride" unfolded at a measured pace.

Tonight, the song John had once described as "heavy" was almost a ballad. The words were mournful, regretful. The live version lacked the invective of the recorded song, and John's wistful "she don't care" was freighted with emotion.

Six thousand enthralled fans — perched on chairs across the wooden floor and seated in risers flanking the stage — sat virtually silent, listening with empathy. As the show entered its final minutes, The Beatles were leaving their faithful with a poignant memory.[1878]

Then, abruptly, everything changed. The pace quickened; the

strumming grew harsh and choppy. As "Ticket to Ride" vamped towards its end, the tone promised hope for the peevish lover left behind. Instead of a complaint, the oft-repeated words, "My baby don't care!" became a firm resolution, a decision to accept fate and move on. Determination replaced despondency.[1879] And cheering the decision to leave the past where it belonged, the room shook with adoration. The fans leapt to their feet, waving their arms wildly.

Running off stage for the benefit of the television audience[1880] and then returning victoriously — as if the audience had eagerly demanded an encore — The Beatles snickered at the silly gimmick.

"And now...an encore," Paul shouted to the others, "seein' as the demand was...uh, nothin'!"[1881] The Beatles giggled, but stepped into centre-stage anyway and glanced towards John.

Without a pause, he gave the nod, the signal. The Beatles bowed, cautiously cutting their eyes at one another. Only a single song stood between them and tangible danger. The boys were vigilant now. Ready to move.

"This song...uh, *chanson...*" Someone off-stage caught Paul's eye, and he was given the direction to exit. "We understand," he responded audibly, on mic. Then, turning back to the audience, he grinned. "This song's our last song, 'n uhm, we'd like you all to clap..." He demonstrated the act of applause. But before he could encourage the crowd to stomp their feet, the willing throng broke into a rhythmic applause-stomp that swelled louder and louder and louder. "Okay!!" Paul grinned. And without delay, "Long Tall Sally" assaulted the room.[1882]

Nothing for the last thirty-some-odd minutes had been this frantic. Paul rushed the stage apron, his hair flying up as he yelled, "I'm gonna tell Aunt Mary 'bout Uncle John!" Shredding the song with Cavern aplomb, he toyed with the lyrics — whilst open-mouthed, John concentrated and studied his fretboard, offering up rhythm, full-on.

After "some fun tonight," George pivoted towards Paul and held nothing back. His lead was vigourous, intricate, right on point. All evening, George had been the group's backbone; each lead line had been remarkable. But for this final number, Harrison pulled out all stops.

Ringo, too, was committed. He shook his wet hair and laughed, savouring the long-delayed chance to perform for a crowd. Like Paul, Ritchie adored the stage, and after a month of film-making in well-sequestered locations, this night was sheer bliss. The drummer let go.

But the instant the final refrain of "have some fun tonight" echoed across the *Palais des Sports*, the boys vanished. In a downpour of applause and screams, they disappeared — were gone.

With Neil, Mal, and Brian frantically steering them down a dank, narrow corridor to some unanticipated back doorway, the boys moved faster than anyone could've imagined. They were breathless but safe and suddenly in the car, without incident. Alf Bicknell careened away, tires squealing.

"I expected it to be worse," George gasped for air and permitted a smile, "but it was *great!*"[1883] The others mumbled agreement. "We were a little rusty, but no one seemed to notice..."[1884]

"*I noticed!*" John exaggerated a pant. "You don't get any time to breathe! 'Rock'n'Roll Music' nearly killed me!"[1885]

"Who's after a bevvy, then?" one of them shouted. There was a brisk and unanimous show of hands. Cheers.

And after the briefest of hotel stopovers, the boys were swept directly to Castell's, the Parisian version of their beloved Ad Lib.[1886] They had earned it.   ·

Notes!

1. Were John and Cynthia actually beginning to struggle in their relationship?

In Lennon, author Tim Riley - discussing the 1965 release of A Spaniard in the Works - say this: "It's not hard to read Lennon's own emotional defection from Cynthia and Julian...seeing as [John] had long since packed himself off with nowhere to go." (Lennon, p. 277)

And Ray Connolly in Being John Lennon says, "Cynthia might have been living a privileged, luxurious life with money to buy whatever she wanted...but she was hardly enjoying a normal family life. And though John might sometimes hate himself and wish he could be more of a family man and not get cross with Julian when the little boy splashed his food around the room, he couldn't. [John] was the way he was, and domestic life bored him." (p. 198)

And in both A Twist of Lennon *and her later book,* John, *Cynthia states that by 1965, her marriage was beginning to unravel. She says that drugs were at the epicentre of all the problems that John and she faced. And the advent of LSD in the spring of 1965 only added to their difficulties.*

2. How accurate is the account of the 9.00 p.m. Palais des Sports show that you have just read?

Please listen to the links provided below for the audio of this concert. The observations in this chapter come directly from those recordings. The screaming isn't so loud that you can't hear what's happening on the stage. And what you'll hear is a surprisingly well-managed performance. After months of making "Help!" and working in studio to record its accompanying LP, The Beatles hadn't forgotten how to mach schau. They put on a superb show.

Indeed, Winn notes that "although it's their first full concert in six months, the songs are performed with high energy and few flaws. Perhaps that's because the set list is nearly identical to the Christmas shows, with the addition of 'Ticket to Ride' and the substitution of 'I Wanna Be Your Man' for 'Honey Don't.'" (p. 329) Winn is correct, of course, but we must remember that The Beatles had concluded the Christmas shows in January, and this concert occurs in late June. Their innate ability to entertain is clearly demonstrated during this performance, five months later.

The song introductions used in this chapter come directly from the audio tape and are, as noted, incomplete. Winn tells us that George Harrison dedicated "Ticket to Ride" to Hubert Wayaffe, the Emcee for the evening's show. (p. 329) I did not include this dedication, not having Harrison's quote in the audio tape to use verbatim.

Several volunteers listened to this tape many, many times to capture the actual verbiage. That is the basis for the account you just read.

Note: *Not included in this chapter is the fact that after the concert, the boys were visited at their hotel by enchanting French singer Françoise Hardy (noted for her 1964 hit* "Tous les garçons and les filles").[1887] *The visit was brief, and then the four Liverpool lads were off to Castrell's nightclub, where they "stayed until dawn." (Miles,* The Beatles' Diary, Vol. 1, *199)*

Sources:

Lewisohn, The Complete Beatles Chronicle, *196.*
Lewisohn, The Beatles: Day by Day, *63.*
Harry, The Ultimate Beatles Encyclopedia, *512.*

The Beatles, The Beatles Anthology, *114.*
Miles, The Beatles' Diary, Vol. 1, *128 and 199.*
Lennon, Cynthia, John, *169 and 171.*
Lennon, Cynthia, A Twist of Lennon, *97-100.*
Coleman, The Man Who Made The Beatles, *243.*
Winn, 328-330.
Freeman, 146.
Riley, Lennon, *277.*
Connolly, 196.
Badman, 160.
Spizer, The Beatles are Coming!, *114.*
Braun, Love Me Do, *75.*
Goldsmith, The Beatles Come to America, *129-130.*
Norman, John Lennon: The Life, *548.*
Badman, 160.
Margotin and Guesdon, 171.
Bicknell, 51.
Brown, 185.
Wiener, 49.
Schultheiss, 134.

https://infogalactic.com/info/The_Beatles%27_1965_European_tour
This website supplies information about The Beatles' 1965 European Tour.

The Beatles - Tour dates (bizhat.com) This website supplies info about every Beatles Tour, including song lists, venues, dates, etc.

Beatles - bootleg Paris,Palais des Sports 06-20-1965 late show - Bing video This is a 31-minute audio of the 9.00 p.m. show at the Palais des Sports.

https://en.wikipedia.org/wiki/Fran%C3%A7oise_Hardy This website gives biographical information about Françoise Hardy, who visited The Beatles at Hôtel Georges Cinq *on 20 June.*

Sullivan Suit by Beatlesuits This website, managed by Beatles wardrobe expert Russ Lease, gives information about the Chesterfield suits that The Beatles were wearing on stage, 20 June 1965.

https://www.fourseasons.com/paris/ This website supplies numerous photos of the Hôtel Georges Cinq.

https://www.bing.com/videos/search?q=beatles+at+palais+des+sports+ paris+1965&&view=detail&mid=CA121D55D1C109587A21CA121D55 D1C109587A21&rvsmid=681905573000AA3A0698681905573000AA3 A0698&FORM=VDQVAP Here is a longer version of the 9.00 p.m. show at the Palais des Sports *on 20 June 1965. This one is 32:50. It is*

clearer as well.
Or use this QR code:

[1834] Norman, *John Lennon: The Life*, 548. John is quoted as saying, "I was used to being served by women, whether it was my Aunt Mimi — God bless you — or whoever, served by females, wives, girlfriends."
[1835] Lewisohn, *The Complete Beatles Chronicle*, 196, Miles, *The Beatles' Diary, Vol. 1*, 199, Bicknell, 51, and The Beatles' European tour begins at Palais des Sport, Paris – The Beatles Bible
[1836] The Beatles' European tour begins at *Palais des Sport*, Paris – The Beatles Bible and Miles, *The Beatles' Diary, Vol. 1*, 199.
[1837] The Beatles' European tour begins at *Palais des Sport*, Paris – The Beatles Bible and Miles, *The Beatles' Diary, Vol. 1*, 199.
[1838] The Beatles' European tour begins at *Palais des Sport*, Paris – The Beatles Bible and Miles, *The Beatles' Diary, Vol. 1*, 199.
[1839] Lewisohn, *The Complete Beatles Chronicle*, 196, Miles, *The Beatles' Diary, Vol. 1*, 199, and The Beatles' European tour begins at *Palais des Sport*, Paris – The Beatles Bible
[1840] https://www.fourseasons.com/paris/ Lovely photos and videos of the George V are available on this website.
[1841] The Beatles' European tour begins at *Palais des Sport*, Paris – The Beatles Bible and Miles, *The Beatles' Diary, Vol. 1*, 199.
[1842] Lewisohn, *The Complete Beatles Chronicle*, 196 and Miles, *The Beatles' Diary, Vol. 1*, 199.
[1843] Lewisohn, *The Complete Beatles Chronicle*, 122, Miles, *The Beatles' Diary, Vol. 1*, 108, Lennon, Cynthia, *John*, 119-121, and Lennon, Cynthia, *A Twist of Lennon*, 97-100. Also, read Vol. 3 in **The John Lennon Series**, *She Loves You*, pp. 263-285.
[1844] Braun, *Love Me Do*, 75, The Beatles, *The Beatles Anthology*, 114, Miles, *The Beatles' Diary, Vol. 1*, 128, Spizer, *The Beatles are Coming!*, 114, Goldsmith, *The Beatles Come to America*, 129-130, Harry, *The Ultimate Beatles Encyclopedia*, 512, and Riley, *Lennon*, 234. Also, read Vol. 3 in **The John Lennon Series**, *She Loves You*, pp. 509-511.
[1845] Lennon, Cynthia, *John*, 169. This is verbatim a 1965 letter to Cynthia from John. I will not endnote each sentence but will endnote again at the end.
[1846] Lennon, Cynthia, *John*, 169. John writes "him" here, but for clarity, I changed it to "Jules." That does not in any way alter the meaning or intent of the sentence or the letter.
[1847] Lennon, Cynthia, *John*, 169. This is the last line of John's 1965 letter to Cynthia. Nothing has been altered...not the spelling, punctuation, or wording.

[1848] Freeman, 146. Bob Freeman, who knew John quite well, states, "In his songs, there was often a yearning for love…John drew on the conflicts in his life for his music and in singing his songs, he attempted to exorcise the confused feelings raised by his relationships with women. While seeking solace in these relationships, he often found himself the victim of them."

[1849] You can hear John's apologies in songs such as "Jealous Guy," "Cold Turkey," "Aisumasen (I'm Sorry)," and "It's Only Love," to name a few.

[1850] Lewisohn, *The Complete Beatles Chronicle*, 196, Miles, *The Beatles' Diary, Vol. 1*, 199, https://www.beatlesbible.com/1965/06/20/live-palais-des-sports-paris/, The Beatles 1965 European Tour (enacademic.com), and The Beatles' 1965 European tour - Infogalactic: the planetary knowledge core.

[1851] Lewisohn, *The Complete Beatles Chronicle*, 196. Lewisohn says, "…the relationship between the Parisian audience and The Beatles was now far warmer than in January 1964."

[1852] Sullivan Suit by Beatlesuits Beatles apparel expert Russ Lease tells us that "early on, [The Beatles] were especially fond of the traditional English Chesterfield models…owning at least 15 different variations." The variation they are wearing on the 1965 European Tour does not have the velvet collar, and the boys wore a black knit tie and white shirt. You can see the tie on this website as well.

[1853] To enjoy the full 31-minute bootleg recording of the Paris *Palais des Sports* concert, including the introductions, listen here: Beatles - bootleg Paris,Palais des Sports 06-20-1965 late show - Bing video Direct quote from Paul McCartney.

[1854] Beatles - bootleg Paris,Palais des Sports 06-20-1965 late show - Bing video

[1855] Beatles - bootleg Paris,Palais des Sports 06-20-1965 late show - Bing video Direct quote from Paul McCartney.

[1856] Beatles - bootleg Paris,Palais des Sports 06-20-1965 late show - Bing video

[1857] Winn, 330 and Beatles - bootleg Paris,Palais des Sports 06-20-1965 late show - Bing video

[1858] Beatles - bootleg Paris,Palais des Sports 06-20-1965 late show - Bing video Direct quote from John Lennon.

[1859] Beatles - bootleg Paris,Palais des Sports 06-20-1965 late show - Bing video

[1860] Margotin and Guesdon, 171.

[1861] Winn, 330.

[1862] Beatles - bootleg Paris,Palais des Sports 06-20-1965 late show - Bing video Direct quote from Paul McCartney.

[1863] Beatles - bootleg Paris,Palais des Sports 06-20-1965 late show - Bing video

[1864] Beatles - bootleg Paris,Palais des Sports 06-20-1965 late show - Bing video In all of the songs from the *Palais des Sports* in Paris, George's solos hold the songs together. He quietly kept the show moving forward.

[1865] Beatles - bootleg Paris,Palais des Sports 06-20-1965 late show - Bing video

[1866] Beatles - bootleg Paris,Palais des Sports 06-20-1965 late show - Bing video

[1867] Coleman, *The Man Who Made The Beatles*, 243.

[1868] Beatles - bootleg Paris,Palais des Sports 06-20-1965 late show - Bing video. Direct quote from John Lennon.

[1869] Beatles - bootleg Paris,Palais des Sports 06-20-1965 late show - Bing video

[1870] Beatles - bootleg Paris,Palais des Sports 06-20-1965 late show - Bing video

[1871] Beatles - bootleg Paris,Palais des Sports 06-20-1965 late show - Bing video

[1872] Beatles - bootleg Paris,Palais des Sports 06-20-1965 late show - Bing video

[1873] Beatles - bootleg Paris,Palais des Sports 06-20-1965 late show - Bing video

[1874] Badman, 160 and Beatles - bootleg Paris,Palais des Sports 06-20-1965 late show - Bing video

[1875] Beatles - bootleg Paris,Palais des Sports 06-20-1965 late show - Bing video

[1876] Beatles - bootleg Paris,Palais des Sports 06-20-1965 late show - Bing video

[1877] Winn, 329 and Beatles - bootleg Paris,Palais des Sports 06-20-1965 late show - Bing video

[1878] Beatles - bootleg Paris,Palais des Sports 06-20-1965 late show - Bing video

[1879] Beatles - bootleg Paris,Palais des Sports 06-20-1965 late show - Bing video

[1880] Winn, 330.

[1881] Winn, 330. Direct quote from Paul McCartney.

[1882] Beatles - bootleg Paris,Palais des Sports 06-20-1965 late show - Bing video

[1883] Badman, 160. Direct quote from George Harrison after the 20 June 1965 *Palais des Sports* concert.

[1884] Badman, 160. Direct quote from George Harrison after the 20 June 1965 *Palais des Sports* concert.

[1885] Badman, 160. Direct quote from John Lennon after the 20 June 1965 *Palais des Sports* concert.

[1886] Bicknell, Alf, 51 and Miles, *The Beatles' Diary, Vol. 1*, 199. Alf, who was there with The Beatles, says, "After the evening concert, we ended up at Castell's, a club not unlike the AdLib. Smashing!"

[1887] https://en.wikipedia.org/wiki/Fran%C3%A7oise_Hardy This website gives biographical information about the lovely Françoise Hardy, who visited The Beatles at *Hôtel Georges Cinq* just after the concert on 20 June.

Monday, 21 June 1965
Hôtel Georges Cinq
Paris

The boys had partied until dawn,[1888] so the bright Parisian morning was given to sleep. But in early afternoon, the boys sauntered onto the balcony patio. Waving to the fans below and perching on the wide concrete balustrade, they posed for the press.[1889]

"What're *you* dressed for?" John eyed Paul's suit, grey-striped shirt, and tie.[1890]

"Whatever you're not, apparently." Paul strolled to the umbrellaed, round table laid out for the four young gods. Casually, he lit a Marlboro and poured a goblet of orange juice from a linen-wrapped, chilled decanter. Without speaking, Paul claimed a seat next to Ringo, who was engrossed in a British newspaper.[1891]

"Looks Good! Feels Good! No Dandruff!" Paul read aloud, peering over Ringo's shoulder at a bold print advertisement.[1892]

Behind very dark sunglasses, Ringo growled,[1893] "No thanks, I'm all *for* dandruff. Proves the hair's real, y' know."

"I had some imported — dandruff." George joined them. His velvet collar was up-turned against a ruffling wind.[1894]

"Adds natural density, y' see." John ambled over, filching a pack of Marlboros from the long red and white carton.[1895]

"Good morning, everyone. Glad you've at last joined the land of the living." Though Brian Epstein's hair was windblown, his finely cut grey suit was impeccable. However, with a nod to casual, he'd unbuttoned it. "Care to peruse the review of last night's concert?" He tendered a newsprint magazine to John and Paul.[1896]

"Um, let's see here," Paul pretended to read. "'The Beatles were as perfect as always.'"

"You've read it entirely wrong, haven't y' son?" John pointed to the review. "It says 'compellin',' not perfect. *Compellin'*. That's what we were!"

"Oh, right, yeah…so it compellingly does."

"'N invidious as well," John over-pronunced, comically. "It says, 'Their invidious domination of the charts wages on."

"Yeah, that, too," George chuckled.

"It's actually a marvellous review, if you'd care to read it in earnest." Brian cut across their nonsense. Though the NEMporer considered himself dispassionate and logical, he was, more frequently, easily provoked.

"Right, then. Well…" Paul began to flick through the article, and John leaned over to scan it as well. Whilst they read the piece, they could hear a dozen cameras clicking.[1897] Everything The Beatles did these days was recorded: their favourite cigs, their choice of orange juice, their news source.

After a few minutes, John glanced up and capitulated. "Not a bad critique — this."

"All right, yeah." Paul agreed.

"It's a *splendid* harbinger," Brian insisted. "An augury of things to come…for the rest of the tour, you understand! And following your *Radio Luxembourg* interview with Chris Denning this afternoon,[1898] we're sure to have record audiences all over…"

"Hold! Wait…what's this?" John had thought the afternoon an opportunity for rest.

"Yes, just a small chat, as it were. In a quarter of an hour." Brian checked his watch. "Either out here or in the suite, as you prefer."

The boys exchanged glances and shook their heads.

"It's down to you, Brian," John sighed. "Just tell us what to do 'n when to do it."

"Well, let's have the suite, then," Brian brightly selected.[1899] "Shall we?"

****

1965 was turning out to be a year of "lasts." Their 26 May appearance on the Light Programme special *The Beatles (Invite You to Take a Ticket to Ride)* had been John, Paul, George, and

Ringo's last exclusive BBC programme, ever.[1900] Then, this afternoon, the quick session with Chris Denning signaled The Beatles' concluding live interview for *Radio Luxembourg's* popular weekly show, "The Beatles."[1901]

These days, the four boys were far too busy to entertain regular radio appearances. They were tugged to the earth's corners and back again.[1902] And though the BBC was bitterly disappointed, Denning put sentiment aside and treated this as just another friendly conversation.

With his journalist's nose for controversy, Denning zeroed in on the lads' MBE nod. Just this morning, British war hero and author Richard Pape had returned his MBE to the Queen, expressing vast indignation at The Beatles' nomination.[1903] "The Beatles' MBE reeks of mawkish, bizarre effrontery to our wartime endeavours," the World War II flyer had raged in the London *Times* and the Glasgow *Herald*.[1904] And Pape, Denning told the listening audience, was just the most recent in a long line of resentful retorts from the Establishment.

"So, tell me...how do *you boys* feel about the award? Truthfully?" Denning knelt on the floor and extended a tethered microphone awkwardly in their direction.[1905]

"I think it's great," Ringo piped up immediately. "And by the way," his eyes sparkled, "*there*, you don't have to kneel, y' know!"[1906]

"Oh, good," Denning chuckled. "Quite an improvement on this, then. Worth the award!" Smiling, he turned towards John. "John, it's widely rumoured that you four were proposed for this distinguished honour by none other than Harold Wilson himself. Have you met Harold Wilson?"[1907]

John crossed his leg, ankle at the knee, and nonchalantly chewed gum. "Harold Wilson?" his eyes twinkled. "I knew him when he was at Decca!"[1908]

The group sputtered laughter. Denning bit his lip and pressed on.

"Now, in uhm keeping with our theme, we'd like to play one of our most requested records on this programme. It's 'Do You Want to Know a Secret?'. Paul, is there anyone or anyones to whom you'd like to dedicate this selection?"

"Oh, right yeah...ta." Paul carefully rubbed the corner of his eye with a finger. "I'd like to send it out to our old friends Bernard

Levin, Wolf Mankowitz, and Donald Zec."[1909] London's razored critics had been extremely hard on The Beatles of late. Mankowitz had been outright antagonistic on the recent "Eamonn Andrews Show," and Zec had all but scalded The Beatles over the proposed MBE award.

Cleverly following suit, Ringo asked to hear "I'll Follow the Sun," indicating his new-found preference for *The Sun* newspaper over the barbed words of both Don Short at the *Daily Mirror* and Judith Simmons of the *Daily Express*, to whom Starr's selection was sardonically dedicated.[1910] But not to sound entirely antagonistic, the drummer added in a cheery afterthought, "also for our fan club secretary, Freda Kelly, 'n for all the dockers in Liverpool!"[1911]

"*Up the Pool!*" someone yelped, and the record spun.

Not to be outdone by Ritchie, George called for "a number for all the miners in Scunthorpe,"[1912] and laughing, he dragged Neil into the fray, forcing Aspinall to give his own dedication on this, the very last "The Beatles" show.[1913]

"Ah well, then," Neil leaned over as close to the microphone as he could from a standing position, "let's have one for Mr. Mal Evans!" The others cheered.

But in a grand *piece de resistance*, John leaned forward slyly and acridly demanded, "Well, Chris, why don't we have a listen, then, to 'Thank You, Girl,' eh? 'N I'd like to send that one out to Mr. Harold Wilson of Hampstead Garden Suburb."[1914]

The Beatles and Neil Aspinall erupted into hacking laughter, and Denning fared no better. John had closed the final episode of "The Beatles" with a droll *entendre* that would make the "last" last. The wicked jest was classic Lennon.

****

Monday, 23 June 1965
En Route from Lyon to Milan

The evening train to Milan was sluggish and deliberate, but the cadence, mesmerizing. John yawned, trying his best to digest

Saul Bellow's *Herzog.* The slim recent best-seller, however, only succeeded in distressing him.

The last fuggin' thing I need, he plunked his feet heavily on the seat in front of him, *is some unhappy story of an unhappy man in an unhappy marriage, desperately writin' letters to try 'n sort it all out.*

"Have y' heard about Brian?" George slid into the seat next to John.

"I think we've *all* heard about Brian," John lifted an eyebrow.

"No, not *that!*" George waved him off. "The disaster! The near-death thingy!"

"Don't be at it, George." John wouldn't bite. "It's not attractive."

"I'm serious! *I'm dead serious...*'n I mean it, even though in a moment that'll sound like a pun!" Harrison lifted a hand in sworn pledge. "Neil just told me right back there that at the Paris show, Brian had this 'great idea' to go up in the control room 'n take a snap of us, y' see, performin' on the stage below."[1915]

"Yerrokay, go on." John yawned again.

"Well, at the very top o' the stairs, there was this low lintel, y' see...like an overhang, what have you, on the doorway, y' know...'n unfortunately, Eppy failed t' see it soon enough...'n he crashed into it. *Smash! Head on!*" George's eyes were wide.

"You're havin' me on now, aren't you, son?" But John was finally engaged. He removed his glasses and rubbed the bridge of his nose.

"No! 'N that's not the worst of it!" George lowered his voice, as if divulging state secrets. "Neil says Eppy hit the barrier so hard that he sorta tripped back 'n staggered...'n he almost fell! Neil says he was *this close* to careenin' down the spiral staircase directly behind him...y' know, the one he'd just run up in such an awful hurry."

"But..." John was riveted.

"But he caught himself in the nick o' time, 'n as you can tell, he lived to manage yet another day."[1916]

"And *that's* the end of your story?"

"It's not a story, John. It's real."

"And that's the end of your um 'reel,' then?" John simulated a movie camera.

"What did y' want me to say...that he plunged to his death 'n died?"

"Well…that would've had more…impact."

"That's awful."

"Your story's awful." John re-opened his tragic novel. "You've forced me right back to ole Saul Bellow."

"I don't know what you wanted me to say." George folded his arms and closed his eyes. "I don't know what you expected!"

"Well, whatever it was, or is," John muttered, "I never seem to get it."

****

Thursday, 24 June 1965
Velodromo Vigorelli
Via Arona
Milan, Italy

The boys had played two houses in Paris, two in Lyon, and today, two shows were slated as well.[1917] The powers-that-be, who had engaged 700 policemen and 400 civilian security staffers — already perspiring in a rugged heat wave — were determined to get their money's worth.[1918] Long before the afternoon show was to commence in the 22,000-person open-air arena,[1919] the narrow-eyed guards were carefully stationed and prepared. They were steeled for the mayhem widely known as "Beatlemania."

But the boys, who had already witnessed several instances of European overreaction to fan frenzy were equally determined that Milan's teenagers would have a good time. As the boys departed in their hired car from the train station, they all stopped in front of their hotel, turned, and waved enthusiastically to the young fans smiling, jumping, and hoisting posters in the street. One 13-year-old girl was the first to initiate the contagious ripple of screams, and instantly, her large, grimacing mother fell upon her, hitting the child repeatedly.

"Fuggin' stop that!" John bellowed, as police rushed to calm rash tempers.

"Horrid woman," Brian agreed quietly, but he placed a staying hand on John's arm anyway. The boy's new book, *A Spaniard in the Works*, was being released this very afternoon[1920] and would be splashed across the news. In fact, John's pre-recorded interview with the BBC Home Service was airing this evening.[1921] The last thing John needed was unfortunate press.

Today, however, it was Paul who — in a rare moment of exposed anger — divulged to a nearby reporter, "*That's* the sort of attitude here from some of the adults. Some of the parents, the big fat mammies, think it's a disgrace for their kids to scream for The Beatles! *We* think it's a bloody shame!"[1922]

"Right," George nodded.

"What he said!" Ringo did the same.

And although John itched to add his own addendum, he saw Brian's sense. Today, he was too visible and too vulnerable to speak up. One freighted word, and John would be crucified.

The author bit his lip and let his eyes say it all.

****

The carefully folded literary reviews were waiting in the suite when the boys returned around 10.00 p.m. — weary from the *Velodromo Vigorelli*. From all over the U.K. and Europe, literary critics were weighing in. And as the boys thumbed through the newsprint, it seemed evident: *A Spaniard in the Works* was an astounding success.

"It's fascinating, of course, to climb inside a Beatle's head to see what's going on there," the London *Times* glowed, "but what counts is that what's going on there is really fascinating!"

"*Hmpf!*" John tossed the article back on the table and got up to mix a Scotch and Coke. Most often now, he turned to marijuana for a much-needed lift. But after shouting over 20,000 hysterical fans at tonight's *soirée*,[1923] he needed something to cool his throat.

"You did all right here, Lennon!" Ringo waved a review at the author.

"Did I?" John asked, with a harsh laugh. "We're generally at cross-purposes — me 'n the press. Most times, we're not even talkin' 'bout the same thing!"

"What d' you mean by that?" Paul had removed his jacket and

tie. He untucked his damp shirt.

"I mean," John fell into an overstuffed chair, "it's neither here nor there what they say…because what they say is *rubbish*."

"As in?" Ringo lifted a palm.

"As in…look at the bit by that Wain character from the *New Republic*." John wrinkled his nose in distaste. "He said my work comes straight out of one source, James Joyce! But as I've said over 'n over, I never even *read* James Joyce 'til lately…'n only then because everyone kept sayin' we're so bleedin' alike that I wanted to know if we were!"[1924]

"Ah, who cares what they say?" Ringo cajoled, and he repeated a Beatles' mantra, "You know how the press is…wrong!"

John sputtered a brief smile; Ringo always had a soothing effect on him. But still, he went on, "Y' know, the plain, unvarnished fact is that I *like writin'*, 'n I'd go on writin'…even if there wasn't any publisher daft enough to publish m' stuff![1925] So, what good would it do me — artistically, I mean — to plagiarize the work of another, when the *only* reason I'm doin' this *at all* is to express how *I* feel?"

Paul nodded. Ringo, too.

"'N look," John took a long quaff, "I don't give a fig if m' work sells or not! I mean, I don't *need* it, do I?"[1926] It was a rhetorical question, but he paused anyway, and Ringo dutifully shook his head. "'N if it doesn't go as well as the first, what follow-up book ever does?"[1927] John's voice rose. "I had a lot of the stories in m' book bottled up in my system, 'n it did me good just to get rid of them, y' know. 'Better out than in,' as they say.[1928] I mean, what's the point of lettin' stuff hang around in a drawer when I know I can get it published, right?"[1929]

"Wait, John…you're goin' on as if the reviews aren't good or the book won't sell," Paul logically pointed out. "But *look*…" He handed John another exceptional appraisal. "They're *all great* — these reviews! They're positive. Almost every one!"

"Yeah, well, y' didn't talk to that fuggin' George Melly who says I owe it all to James Joyce!" John's voice rose. "'N then, carried on to say that *our songs* 'owe a real debt' to Muddy Waters 'n Chuck Berry! *Hmpf!*"[1930] John threw a long drink back. "So, I told him, I said it was nothin' of the sort…'n that I could eat 'em all for breakfast! But he wouldn't listen! He refused to believe it!"[1931] John drank again. "So, pardon me if I'm anti-critic, y' know, from the very get-go! I don't want to get drawn into their filthy web of whatever it is their filthy web is made of..."

"Lies," Ringo suggested. "I've heard it's lies."

"What's the topic of *this* conversation?" George ambled in from the shower, rubbing his wet hair with a towel.

"Uh," Ringo gestured towards George's towel, "apparently, you missed the word...that we're goin' out, y' know."

"Yeah? *Apparently*, no one told me." George looked accusingly at each of them.

"No worries." Paul smiled and flashed a bright thumbs-up. "The shower was a lovely idea, regardless! You were rancid."

"You think *you're* any better?" George arched an eyebrow.

"No, no...I'm off to the loo straight away...that is, if you'll stay 'n play nursemaid to Long Lost John here."

"I don't need a fuggin'..." John snarled.

"He's a long string o' misery, our John," Ringo stage-whispered to George.

"Yeah? What's wrong with him now?" George muttered back.

"Oh, his book is selling bazillions, 'n the reviews 're all top-notch," Paul confided.

"Oh, well that sorts it, then." George smiled his signature smile. "John prefers gloomy, y' see. He isn't good with glad tidings of great joy which shall be to all people."

"Right," Paul sniffed. "He's a birrova Beatle, isn't he?" The others smirked and winked at one another. And as John flipped them his vilest back-handed V,[1932] they collapsed into laughter and headed off to their rooms to dress.

Tonight, they would fête *A Spaniard in the Works* and its author with a real "book release party," a Merseyside celebration of mammoth proportions...whether Long Lost John wanted one or not.

****

Brian Epstein's Suite
Milan, Italy

10.20 p.m.

It was Brian, not John, who truly needed cheering, and Brian's concerns were far from imaginary. They were confirmed in statistics.

The afternoon show at Velodromo Vigorelli had been less than one-third sold out.[1933] And instead of spacing the fans together, leaving the empty seats far above them or off to the sides, the attendees had been spaced out widely, revealing ugly gaps no one could fail to notice[1934] — diminishing fan fervour and fanning fatalistic rumours in the press. And although the evening's 9.30 p.m. concert had been a grand success, with 20,000 of the 22,000 seats occupied,[1935] Brian was still anxious and apprehensive.

The Beatles at the 9.30 p.m. show
at the Velodromo in Milan on 24 June 1965.
Permission purchased from Getty Images
https://www.gettyimages.com/detail/news-photo/the-british-rock-group-the-beatles-playing-at-vigorelli-news-photo/152217166?adppopup=true

"Where were the fans, Neil?" He had summoned the trusted roadie and former accountant to his suite. "The boys are doing well on the Italian charts, but the concert-goers were...negligible.[1936] Have the boys lost their touch? Am I missing something that everyone else knows?"

"Well, you *are* missin' somethin', Brian." Aspinall, as always, was particularly frank. "Faith in the lads — that's what."

Brian slumped, his hands falling to the back of the elegant sitting room settee. "Be kind, Neil. I'm so low, and nothing is going right."[1937]

"I know it might *look* that way, but…" Aspinall hesitated. Already, he realised, he had jeopardized his job by replying bluntly. Brian had sacked smart, long-standing employees for much, much less.[1938]

"Please, see things from my point of view," Brian elucidated. "There were only 7,000 seats occupied this afternoon. *Seven thousand* in a stadium that could have easily housed three times as many! So, when I say 'negligible'…"[1939]

"All right," Neil nodded, wishing he'd been offered a drink. Ordinarily, Brian was the epitome of courtesy and good manners, but tonight Eppy was too apprehensive for niceties. For the first time since 9 November 1961, The Beatles' manager seemed sincerely doubtful of the lads' *elan*.

Hating to disagree with the NEMporer, Neil dove cautiously in. "Look Brian, could y' have imagined 7,000 punters in the hall when you drove the boys over to New Brighton Tower Ballroom to play Boxin' Day 1961?[1940] If I remember correctly, you termed that night 'a grand success,' but there was *nowhere near* 7,000 fans there!"

"Yes…but clearly…that was then, and this is now. I have…we all have great expectations, as it were." Brian rolled his hand to deem the logic self-evident.

"Yeah, sure, I know. But…" Neil squared his shoulders and stood taller. "It was *swelterin'* out there this afternoon. Those poor people in the stadium were nearly keelin' over. I mean, it was 37 degrees, in the shade![1941] 'N yeah, I know those of us on tour lose track of time, but it's a *Thursday*…a school day, a work day.[1942] No one much is free of a Thursday afternoon, are they?"[1943] He paused to ascertain if any of this was sinking in. And it was.

"Yes…I see," Brian nodded. He strolled to the large, plate-glass window and scanned the hot, humid rows of stucco flats and businesses, glittering against the matte-black summer night.

"But most of all," Neil braced himself and ventured one more bold observation, "the tickets…"

"Yes. Go on."

"They're too dear, Brian. They're more than the ordinary person here can afford."

Epstein swiveled around, and eye-to-eye with the NEMporer, Neil released a shuddering breath. "Look, the cheapest is 11s 4 d, 'n the most expensive is £4. And yeah, either of these extremes is fine, 'cause there's always people who'll grab up the cheap seats, 'n there're always people who can afford the pricey ones as well. But in between..."[1944] Neil shrugged. "Those in between are just too much, y' see. No one fits the in-between. You're either rich here, or y'er dead skint, right? No one's a medium."[1945] He smiled slightly, to soften the blow.

"Oh," Brian blushed, pulling the back of his hand across his lips.[1946] "I hadn't thought of that."

"Well, to be honest, I hadn't either," Neil confessed. "But I asked questions, 'n like any good accountant, I made notes."

Brian nodded, making note himself. "So, not to be tedious, but other than the weather, the day of the week, and the prices...?"

"Other 'n that," Neil chuckled lightly, honoured to be valued and trusted, "we're all perfectly fine. C'mon Brian, you saw how it was. The boys did well, both houses. They always do the job, no matter what. 'N what with John's book goin' a bomb[1947]...we're all fairly happy, right?"

"Yes," Brian said stiffly, lying. These days he was far from "fairly happy," but that was an entirely private matter. "Yes, of course we are...just as you say. All of us...we're fine...we're all just fine."

****

After Neil departed to join the others at some night spot or another, Brian doffed the suite lights, tugged an ottoman and its matching chair to the sliding glass window, and wedged the heavy glass open. He filled his brandy snifter, and just before sitting back, removed his shoes for the night. Italy was too beautiful to miss.

As late as it was, footpath cafés still carried sounds of laughter and the aromas of fresh bread and rich cuisine. Silhouetted shadows of couples sipping wine against the buttery backdrop of flat lights transformed private balconies into miniature *teatros*. And with Friday but hours away, an aura of flight-from-humdrum floated over the city.[1948] Its revelry, however, excluded Brian.

Loneliness...the manager mulled...*my greatest fear. And though I know full well that one inflicts loneliness on oneself, to a great extent, I have no inkling how to change that.*[1949] Brian toyed with the idea of getting up and dialing in a radio station for company. But too often these days, music only made him sad.

Brian owned full responsibility for his solitary life. He realised that more and more, he was withdrawing from the world, setting himself apart from everyone he knew.[1950] Recently, he'd relocated his office from the busy Sutherland House building into a secluded suite in Stafford Street called "Hilly House"[1951] — a decidedly more serene locale, much more conducive to work. But with only his long-time friend (the former manager of Liverpool's Great Charlotte Street NEMS) Peter Brown there to assist him,[1952] Brian had cut himself off from the congenial shuffle of calls, conversations, queries, drop-ins, and appointments that had characterized his daily life in London.[1953]

Brian was now isolated.

In fact, Hilly House served as an escape room, of sorts, from the slew of NEMS acts — such as The Big Three and Tommy Quickly —who weren't progressing as well as Brian had once hoped.[1954] Because Peter Brown had been forbidden to give out the Hilly House telephone number to *anyone*, Brian was now able to side-step anxious calls and visits from his struggling groups and solo acts. And lately, even hitmakers Gerry and the Pacemakers and Billy J. Kramer were pigeonholed into the ranks of "the patently ignored." Overwhelmed with work, Brian had begun circumventing them as well. In the early months of 1965, NEMS had sprawled far out of Brian's acumen and control.[1955] And in reply, he shrank from it — he intentionally looked away.[1956]

Only The Beatles still claimed Brian's full attention.[1957] Well, The Beatles and Cilla. Brian had never diminished his faith in the magic that was Cilla Black. Nor would he.

When Cilla captured two Number Ones last year with "Anyone Who Had a Heart" and "You're My World," Brian's vacillating moods had soared to unprecedented happy heights.[1958] And despite his absorption with this European Tour and John's new book, Cilla was still on his mind. Brian was ever searching for her next hit, her next big venue.

But with the exception of Cilla and the boys, Brian had little to make him glad these days. His gambling obsession was growing.[1959] His personal life was worse.[1960] And wrongly, he assumed that no one cared.

Never dreaming that every single NEMS employee coveted his attention, trust, and affection, Brian rarely spoke to any of them. Never aware of their utter admiration for him, he doubted his own charisma, and frequently, even his competence. Terrified that he would be discovered for the sham he believed he was, Brian edged farther and farther into seclusion. Isolation was his protection, his cover.[1961]

Work, too, provided the wall behind which Brian shielded himself. It was unbroken. Signing a copy of *A Spaniard in the Works* to his friend, John acknowledged Brian's obsession with endless tasks — work that precluded any other activity. John had scribbled:

Brian

I hope yur ok?

P.S. Make sure you bloody
read it!

Love,

John[1962]

Of course, Brian hadn't read it. *Not yet, anyway.* And even to himself, Brian made excuses. *I've been far too overwhelmed to...*

Brian stopped. He sighed and tried to imagine where the boys had gone to revel this evening and what deviltry they'd devised...together. In the street below and the balconies beyond, everybody seemed to be paired with somebody. But on this lively midsummer night in loveliest Milan, Brian Epstein sat alone. He ached for companionship.

****

Sunday, 27 June 1965
Rome

Brian Epstein was not the only lone wolf in Italy. Marcello Geppetti had made a name for himself by being singularly inimitable — by daring to photograph subjects no one ever captured: the irreverent, the unplanned, the unposed.[1963]

He'd begun his career on a traditional path, taking a job with the Giuliani and Rocca agency and then advancing to the more prestigious Meldolesi-Canestrelli-Bozzer agency, where respect and conformity were the norm.[1964] But as Geppetti increasingly rejected the notion that "the best photo was the carefully premeditated shot," he grew more and more estranged from standard work. He found himself falling for the extemporaneous moment.[1965] He felt the tug of freelance.

When a vicious fire in Rome's renowned *Ambasciatori* Hotel threatened the lives of young, international visitors, Geppetti grabbed his camera and took horrific — though stunning — photos of desperate, half-naked tourists hurling themselves from windows to escape the brutal flames.[1966] Geppetti's photographs, graphic and powerful shots, said all one needed to know about the ruthless fire. But when the Catholic Church condemned Geppetti's work as "obscene" and demanded the photos be removed from public display, Geppetti fumed and abandoned corporate photography altogether. He struck out on his own.[1967]

Working as a freelance "collaborator" with the revered Italian newspaper *Momento Sera,* Geppetti was immediately heralded for discovering "headlines without words."[1968] He was applauded for securing shots of clandestine celebrities without their approval and was well-paid for his extemporaneous glimpses into the hidden lives of "the beautiful people."[1969]

Geppetti cunningly captured a steamy kiss between Richard Burton and Elizabeth Taylor, when both were married to other people — and he was threatened by an enraged Anita Ekberg armed with a bow and arrow, the photo of which was an emotional *tableau*![1970] Recklessly zipping here and there on his wieldy Vespa and sporting his beloved Leica camera around his neck, Geppetti covered student protests, clandestine affairs, and political unrest.[1971]

Today, however, he was after an unkempt rock'n'roll sensation from England called The Beatles.[1972] *This,* he thought, *will be most fascinating!*

****

Sunday, 27 June 1965
Androsquo Airport[1973]
Rome

Geppetti frowned, manoeuvring his Vespa through the thick, humid darkness to Rome's Androsquo Airport.[1974] *Past sunset...and still inhumanly scorching! Agh, shades of Dante!*

Geppetti parked his motorbike and threw a furtive look at the swarm of "corporate photographers" — serious older men from standard newspapers, magazines, and music journals. He smirked as they perspired in their rumpled suits and neck-cinching ties. The only article of apparel Geppetti had in common with them was a press pass. Everything he owned was entirely casual, including the pink-striped, short-sleeved shirt he'd thrown on this afternoon. His thick, curly hair had been blown awry. His sideburns were wide and bushy. A cigarette dangled from Geppetti's mouth, littering ashes here and there.[1975] No one would have thought him one of the world's most innovative and courageous photographers.

**Marcello Geppetti, the original
paparazzi, who photographed
The Beatles, June 1965**
Photograph from Wikimedia Commons

Without speaking to a soul, Geppetti looped through the crowd, sussing out the most advantageous spot. He lit a cig from one he tossed to the ground. He waited.

But Geppetti never lingered long at news scenes. He always arrived just in time to do his job.

Within minutes, The Beatles' plane landed to harsh shrieks…squeals from hundreds of perfumed, female denizens — some too young to be so infatuated. Others, too old to be potential objects of the boys' affections. Geppetti scanned the overwrought mob, chuckled, and snapped away. This craze he'd heard so much about was far from over-blown. "Beatlemania" was more passionate than Geppetti had ever anticipated.

As the cumbrous plane bowled down the runway, cries swelled. Geppetti swung around, capturing a grinning group of teenage boys hoisting a portrait they'd crafted of the British four. A wailing cluster of girls in tight-knit, sleeveless, turtle-neck jumpers, fitted skirts, and high heels reached out, hysterically hopeful.[1976] And a tight-lipped line of white-uniformed policeman stood together, frightened and primed for action.[1977]

What sort of demi-gods breathed all this to life? Geppetti wondered, as the door of the plane slowly lifted — a mechanical mouth gaping in shocked surprise.

Then, there they were…*well, two of them, anyway.* The first, wearing a Lenin-cap pulled low over his forehead, Geppetti instantly recognized him from recent publicity for the boy's new book. *Ah, John Lennon!* Geppetti snapped away. And right behind the lauded author, a slim young man emerged with an ugly crease in his fringe and a dark sport coat buttoned clumsily, too high on his chest. The photographer would later discover the thin, unsmiling Beatle to be young lead guitarist George Harrison.[1978]

Both of the musicians, carrying travel bags, appeared road-worn. Their hair was greasy and shaggy, and if they had washed it at all, they had slept in it wet. As the boys clomped down the metal stairway, neither offered a scrap of a smile.

Seconds later, a third band member — this one smartly-tailored in a dark jacket, blue shirt, dress slacks, and sunglasses — exited. Carrying a small suitcase and peering over the crowd with concern, the boy hung back, waiting for his mate. At last, the final Beatle — in a white coat, white shirt, and tan slacks — edged forward, flicking a smidgen of a smile at the chumming reporters.[1979]

"Paul! Ringo!" A random journalist shouted as the boys descended to the tarmac, and Geppetti assigned names to faces as he fired away.

Walking straight towards Geppetti, John Lennon never

registered the photographer or his camera. The cap sat so low on the boy's forehead that he was forced to lift his chin to see. The manoeuvre gave Lennon an air of confidence bordering on conceit, but when someone barked out his name, the Beatle jumped and immediately swiveled around. Like everyone else in this volatile mob, John Lennon was on edge. He had to be.

Whilst Harrison chatted with a tall and handsome member of their entourage (whom Geppetti later identified as Neil Aspinall) and Ringo strode along beside another obviously trusted colleague — a giant of a man designated as roadie Mal Evans — John strode out in front, lips slightly parted in a hesitant gape. Lennon never smiled, never frowned. He moved singly-mindedly, setting a bead on the terminal.[1980]

At the entrance to the building, the crowd thickened. Bodies pressed together at the narrow glass entranceway; photographers angled for position; journalists elbowed one another. Geppetti was one of the first inside, and he swung around, just in time to snap Ringo chuckling at some random comment and John biting back frustration as he was uncomfortably smothered in the fray. Mal Evans stepped protectively behind John and the throng, shielding the boy when the crowd became a threat. But although John's eyes hinted fear, his face only signaled exasperation.[1981]

It was *this* that drew Geppetti's interest: the taut, thin line of distaste that sat upon the Leader Beatle's visage, the scowl of repugnance towards the swarm. What Geppetti saw — and captured — was Lennon's undisguised disillusionment.

Ringo, George, and Paul, the photographer observed, were wearing sport jackets and traveling as celebrities were expected to do. John alone had donned a blousy, untucked, full European-styled chemise — a sort of painter's smock — unbuttoned at the neck to reveal a worn black T-shirt tossed over dark jeans.[1982] It was the sort of garb better suited to the *Left Banque* or an art college — hardly the favoured attire of a rich, young rock'n'roller.

This Lennon, I like! Geppetti smirked, snapping another photo of John chatting comfortably with Paul McCartney.[1983] Serious, aloof, and no one's fool, the rhythm guitarist seemed insistent on his own boundaries. Marcello empathized. That was where *he* lived as well.

However, as Lennon brushed past him for a second time, Geppetti blinked back a gasp. He could see the raw, irritated redness of the boy's eyes, and he detected a quick glint of bright light off an iris.

Contact lenses! Geppetti was shocked. *John Lennon's wearing contact lenses![1984] On the one hand, he emits an aura of oblivion to what others think, but here, he proves that he cares very much! Indeed, this Lennon endures discomfort...for the sake of "fitting in."*

Geppetti moved quickly, squeezing into position, inching closer to John than before. The talented *paparazzo[1985]* held his breath, focused his lens, and snapped a very intimate portrait.[1986]

Ah, Geppetti breathed, lowering his camera and letting John pass, *there's more to this fretful dreamer than one would expect...depths that the fans cannot comprehend. Try as he might to conform, the "Beatle Life" will never be John Lennon's stopping-off point. Soon, he'll ache to break free. Soon, he'll be compelled to do so.* Geppetti sighed and patted his Leica fondly. *Lennon may struggle to be what the world expects, but behind the looking-glass, he is an* artiste. *And soon, he will no longer be able to deny it.*

****

Friday, 2 July 1965
Plaza de Toros de Las Ventas
Madrid, Spain

They had almost reached the final day. One more performance in Barcelona tomorrow night, and the boys would be returning home.[1987] *One more to go, 'n not a moment too soon!* John thought.

The Beatles had played four shows — two each day — at the *Teatro Adriano* in Rome on 27 and 28 June. Then, they'd performed at the *Palais des Expositions* in Nice, France on 30 June. And now tonight — hoping to outdo the great matadors — the boys were once more stepping into the bullring, in Madrid's magnificent *Plaza de Toros de Las Ventas*.[1988]

"Wath's the reathon for thingin' here, Mith-ter?" John

parodied the well-known Castilian lisp.[1989]

Brian glanced at him briefly, waved him away, and continued his conversation with venue's promoter. John wandered off towards the others, who chatted, smoked, and waited to take the stage, antsy for tour's end.

The last few days had been irritating in a myriad of ways. The torturous heat wave had persisted, making outdoor performances dizzying, almost unbearable. As one would guess, attendance had been disappointing as well. Genoa's 25,000-seat stadium had seen only 5,000 fans during the boys' blistering afternoon show, and even Rome's *Teatro Adriana* had been half-full.[1990] Though none of The Beatles had made "heavy weather" about it, the slight crowds hadn't escaped their notice. And now, the ever-present press queries of "How long do you think *you'll* last?" began to feel ominous. Each successive press conference felt a tad more antagonistic.

The Beatles onstage at the *Teatro Adriana*, Rome, 1965
Photograph from Wikimedia Commons

**George and John at the Beatles Press Conference,
held at the *Parco dei Principi* Hotel, Rome**
Photograph rights purchased from Alamy.com

Brian had done his best to alleviate The Beatles' worries and to mitigate the slog of performing the same songs over and over. He'd even been atypically lenient with their chicanery, discounting some of their antics of late.

In Rome, when the four had refused to admit Noël Coward to their dressing room — following the actor/playwright's very public and disparaging remarks about The Beatles' MBE nomination — Brian hadn't cajoled the boys into welcoming the man.[1991] When the infuriated Coward had haughtily instructed Brian's assistant, Wendy Hanson, "to go and fetch one of them," and Paul had reluctantly capitulated, giving Coward the short shrift of an extremely brief audience,[1992] Brian hadn't uttered a syllable of rebuke. Not one word.

When Paul had begun giggling uncontrollably during Ringo's Rome performance of "I Want to Be Your Man," Brian had merely folded his arms and pursed his lips. McCartney had exited the boards briefly, trying to pull himself together, but the boy's return had only resulted in further infectious laughter. Soon, the hilarity had spread to the all-too-willing John.[1993] And although George had been galled and very vocal about "the juvenile behaviour from you lot," Brian had restrained himself from censuring the lads as well. Recalling John's repeated observation that "It's a real grind — this!" Brian had permitted the group leeway.

Even when John had babbled nonsense lyrics to "I'm A Loser" in Rome's *Teatro Adriano* or when George had yelped the "Help!"-inspired battle cry of "Kailiiii!" as an on-stage mic-check[1994] or when Paul had solemn-facedly told a reporter that he "had Ringo's autograph mounted on a wall in my toilet,"[1995] Brian had said nothing.

Instead, he'd spent his energy trying to arrange happy diversions for the four. Flouting gut-twisting fear, Brian had agreed to let the Alfa Romeo Racing Team shuttle The Beatles — one boy per car — from Milan to Genoa.[1996] And in Nice, he'd agreed to let the four scarper off to the *La Fiesta* nightclub, a hot spot that hazardously combined liquor with a tricky Go-Kart track.[1997] Although everything about that adventure had whispered "Danger!", Brian had been uncharacteristically agreeable. Frequently, he'd even served as a listening ear when the boys found themselves worn and exasperated.

"Beatles-karting" à Villeneuve-Loubet

**John and Ringo (top row), George and Paul (bottom row)
at the Go-Kart track in Nice, France on 30 June 1965**
Photograph used by kind permission of https://www.meetthebeatlesforreal.com
and Sara Schmidt, who owns the website.

Tonight was one of those moments.

"Why're we playin' to all these bloody government officials?!" Paul had raged in the dressing room. "The kids're our *real audience*, but they're *outside*! We should be playin' to the people outside, y' know...let 'em in!"[1998]

"I can't stand it when the audiences are too old!" John had quickly jumped aboard. "'N if *that's* what it looks like out front, Brian, I reckon I'll be off..."[1999]

"I understand." Brian had held their eyes, in sincere empathy. "Truly, I do."

"It just doesn't seem natural," John had groused on, "to see older people out there lookin' at us!" But he had combed his hair anyway, preparing to take the stage. "I mean, it's nice to see *anybody*...don't get me wrong. But I always think old people should be at home...doin' the knittin' or somethin'!"[2000]

And nodding in earnest empathy, Brian had sent them onto the stage with no resolution to their problems, but with a feeling that their complaints had been heard. It was something. It was the very best Brian could offer.

****

By the end of the evening, however, the average age of the Madrid punters had become the least of The Beatles' concerns. Over-zealous police had transformed this next-to-last night of the European Tour into an ugly *mêlée*.

"Just shy of the fuckin' Garston Blood Baths!" John's face was blanched and grim.

"...the first time I've really seen kids gettin' beaten up," Ringo said, smoking with shaky hands.[2001]

"It was violent, Brian." George's face was dour. They were all rattled — honestly stunned.

"I-I know but...but try to put it in context," Brian stammered. Spain was his home-away-from-home, and he understood the culture all too well. "These young ladies...have *always* been chaperoned. Heavily chaperoned, I assure you. And the way they responded to you tonight...well, that *isn't* the way young ladies of Madrid are expected to conduct themselves. To the powers-that-be, including their parents, that sort of behaviour was...crass. Vulgar. Bordering on lunacy."

"Right," John toweled off, loosening his tie. "All the more reason to head home, straight away. The sooner we're out of here, the fuggin' better!"

Brian sighed and hung his head. He adored the *Côte d'Azur*. For years, he had been enamoured with its June nights, awash in a lush, ripe, matchless warmth. And he'd been equally entranced with the raw and brutal bullrings, scented with fear, blood, and death. In Spain alone, Brian felt vital and alive. And he had wanted his boys to relish it, as well. But the translation, he'd found, was problematic.

Opening his mouth to explain, Brian stopped.

In a rare instance of awareness, he "saw" his boys. He saw them with an outsider's eyes: rumpled and sweating lads, young men at best. They were, he thought, boys from cosy Liverpool families, boys who regularly took tea and sang Irish folk songs, boys who watched telly and prized Cadbury's Fingers, boys exhausted from months of non-stop work with only moments, here and there, of fun. They were boys isolated and far from home. George's gaunt visage had grown even thinner. John's face was tired and sad.

**A very tired George Harrison and John Lennon
on the 1965 European Tour**
Permission purchased from Alamy.com

"Right, yeah. We know the score." John anticipated the pep talk Brian yearned to deliver. "You'll say there's nothin' for it. You'll tell us we have to 'get on with it.'"

"No, no, not at all," Brian shocked even himself. "What happened tonight between the police and your fans...it was completely out of order. And I give you my word: from now on, I shall speak sharply to our promoters about this sort of...vicious scene. *No one* should be harmed at a Beatles concert. Especially not..."

"Well," John cut across him, slyly, "unless it's a nasty critic with a bad review."

And desperate for anything to lighten the mood, they all laughed. Brian as well.

"Just one more show tomorrow night," Brian coaxed.

"One more rousin' round of 'A Hard Day's Night,' 'n 'Ticket to Ride'!" John chimed in.

"One more go at 'Everybody's Tryin' to Be My Baby,'" George half-sang.

" Y' never know..." Ringo threatened, "*I* might even try out 'Long Tall Sally'!"

"Ah, give the boy a coconut!" Paul swept his hand at the drummer.

And as the "soldier on" crept back into their faces, Brian hurriedly folded the London newspaper proclaiming, "No Full Houses Yet for The Beatles!"[2002] and tucked it away. Negative press was the last thing The Beatles needed to see.

"Where're we goin' lads?!" John drudged up the hackneyed mantra.

"Well, I don't know about you lot," Ringo spat, "but after tomorrow night, *I'm* goin' home!"

"Right!"

"Hard agree, Ritchie!"

"Cheers!"

Even in the best of attitudes, 1965 was asking more of The Beatles than they had to give. Their veneer was still quite attractive, but all of them knew it: the varnish was paper-thin.

Notes!

Did the press's unrelenting emphasis on the fact that the European

concerts had failed to "pack the stadiums" worry Beatles Press Agent Tony Barrow? Did he think the boys were losing their appeal to the public?

In his book John, Paul, George, Ringo & Me, Tony Barrow states, "It was inevitable that having spent 18 months helping to build up The Beatles with positive stories, the press were by now only too ready to take a knock at us on unsold concert tickets. An Associated Press report from Rome suggested that on the European mini-tour, there had been 'no full houses yet for The Beatles.' In Genoa, 'the audience barely reached 5,000, including 1,000 police on hand to keep the order.' Perhaps, said AP, 'the current heatwave was keeping the crowds down.' To be frank, I never thought of the continental European market as being close to the epicentre of Beatlemania. As long as I was getting healthy feedback from our U.S. concert promoters about the brisk business being done at advance box offices over there, I was satisfied that John, Paul, George, and Ringo were not losing their touch in the part of the world that mattered." (p. 150)

However, the diminished audiences **would not** have escaped the notice of The Beatles and most especially of John, with his fragile ego. In The Complete Beatles Chronicle, Mark Lewisohn observes, "Mostly, the [European] tour was remarkable for what it didn't produce — sold-out concert venues. Maybe once or twice over the previous two years a Beatles show hadn't been seen by a capacity house, but here it was a regular occurrence. Fewer people, too, were now at airports to welcome or bid farewell to the group. Certainly there remained huge numbers of fans following The Beatles' every move, and creating chaos at every juncture, but Beatlemania had noticeably diminished since 1963." (p. 180)

And because the boys were only human, this trend had to be a bit "niggling."

Sources:

Lewisohn, The Complete Beatles Chronicle, 51, 180, 194, 196-198, and 203.
Lewisohn, The Beatles: Day by Day, 64.
Harry, The Ultimate Beatles Encyclopedia, 125, 182, and 679-680.
Harry, The John Lennon Encyclopedia, 830-834.
Winn, 321, 328-332, and 335.
Miles, The Beatles' Diary, Vol. 1, 199-200.
The Beatles, The Beatles Anthology, 186-187.
Barrow, 149-150.
Connolly, 198.
Coleman, Lennon, 240, 242, 244-246, and 254.

Coleman, The Man Who Made The Beatles, *251, 252, and 255.*
Winn, 331-332.
Davies, Hunter, The John Lennon Letters, *91.*
Badman, 160.
Barrow, 150.
Gould, 281.
Brown, 175-177 and 252.
Hill, John, Paul, George & Ringo, *206-207.*
Wiener, 49.
Robertson, Lennon, *40-41.*
Joseph, Jennifer, "Foreword to The English Language Edition," *The Beatles in Rome 1965, 1.*
Morola, Adriana, "In the Thick of It," The Beatles in Rome 1965, *4.*
Geppetti, Marcello, The Beatles in Rome 1965. *Marcello's photographs of The Beatles in Rome 1965 fill this book. They are unique and quite revealing.*
Schultheiss, 134-136.
Bicknell, 54.

♫ *The Beatles at Hôtel George V Paris 1965 - Bing video* *This website has a video collage of photos from 21 June 1965 on the patio of the Hôtel Georges Cinq.*

Day off in Paris – The Beatles Bible *This chronicles the events of 21 June 1965.*

June 20 | Absolute Elsewhere: The Spirit of John Lennon | Beatles History *This article also includes the events of 21 June 1965.*

https://www.fabfourstore.com/the-beatles-50-years-ago-today-june-21-1965-monday

The Beatles - A Day in The Life: June 21, 1965 (Monday). Beatles Radio: The Beatles, Solos, Covers, Birthdays, News The Fab 4 and More!

21 June 1965 - France, Paris Day off - Beatles & Solo Photos & Videos Forum (tapatalk.com)

Richard Pape (Author of Boldness Be My Friend) (goodreads.com) *This website supplies the direct quote from Richard Pape regarding The Beatles' nomination for the MBE.*

Richard Pape | Military Wiki | Fandom (wikia.org) *This is a second biographical source on Richard Pape.*

https://www.beatlesbible.com/1965/06/24/john-lennon-a-spaniard-in-the-works-published/ *This web page discusses the press reactions to*

John's second book of poetry and prose.

Cilla Black Biography – Facts, Childhood, Family Life, Achievements (thefamouspeople.com) This website gives a biography of Cilla Black.

Marcello Geppetti - Wikipedia This website contains biographical information about "the first paparazzo," Marcello Geppetti.

https://marcellogeppetti.com/ This is the website of Marcello Geppetti. It is in Italian, but don't miss it. The photo collection is stunning.

Beatles in Rome 1965: Marcello Geppetti: Hardcover: 9781933149127: Powell's Books This website furnishes details about The Beatles' time in Rome 1965 and about Geppetti.

https://tinyurl.com/y4rjd2u5 This photo of Marcello Geppetti was used for the description of the photographer in this chapter.

the beatles at androsquo airport 1965 - Bing images This web page features myriad photos of The Beatles landing at Androsquo Airport, Rome.

Live: Teatro Adriano, Rome, Italy – The Beatles Bible This website gives brief details of each day of the 1965 European Tour. This page is an account of the four Rome concerts and the meeting of Paul and Noël Coward.

(20+) M O T L E Y M I N D - Posts | Facebook This is a photo of Brian Epstein and Paul McCartney at The Beatles' Rome press conference in the Parco dei Principi Hotel.

http://www.meetthebeatlesforreal.com/2015/06/the-press-in-rome.html#comment-form One of Geppetti's photos and three additional photos of the press conference in Rome are found here.

http://www.meetthebeatlesforreal.com/2012/12/go-karts-part-2.html Sara Schmidt's excellent site also supplied these photos of The Beatles enjoying the Go-Kart track in Nice, France on 30 June 1965.

https://www.gettyimages.com/photos/milan-at-night-1960s?phrase=milan%20at%20night%201960s&sort=mostpopular This website furnished 1960s photos used for the descriptions of Milan in this chapter.

https://www.beatlesbible.com/1965/06/26/live-palazzo-dello-sport-genoa-italy This web page chronicles the events of The Beatles' 1965 visit to Genoa, Italy.

Erichsen, Gerald, "Where Did Spaniards Get Their Lisp From?" ThoughtCo.com, 12 January 2019, found at Origins of the 'Lisp' of Spain (thoughtco.com)

https://www.beatlesbible.com/1965/06/27/live-teatro-adriano-rome-italy/ This website supplies information about The Beatles at the Teatro Adriana in Rome, June 1965.

https://www.youtube.com/watch?v=HMGi3v5XRck This 3-minute, colour YouTube clip will let you see The Beatles performing "She's A Woman" at the 4.30 p.m. Velodromo Vigorelli concert in Milan. Or use this QR code:

[1888] Bicknell, 54 and Miles, *The Beatles' Diary, Vol. 1,* 199.

[1889] ♫ The Beatles at Hôtel George V Paris 1965 - Bing video This is a collage of photos of The Beatles at the Hôtel Georges Cinq on 21 June 1965. All descriptions in this portion of the chapter come directly from these photos.

[1890] ♫ The Beatles at Hôtel George V Paris 1965 - Bing video In this video, note that Paul is the only one in a suit and tie. John wears a long-sleeved red shirt and slacks. George wears his Chesterfield coat with upturned collar, an open-necked pale pink shirt, and no tie. Ringo sports a black turtleneck, but has his suit coat on the back of his chair. It's a warm June day, so the coat would possibly have been too warm to wear.

[1891] ♫ The Beatles at Hôtel George V Paris 1965 - Bing video The details of the cigs, orange juice in chilled decanter, and Paul being seated beside Ringo, who is reading newspaper come from this videos. Also, the large carton of Marlboro cigarettes on the table is pictured as well.

[1892] ♫ The Beatles at Hôtel George V Paris 1965 - Bing video The advertisement that Paul reads aloud is found in the upper left hand page that Ringo is perusing in this video.

[1893] ♫ The Beatles at Hôtel George V Paris 1965 - Bing video

[1894] ♫ The Beatles at Hôtel George V Paris 1965 - Bing video

[1895] ♫ The Beatles at Hôtel George V Paris 1965 - Bing video

[1896] ♫ The Beatles at Hôtel George V Paris 1965 - Bing video You can see several photos of John and Paul reading the magazine section review together in this photo collage video.

[1897] ♫ The Beatles at Hôtel George V Paris 1965 - Bing video

[1898] Lewisohn, *The Complete Beatles Chronicle*, 197 and The Beatles - A Day in The Life: June 21, 1965 (Monday). Beatles Radio: The Beatles, Solos, Covers, Birthdays, News The Fab 4 and More!

[1899] The Beatles - A Day in The Life: June 21, 1965 (Monday). Beatles Radio: The Beatles, Solos, Covers, Birthdays, News The Fab 4 and More! and *Day off in Paris – The Beatles Bible* These sources all confirm that the Chris Denning interview took place in The Beatles' suite.

[1900] Lewisohn, *The Complete Beatles Chronicle*, 194, Miles, *The Beatles' Diary, Vol. 1,* 196, Robertson, *Lennon*, 40, and Winn, 321.

[1901] Lewisohn, *The Complete Beatles Chronicle*, 197, Badman, 160, and Winn, 331.

[1902] Howlett, *The Beatles at the BBC*, 67.

[1903] Schultheiss, 134, Badman, 160, and Winn, 331.

[1904] "Author Returns His Military Medal," The *Times*, 22 June 1965, p. 10 and *Glasgow Herald*, 22 June 1965. These printed reports of Pape's comments would emerge the day after Denning informed The Beatles of the World War II flyer's ire.

[1905] Badman, 160.

[1906] Badman, 160. The entire quote is verbatim from Ringo Starr.

[1907] Badman, 160. Badman is the source of the "Have you met Harold Wilson?" question, asked by Chris Denning of John Lennon.

[1908] Badman, 160. Direct quote from John Lennon.

[1909] Lewisohn, *The Complete Beatles Chronicle*, 197 and Winn, 331.

[1910] Lewisohn, *The Complete Beatles Chronicle*, 197 and Winn, 331.

[1911] Lewisohn, *The Complete Beatles Chronicle*, 197.

[1912] Lewisohn, The Complete Beatles Chronicle, 197.

[1913] Lewisohn, *The Complete Beatles Chronicle*, 197.

[1914] Winn, 331. Direct quote from John Lennon. Winn tells us that you can hear this interview on the CD-R *City of Light*.

[1915] Badman, 160. All of the events of Brian's near-tragic accident at the *Palais des Sports* are true and are found in Badman's account. I'm not going to endnote every line of George's story, but will endnote again at the end.

[1916] Badman, 160. This is the end of George's true story of Brian's collision and near fall at the *Palais des Sports* in Paris.

[1917] Lewisohn, *The Complete Beatles Chronicle*, 196-197, Miles, *The Beatles' Diary, Vol. 1,* 199, Winn, 328-332, Hill, *John, Paul, George & Ringo*, 206-207, Robertson, *Lennon*, 41, and Wiener, 49.

[1918] Lewisohn, *The Complete Beatles Chronicle*, 197 and The Beatles' 1965 European tour - Infogalactic: the planetary knowledge core.

[1919] Lewisohn, *The Complete Beatles Chronicle*, 197, Miles, *The Beatles' Diary, Vol. 1,* 199, Wiener, 49, Schultheiss, 135, and https://www.beatlesbible.com/1965/06/24/live-velodromo-vigorelli-milan-italy/

[1920] Lewisohn, *The Beatles: Day by Day*, 64, Miles, *The Beatles' Diary, Vol. 1*, 199, Hill, *John, Paul, George & Ringo*, 207, Robertson, *Lennon,* 41, and Wiener, 50.

[1921] Lewisohn, *The Beatles:Day by Day*, 64.

[1922] Badman, 160-161. Direct quote from Paul McCartney.

[1923] Lewisohn, *The Complete Beatles Chronicle*, 197, Miles, *The Beatles' Diary, Vol. 1*, 199, Schultheiss, 135, and John Lennon's A Spaniard In The Works is published – The Beatles Bible.

[1924] Harry, *The John Lennon Encyclopedia*, 834 and Connolly, 198. Harry says that Wain wrote the mentioned review of *A Spaniard in the Works* for the *New Republic*. Connolly says that John had purchased a copy of *Finnegan's Wake* "to discover what it was that, according to some critics…had influenced him."

[1925] https://www.beatlesbible.com/1965/06/24/john-lennon-a-spaniard-in-the-works-published/ Direct quote from John Lennon.

[1926] https://www.beatlesbible.com/1965/06/24/john-lennon-a-spaniard-in-the-works-published/ Direct quote from John Lennon.

[1927] https://www.beatlesbible.com/1965/06/24/john-lennon-a-spaniard-in-the-works-published/ Direct quote from John Lennon.

[1928] https://www.beatlesbible.com/1965/06/24/john-lennon-a-spaniard-in-the-works-published/ Direct quote from John Lennon, except for "as they say."

[1929] https://www.beatlesbible.com/1965/06/24/john-lennon-a-spaniard-in-the-works-published/ Direct quote from John Lennon, except for the word "right."

[1930] Coleman, *Lennon*, 244. George Melly was a singer who wrote a review of *A Spaniard in the Works* for the *Observer*.

[1931] Coleman, *Lennon*, 244. This is a direct quote from John Lennon.

[1932] Lewisohn, *The Complete Beatles Chronicle*, 203. Check the photo on this page to see John doing this very thing!

[1933] Winn, 332 and Harry, *The Ultimate Beatles Encyclopedia*, 680. Direct quote from Winn.

[1934] Miles, *The Beatles' Diary, Vol. 1*, 198, and Winn, 332.

[1935] Lewisohn, *The Complete Beatles Chronicle,* 197 and https://www.beatlesbible.com/1965/06/24/live-velodromo-vigorelli-milan-italy/

[1936] Harry, *The Ultimate Beatles Encyclopedia*, 680.

[1937] Coleman, *The Man Who Made The Beatles*, 255. Direct quote from Brian Epstein.

[1938] McCabe, Peter and Robert Schonfeld, *John Lennon: For the Record*, 96 and Harry, *The Ultimate Beatles Encyclopedia*, 644. Bill Harry discusses the dismissal of Derek Taylor as Brian's Personal Assistant in 1964 because Brian accused Derek of "riding in a limousine meant for him." And in McCabe and Schonfeld's interview with John Lennon, he says, "[Brian] had hellish tempers and fits and lockouts and he'd disappear for days."

[1939] Lewisohn, *The Complete Beatles Chronicle*, 197, Harry, *The Ultimate Beatles Encyclopedia*, 680, Miles, *The Beatles' Diary, Vol. 1,* 199, and Winn, 332.

[1940] Lewisohn, *The Complete Beatles Chronicle*, 51.

[1941] Lewisohn, *The Complete Beatles Chronicle*, 197 and Miles, *The Beatles' Diary, Vol. 1*, 199. The exact temperature comes from the newspaper article in Lewisohn's book and is in degrees Celsius.

[1942] Lewisohn, *The Complete Beatles Chronicle*, 197, Barrow, 150, and Miles, *The Beatles' Diary, Vol. 1*, 199. Both the heat and the scheduling issues on a work day are discussed by Miles. And Lewisohn includes an Associated Press newspaper article entitled "No Full Houses Yet For The Beatles: Heat Wave's Effect on the Tour."

[1943] Miles, *The Beatles' Diary, Vol. 1*, 199.

[1944] Lewisohn, *The Complete Beatles Chronicle*, 197. The newspaper article on this page furnished the ticket prices and the explanation that Neil is offering.

[1945] Lewisohn, *The Complete Beatles Chronicle*, 197. The newspaper article on this page furnished the ticket prices and the explanation that Neil is offering.

[1946] Coleman, *The Man Who Made The Beatles*, 251.

[1947] I rarely explain the Scouse phrases in the book since they're in the glossary, but this one might be misconstrued. To "go a bomb" in Liverpool is to explode with success. Neil was thrilled with the reviews and sales of John's book on Day 1.

[1948] https://www.gettyimages.com/photos/milan-at-night-1960s?phrase=milan%20at%20night%201960s&sort=mostpopular The description of Milan at night in the 1960s is derived from these images.

[1949] Coleman, *The Man Who Made The Beatles*, 244 and 246. Direct quote from Brian Epstein except changing "greatest fear" to "supreme fear" so that "greatest" wouldn't be repeated twice in one sentence.

[1950] Coleman, *The Man Who Made The Beatles*, 244 and Taylor, Derek, *It Was Twenty Years Ago Today*, 21. In Taylor's book, he reprints a letter addressed to him from Brian Epstein. Brian's salutation reads "[From] Brian Epstein, Manager and Frequent Loner." Brian was well aware of the fact that he was isolating himself more and more from society. In Coleman's book, Wendy Hanson refers to Brian in 1965 as "inconsolably depressed." (p. 244)

[1951] Brown, Peter, 175 and Harry, *The Ultimate Beatles Encyclopedia*, 125.

[1952] Brown, Peter, 175, Schultheiss, 135, Harry, *The Ultimate Beatles Encyclopedia*, 125, and Harry, *The John Lennon Encyclopedia*, 133. Peter Brown assumed management of the Great Charlotte Street NEMS in Liverpool aound the time that Brian left for London.

[1953] Brown, Peter, 175.

[1954] Brown, Peter, 176-177.

[1955] Brown, Peter, 254. Brown states, "NEMS Enterprises...had swollen to literally unmanageable size...on the one hand, struggling to contain the Beatle phenomenon, [Brian] continued to sign up any new act which caught his increasingly capricious fancy." New acts included Sounds Incorporated, Cliff Bennett and the Rebel Rousers, Paddy, Klaus & Gibson, and the Rustics.

[1956] Brown, 176-177.

[1957] Coleman, *The Man Who Made The Beatles*, 254. Coleman quotes famous deejay Alan Freed as saying of Brian, "The manager needed to have no other ties...all the love he would have given to anybody was given to The Beatles."

[1958] Cilla Black Biography – Facts, Childhood, Family Life, Achievements (thefamouspeople.com) This website furnishes information about the biography and discography of Cilla Black.

[1959] Coleman, *The Man Who Made The Beatles,* 241-242. Coleman says, "Brian's forays into gambling were becoming habitual." (p. 241) And Gerry Marsden, who warned Brian "that his gambling habit was increasing," observed, "He'd win eleven thousand pounds one night and lose fifteen thousand the next. I used to tell him he was stupid, but Brian got a kick out of it, and it was his money!" (p. 242)

[1960] Coleman, *The Man Who Made The Beatles*, 252.

[1961] Coleman, *The Man Who Made The Beatles*, 252 and 255. Coleman observes, "Coupled with [business] pressures was inner loneliness…Brian faced all his worries in solitude." (p. 252) His secretary, Joanne, said, "He was always searching for love…and yet, it was all around him. There was incredible love and loyalty for Brian. But he was so lonely, and he wasn't close to people…he didn't realize [sic] there were many people around him who did care for him." (p. 255)

[1962] Davies, Hunter, *The John Lennon Letters,* 91.

[1963] Joseph, Jennifer, Preface to The English Language Edition of *The Beatles in Rome 1965*, 1.

[1964] Marcello Geppetti - Wikipedia and https://marcellogeppetti.com/ Both websites contain biographical information about Marcello Geppetti. The second site is in Italian; however, it gives you access to his photo collection. You will be impressed!

[1965] Joseph, Preface to *The Beatles in Rome 1965* and Merola, Adriana, "Art in the Thick of It," *The Beatles in Rome 1965*, 4.

[1966] Merola, 4.

[1967] Merola, 4.

[1968] Marcello Geppetti - Wikipedia and Merola, 5. Merola calls Geppetti's employment status with *Momento Sera* "a collaboration."

[1969] Marcello Geppetti - Wikipedia and Merola, 5.

[1970] https://marcellogeppetti.com/ and Marcello Geppetti - Wikipedia

[1971] Merola, 4.

[1972] Merola, 4. Merola says that Geppetti and other photographers of his genre, who became known as *paparazzi* after the making of the film *La Dolce Vita*, "unmistakably changed things…they went beyond the motion picture veneer, catching the human aspect…"

[1973] rome androsquo airport 1965 - Bing images This website will allow you to see Geppetti's photographs of The Beatles landing at Androsquo Airport.

[1974] Beatles in Rome 1965: Marcello Geppetti: Hardcover: 9781933149127: Powell's Books

[1975] https://tinyurl.com/y4rjd2u5 The description in this chapter of Geppetti comes from this photo.

[1976] Geppetti, *The Beatles in Rome 1965*, 18.

[1977] Geppetti, 19.

[1978] Geppetti, 6.

[1979] Geppetti, 7. These descriptions are from Geppetti's photo of Paul and Ringo exiting the plane.

[1980] Geppetti, 8, 9, and 10. There are five photos on these pages depicting this scene. You can see Mal grinning beside Ringo and George chatting with Neil. You can see John turning his head toward someone in the crowd.

[1981] Geppetti, 11 and 12. You can see Mal right behind John as the crowd grows. As they enter the airport doors, you can see that John has been wedged almost against the wall.

[1982] Geppetti, 13. Here, you can see John's black smock, T-shirt, and dark jeans in the photo.

[1983] Geppetti, 13.

[1984] Geppetti, Marco, "My Father," *The Beatles in Rome 1965*, 23. This article is written by Geppetti's son, Marco, about Marcello Geppetti's photos of The Beatles in June 1965.

[1985] Joseph, Preface to *The Beatles in Rome*, 1.

[1986] Geppetti, 24-26. There are three incredible "head shots" of John taken by Geppetti on these pages. They were actually taken at The Beatles' press conference at the *Parco dei Principi* Hotel.

[1987] Lewisohn, *The Complete Beatles Chronicle*, 197, Lewisohn, *The Beatles: Day by Day*, 64, Winn, 332-335, Wiener, 49, Schultheiss, 135-136, Robertson, *Lennon*, 41, and Miles, *The Beatles' Diary, Vol. 1*, 199-200.

[1988] Lewisohn, *The Complete Beatles Chronicle*, 197, Lewisohn, *The Beatles: Day by Day*, 64, Winn, 332-335, Wiener, 49, Schultheiss, 135-136, Robertson, *Lennon*, 41, and Miles, *The Beatles' Diary, Vol. 1*, 199-200.

[1989] Erichsen, Gerald, "Where Did Spaniards Get Their Lisp From?" ThoughtCo.com, 12 January 2019, found at Origins of the 'Lisp' of Spain (thoughtco.com)

[1990] Lewisohn, *The Complete Beatles Chronicle*, 197, Winn, 332-333, Barrow, 150, and Miles, *The Beatles' Diary, Vol. 1*, 199.

[1991] https://www.beatlesbible.com/1965/06/27/live-teatro-adriano-rome-italy/ This website notes that Noel Coward had called The Beatles "devoid of talent."

[1992] Miles, *The Beatles' Diary, Vol. 1*, 199-200 and https://www.beatlesbible.com/1965/06/27/live-teatro-adriano-rome-italy/

[1993] Miles, *The Beatles' Diary, Vol. 1*, 199.

[1994] Winn, 333.

[1995] Winn, 332. The interviewer in this 26-27 June chat with The Beatles at the *Parco dei Principia* Hotel identifies the speaker as John, but Winn correctly points out that Paul McCartney is actually doing the talking.

[1996] The Beatles, *The Beatles Anthology*, 186, Miles, *The Beatles' Diary, Vol. 1*, 199, and https://www.beatlesbible.com/1965/06/26/live-palazzo-dello-sport-genoa-italy.

[1997] Miles, *The Beatles' Diary, Vol. 1*, 142 and http://www.meetthebeatlesforreal.com/2012/12/go-karts-part-2.html.

[1998] The Beatles, *The Beatles Anthology*, 186. Direct quote from Paul McCartney. The first and second sentences have swapped places, but the words are all exactly the same.

[1999] The Beatles, *The Beatles Anthology*, 186. Direct quote from John Lennon.

[2000] The Beatles, *The Beatles Anthology*, 186. Direct quote from John Lennon, except for the words "don't get me wrong."

[2001] The Beatles, *The Beatles Anthology*, 186. Direct quote from Ringo Starr.

[2002] Lewisohn, *The Complete Beatles Chronicle*, 197 and Barrow, 150. You can see the Associated Press newspaper article in Lewisohn's book.

**The Beatles might have been weary
of touring,
but the fans were still eager for them!**
Poster from Wikimedia Commons

July 1965

Chart Toppers

"(I Can't Get No) Satisfaction" - The Rolling Stones
"I Can't Help Myself" - The Four Tops
"Mr. Tambourine Man" - The Byrds
"I'm Henry the VIII, I Am" - Herman's Hermits
"What's New Pussycat?" - Tom Jones[2003]

In The News

2 July: The Civil Rights Act of 1964 goes into effect in the U.S., creating the Equal Employment Opportunity Commission (EEOC) to protect against "workplace discrimination" based on race, sex, religion, or national origin.

3 July: Soviet Communist Party Chief Leonid Brezhnev states publicly that the USSR possesses "orbital missiles" that could target and be fired upon any location on Earth.

9 July: The "flashcube" (developed by Sylvania Electronics) is released by American camera maker Kodak. This invention enables photographers using Instamatic cameras to take four indoor photos in succession.

19 July: Filming begins on a new science fiction TV series by Gene Rodenberry entitled "Star Trek."

22 July: Quite unexpectedly, Sir Alec Douglas-Home resigns as head of the Conservative Party in the U.K.[2004]

Sunday, 4 July 1965
London Airport
Heathrow

Noon[2005]

Smiling and waving, The Beatles tarried on the London Airport tarmac. They sopped up the familiar of home...the insouciant British girls, waving and wailing devotion. One thousand unfettered fans, who had loitered for hours to see their boys return, let The Beatles know they were loved.[2006] But the press was not as convivial.

Press: Paul, we hear that *not one* of your European concerts was sold out. In fact, many were only half-booked. Is that true?
Paul: (With a charming wink) Really, the entire visit was a knockout! (He continued to wave and point to various fans on the rooftop deck.) There were some reports that The Beatles were "a flop" in Milan. Well, there were 10,000[2007] at the first show and 22,000 at the second. (Paul eyed the reporter, coolly.) I don't think *that* was too bad. We thought they wouldn't know anything about us![2008]

Press: George, what's your opinion of the tour? Were you disappointed in the number of fans who turned out?
George: (Shrugging and smiling at the frenetic crowd) We thought the whole tour was great. I think the press that said we "flopped" was misleading. Barcelona and Milan were fantastic! In Milan, it was a knockout playin' in a cyclin' stadium, and in Spain, we played a bullring. Great![2009] (George chuckled and waved at a group of girls hoisting a banner that proclaimed "Gorgeous George!")
Press: So, what happens now?

George: Now, we're waitin' to see what happens with our new single. If it doesn't go to the top, then the knockers can have a go.[2010]

Press: And for the *record,* as it were, what might that new single be?

John: "Help!" and "I'm Down." It's comin' out in just a few days, we think.[2011]

Press: Does "Help!" reveal anything about the plot of the new film, then?

John: (Shrugs) We never write to fit with the story line, but this one seemed to fit okay.[2012]

　　And with that, The Beatles were off — grinning and applauding for their fans, to the delightful music of cheers. Almost to the car, John halted abruptly, and using one side of his short, white jeans jacket as a cape, he assumed his newly-discovered "matador's pose," [2013] a subtle allusion to *A Spaniard in the Works.*

　　"Shameless plug, yew!" George barked in his ear.

　　"Well, if y' write the book," John yelled back, " y' have t' sell the book!"

　　And snickering, The Beatles piled into the limo — once again, making their famous, dramatic, and hasty exit.

Sources:

Lewisohn, The Complete Beatles Chronicle, *180 and 197-198.*
Lewisohn, The Beatles: Day by Day, *64.*
Miles, The Beatles' Diary, Vol. 1, *200.*
Badman, *160.*
Schultheiss, *136.*
Robertson, Lennon, *41.*
Winn, *335.*

The Beatles return to England, from Spain, London Heathrow Airport,...
News Photo - Getty Images *This is an excellent photo of the boys on the tarmac. You can see the short white jeans jacket John lifted as a brief cape. Note that George is wearing John's traditional "Lenin cap," whilst John has on a white one. You can also see Neil Aspinall and Mal Evans.*

The Beatles at London's Heathrow Airport. The Beatles returned home...

News Photo - Getty Images This is a closer image of the "landing party."

The Beatles at London's Heathrow Airport, July 4, 1965. They had just returned from a successful tour of France, Italy, and Spain : beatles (reddit.com) Here is a full-length view, revealing John's houndstooth slacks and trendy white belt, to match the jacket and cap.

Travel: Barcelona to London – The Beatles Bible This web page gives brief information about The Beatles' return flight to London, 4 July 1965.

[2003] All US Top 40 Singles For 1965 - Top40Weekly.com

[2004] July 1965 - Wikipedia One other event of note for July 1965 was the birth of J.K. Rowling on 31 July.

[2005] Lewisohn, _The Beatles: Day by Day_, 64 and Miles, _The Beatles' Diary, Vol. 1_, 200.

[2006] Miles, _The Beatles' Diary, Vol. 1_, 200.

[2007] Badman, 161. In Badman's book, the number is given as **100,000**, but that is obviously a misprint. The upcoming Shea Stadium performance would only hold, 60, 000. The Barcelona concert wasn't twice as large as Shea. The correct number must have been 10,000.

[2008] Badman, 161. Direct quote from Paul McCartney.

[2009] Badman, 161. Direct quote from George Harrison.

[2010] Badman, 161. Direct quote from George Harrison.

[2011] Badman, 161. Direct quote from John Lennon.

[2012] Badman, 161. Direct quote from John Lennon.

[2013] Hill, _John, Paul, George & Ringo_, 207. Here, you can see John doing this exact same pose, one day earlier, in Barcelona.

Tuesday, 13 July 1965
Kenmore
Weybridge, Surrey

"I truly can't understand your logic!" Cynthia blinked. All of June, whilst her husband had been away on tour, she had missed him terribly. She'd even sat, misty-eyed, in front of the radio when they'd aired John's clever BBC Home Service "World of Books" interview.[2014] She had sniffled into a tissue at the sound of his voice. But now that John was home again, they were already at each another.

"I didn't ask you to understand, did I?!" John shuffled out of the room — his robe hanging open; his face bristly and hair uncombed.

Cynthia huffed and followed after him, trying to convince her husband to "do the right thing." "You're famously put off when Paul records a song without you, but *now,* you say you're happy to let him accept an award on behalf of the group...an honour that will, no doubt, be photographed for the newspapers and perhaps even recorded for telly as well!"

"Yeah well, I've had enough of that shite!" John shouted.

Cynthia threw her eyes to the ceiling. *Men! They deem women 'a fathomless mystery.' But* this*!* She shook her head in bewilderment.

At that very moment, The Beatles were being fêted at London's elegant Strand Hotel for once again capturing several prestigious Ivor Novello awards for songwriting excellence.[2015] Admittedly, this wasn't the first time the boys had been selected for the honour. On 25 October 1964, the lads had garnered four Novellos: one for the Most Broadcast Song, "She Loves You." A second for the Best-Selling Record, also "She Loves You." A third for the Second Top-Selling Record, "I Want to Hold Your Hand,"

and the *pièce de résistance*, the award for Most Outstanding Contribution to Music in 1963.[2016] The Beatles had, essentially, "run away with" every coveted prize, and John had been there, reluctantly smiling for the fawning press.

But despite today's congratulatory banquet being a recurrence, the Novello was a coveted award that would most assuredly be accompanied by a flurry of publicity. And Cynthia knew that tomorrow morning — when thousands newspapers flapped upon damp doorsteps — Paul's smiling photo at the lavish affair would only agitate John.

"Look, it's too late, anyroad." John trudged upstairs, the belt of his robe trailing behind him whilst Mimi, their constantly curious cat, followed, batting at the frayed tie.

"Not if you hurry! I could ring Alf...he could almost be here by the time you're..."

"Look Cyn," John sighed, "we all agreed in the airport...Paul's the one for this. He's our 'Johnny on the Spot,' as it were."[2017]

"But that's just *it*!" Cynthia hated herself for arguing. When John set his mind on a thing, nothing would alter the course. "Paul's not Johnny! He's not *you*! And I'll wager those awards this afternoon are all yours!"

John spun around, his belt flying up and accidentally batting Mimi on the ear, "Bad wager, Powell! Because y'er *not* right. If fact, y'er dead wrong!"

"What?" Cynthia's face clouded. "What exactly were the awards, then?"

"Well, let's see," John hissed, "first, we have the award for The 'A' Side of the Record Issued in 1964 that Achieved the Highest Sales," He paused. "And *that*, jadies'n lents, goes to Paul McCartney's 'Can't Buy Me Love.'"[2018]

"Oh."

"Don't feel bad for me, Powell." John's voice dripped with venom. "I *was* nominated...for an innovative, little record called 'I Feel Fine.' But unfortunately, as all good billiards players say in America, 'Dem's da breaks, luv.' 'Can't Buy Me Love' won the day 'n that's that."[2019]

"John, I..."

"No, no, wait! There's more!" John snatched up his belt and tied it. "The Beatles also won a cherished Ivor Novello for The

Most Performed Work of the Year…which again turns out to be 'Can't Buy Me Love.' 'N yes, before you arsk…I was nominated for 'A Hard Day's Night,' but as y' can see, I was clearly overlooked."[2020]

"Well, it's…it's not as if…" Cynthia stammered.

"Don't pity me!" John snarled. "From all reports, 'A Hard Day's Night' won the award for the Year's Outstandin' Theme from Radio, TV, or Film,' so I wasn't entirely 'belly up,' as they say."

"John, I never…"

"But all right, all right! Have it your way! As m' last big single proclaimed to all 'n sundry, 'I'm a Loser.'"[2021] John gave his wife a hard stare.

John's sarcasm rarely failed the mark. And today was no exception. Cynthia bent down and scratched Mimi behind the ears. It was all she could think of to fill the silence.

"Why do the others think you're not attending?" she asked her husband, softly. John had scored hit after hit in 1964. He had dominated the *A Hard Day's Night* LP. In truth, the record had been comprised almost entirely of Lennon compositions. Now, to have his merits assessed in such a lopsided fashion — Cynthia supposed she was even angrier than John.

"I told the others that after all the roolya-broolya 'n 'rigama-roar' of the MBEs, I didn't want to put myself out there again. I told 'em I was tired of the fuggin' furore." John shrugged, "I said I didn't want to hear another word of it."[2022]

"And they swallowed that?" Cynthia arched a carefully-penciled eyebrow.

John's snort was indignant. "Paul said he's usin' that as a springboard for his acceptance speech, as it were. He's gonna say he hopes people won't start sendin' their Ivor Novellos back, once they've heard we've won a few."[2023]

Cynthia mimed a smile. She stood and brushed the heavy fringe out of her eyes. "Well, at least you enjoyed a morning lie-in, then."

"Right…" John continued up a second staircase to the attic game room where his elaborate Scalextric race cars[2024] were waiting for a spin.[2025] "One day without a million deadlines…or a million eyes on me."

Cynthia followed after him. "This morning's entertainment

headlines say your American LP — *Beatles VI* — just went to Number One."[2026]

"Well, I've no objection to a million ears." John quirked a corner of his mouth. "They're virtually non-invasive — ears." He flipped on the game room lights and headed for his prized electric slot car set.

"John, I hope you didn't want to attend that luncheon. I hope you weren't..."

"The only thing that interested me in the *slightest* was meetin' ole Billy Butlin himself." John bent over, arranging the cars on the track. "He's the one dispersin' the awards, y' know."

"Butlin?"

"*Sir* Billy Butlin to you, gerl."

Cynthia made a face.

"You know Butlin...the very one who started the very famous holiday camps,[2027] includin' the one in Skegness where Rory 'n the boys were performin' when we shanghied Ringo out from under their very noses!"[2028]

"Ringo was at Butlin's when you asked him to join the group?" Cynthia frowned.

Butlin's Holiday Camp postcard, 1940
Photograph from Wikimedia Commons

"Don't you recall? It was August…the height of the summer season, 'n Rory 'n the Hurricanes were up there, headlinin' the show…so, me 'n Paul, we drove up 'n forced ole Johnny Guitar to tell us where Ritchie was…'n right then 'n there, we persuaded Starkey to jump ship 'n join us…"[2029]

"And the rest, as they tritely say, is history." Cynthia smiled. "I guess I never really knew the details."

"I can't imagine why not."

"Well…um…I believe I was planning a small, intimate, but quite eventful wedding…in only a day or so…"[2030]

"Right yeah, that." John cut his eyes at her, coyly. "I remember *that* as well."

Cynthia sighed, wistfully. "I probably wasn't the best bargain you made that week, was I?" She ached for some sort of compliment, however small.

John fidgeted with the Scalextric set, making adjustments on the track, and biting his lip for a moment. Then he regarded his wife with honest eyes. "Y' know, we did some things that week that I'll always regret, but Ringo wasn't one of 'em…'n you, Cynthia Powell, weren't, either."

"Well, thank you…I think."

John snickered and hopped up. "Ah, forget the fuggin' cars, gerl! Let's go 'n find Jarlett 'n see what she can conjure from the ole magic cupboard."[2031]

And set on making the most of a day off, Cynthia began planning their uncharted afternoon. John said very little but willingly agreed to everything she wanted to do.

Notes!

Though in 1965, John and Cynthia were beginning to experience difficulties in their marriage, they were in no way anticipating divorce and were still very much in love. In the decades that have passed since that time, the legend that they were "never in love" has taken root. But nothing could be farther from the truth.

In fact, recalling her August 1962 wedding, Cynthia states in her 2005 book, John: *"Accounts of our wedding have often portrayed it as a miserable, last-minute shotgun affair…Again, it's a long, long way from the truth. It was last-minute, which meant that we had no flowers, no reception, no beautiful dress and no photographer, but it wasn't miserable. In fact, it was the opposite: we were very happy. And John —*

who was never one to do things the conventional way — was the most determined of us that it would go ahead...We giggled about being Mr. and Mrs., teased each other about being boring old marrieds and pictured ourselves together in our rocking chairs. Our map of the future had changed, but we began to like the idea and John rose to the occasion, becoming gentle and protective toward me." (p. 94)

And of 1965, Cynthia reports, "We had lots of fun at Kenwood..." She says that in the Scalextric room, "[John] and Julian would team up together against the opposition and the race would be played out amid whoops, screams and shouts of 'Cheat! Your car's been souped up. Mine's been fixed.'" (p. 167) Cynthia admits that in 1965 and 1966, "the chasm between us was widening..." (p. 195) but the Lennons' happy days were not yet over and done.

Sources:

Lewisohn, The Complete Beatles Chronicle, *198.*
Lewisohn, The Beatles: Day by Day, *64.*
Harry, The Ultimate Beatles Encyclopedia, *332-333 and 623-624.*
Harry, The John Lennon Encyclopedia, *410.*
Miles, The Beatles' Diary, *Vol. 1, 67 and 200-201.*
Lennon, Cynthia, A Twist of Lennon, *78-81.*
Lennon, Cynthia, John, *94-95, 166-167, and 195.*
Winn, 335-336.
Goldman, 191.
Spitz, 345-346.
Norman, Shout!, *162.*
Norman, John Lennon: The Life, *271-272.*
Coleman, Lennon, *177-178.*
Starr, Michael Seth, Ringo: With a Little Help From My Friends, *53-54.*
Stark, 120.
Wiener, 50.
Robertson, 41.
Schultheiss, 136.

<u>*Lennon and McCartney receive five Ivor Novello awards – The Beatles Bible*</u> *This web page provides brief information about Paul McCartney accepting the Ivor Novello Awards on behalf of The Beatles, 13 July 1965.*

<u>*JULY 13, 1965 – Paul McCartney was presented with five Ivor Novello Awards – The Beatles (beatlesdaily.com)*</u> *This web page provides more information about The Beatles' 1965 Ivor Novello Awards.*

<u>*13 July 1965 - UK, Savoy Hotel on the Strand, London - Beatles & Solo*</u>

Photos & Videos Forum (tapatalk.com) This is a video of Paul McCartney accepting the Ivor Novello Awards from Sir Billy Butlin.

http://www.dmbeatles.com/history.php?year=1965&month=07 This web page discusses the events of 13 July 1965.

https://en.wikipedia.org/wiki/Billy_Butlin This web page gives information about entrepreneur Billy Butlin, who founded the very successful Butlin's Holiday Camps in England.

Scalextric - Wikipedia This website supplies information about the British electric slot car racing set owned by John Lennon.

[2014] Miles, *The Beatles' Diary, Vol. 1,* 200 and Schultheiss, 136.

[2015] Lewisohn, *The Complete Beatles Chronicle*, 198, Lewisohn, *The Beatles: Day by Day*, 64, Winn, 335, Miles, *The Beatles' Diary, Vol. 1,* 201, Robertson, *Lennon*, 41, and Wiener, 50. Some reports of this event say that John "forgot" to show up. But Barry Miles correctly informs us, "John refused to attend. He had been upset by the press comments about their receiving the MBE and did not want to put himself on show again.".

[2016] Harry, *The Ultimate Beatles Encyclopedia*, 332-333.

[2017] Winn, 336. Winn says that at London Airport on 4 July, "Paul drew the short straw and agreed to represent The Beatles at the annual Ivor Novello Awards luncheon."

[2018] List of awards and nominations received by the Beatles - Wikipedia and Lewisohn, *The Beatles Day by Day*, 64. Most sources claim that The Beatles won five Ivor Novello awards in 1965. Lewisohn is correct in saying they actually won only three, although they were nominated for five awards.

[2019] List of awards and nominations received by the Beatles - Wikipedia and Lewisohn, *The Beatles Day by Day*, 64.

[2020] List of awards and nominations received by the Beatles - Wikipedia

[2021] List of awards and nominations received by the Beatles - Wikipedia and Lewisohn, *The Beatles Day by Day*, 64.

[2022] Miles, *The Beatles' Diary, Vol. 1,* 201. Miles states, "John refused to attend. He had been upset by the press comments about their receiving the MBE and didn't want to put himself on show again."

[2023] Lewisohn, *The Beatles: Day by Day*, 64, Miles, *The Beatles' Diary, Vol. 1,* 201, and *Lennon and McCartney receive five Ivor Novello awards – The Beatles Bible*

[2024] Scalextric - Wikipedia This website gives information about the electric slot car racing set owned by John Lennon. Scalextric cars had been invented by Fred Francis in England, 1956. The Beatles had a set, to keep them amused backstage on their 1964 U.K. Tour. John liked it so much that he had an elaborate set, complete with speakers that produced authentic track sounds, installed in Kenwood.

[2025] Goldman, 191. Goldman tells us that John had "two rooms in the attic" for his "lavish layout of electrically-powered model cars" complete with "speakers that blared out the roar of accelerating engines, the squealing of tires, and occasionally, the explosive sounds of a deadly crash."

[2026] Lewisohn, *The Beatles: Day by Day*, 64, Miles, *The Beatles' Diary, Vol. 1*, 201, and _Lennon and McCartney receive five Ivor Novello awards – The Beatles Bible_

[2027] https://en.wikipedia.org/wiki/Billy_Butlin This page supplies a biography of Sir Billy Butlin, the entrepreneur who founded Butlin's Holiday Camps.

[2028] Harry, *The Ultimate Beatles Encyclopedia*, 623-624, Miles, *The Beatles' Diary, Vol. 1*, 67, Spitz, 345-346, Norman, *Shout!*, 162, Norman, *John Lennon: The Life*, 271-272, Starr, Michael Seth, *Ringo: With a Little Help from My Friends*, 53-54, Coleman, *Lennon*, 177-178, and Stark, 120.

[2029] Harry, *The Ultimate Beatles Encyclopedia*, 623-624, Miles, *The Beatles' Diary, Vol. 1*, 67, Spitz, 345-346, Norman, *Shout!*, 162, Norman, *John Lennon: The Life*, 271-272, Starr, Michael Seth, *Ringo: With a Little Help from My Friends*, 53-54, Coleman, *Lennon*, 177-178, and Stark, 120. Sources differ on how Ringo was invited into The Beatles. Many sources say that John telephoned him at Butlin's and said "You're in." Other sources, including Bill Harry who was close friends with John and Paul during (and after) the summer of 1962, say that they drove up to Butlin's in Skegness, Scotland to convince Ringo to join them.

[2030] Lennon, Cynthia, *John*, 94-95 and Lennon, Cynthia, *A Twist of Lennon*, 78-81. Cynthia was busy planning her wedding to John, which took place on 23 August 1962.

[2031] Harry, *The John Lennon Encyclopedia*, 410. John is referring to Dorothy "Dot" Jarlett who "was initially hired to look after Julian…but who soon began to take on other household chores, ranging from cooking and cleaning to checking the fan mail…"

Thursday, 29 July 1965
London Pavillion, Picadilly Circus
London

"Princess Margaret's delayed her holiday for this, y' know,"[2032] Ringo fidgeted nervously in the back of the fat, black limousine.[2033]

"Lord Snowden...not to be forgotten...as well." Paul winked and clicked his cheek.

"Who?" John chewed gum and gripped Cynthia's hand even tighter.[2034] His starched tuxedo shirt was chafing, and the warm July night was doing nothing to solve it.[2035]

The boys laughed, but minimally. The only thing they hated more than wearing formal attire and viewing themselves on film was attending the official banquets that always concluded these extravagant premières. Nothing about this evening was appealing.

"*You've* had quite the week, haven't you?" George elbowed Ringo playfully. "Estate owner!"[2036]

"Ah, Sunny Heights isn't really an estate," Ringo chuckled throatily. "It's just a much larger home than the ones *I've* been used to!"[2037]

Only yesterday, Ringo and Maureen had officially purchased their own St. George's Hill Tudor in Weybridge, Surrey, complete with thickly wooded acreage, a whimsical tree house, a goldfish pond, and an expansive garage, large enough for Ringo's four cars and nine meandering cats.[2038] Sunny Heights, located only a mile and a half from John's house, boasted a kennel for Ringo's peach-coloured poodle, Tiger,[2039] and two Airedales — though they were almost always under foot. The rambling home even provided the Starrs with an air raid shelter, should the need arise.[2040]

"I had it in m' mind to be more like John, y' see." Ringo slid his eyes to Lennon. "Stockbroker belt, Tudor home, lovely wife...livin' the fat life out in Weybridge."[2041] Ringo grinned.

"Well, if it's livin' like John y'er after, you'll have to work on bein' perpetually browned off, then, won't you?" George snickered.

"Hardee-har-har," John sniffed, indignantly.

"How very dare you?" Cynthia patted her husband's arm protectively, though she knew it was all in fun.

The limo, which had swept briskly along the roadway, was now reduced to a crawl as the stars of "Help!" rolled into Piccadilly, congested with over 10,000 exuberant fans who had begun assembling at 8.00 that morning.[2042] Two hundred and sixty policemen braced themselves against potential mayhem. (Even the priceless statue of Eros had been boarded up for protection.)[2043] Now, the security team cast uneasy glances at one another.

Ignoring them, the Beatles' loyal hoisted banners proclaiming, "WELL DONE, BEATLES!" and "IT'S TOPS!"[2044] The London Pavilion's marquee boasted, "THE BEATLES in *Help!*" And Piccadilly bulged — not just with ecstatic teenaged girls but also with mums in flats and frocks, male college students, and well-heeled businessmen, curious about the "so-called British phenoms."[2045] As the car slowed in front of the metal-gated red carpet and The Beatles alighted beneath the striped awning, cheers shifted to screams.[2046]

"George Harrison!" an enthusiastic reporter leaned over the ropes and pointed his microphone in the lead guitarist's direction, "You four look quite smart! Do you prefer black tie?"

"No, we'd be much happier in jeans and T-shirts!"[2047] George retorted. Those who heard the jab collapsed in laughter. Most screamed on.

But before the next audacious reporter could insinuate himself into The Beatles' grand entrance, the crowd spontaneously broke into song. "Happy birthday to you, Happy Birthday to you, Happy Birthday Dear Ringo...Happy Birthday to you!!!!!!!!"[2048] Tomorrow would be Richard Starkey's 25th, and feeling a tad "on-in-years," he relished the fans' devotion. The drummer laughed and lifted the hand clutching his cig.[2049] He waved.

Then, just as they'd been instructed to do, the boys gathered for mandatory photos. George and Paul moved to the outside of the assemblage, whilst John, Cynthia, Ringo, and Maureen took "centre stage." Cynthia leaned her head against John's shoulder, her blonde hair cascading from a high clip and falling against her fur-trimmed tapestry jacket. Maureen stood, lightly smiling in an elegant Grecian up-do that highlighted her neck and graceful empire-waisted gown.[2050]

In seconds, the troupe rearranged, with Paul, Maureen, and Ringo in one smiling cluster and John, Cynthia, and a distracted George looking away in another.[2051] Just behind them, as in almost every pose, Brian was keeping watch.[2052] Never the centre of attention, the manager looked on, possessively.

At the entrance to the Pavilion, the others waited: Walter Shenson with his wife, Gerry; music publisher Dick James with his son Steven;[2053] and Victor Spinetti — whom the fans had adored in "A Hard Day's Night." They had arrived[2054] to a wave of squeals. And typically jubilant, Roy Kinnear was enjoying the well-deserved celebration.

**Victor Spinetti, who starred with The Beatles
in "A Hard Day's Night" and "Help!"**
Photograph from Wikimedia Commons

"Just a few close friends, eh?" John joined them, waving to the crowd.

"A select few," Spinetti deadpanned.

"'N a light meal after." Paul placed a hand on his jacket front.

"Only if we sing fer our supper, son." John escorted Cyn towards the door.

"I believe *that* can be arranged," George pointed the way. "I think we have the very thing…on film."

And steeling themselves for the worst, The Beatles trailed into the magnificent theatre for presentation to Lord Snowden and Princess Margaret…and for another glance at the bizarre United Artists film that they had made but never quite understood.

****

It wasn't as dreadful as they'd remembered from their earlier sneak peek. At moments, the film was genuinely funny. And there were plenty of fond memories from the Bahamas and Austria and even street stops around London to share with another. "Remember when we…" and "Oh yeah, that's where Mal…" the boys snickered.[2055]

The Pavilion audience was unabashedly enthusiastic. Laughter over the chase scenes. Applause for the songs. Murmurs of a good sort.

"I enjoyed 'A Hard Day's Night' very much,"[2056] Princess Margaret — alluring in a gauzy, white, ruffled-back dress with pale grey polka-dots — offered her hand to each of them. "And I've been looking forward to this latest one!"[2057] Her compliment had seemed genuine and from the wide smile she'd worn, The Beatles supposed that their royal fan hadn't been disappointed.

If he was honest with himself, John hadn't been dissatisfied, either. He couldn't legitimately stamp it a complete failure.

"'Help!' as a film," he told a reporter as they exited the Pavilion "is like 'Eight Days a Week' as a record. A lot of people liked that record. But neither was what we really wanted. They were both…a bit manufactured. The film won't harm us," John shrugged, "but we weren't in control."[2058]

"John! *John Lennon!*" a second journalist bellowed as John manouevered Cynthia towards the car. "One more question! Just one!" John glanced in his direction, and the reporter elbowed his colleagues aside to stand out.[2059] "John," the man cupped a hand around his mouth, "have you heard the rumour that the Weybridge golf club is refusing to permit entry to Ringo and you, even though you both now live in the neighbourhood?"[2060]

For an instant, John was stunned. No one likes being disliked. But stiffening his neck, he shot back, "We don't even *like* golf!"[2061] He looked at Cynthia and sputtered indignantly, "In fact, we very nearly didn't *buy* the house when we heard that there was a golf course in the back of it, because I was frightened of people runnin' all over my garden lookin' for their golf balls!"[2062] Even without his glasses, John could see Brian pacing at the limo's doorway, so he quickly rattled off, "We haven't asked to be members of their club, and we won't be doin' so. Neither of us have the slightest interest in the sport!"[2063]

"Right, but..." the journalist pressed ahead. But giving the man a mock-salute, John and Cynthia walked on.

"The whole thing is a fast-paced comic strip, really." They heard George critiquing the film as they moved past. "Just a string of events, y' see."[2064]

"And your producer, Dick Lester? How was *he*, George?" a newsman followed up.

"Oh," George smiled and began to edge towards the car, "I think we pushed Dick Lester to the limit of his patience. But he was very, very easy-goin' and a pleasure to work with."[2065] Then, nodding "goodbye," Harrison ducked inside the Rolls, the door swinging shut behind him.

To a surge of applause and shrieks, The Beatles and their entourage were off to the Dorchester Hotel, leaving scores of fans, wide-eyed and open-mouthed, sighing in Piccadilly.

****

Friday, 30 July 1965
Kenwood
Weybridge, Surrey

Noon

Last evening's dinner in the Dorchester's Orchid Room[2066] had been magnificent: faintly-scented white flowers, exquisite appointments, sparkling wine, sinful desserts, and tasteful instrumentals. Brian had been ebullient. John had been chatty. And thinking back over it all — as she snuggled under her high-count, white cotton sheets — Cynthia smiled contentedly.

It had been the perfect midsummer's night. Cynthia had discarded her tapestry jacket in the limo. And Jane Asher had arrived in a sleeveless, alabaster Edwardian gown.[2067] Even at 9.00 p.m., the evening had been unseasonably warm. Brilliant for a party.

During dinner, scores of guests had come by to express their delight with the film.

"Ingenious Bond spoof!"

"Well done, you four!"

"Can't wait to give the record a listen!"

And according to Brian, the various seaside towns — Barnstaple, Brighton, Clacton, Lowestoft, Plymouth, Ramsgate, Weymouth, and Worthing — that had simultaneously premièred "the flick"[2068] (as they said in America) — had teemed with rave appraisals. Now, tucking John into the covers, Cynthia edged from the bed, grabbed her robe, slippers, and glasses, and tiptoed downstairs to snag the reviews.

Dot Jarlett had already seen the papers, and as she handed Julian to Cynthia, her face was guarded.

"Should I?" Cynthia nuzzled her son's neck, making him squirm and giggle.

"Well, first off, you'll notice the boys are splashed all across *the entire front page*! They've become such an institution that even their films are headline news!"[2069]

"And...did we do well?" Cynthia bit her lip.

"Some say 'aye.' Some, 'nay.'" Dot reported. "It's not blanket approval, as with the last film. But no one ignored it."

"Well," Cynthia accepted a cup of tea, "let's see what's what."

The Spectator acknowledged the Bond parody, proclaiming: "Beatles on the Bond Trail,"[2070] and the reviewer was primarily positive, giving kudos to Ringo as "the most individual character."[2071] But the press persisted with their long-standing perspective that the boys were virtually indistinguishable. Starr, the reviewer said, "is the oddity…so far as any of them can be called that."[2072]

"What's that quote from the film?" Cynthia snickered, "'They're all the same in their similitude!' or something of that nature."

"Well personally, I can't see it!" Dot shook her head. "To me, they're as different as plum and pudding!"

"'Help!'" Cynthia read aloud whilst Julian scrambled down to play, "'is almost consistently funny, sometimes almost confusingly fast, and above all, a contrast to its predecessor.' I'd call that a compliment, wouldn't you, Dot? That the boys have done something entirely unique?"

"Hmmm, yes, but read on."

"All right," Cynthia took a quick sip of tea and adjusted her glasses. "'Help!'s social satire is directed as much inward as outward…The Beatles put latch keys into four identical front doors which, with carefully primitive exteriors, all open into a single opulent interior, a schoolboy millionaire's dream of gadgets and instant marvels — sunken beds, rising Wurlitzers, orangeade-making machines, and pigeon-holed sandwiches…'"[2073]

"A *schoolboy* millionaire's dream!" John barked from the doorway. He stood forlorn, in wilted pyjamas, an undone robe, and no slippers. "But *we* had nothin' to do with any of that! It was all made up…concocted without us! We just showed up 'n did what we were told to do when we were told to do it!"

"Oh, that's a negligeable part of the whole article, John." Cynthia handed him the newspaper. "It's really quite a lovely review."

"Here," Dot Jarlett fished through the folded papers and handed the Lennons another. "Don your specs and take a gander at that one."

John had left his glasses upstairs, so he handed the paper off to Cyn.

"All right, then." Cynthia cleared her throat, "This is Kenneth Tynan, writing in the *Observer*. He notes, 'The Beatles themselves are not natural actors…'"[2074]

"Got that right," John snorted, taking a sip of Cyn's tea.

"'…nor are they exuberant extroverts…'"[2075]

"I see he never caught us in the Cavern."

"Their mode," Cynthia went on, "is dry and laconic, as befits their flat and skeptical Liverpool accent..."[2076]

"Said the muzzied journalist..." John intoned.

"Realising this," Cynthia read, "Lester leaves it to his cameraman (David Watkin)..."[2077]

"Nice plug, eh David?"

"...to create the exuberance, confining The Beatles to dead-pan comments..."[2078] Cynthia read.

"Watkin never confined us to fuggin' anythin'!"

"It's a misplaced modifier, John. Tynan's referring to Dick Lester."

"Go on."

"Where was I?" Cynthia ran her finger down the page. "Oh here: 'confining The Beatles to dead-pan comments and never asking them to react to events with anything approaching emotion. He capitalizes on their wary, guarded detachment. 'There's somebody been in this soup,' says John, having calmly dredged from his bowl a season ticket and a pair of spectacles."[2079]

"Wait, wait! He left out the best part...the, 'I like a lot o' seasoning in me soup' part. That's m' favourite line of the film!" John scowled. "Craggy bastard."

"Um...okay." Cynthia tried again. "'Not a bit like Cagney,' is George's response when..."[2080]

"*That's it!* I've heard enough." John slurped down the rest of his wife's lukewarm tea and slid the cup across the kitchen counter. "Let's chuck it all in favour of bacon butties."

Dot sighed relief. She had cleverly tucked the *Daily Worker* critique near the bottom of the pile, hoping John would tire before discovering it. The short but scathing review had been anything but kind to The Beatles.

"Save me..." it had read, "from the unabridged, unhinged lunacy that has no roots, no meaning, no sequence, no consequence, no let-up, no pause! Save me (notwithstanding some occasional peaks of inspired nonsense) from the ruthless elegance, this unrelenting *Sunday Colour Supplement* assault upon the senses!"[2081]

No, Jarlett thought as she happily opened the bread bin, *save me from being here when John Lennon reads the* Worker *review! I hope to be far, far away when that one surfaces!* And happily changing the subject to "who wore what" last night, Dot dexterously directed the conversation to happier ground.

****

John collapsed on the sun-parlour settee and tugged a light throw across his bare feet. He wanted to do something — and nothing. He had every intention of being productive and not one desire to do so. He didn't want to sleep or talk or watch telly. He loitered.[2082]

John knew he'd been tendered only the positive reviews of "Help!" He surmised that "Auntie Dot"[2083] had concealed the others...or at least stacked them on the bottom of the pile. But it was no state secret that the film wasn't as good as the last. He'd said so himself plenty of times.[2084] They all had.[2085]

What John didn't say, and what he couldn't help thinking now was how apt the whole script really was. The Beatles — always loping from one end of the world to the next, untethered to stability or reality — were in constant danger...danger of being sacrificed ("jolly, with a knife!") on the altar of public opinion, sacrificed to the Goddess of Money or the Lord of Desire.

They were perpetually asked to do anything and everything ("Wear these clothes." "Use these words." "Stop smoking in public!" "Silence your opinions!" "Hide your love away.") for a slim chance at survival. They were commanded to don eternally jovial masks of "slapstick schoolboys" in hopes of evading the danger at hand. Failure was always prowling — a mere step or two behind. And so, holding together as they ran pell-mell, the Fab Four narrowly averted peril, day after murderous day.[2086]

Notes!

John's feelings about The Beatles' constant evasion of impending danger are seconded by Peter Brown, Brian's assistant in the new Hilly House location of NEMS. In Carlin's biography, Paul McCartney: A Life, *Brown states, "[Beatlemania] was just madness. The whole point was that it wasn't wonderful. What it was, was stressful; you were always running out. And they always had to be bigger and better than they were before, no matter what they were doing. So really, there was nothing wonderful about any of it, except the results." (p. 104)*

George Martin had expressed a similar sentiment in 1964, when he said, "I've seen the stresses to which [the boys] were subjected, and it was absolute hell. Wherever they went, there were hordes of people trying to get hold of them, trying to get their autographs, trying to touch them...[I remember] almost being kicked out of an aircraft by reporters who wanted to get on. Another time, I was in a lift, stuck between floors because too many people had crowded in...The only peace they got was when they were alone in a hotel room, watching television and hearing the screams outside. That was about it. A hell of a life, really." (The Beatles, The Beatles Anthology, 155.)

Sources:

Lewisohn, The Beatles: Day by Day, 65.
Lewisohn and Howlett, In My Life: John Lennon Remembered, 36.
Harry, The Ultimate Beatles Encyclopedia, 410 and 633-634.
Harry, Beatlemania, Vol. 4: The History of The Beatles on Film, 31-32.
The Beatles, The Beatles Anthology, 169.
Miles, The Beatles' Diary, Vol. 1, 202.
Starr, Michael Seth, 147-148.
Clayson, Ringo Starr: A Life, 142, 148, and 151.
Wiener, 50.
Wells, 29 July 1965 (six pages, including photos).There are no pages in this book. Look for the date heading.
Spitz, 572-573.
Bicknell, 61.
Hill, John, Paul, George & Ringo, 207-209.
Robertson, John, "Help! The End of the Beginning," Trynka, The Beatles: Ten Years That Shook the World, 167.
Coleman, Lennon, 254-257 and 262.
Friede, Titone, and Wiener, 91.
McKinney, Devin, Magic Circles: The Beatles in Dream and History, 72-83.
Gould, 274-275.
Carr, The Beatles at the Movies, 72.
Carr, Roy and Tony Tyler, The Beatles: An Illustrated Record, 42-43.
Carlin, Paul McCartney: A Biography, 104.
Yule, 106.
Schaffner, 41.
Shotton and Schaffner, 110.
Badman, 163.

World première of Help! – The Beatles Bible This concise synopsis of events at the premiers of "Help!" includes a good photo of Princess Margaret and Lord Snowden shaking hand with The Beatles.

Meet the Beatles for Real: Ringo at Sunny Heights This true story of a fan who met Ringo affords a rare glimpse of Ringo out in front of Sunny Heights.

https://www.beatlesbible.com/1965/07/24/ringo-starr-buys-sunny-heights-weybridge/ This article about Ringo's purchase of Sunny Heights supplies two excellent photos of the lovely home.

Meet the Beatles for Real: Help! *for Beatle fans There are excellent photos of the crowd around Piccadilly for the arrival of The Beatles here.*

https://dmbeatles.com/history.php?year=1965 Brief mention of the London première in this listing of Beatles events in 1965.

29 July 1965 - World première of Help! *- Beatles & Solo Photos & Videos Forum (tapatalk.com) This website supplies additional information about the prmiere of "Help!"*

[2032] Miles, *The Beatles' Diary, Vol. 1*, 202 and World première of *Help!* – The Beatles Bible

[2033] Miles, *The Beatles' Diary, Vol. 1*, 202, Harry, *The Ultimate Beatles Encyclopedia*, 410, and Bicknell, 61. Miles says that The Beatles "arrived in a black Rolls Royce." Alf Bicknell writes as if he was the one driving the limo. He says, "A big 'do' at the Dorchester Hotel to celebrate the première of the film. Quite a hectic night, just as we expected." But he doesn't state he's driving, and generally, he does. Harry says that each Beatle arrived in a separate limo with his significant other.

[2034] Harry, *The Beatles Ultimate Encyclopedia*, 410 and Hill, *John, Paul, George & Ringo*, 207. Harry says that Cynthia was with John; Maureen was with Ringo, and Jane Asher was with Paul. He does not mention Pattie Boyd being present. Photos in Hill's book show both Cynthia and Maureen at the première.

[2035] Miles, *The Beatles' Diary, Vol. 1*, 202. Barry Miles calls 29 July a "humid summer evening."

[2036] Miles, *The Beatles' Diary, Vol. 1*, 202 and World première of "Help!" – The Beatles Bible

[2037] Harry, *The Ultimate Beatles Encyclopedia*, 633-634, Miles, *The Beatles' Diary, Vol. 1*, 202, Starr, Michael Seth, 147-148, Spitz, 573, and https://www.beatlesbible.com/1965/07/24/ringo-starr-buys-sunny-heights-weybridge/ Spitz calls Sunny Heights "a small but graceful estate."

[2038] Starr, Michael Seth, 147-148 and Harry, *The Ultimate Beatles Encyclopedia*, 634.

[2039] Clayson, *Ringo Starr: A Life*, 142.

[2040] Starr, Michael Seth, 147-148.

[2041] Lewisohn and Howlett, *In My Life: John Lennon Remembered*, 36. "Living the fat life out in the comfortable, conservative Weybridge area near London" is a quote from Lewisohn and Howlett.

[2042] Harry, *The Ultimate Beatles Encyclopedia*, 410 and Harry, *Beatlemania, Vol. 4: The History of The Beatles on Film*, 32. Harry says there were 12,000 fans present a year earlier for the première of 'A Hard Day's Night' so "the number had dropped about 2,000. I doubt that anyone noticed this slight dip."

In his *History of The Beatles on Film*, he notes that the fans had been assembling in Piccadilly since 8.00 a.m. and were just as enthusiastic as ever.
[2043] Harry, *The History of The Beatles on Film*, 32.
[2044] Wells, *The Beatles, 365 Days*, 29 July 1965. (Six pages including photos.)
[2045] Wells, 29 July 1965 and Clayson, *Ringo: With a Little Help*, 151. This description comes from the photo in Wells's book. It's interesting to note that although several sources refer to the evening as "humid" and note the "midsummer temperatures," many people in this photo are wearing jackets or coats. Additionally, you can see that many in the crowd are adults. Michael Seth Starr observes that in the summer of 1965, "Beatlemania was still in full swing, but the cracks were beginning to show in the band's young fan base."
[2046] 29 july 1965 beatles london première help images - Bing images In this photo, you can see the metal gate set up in front of the London Pavilion and the striped awning over the entrance.
[2047] Hill, *John, Paul, George & Ringo*, 207. Direct quote from George Harrison.
[2048] Harry, *The Ultimates Beatles Encyclopedia*, 410.
[2049] 29 july 1965 beatles london première help images - Bing images Despite Brian Epstein's admonition not to smoke in public, The Beatles kept doing just that. You can see Ringo in front of the London Pavilion on 29 July in this photo, smoking as he poses for the press.
[2050] 29 july 1965 beatles london première help images - Bing images The photo described may be found here.
[2051] 29 july 1965 beatles london première help images - Bing images This is the second photo described.
[2052] 29 july 1965 beatles london première help images - Bing images You can clearly see Brian in this shot, but if you'll look closely, you can see part of his head in almost every photo, just behind The Beatles.
[2053] Harry, *The Ultimate Beatles Encyclopedia*, 410.
[2054] Wells, 29 July 1965 and Carr, Roy and Tony Tyler, *The Beatles: An Illustrated Record,* 42. In Wells's book, you can see the London Pavillion première programme that all four Beatles signed that night for Victor Spinetti on this page. And in Carr and Tyler's book, you can see Victor Spinetti directly behind Maureen Starr in the photo on p. 42.
[2055] Carr, *The Beatles at the Movies*, 72. Paul is quoted as saying that during the making of *Help!*, "there were some interesting moments in it for all of us...going skiing was good fun..."
[2056] Hill, *John, Paul, George & Ringo*, 208. Direct quote from Princess Margaret.
[2057] Harry, *The History of The Beatles on Film*, 32 and 1965 beatles met lady margaret and lord snowden july première - Bing images You can see Princess Margaret's dress in this photo. Direct quote from Princess Margaret to Ringo.
[2058] Robertson, John, "Help! The End of the Beginning," Trynka, *The Beatles: Ten Years That Shook the World*, 167.
[2059] The Beatles, *The Beatles Anthology*, 155. George Martin says, "The [Beatles] were besieged by reporters who weren't very nice people, they tend to use elbows and feet to kick people, and each other, out of the way."

[2060] Badman, 163. The news, Badman tells us, was released with press sources the following day.

[2061] Badman, 163. Direct quote from John Lennon.

[2062] Badman, 163. Direct quote from John Lennon.

[2063] Badman, 163. Direct quote from John Lennon.

[2064] Robertson, John, "Help! The End of the Beginning," Trynka, *The Beatles: Ten Years That Shook the World*, 167. Direct quote from George Harrison.

[2065] The Beatles, *The Beatles Anthology*, 169. Direct quote from George Harrison.

[2066] Miles, *The Beatles' Diary, Vol. 1*, 202.

[2067] Miles, *The Beatles' Diary, Vol. 1*, 202.

[2068] Miles, The Beatles Diary, Vol. 1, 202, and 29 July 1965 - World première of *Help!* - Beatles & Solo Photos & Videos Forum (tapatalk.com)

[2069] Schaffner, 41. Schaffner tells us that "…London's major newspapers devoted the whole front page [the day after the première] to pictures of The Beatles and reviews of the new film."

[2070] Harry, *The History of The Beatles on Film*, 32.

[2071] Harry, *The History of The Beatles on Film*, 32.

[2072] Harry, *The History of The Beatles on Film*, 32. Direct quote from the review by the *Spectator*.

[2073] Harry, *The History of The Beatles on Film*, 32. Direct quote from the review by the *Spectator*.

[2074] Harry, *The History of The Beatles on Film*, 34. Direct quote from the *Observer*.

[2075] Harry, *The History of The Beatles on Film*, 34. Direct quote from the *Observer*.

[2076] Harry, *The History of The Beatles on Film*, 34. Direct quote from the *Observer*.

[2077] Harry, *The History of The Beatles on Film*, 34. Direct quote from the *Observer*.

[2078] Harry, *The History of The Beatles on Film*, 34. Direct quote from the *Observer*.

[2079] Harry, *The History of The Beatles on Film*, 34. Direct quote from the *Observer*.

[2080] Harry, *The History of The Beatles on Film*, 34. Direct quote from the *Observer*.

[2081] Harry, *The History of The Beatles on Film*, 32. Direct quote from *The Worker*.

[2082] Shotton and Schaffner, 110. Pete Shotton states, "…John grew increasingly reluctant to abandon his favourite settee, his TV, and his Dylan records…"

[2083] Brown, Craig, 270. Brown quotes the catalogue for the 5 November 2011 sale of John Lennon's tooth, which read, "John had a warm relationship with Dot [Jarlett] and her family, often referring to her as Aunty Dot."

[2084] Yule, 106. John's opinion that The Beatles were "guest stars in their own movie" is repeated along with his summation that the concept was "bullshit."

[2085] Gould, 274. Gould quotes Paul McCartney as saying, "*Help!* wasn't great, but it wasn't our film — we were sort of guest stars. It was fun, but basically, as an idea for a film, it was a bit wrong."

[2086] McKinney, Devin, *Magic Circles: The Beatles in Dream and History*, 72-74. I highly recommend that you read Chapter 2: "Ascension/Sacrifice: *A Hard Day's Night* and *Help!*" which develops this theory in much lengthier and more detailed terms.

Friday Morning, 30 July 1965
NEMS Enterprises
Hilly House
London

The news had been leaked to the world at large: The Beatles would no longer be at the beck and call of the fans or the press. In light of "less than favourable" reviews of both "Help!" and John's *A Spaniard in the Works,* Brian and Tony Barrow had decided to reduce the boys' public exposure — to cancel the majority of their appearances, forthwith.[2087]

John was over the moon with it. For months, he'd insisted that "absence makes the heart grow fonder," pointing out that "Fans can't even walk down the street without havin' us starin' at 'em! It's at saturation point, really."[2088]

The Beatles truly were omnipresent.

"It's been Beatles, Beatles, Beatles!" George backed John up. "We need *less* exposure 'n not more!"[2089]

"Even *I'm* sick of us!" Ringo nodded. "Records, books, films, interviews, radio programmes, shows on telly, bits in the news..."

"Yes, I know," Brian cut across him, "but it's always been my belief that staying accessible to the fans is..."[2090]

"*Accessible!?*" John exploded. "We're virtually stalkin' the fans, Brian!"

And so, it came to pass, in the land called The Smoke, that an edict went out across the land: No further radio chats, television specials, interviews, quick walk-ons during "Sunday Night at the Palladium," or (as requested) sightings of The Beatles on "The Lucy Show" (even at the outrageous rate of $100,000 for less than a minute).[2091] None. Until the middle of August 1965 — when the boys would depart for their North America Tour — the lads from Liddypool would give no more live performances.[2092] The Beatles could be heard, but not seen.

****

Not everyone, however, was happy with the media blackout. Rumours that had swiftly spread across America — after a January *New York Times* article speculating that The Beatles might not return to the States in 1965 — now resurfaced.[2093] For the first time, fans were told that last autumn a heated tax disagreement had arisen between the boys and Brian Epstein, and the U.S. Treasury.

The Treasury had withheld a rather significant portion of The Beatles' $2.8 million earned on tour in August and September of 1964. The funds had been requistioned as tax payment, required under the Anglo-American Tax treaty. Because The Beatles were also paying an ungodly portion of taxes to Britain, the additional American requirement seemed chokingly unjust.[2094] And initially, the boys had balked.

Now, with The Beatles mysteriously stepping away from the microphones of the world, new questions about their upcoming tour began to be whispered and finally, asked aloud:

"Are The Beatles really coming to America?"

"Will they honour the concert tickets already sold?"

"Will thousands of fans be bitterly disappointed?"

Brian and Tony Barrow worked overtime to pacify frantic fans and to set the record straight. In Los Angeles, Portland, Chicago, and Atlanta, "Beatle People" were in a tizzy.

And the "British loyal" reacted even worse. Accustomed to seeing John, Paul, George, and Ringo regularly on *Ready, Steady, Go* and *Top of the Pops* and *Thank Your Lucky Stars*, the punters were outraged to discover that The Beatles had audaciously called "an intermission."[2095]

Anne Laury of Harrowgate, England posted a fiery missive to NEMS: "Those boys have become far too big for their boots, and it's time fans paid them back and quit forking out their hard-earned pocket money to buy their records!"[2096]

Brian huddled over his desk, as one U.K. letter after another spat invective towards the Fab Four. "I used to be one of The Beatles' biggest fans," a hand-written missive angrily began,

"BUT *now*, I'm beginning to wonder..."[2097]

It was Brian's most horrid nightmare realised — the very scenario he'd always struggled to avoid. Despite Peter Brown's stalwart words of encouragement, the NEMporer cleared his throat constantly and laboured to breathe.

Have I let my emotional involvement with the boys get the better of me? Has empathy for their lined faces and trailing energy swayed me wrongly?

Unfortunately, even the latest *New Musical Express* poll reflected growing resentment towards John, Paul, George, and Ringo. "The Beatles are now taking a leaf from Mr. Presley's book!" one embittered fan accused.[2098]

Brian shook his head and sighed. It seemed that in trying to rescue his boys, he'd set the fans afloat. In trying to "pay Peter," he had inadvertently "robbed Paul."

****

Friday Afternoon, 30 July 1965
Saville Theatre
Shaftesbury Avenue
London

Paul — the real Paul — was not best-pleased. He thought the cancellation of their public appearances imprudent, and he said so.

"It's not *us* the public's tired of!" Paul made his case. "It's the *image* that's bein' portrayed of us, y' see. Things are changin', Brian. The direction's movin' away from the poppy stuff like 'Thank You, Girl' and 'From Me to You' and 'She Loves You.'"[2099]

Even The Beatles' films, Paul felt, were failing to keep pace with the current market. "'Help!' was a comic book of sorts,"[2100] Paul shrugged, "'n that's all well 'n good, I suppose, but the fans are maturin' past that.[2101] And that's why they're not as...well, as thrilled as before."

Brian nodded thoughtfully, taking it in.

"Look, Eppy," Paul went on, "look, I know John loves

rock'n'roll, 'n so do I! So do I! But...well, the move today's toward *rock*.[2102] So, we have to keep up, don't we? We have to keep movin' ahead, not pullin' away."

"And how exactly are we pulling away?" Brian lifted his chin.

"Well, the rumour is," Paul leaned over and doffed his cig in a tall, backstage sand bucket, "we're cancellin' the U.K. Tour."[2103]

"It is a consideration." Brian's eyes slid sideways. He committed to nothing.

"Well, there y' have it,then...I think that would be a mistake." Paul was frank. "In just a coupla days, y' know, we're headin' to America to spend weeks with the fans over there. And that's grand, yeah. But then, when we come home, is it right to ignore the very ones who put us on the charts in the first place?"

"*Ignore*?!" Brian brushed the back of his hand across his lips. "You think we're ignoring them?"

Paul smiled pleasantly.

"The whole reason you're here in Saville Theatre this afternoon," Brian stiffened, "the whole reason I opened my own personal theatre to you four[2104] — scheduling this private rehearsal for you — is so that you'll be ready for your appearance on ABC's *Blackpool Night Out* tomorrow evening.[2105]

"And if I'm not mistaken, only the U.K. fans will be privy to that programme. Furthermore, only the U.K. fans will hear the interview you're about to do with Dibbs Mather, as well as the second interview with Lance Percival, later on tonight."[2106] Brian's neck was aflame with hives.

"True," Paul sniffed. "And that's good. Very good." He gave a quick sideways nod of concord.

"But?"

"But I think we should consider doin' the Autumn Tour as we always have." Paul didn't back down. "I think we owe it...or *want to give it*, as it were...to the fans who've been with us all along, from the very start."

"And John 'n the others? How do *they* feel about it?"

"Well, I dunno. I don't speak for them, do I?"

"I see." Brian chewed on his bottom lip. "Well, let's give the idea some thought and perhaps listen to what the others have to say over the next few days...as Tony and Arthur Howes[2107] and I have tried to do. If you hear the others out and still feel strongly about the Autumn Tour, then *possibly*, we can reconsider. But I must do what's best for everyone involved. I'm sure you understand that."

"Right, yeah. It takes four votes…just the way it always has." Paul tightened his tie. "And my vote is to do the tour." And with a quick click of his cheek and a swift nod, Paul shuffled off to join the others in the dressing room.   .

****

John was grateful for the rehearsal. They hadn't played a note together since the European Tour. And although he was constantly strumming his guitars in Kenwood, John was rusty at performing and sloppy with the lyrics.

The Beatles, however, had incredible muscle memory, and in less time than they'd thought possible, they pulled the *Blackpool Night Out* act together. John led them through "Ticket to Ride," "I Feel Fine," and "Help!". Ringo gave "Act Naturally" a go. And Paul refined "Yesterday" before belting out "I'm Down."[2108] It all came back to them swiftly.

Then, with only 13 days to go before yet another departure for the States and Canada, the boys applied themselves to their tour playlist.[2109] Of course, John's "Ticket to Ride" — which had been Number One on the *Billboard* charts in May and had only dropped from the chart a week ago — was included.[2110] His film theme, "Help!" — which hadn't yet charted in America, as the film's American release was set for 11 August[2111] — would be promoted to the hilt.[2112] And the raucous "I'm Down" would certainly be included.

Some of the old classics, such as "I Wanna Be Your Man" and the boys' potboiler, "Twist and Shout," would naturally be showcased. George's charming "Everybody's Trying to Be My Baby" was included. And unsurprisingly, a gem from the new *Help!* LP, John's "Dizzy Miss Lizzy," would be incorporated into the shows. Paul's Ivor Novello award-winning tune, "Can't Buy Me Love," and his single, "She's A Woman," would make the grade. And two of John's favourites, "Baby's in Black" and "A Hard Day's Night," rounded out the bill.[2113] So, for the next hour or so, the boys turned their attention to America, rehearsing the songs they knew so well but had played so little during the eventful

jude southerland kessler

weeks of July.

Sitting restlessly in the musty Saville Theatre, Dibbs Mather coughed and fidgeted, waiting for his chance to chat with the Liverpool troupe. Mather had spoken with them several times previously,[2114] but today, he was to conduct an interview for distribution by the BBC Transcription Service, to be used by British Information Service as a promotion for British culture all over the world.[2115]

Four o'clock. Mather glanced at his watch again. The rehearsal was lively, but the theatre was dark and cool, and the afternoon stretched on. The journalist yawned.

Brian Epstein — in a striking suit from Gieves & Hawkes in Savile Row[2116] — edged down the aisle and found a seat beside Mather. They shook hands. Mather sat up straighter and hoped his tie was tight. Epstein was never rude, but he had a way of looking at you that indicated instant antipathy or approval.[2117]

"Thank you for your patience, Dibbs," the manager intoned. "I realise it's taking a bit longer than anticipated, but the lads're not only preparing for tomorrow's venue, you understand; they're also brushing up for the imminent North American jaunt."

"Not to worry, Brian." Mather was self-consciously gracious. "I'm at your disposal."

The NEMporer smiled slightly, with a single nod.

"Enchanting art deco theatre you have here." Dibbs swept his hand at the elegant walls and ceiling. "I understand the building is yours these days?"[2118]

"Well," Brian ducked his chin, "I've a long-term lease with Bernard Delfont, as it were. I thought my clients might make use of it, for various purposes.[2119] And well, I love the theatre. Always have…from my youth."[2120]

"Yes, just so." Mather nodded. Although he was Australian-born, Mather had been in London long enough to adopt its catch-phrases.[2121] "Tell me, Brian, did you perhaps find an opportunity to speak with John about reading from his new book this afternoon?"

"Yes," Brian stood as he saw the boys concluding the rehearsal and removing their guitars. "He's worked up something with the others, I believe. In fact," Brian observed, "I think the boys are ready for you right now."

"Wonderful!" Mather stood and stretched. "I have everything

all set in the dressing room."

"Excellent!" Brian moved towards the stage. "I'll send them your way in moments."

And in less than a quarter of an hour, The Beatles were gathered around Mather's portable reel-to-reel recorder and fat microphone. Ties loosened and postures relaxed, they were ready to record.

****

John: (Looking at the others and pointing to "The National Health Cow" in his copy of *A Spaniard in the Works*) Are we gonna read one?[2122]

Paul: (Nodding) Yeah, go on, read that.

John: (Grinning slyly) Why don't we *all* read it?

Paul: Couldn't. It's double-tracked.

John: Okay. "The National Health Cow," page 62. "I strolled into a farmyard when no one was about/ Treading past the troubles, I raised my head to shout." (Looking up and offering commentary) Don't like that. (Reading again)"'Come out, the cow with glasses' I called and rolled my eye/ It ambled up toward me, I milked it with a sigh/ 'You're just in time' the cow said, his eyes were all aglaze/ 'I'm feeling like an elephant, I aren't been milked for days,'/ 'Why is this' I asked it, tugging at its throttles/ 'I don't know why, perhaps it's 'cause my milk comes out in bottles'."

All: "That's handy for the government." I thought, and in a tick/ The cow fell dead all sudden, I'd smashed it with a brick!" (Guffaws all round)

Paul: (Unsolicited) Yeah, well, *I'm* doin' a lot of symphony work on my own at the moment.

John: Who's that talkin'?

Paul: This is Paul. Doin' a lot of symphony work, 'n um...

George: 'N *I'm* branchin' out as fullback for West Ham United.

John: Who's *that* talkin'?

Paul: That's George. 'N I've also got comin' up, the lead in the new Tarzan film.

John: Who's *that* talkin'?

Paul: Paul. Well, that ought to be…y' know, promisin', as it offers me full scope for my actin' 'n physical abilities!

Dibbs Mather: This may destroy the image that's already built of The Beatles!

Paul: No, I don't think it will, actually, 'cause…

George: (Shaking his head) No, it won't, y' know.

John: Who's *that* talking?

Mather: (Smiling) Mr. Dibbs.

Paul: (Trying not to giggle) 'Cause John sort of built up a bit of a Tarzan image.

Mather: This business about image, though. Most of the other pop singers get into trouble for what — drunken driving or drugs or something or other. You seem to be pretty clean.

Paul: (Batting his eyelashes innocently) Yeah, we're not like that. Oh, yeah.

Mather: How do you keep so clean?

John: Yeah, we're…

Paul: (Quickly cutting across John) Clean. Washin' 'n that 'n…

John: 'Cause we get somebody to drive us, y' see.

Ringo: (Chuckling) We're friendly with the police.

Mather: Has it got anything to do, would you say, with the kind of…um, upbringing that you had in Liverpool?

John: (Laying on thick Scouse) Yeah, well, it's just mainly sort of, er… y' know, the background, like.

Paul: Y' know, once a scruff, always a scruff!

John: Y' know, you get a sort of clean-livin' image, like, comin' from there, like. Y' know.

Paul: What we always used to say was that you can take a boy out of Liverpool, but you can never take Liverpool out of a boy.

John: Who's *that* talking?

Paul: Paul.[2123]

Mather: Do you prefer it to wor-working in front of an audience?

John: Uh, no. No, it's — it's quite good makin' films. Said John, whimsically.

Mather: The new film, "Help!", how did you enjoy it?

John: It was a wonderful experience, I must say, 'specially workin' with such great actors as Leo McKern 'n John Bluthal 'n Victor Spinetti 'n Eleanor Bron…

George: (Leaning in) This is John talking. John.

Paul: John talking.

George: John talking.

John: (Smiling and shaking his head) ...'n Roy Kinnear. It was a wonderful experience!

George: This is George talkin', sayin', "John's talkin'."

John: This is...They can't *hear John talkin'* when George keeps saying that!!!

George: (Snickering) I'm telling them who it is talkin'!

Paul: (Didactically) Now, George and John! Now, now, boys.

Mather: Is there any likelihood that any of you will branch out into the cinema, as actors later?

John: Not likely. 'N we're not gonna let Ringo branch out...unless *we* get a percent!

Paul: (In mock-horror) *Cut!* Okay, cut it, Harry! Cut it there!

Mather: And as...and as a result of this, and your increasing popularity, how's it affected you? Is it possible you're going to become bored with being The Beatles for year after year at the top?[2124]

John: You don't get bored, 'cause there's...so many different things that happen, like MBEs or premières, and they're all different, y' know. So, soon as you start getting bored with somethin' like a tour, the tour's over, 'n somethin' else starts. So, you don't get a chance to get bored. 'N there's always Ringo, isn't there?

(Laughter)

Mather: If you had not been so rich and famous, what do you think you might be doing now?

John: We'd probably be bummin' 'round, y' know.

Ringo: We'd be playin', only...

Paul: Still workin' in clubs 'n things.[2125]

George: (Nodding) Yeah.

Ringo: (Shrugs) Y' know.

Mather: And Paul would've been teaching?

Paul: I *might've* been teachin', but I — I would've hated it, I think. Y' know, we — I think all of us might have been — if we hadn't stuck with the group, it might have just ended up, y' know, like George bein' an electrician 'n Ringo bein' a fitter, 'n John bein' a...a bum. 'N y' know, us...

George: I think we would've been...

Paul: ...just doin' things we didn't enjoy much.

George: ...we would've been probably playin' modern jazz now in some crummy club.

John: (Shocked) *Do you?!*

George: (Nodding) Yeah.

John: Do we *like* modern jazz?

George: 'Cause — no, 'cause we would've been so fed up playin' the same things that we would have progressed, but now we — we don't progress 'cause we play the same things every time we play somewhere. Y' see? Y' know what I mean?

Mather: But isn't this a — it's a kind of a progression though, in the, uh... in the style...has it altered slightly?

George: Yeah, but — yeah, *slightly*, but the thing is, we used to improve at a much faster rate, before we ever made records. Well, *I* think so, because we used to get so fed up playin' the same things, so we'd always learn new songs all the time.

John: (Nodding) You'd have to improvise every time. Or even with the old songs, you'd do 'em different almost any time, but when you make records, you've got to reproduce, as near as you can, the records, so you don't really get a chance to improvise or improve your style.[2126]

Mather: Well, listen — listen, Paul...does this mean that you might've branched out into a different, um... a different style of music?

Paul: It *may* — probably wouldn't have been all *that* different. 'Cause we've tried anyway to change gradually, just to keep bein' a bit different. And uhm, we used to play all rock stuff. And then we started doin' — had a sort of period of doin' — er, a few sort of ballads 'n things, 'n it got a bit — the general thing got a bit fruitier. Then we went all back to rock stuff 'n things 'n — y' know, we keep tryin' to change, so we might've been doin' somethin' different now, I don't know.[2127]

****

Actor/comedian Lance Percival, who provided the voices of Ringo and Paul in the Beatles cartoons and interviewed the boys for his radio programme, *Lance A'GoGo*.
Photograph from Wikimedia Commons

Interviews, the boys thought, were all basically the same. Same topics, same answers, similar jibes. The Beatles were rarely harsh but never completely honest. They were rarely drab, but the edge no longer cut. And as popular comedian/actor Lance Percival supplanted Dibbs Mather at the helm, the well-worn act commenced all over again.

"*You* look like the end of the road," George muttered to John as Percival replaced Mather's equipment with his own.

"Na, I'm just not the bustlin' dual carriageway I once was."

"'N what's *this one* after findin' out?" George thumbed towards the star of the Light Programme's show, *Lance A'GoGo*.[2128]

"Oh, the usual…How's the film? Is Paul married? How long do you think *you'll* last?"[2129]

"Hey," George asked Percival directly, "what are *you* after findin' out, hey?"

But being the splendid extemporaneous comic he was known to be, Percival doled out a faultless Ringo Starr accent, "Ah, get home with you lot! Yew and yer ilk!"[2130] And to genuine braying, The Beatles surrendered their antipathy towards interviews and settled back, ready to record yet another predictable chat in a long, long day.

Notes!

Was Paul actually as enthusiastic about touring as he appears in this chapter?

By mid-1965, John and George made no bones about their disenchantment with touring. They wanted to spend more time in studio and less time on the road. But Paul (and formerly, Ringo...who was only a bit less enchanted in 1965 because of his marriage to Maureen and the impending birth of his new baby) still enjoyed touring.

*When asked later about his experience on the 1965 North American Tour, Paul said, "These were great times, even if you didn't enjoy all of the events that much you could still go home to Liverpool and say, "Well, you know who I met?" I mean, to meet Elvis or anybody like that...it was very impressive." (The Beatles,*The Beatles Anthology, *192)*

Sources:

Lewisohn, The Complete Beatles Chronicle, *198.*
Lewisohn, The Beatles: Day by Day, *65.*
Harry, The Ultimate Beatles Encyclopedia, *577.*
Harry, The Encyclopedia of Beatles People, *160.*
Howlett, The Beatles at the BBC, *73-74.*
Everett, The Beatles as Musicians: The Quarry Men to Rubber Soul, *296.*
The Beatles, The Beatles Anthology, *192.*
Miles, The Beatles' Diary, Vol. 1, *202.*
Frontani, 87 and 90.
Coleman, The Man Who Made The Beatles, *217, 219, and 247.*
Spitz, 571-573.
Winn, Way Beyond Compare, *336-337.*
Creasy, Beatlemania! The Real Story of The Beatles U.K. Tours, 1963-1965, *308.*
Gunderson, Some Fun Tonight!, Vol. 2, *45.*
Wiener, 50.

Rehearsals for the North America tour – The Beatles Bible *This website gives a brief account of what occurred on this day of rehearsals at the Saville Theatre.*

The Beatles - A Day in The Life: July 30, 1965 (Friday) -Beatles Fab Four Store Exclusively Beatles Only Official Merchandise
This website also gives a succinct account of 30 July at the Saville Theatre.

https://www.forums.stevehoffman.tv/threads/the-beatles-interviews-database.680834/ This exceptional website from Steve Hoffman provides many rare transcribed Beatles interviews, including the interview in this chapter.

In The Life Of...The Beatles: The Beatles - Attack of the FILLER BEEBS, episode two This website gives an overview of a Beatleg that provides the Dibbs Mather interview on 30 July 1965. It is called "Attack of the FILLER BEEBS, Episode Two."

https://www.imdb.com/name/nm0558443/bio This is the IMDb biography of BBC interviewer Dibbs Mather.

Lance Percival - Wikipedia This website supplies a succinct biography of comic actor Lance Percival.

Lance Percival - Biography - IMDb This is the IMDb biography of Lance Percival.

All US Top 40 Singles For 1965 - Top40Weekly.com This website supplies information about hit songs in any month/year in the past.

https://www.beatlesbible.com/1965/04/01/brian-epstein-takes-over-saville-theatre-london/ This website furnishes information about Brian Epstein's lease of the Saville Theatre.

[2087] Spitz, 572-573.

[2088] Spitz, 572. Direct quote from John Lennon. The order of the two sentences has been reversed.

[2089] Spitz, 573. Direct quote from George Harrison. The order of the sentences is reversed.

[2090] Spitz, 573.

[2091] Spitz, 571-572.

[2092] Spitz, 573.

[2093] "U.S. and British Taxes Vie to Shear Beatles," *New York Times*, 3 January 1965, late ed.: 84, found in Frontani, *The Beatles: Image and the Media*, 90.

[2094] "U.S. and British Taxes Vie to Shear Beatles," *New York Times*, 3 January 1965, late ed.: 84, found in Frontani, *The Beatles: Image and the Media*, 90.

[2095] Spitz, 572.

[2096] Spitz, 572. Direct quote from the letter by Anne Laury.

[2097] Spitz, 572. Direct quote from fan letter to NEMS.

[2098] Spitz, 572. Direct quote from fan speaking out to *NME* poll takers.

[2099] Spitz, 573. Direct quote from Paul McCartney, beginning with, "Things are changin'."

[2100] Frontani, 87.

[2101] Spitz, 573.

[2102] Spitz, 573.

[2103] Spitz, 572, Lewisohn, *The Beatles: Day by Day*, 65, Miles, *The Beatles' Diary, Vol. 1*, 202, and Creasy, *Beatlemania! The Real Story of The Beatles UK Tours 1965-1965*, 308.

[2104] https://www.beatlesbible.com/1965/04/01/brian-epstein-takes-over-saville-theatre-london/

[2105] Lewisohn, *The Complete Beatles Chronicle*, 198, Lewisohn, *The Beatles: Day by Day*, 65, Miles, *The Beatles' Diary, Vol. 1*, 302, and Wiener, 50.

[2106] Lewisohn, *The Complete Beatles Chronicle*, 198, Winn, 336-337, Lewisohn, *The Beatles: Day by Day*, 65, Miles, *The Beatles' Diary, Vol. 1*, 302, and Wiener, 50.

[2107] Harry, *The Encyclopedia of Beatles People*, 160. Arthur Howes was the U.K. Tour promoter for The Beatles, year after year.

[2108] Lewisohn, *The Complete Beatles Chronicle*, 198. Lewisohn provides the list of the songs the boys are preparing for the *Blackpool Night Out* performance.

[2109] Lewisohn, The Complete Beatles Chronicle, 198 and *Rehearsals for the North America tour – The Beatles Bible*

[2110] All US Top 40 Singles For 1965 - Top40Weekly.com

[2111] *Help! (film) - Wikipedia*

[2112] All US Top 40 Singles For 1965 - Top40Weekly.com

[2113] Gunderson, *Some Fun Tonight!, Vol. 2*, 45.

[2114] Howlett, *The Beatles at the BBC*, 73. Howlett reminds us that Mather had conducted an interview with The Beatles at the Gaumont Theatre in December of 1963, famously asking them what they were planning to do once their "15 minutes of fame had expired."

[2115] Lewisohn, *The Complete Beatles Chronicle*, 198.

[2116] Coleman, *The Man Who Made The Beatles*, 219.

[2117] Coleman, *The Man Who Made The Beatles*, 217. Coleman says 'Brian was not aggressive when he met people but you knew you were being scrutinized personally."

[2118] Coleman, *The Man Who Made The Beatles,* 247. Coleman says "[Brian's] love of the stage had never faltered. Now, as an established impresario, he had an alternative to acting: owning a theater…and on April 1, 1965, after short negotiations, Brian became the leaseholder of the Saville Theatre in Shaftesbury Avenue."

[2119] Lewisohn, *The Complete Beatles Chronicle*, 198 and Harry, *The Ultimate Beatles Encyclopedia*, 577. Harry tells us that in April 1965, Epstein leased the Saville Theatre from Bernard Delfont for three years. The only other NEMS group that actually used the theatre during Brian's tenancy was Gerry and the Pacemakers. However, many outstanding acts did appear at the spectacular West End art deco theatre under Epstein's purview: Del Shannon, Fats Domino, the Bee Gees, Cream, Pink Floyd, Bo Diddley, Ben E. King, Procol Harum, the Zombies, the Yardbirds, and many more.

[2120] Harry, *The Ultimate Beatles Encyclopedia*, 577.

[2121] https://www.imdb.com/name/nm0558443/bio This is the IMDb biography of Dibbs Mather.

[2122] Hoffman, Steve, Beatles Database Interviews found at: https://www.forums.stevehoffman.tv/threads/the-beatles-interviews-database.680834/ My sincere thanks to Steve Hoffman for the incredible transcription work he has done with rare Beatles interviews such as this one. This is the first line of the 30 July 1965 interview between The Beatles and Dibbs Mather of the BBC. I'm not going to endnote every line, but will endnote again on the last line.

[2123] There is a break in the recording here…when we pick it up again, the boys are discussing "Help!"

[2124] Howlett, *The Beatles at the BBC*, 73-74. This portion of the interview is also found in Howlett's book. This is the first line from Howlett. I'll footnote again at the end. (Howlett's version is abridged, leaving out portions of the quotes.)

[2125] Howlett says that Paul is saying "clubs in England" and Hoffman says "clubs and things."

[2126] Howlett, *The Beatles at the BBC*, 74. This is the end of the abridged interview in Howlett.

[2127] Hoffman, Steve, Beatles Database Interviews, https://www.forums.stevehoffman.tv/threads/the-beatles-interviews-database.680834/ This is the last line of the 30 July 1965 interview between The Beatles and Dibbs Mather of the BBC.

[2128] Lewisohn, *The Complete Beatles Chronicle*, 198, Lance Percival - Biography - IMDb, and Lance Percival - Wikipedia.

[2129] John is punningly referring to Percival's 1964 comedy musical, "It's All Over Town."

[2130] Lance Percival - Wikipedia Percival provided the voices of both Paul and Ringo in the Beatles cartoons in 1965. And later, he was selected to be the voice of "Old Fred" in *Yellow Submarine*.

August 1965

Chart Toppers

"I Got You Babe" – Sonny and Cher
"Unchained Melody" – The Righteous Brothers
"California Girls" – The Beach Boys
"Help!" – The Beatles
"Like A Rolling Stone" – Bob Dylan[2131]

In The News

6 August: President Lyndon Johnson signs the Voting Rights act, eliminating the practice of making voters take literacy tests. This increases the number of African American voters up to 60% in U.S. Southern states by 1969.

11 August: In Watts, California, during the arrest of Marquette Frye for drunken driving, a row breaks out between Frye and his mother that escalates into violence. Onlookers become involved and the Watts riots break out, ending six days later, after the deaths of 34 people.

16 August: The Soviet Union releases the first photos of the dark side of the moon, sent to Earth by the Zond 3 spacecraft.

19 August: The second Auschwitz trial ends, sentencing 17 persons to life imprisonment for the torture and death of thousands of prisoners at Auschwitz during World War II.

28 August: Subway, which will emerge as the world's largest fast-food chain, opens its first store in Bridgeport, CT.[2132]

Tuesday, 3 August 1965
Kenwood
Weybridge, Surrey

Cynthia had hoped that John's last few days at home would be spent with her. Vainly, she had even imagined an amorous weekend getaway. But John found little time for her these days.[2133] Disentangled from his innumerable publicity appearances, John had turned his attention to a long-time passion: getting his Aunt Mimi installed in a new house.[2134]

"Queen Mary," as Cynthia was wont to call her, had been as obdurate about remaining in Mendips as she'd been about voicing her misery beneath the fans' constant bombardment. For months, John's aunt had grumbled of the public's "wearying intrusions."[2135] But when John had urged her to relocate, Mimi had held firm in her insistence that Mendips was "home."[2136]

In early summer, however, her tone had begun to change. Mimi had finally begun hinting that she'd had enough public scrutiny.

"I wasn't feeling at all well," Mimi had recently whinged over the telephone, "and was having a lie-down — leaving the back door open for the doctor to come in — when I heard odd noises downstairs. Voices. Muffled laughter. So, recruiting a heavy doorstop as a weapon, I crept cautiously towards the kitchen...only to find two quite surprised young ladies, *of sorts*, sitting at the kitchen table...covered in a sea of toffee wrappers!"[2137]

"Er, sorry Mimi," Cynthia had tried to sound sympathetic, though similar things happened regularly in Kenwood. "That's horrendous. I'll be sure to alert John as soon as he returns from Spain."

"Yes, have him ring me immediately...first thing! These invasions *have* to stop!"

In early July, when John had heard the story for himself, Mimi had appended yet another woe: "I have no friends at all here these days, John. Everyone's moved on! It's just me and the bedeviling fans!"[2138]

"Well…y' do have yer family,"[2139] John had smiled, repeating the very words Mimi had always said to him.

"Oh, that lot!"[2140] Mimi had spat. "*Hmpf!* I hardly ever see them anyway! They only come around when they want something!"[2141]

And so, throughout July, John had begun considering properties for his aunt. Mimi had specified that she would only relocate to the southeast coast of England,[2142] "somewhere with a more temperate climate…closer to the water."

So, when Cynthia invited Mimi to spend a few days in Weybridge, John and his aunt had put their heads together over a road map and several pages of property listings, sent to them by an agent from the respected Rumsey & Rumsey real estate office of Dorset.[2143] They sat in the parlour all Saturday afternoon, only calling it a day just prior to the airing of John's pre-recorded television interview on BBC-2's *Music International.*[2144]

"Well, we've finally shortlisted three houses,"[2145] John announced as Cynthia brought in a tray of tea and biscuits for them and warmed up the telly.[2146]

"All far too large for me!" Mimi sputtered. "A bevy of bedrooms! Elegant parlours with sweeping views of the water. Much…*much* too much!"[2147]

"Only what y' deserve," John said. No matter what, his bony aunt always had his heart.[2148]

"Soft-soap, John Winston!" Mimi accepted a steaming cup with a perfunctory nod to her hostess.

"Ah, c'mon, Gertie!"[2149] John teased.

"Hush!" Mimi feigned rebuff. When John scrambled to hug her, she tensed and popped his hand. "*Shhh!* You're on television, and I'm *trying* to pay attention!" And for the next few minutes, all talk of real estate was tabled for a discussion of Lennon and literature.

****

En Route from Weybridge to Dorset

This morning — chauffeured by the Lennons' new personal driver, former Welsh guardsman Les Anthony[2150] — John, Cynthia, Julian, and his aunt were off in the Rolls for a full day of house hunting near Dorset and Bournemouth.[2151]

"A holiday community, Mim!" John cried, as they motored southwest from London towards Winchester. "The very place where the well-heeled, as you'd say, come to winter. I think it's one of the most beautiful spots in the world."[2152]

"Do you?" Mimi perched on the leather seat with her purse on her lap. "But really…they're awfully dear, aren't they?"[2153]

"Well, believe it or not," John boasted. "I can afford it." He itched to add something about making his living with the guitar, but wanting the day to remain undisturbed, he restrained himself.

The closer they drew to the seaside, the lovelier the landscape. They rolled down the windows to take in the thick, salt air. Julian squealed at the first glimpse of the aqua bay and the long-winged birds swooping down low and soaring up high. Cynthia gasped. John had butterflies and prayed that when Mimi saw the cheery homes they'd selected, she'd at last realise how far he'd come and how much he'd achieved.

****

Poole
Dorset

They rumbled into Poole in early afternoon, pausing for a light lunch in a footpath café, overlooking the town. Poole was picture-postcard: contented families feeding the swans; lazy, strolling tourists on Rockley Point Beach;[2154] and the colourful snaking row of crowded souvenir shops and restaurants.[2155] But Poole's seaside lure was well-balanced by the aged beauty of Brownsea Castle[2156] and by the silver spires of churches and cathedrals.

Poole, England
Photograph from Creative Commons

"Y' can really feel the ocean, can't y' Mim!" John took a cleansing breath. "It's great here!"

"Yes," Mimi nodded. "A brilliant August afternoon." Bright sun, an assortment of stout clouds, and her nephew's attention focused entirely upon her. Mimi was content.

Meeting their agent, the group moved painstakingly through the chosen houses, taking ample time to ask questions and make a prudent decision. But somehow, nothing seemed quite right.

"Well, there *is* a new listing, just on the market," the agent lifted a palm. "The family's still living there, temporarily, but they're more than happy to have you take a look, if you'd like."

"Oh, we certainly couldn't impose." Mimi's lips drew thin.

"I could." John waved his hand towards the car. "Let's go!" And within moments, the entourage was standing in front of 126 Panorama Road.[2157]

The neat-as-a-pin house that the agent had saved for last was, as Mimi proclaimed, "head-and-shoulders-above-the-rest" — an L-shaped, six-bedroom semi-bungalow with a low-pitched roof and spacious parlour, affording magnificent views of the harbour. Nestled behind a thick banque of trees on the water's edge, the ivy-covered home was exactly the quaint hideaway Mimi had envisioned:[2158] a secluded place to read, write letters, tend gardens, and watch the sunset over splendid turquoise waters.

Mimi, however, refused to enter the home. She waited primly in the garden, staring alternately at the rippling inlet and the glistening bay windows spanning the rear of the house.[2159] But when John completed his tour and joined her, she didn't even request an evaluation of the interior. "John, I do believe *this* is the one," she almost whispered.

"Well, if you don't have it," her nephew said, quietly, "I'll live here."[2160]

And returning to the agent's office to sign the official papers, the deed was done.

****

Kenwood
Weybridge, Surrey

"You've found the perfect roost, Mim!" John crowed over a late supper. "Built-in bookcases, a fireplace…a long hallway perfect for pictures of yer famous nephew!"[2161]

"*Hmpf!*" Mimi snorted. "We shall see what we shall see."

"Yeah, well," John glanced sheepishly at his wife, "I know it's a bit more than we paid for Mendips, but seaside properties, y' know…"

"Location, location, location!" Cynthia smiled. "After all, on prestigious Sandbanks Bay, one expects to spend a bit more."[2162]

Mimi pursed her lips and lifted a cautionary index finger. Discussing finances at the family dinner table was beyond the pale.

"Wasn't it a lovely afternoon!" Cynthia swiveled to something more acceptable. She was sincerely happy for Mimi and even happier for John. If John had accomplished something that made him feel valued in his aunt's censorious eyes, then any amount of money was worth it.

"It *was*." Mimi doled out the rare Mary Elizabeth compliment. "All the way to the shore and back! A joy." She indulged in a small sip of wine. "Maybe I can have some peace now."[2163] And you can bring Julian down now and again. He can enjoy the sea and the sand."[2164]

"Oh, he'd love that!" Cynthia nodded.

"Of course," Mimi said, pointedly, "*you* must be there as well, John. After all, you're the one who brought this all to fruition."

And hanging his head over his plate to hide his delight, John grinned. They all saw it. In this bright moment, everyone was happy.

Mimi Smith's home in Poole, "Harbour's Edge"
Photo used by kind permission of the *Daily Mail*

Notes!

1. What was the cost of Mimi's new home in Poole?

"...In Panorama Road," Philip Norman tells us in John Lennon: The Life, *John bought his aunt "a luxurious bungalow named Harbour Edge[2165] [which] had just come on the market priced at a hefty £25,000." (p. 392) It was located in Canford Cliffs, "a suburb of expansive modern homes that overlooked neighboring Poole Harbour." (Norman, p. 392) The home cost more than John and Cynthia had spent on Kenwood but it didn't*

require as much renovation and made Mimi quite happy. Cynthia, in her book, John, *stated, "...we paid twenty-five thousand for the bungalow. It was worth more than our house because it was in such a sought-after position, right on the beach."*

According to the respected Rumsey & Rumsey real estate company, John did make one improvement to the home. "John," they stated, "had a balcony made with a white-painted wrought iron balustrade of seven hearts from which [Mimi] would sit and watch the boats go by."[2166]

2. In the summer of 1965, was John spending less time with Cynthia?

In her first book, A Twist of Lennon, *Cynthia writes of this time: "Although you might think that I had all any woman could wish for, life could be very lonely. John spent weeks and months away from home; there seemed to be very little time for us to be as close as we were in the early days, and we seemed to be pulling in opposite directions." (p. 147)*

Cynthia also states that when all of The Beatles declined to allow their families to attend the MBE investiture, later in 1965, she realised that "The Beatles were very happy to have their women subservient in the background. It made life easier for them. The northern male chauvinism was quite strong within the group and...we were all conditioned to some extent in our roles, to be seen and not heard. (pp. 146-147)

Similarly, in Burns's book, The Guitar's All Right, *Mimi told Burns that when she visited John and Cynthia in Kenwood, "Cynthia would come downstairs dressed to the nines, looking quite lovely, and hoping for an evening on the town, but John would be too tired." (p. 59) Mimi warned him that he had to be more attentive to his wife." (p. 59) If Mimi, who had never cared for Cynthia, saw this, the neglect must have been obvious indeed.*

Sources:

Lewisohn: The Beatles: Day by Day, *65.*
Lennon, Cynthia, John, *174-175.*
Harry, The Ultimate Beatles Encyclopedia, *611.*
Harry, The John Lennon Encyclopedia, *822-823.*
Harry, The Encyclopedia of Beatles People, *291.*
Norman, John Lennon: The Life, *389-392.*
Burns, 45 and 59.
Brown, Craig, 277-279.
Brown, Peter, 184-185.
Coleman, Lennon, *227.*
Coleman, The Man Who Made The Beatles, *242-243.*

Spitz, 573-574.
Connolly, 407-408.
Burrows, 69.
Kenny, 173-174.
Miles, The Beatles' Diary, Vol. 1, *203.*
Womack, The Beatles Encyclopedia, Vol. 2, *845.*
Goldman, 191.
Hill, John, Paul, George & Ringo, *210.*
Freide, Titone, and Wiener, 196.
Baird, Imagine This, *274-275.*
Robertson, Lennon, *41.*
Tremlett, 61.

John Lennon's aunt Mimi and Sandbanks – Nick Churchill This is a superb article by Nick Churchill on Harbour's Edge and Mimi's time there. There is an excellent photo of Mimi sitting outside her new home.

poole england 1965 images - Bing images These are images of Rockley Beach in Poole.

cd97a421eb9521a33a9d4094ba3a5e31.jpg (600×360) (pinimg.com) This is an image of Poole in 1965.

poole - Bing images This is an image of Brownsea Castle in Poole.

Sandbanks Property 'Harbours Edge' Owned By John Lennon For Sale (housebeautiful.com) This article contains accurate facts about John purchasing Harbour's Edge for Mimi, but the house in the photos is not the original. However, you can see the view that Mimi enjoyed from the windows in her rear parlour.

John Lennon on Sandbanks (rumseyofsandbanks.co.uk) This article does contain a photo of the original home Mimi lived in, as well as great photos of Sandbanks Peninsula, the ledger at Rumsey & Rumsey Real Estate listing Mimi's property, and a 1965 ad for the real estate company.

[2131] List of Billboard Hot 100 top-ten singles in 1965 - Wikipedia
[2132] August 1965 - Wikipedia
[2133] Lennon, Cynthia, *A Twist of Lennon*, 147 and Burns, 59.
[2134] Norman, *John Lennon: The Life*, 389 and Brown, Peter, 184. In Norman's book, Mimi says that John "was always nagging on at me to move...I think he was worried about me living [in Mendips] on my own. I had a dizzy spell and fainted one day after I had to answer the phone." Brown says, "John begged [Mimi] to move out on many occasions, offering to buy her any house she wanted..."

[2135] Lennon, Cynthia, *John*, 174. Cynthia says, "Mimi was no longer happy in Liverpool and complained to us every time we phone her."

[2136] Norman, *John Lennon: The Life*, 389.

[2137] Kenny, 173.

[2138] Lennon, Cynthia, *John*, 174.

[2139] Lennon, Cynthia, *John*, 174.

[2140] Lennon, Cynthia, *John*, 174. Direct quote from Mimi Smith.

[2141] Lennon, Cynthia, *John*, 174. Direct quote from Mimi Smith.

[2142] Kenny, 172.

[2143] Lennon, Cynthia, *John*, 174-175, Brown, Peter, 184, and https://www.rumseyofsandbanks.co.uk/blog/john-lennon-on-sandbanks

[2144] Miles, *The Beatles' Diary, Vol. 1*, 203.

[2145] Lennon, Cynthia, *John*, 175 and https://www.rumseyofsandbanks.co.uk/blog/john-lennon-on-sandbanks Cynthia says they shortlisted four homes, but according to documents at Rumsey & Rumsey, one of the houses (the one Mimi purchased on Panorama Drive) didn't come on the market until the day the Lennons and Mimi were in Poole. Cynthia probably thought the bungalow had been on the "to see" list all along.

[2146] http://www.repairfaq.org/samnew/tvfaq/tvoldtrwp.htm This is a discussion of why television sets, as late as the 1970s, needed "warming up" prior to viewing.

[2147] Burns, 44 and https://www.rumseyofsandbanks.co.uk/blog/john-lennon-on-sandbanks Some sources indicate that the house had four bedrooms. The real estate office of Rumsey & Rumsey, who still has original paperwork on the home, specifies that it was a six-bedroom home.

[2148] Lennon, Cynthia, *John*, 174. Cynthia says, "Mimi always had John's heart."

[2149] Brown, Craig, 279. Mimi states that John used to ring her up and say, "Hello, is that you, Gertie! Never mind, Gertie!"

[2150] Bicknell, 65, Brown, Peter, 184, and Goldman, 191.

[2151] Lennon, Cynthia, *John*, 174, Bicknell, 65, and Norman, *John Lennon: The Life*, 392. Alf says that John had his personal chauffeur, Les Anthony, drive Mimi, Cynthia, Julian, and himself to Poole. Cynthia says that they took "the Rolls."

[2152] Harry, *The John Lennon Encyclopedia*, 823 and Burns, 45. Mimi told Burns, "John insisted…it was the most beautiful spot in the world." Harry says, "John said, 'It was the most beautiful place I've ever seen.'"

[2153] https://www.rumseyofsandbanks.co.uk/blog/john-lennon-on-sandbanks Rumsey & Rumsey state in this article that most houses on Sandbanks Peninsula in 1965 cost around £3,000 or $50,000. Mimi's house, Harbour's Edge, cost £25,000…in today's market, approximately $400,000.

[2154] poole england 1965 images - Bing images This is Rockley Beach in 1965.

[2155] cd97a421eb9521a33a9d4094ba3a5e31.jpg (600×360) (pinimg.com) An excellent photo of Poole in 1965.

[2156] poole - Bing images A photo of Brownsea Castle, Poole.

[2157] Harry, *The John Lennon Encyclopedia*, 823 and
https://www.rumseyofsandbanks.co.uk/blog/john-lennon-on-sandbanks The
Rumsey & Rumsey website says that Mimi had to ride the ferry from
Harbour's Edge to the closest grocery store, so the cars might have had to
travel by ferry from their last house-hunting location out to Panorama Road.

[2158] Burns, 45 and Spitz, 573.

[2159] Spitz, 573 and Brown, Peter, 185.

[2160] Burns, 45, Brown, Peter, 185, and Norman, *John Lennon: The Life*, 392.
Direct quote from John Lennon, according to Mimi. Some sources use, "If you
don't **want** it, Mimi, I will."

[2161] Burns, 45.

[2162] Brown, Craig, 277.

[2163] Lennon, Cynthia, *John*, 174. Direct quote from Mimi Smith.

[2164] Lennon, Cynthia, *John*, 174. Direct quote from Mimi Smith.

[2165] Bill Harry, Kenneth Womack, Peter Brown, Craig Brown, Nick Churchill,
and the Rumsey & Rumsey website refer to Mimi's house as Harbour's Edge.
Norman calls it Harbour Edge.

[2166] https://www.rumseyofsandbanks.co.uk/blog/john-lennon-on-sandbanks

Thursday, 12 August 1965
Kenwood
Weybridge, Surrey

Although "Help!" had been out for weeks in the U.K., it had been released only yesterday in a very select 250 American movie theaters.[2167] Other American venues would wait a week or more to watch The Beatles in action. But the critics were already pouncing on the film, and in a dervish of assessment — some reviews, warm and affirming, and others, fairly lukewarm — John and the boys were off on tour tomorrow morning.

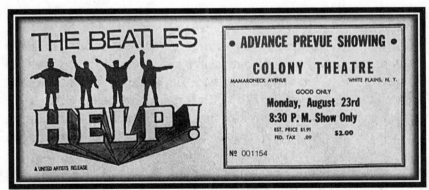

**Prevue Ticket to "Help!" from White Plains, NY
for 23 August 1965**
From the author's collection

Although Alf Bicknell had already collected his baggage, John was ambling about Kenwood, scrounging up loose items, here and there — things he'd forgotten to pack and was sure he'd need: a plastic case containing two foam rubber ear plugs, nose plugs (in case of a swim), Cynthia's favourite satin sleeping mask, a half-full tin of Zubes lozenges and a bottle of Aspero (just in case), a handful of fountain pens, a small stack of torn notepaper for his pockets (to collect random observations and ideas), and an uncracked copy of James Michener's exhaustive new biography of Charles Darwin, *The Source*. Knowing that Mimi would be proud of him for being "at the ready," John carefully stowed these treasures in his worn, zippered, airline bag.

The house was quiet. Cynthia and Julian, out for a "treasure trove stroll," were already melancholy. Over a late breakfast of bacon butties and tea, Cyn had tried to be chirpy, informing John that Brian had rung with good news of the American film critiques.

But when John had returned the call, Brian had admitted, reluctantly, that the reviews weren't unanimously stellar. The *New York Times* had declared that "Help!" lacked whatever had made "A Hard Day's Night" special, despite "interesting camera tricks."[2168] And the *Los Angeles Times* had dismissed the film as "ferociously ephemeral."[2169] The *New Yorker*'s Brendan Gill had pronounced the movie, "hit or miss,"[2170] and even *Playboy* — who had always been supportive of the band's efforts — had christened the United Artists offering "funny but forced."[2171] On the eve of the North American Tour, that dearth of endorsement had soured John's pending departure. He felt a anxious...a sense of foreboding.

Last August, despite the initiation of Kenwood's massive renovations and the large measure of work still required to complete The Beatles' upcoming LP, *Beatles for Sale*, John had been elated at the prospect of several thrilling weeks in America. Last year, John had anticipated it all: the boisterous, screaming airport receptions; the swank hotels; the balmy nights in Hollywood; and the haunting, sweet sound of Dixieland jazz and soulful blues in "good ol' New Orleans." But now, he knew that for The Beatles every city would resemble every other city, and nothing he longed to see could ever be seen.[2172]

John had come to expect "a room and a car, and a car and a room, and a room and a car," as he'd told reporter Ray Coleman.[2173] John had come to expect nothing at all. Except, he hoped, for Elvis. John still wanted to meet Elvis. He'd made that clear.

Hurriedly plundering the sunroom's cabinet drawers for anything that might prove useful abroad, John plowed through

Beatles buttons, badges, and souvenirs, random foreign coins, matches and half-used candles, loose stamps and dog-eared postcards he'd mailed to Cyn and Julian from last year's America jaunt, bits of chipped bric-a-brac, an odd assortment of matchbooks from the London clubs — the Ad Lib and the Pickwick — and...

"What's this, hey?" John said to no one.

Scuffed and discoloured from years in the "rubbish" drawer, the ragged booklet hadn't aged well. Dated — oddly enough — 13 August 1960, the worn, yellowed passport was expiring tomorrow.[2174] Stuart Fergusson Victor Sutcliffe of 53, Ullet Road, Wavertree, Liverpool, England[2175] would no longer be able to travel abroad. Not with this certificate.

Stu Sutcliffe and John Lennon,
circa 1960

"Stu." John carried the weathered passport to the window and turned it in his hand. *Some photograph!* John gnawed his bottom lip and blinked. *So, y'er here, are y', Sutcliffe...come 'round to see me off, as it were?*

*Ah, Johnny....*John could almost hear his soulmate chuckle. *Give over, old son! Why go ter bits over those ragged reviews? What d' they matter, in the long run, right?*

"That's what you say."

*"'N that's what I mean! Look, The Beatles virtually **live** at Number One. 'N soon, y'er gettin' a fuggin' MBE! An MBE, for chrissakes!!!! We never even imagined that one, in all our vain imaginin's! Mary Elizabeth must be Lady Muck o' Muck Hall over it!!! Though she'd never let on.*

John chuckled. He nodded.

'N look at yew, lad...off to America once again...third time's the charm, eh? Toppermost of the poppermost!!! Right up there! Just the way we said! A star.

"Rambullon, Sutcliffe!" John retorted, squinting his eyes against the setting sun, failing but still radiant over the rolling, forested knolls of Kenwood. "It's not as good as all that. It only *looks* as good as all that."

Yeah, well, I may not be there, but I still know what's what! I mean, look what transpired Sunday last when y' ventured out of an evenin' — George 'n Pattie, 'n you 'n Cyn. The Animals at the Jazz Fest, wasn't it? Compliments of Eric?[2176]

"*You* certainly keep up..." John muttered.

*But the fans wouldn't leave you alone, would they? 'N not because they wanted to make yer life miserable...but because they fuggin' **love** you, John. To fuggin' distraction! Thousands 'n thousands of 'em. Millions! More than we ever dreamed! And **we dreamed!***

"*Hmpf!*" John spied Julian, trundling back towards the house, his mother directly behind him. Proudly clutching a sizeable stone, the lad waved it proudly at his father. "Treasure trove!" John mouthed and waved back. Cynthia smiled, too, but John could read her eyes: sadness.

Cynthia Lennon, 1965
Photograph purchased from Alamy.com
OY5726700

John heard Stu's whisper. ***She*** *loves you as well — Cyn. You may think you've outgrown each other, Johnny...that you've wandered off down two radically different paths. 'N maybe y' have, son, right here 'n now...but from where I stand, it's not too late to reconnoiter. We make our own reality, John. We always have a choice...*[2177]

"Do we? I wonder."[2178] John argued. "I mean, how much is

preordained? 'N what if there are *two* paths that are *equally* pre-ordained? There could be *hundreds* of paths where one could go this way or that way...[2179] How can we know if we've made the right choice...if we're with the right person, if we're doin' what we're supposed to be doin', where we're supposed to be doin' it?"

Is that rhetorical, or are y' really arskin'?

"I'd really like to know."

*Well, for my part, the thing that makes life most attractive is the chance to move forward **without** knowin' what comes next. Later, I mean, you'll know it all. The answers'll be easy. But where you are, y' have to figure it out, work at it, unravel it.*

*Look at it this way, John, I went to Hamburg under rabid protest, only because you fuggin' **made** me go, right? But once there, what happened? I found Astrid, or rather, she found me. And with her, I found love. I'd've never found **that** if I hadn't taken the leap...right?*

*And although you made me (forced me to!) leave m' work at Liverpool College of Art behind for **your** brand of art, your rock'n'roll...in Hamburg, I found Paolozzi, 'n he agreed to mentor me... 'n ultimately that lifted m' art to a whole new level, y' know.[2180] It was the chance of a lifetime!!*

*Piece by piece. **That's** the beauty of life, as I remember it, John. An ever-changin' kaleidoscope, an emergin' mosaic, a detailed, muraled landscape gradually revealed. You have to wait for the finished work, the inlaid masterpiece. And if you can't envision the "whole" from the very start, then you have to take a terrifyin' leap of faith to move forward. People do that, more often than not, y' know.*

"Right, well...that's the problem." John sighed. "I don't know *what* I believe! I don't even know what I *want* or what I *feel*! Sometimes, I think I'm happiest bein' here at home, a dad to Julian, 'n a couple — me 'n Cyn. I mean, a few weeks ago, I even told her that from now on when I go off on tour, I'm takin her 'n Jules with me…as often as I can."[2181]

All right. So…

"But the problem's this," John collapsed onto the yellow chaise lounge his Auntie Mater had given Cynthia and him.[2182] "I want to do right by Cyn…'n by Julian. I want to love them the way I'm 'supposed to,' y' know. I mean, I don't want to fail at this shite, Stu! No one does, right?"

Well, not consciously, but…

"…but I've *no idea* how to love! I don't even know how to start, when it comes right down to it! I mean, where I came from, 'love' got the short shrift. I *never* felt I had *any*! Not from me Dad or Mim or even — in the way *I* wanted — from me mum….So, how can I have a feeling when I don't *know* if it's a feeling? How can I have feelings when my feelings have always been *denied*?!"[2183]

You hafta try, John. Everyday. Get up 'n fuggin' try! 'N some days you'll fail entirely, won't you? But…Just. Go. Forward.

"How can I 'go forward' when I don't even know which way I'm fuggin' facin', Stu?!!"[2184] John threw out his hands, exasperated. "How can I go forward when I've no idea which way to go, which way to turn?"[2185] John sighed and folded his arms tightly across his chest. He closed his eyes. And for a moment, silence permeated. Then, John almost whispered, "*How* can I go forward, into somethin'…somethin' I'm not even sure of…"[2186]

And for a long while, neither of them said a thing.

I wish I could tell you, Stu finally began, softly. *I wish I could honestly say that life is long, and you'll figure it out at last. But, well…*Stu let the end of his sentence fall dramatically away. *Look, all I can tell y' for now is that even though you feel that the world's tough — too tough, I know — you've got to be strong, John.*[2187] *Really strong. Not just for Julian…or Cyn…or even for me…but strong enough to do what y' came to do, son. That's the gig.*

"Yeah, great," John mumbled in the slurred accents of exhaustion and fatigue. "The gig…finish it…hold on…fine." For some time, the room was still. John breathed rhythmically, heavily. And then, "Stu…" he muttered. "The gig." Silence. "Tell me what it is…"

But the room grew thick with silence and murky light. And before Cynthia and Julian had finished their trek and swept into the sun room with hands full of bright treasures, John had decided that Stuart Fergusson Victor Sutcliffe of 53, Ullet Road, Liverpool, would be traveling to America with him, passport or no. And bone-knackered, John had curled into a tight, protective ball and had fallen fast asleep.

Notes!

For those who had loved (and continued to love) Stuart, he was never far away. When Colin Fallows interviewed Astrid Kirchherr for Stuart Sutcliffe: a retrospective, *Astrid revealed, "I have never met in my whole life, and I am seventy now and I was married after Stuart, I've never met a person who was so interesting, so loveable and so intelligent, so funny and so full of humour as Stuart.*

"I remember him every day. I think of him every day, and I talk to him when I'm in trouble and don't see any way out. That has been with me all the time. As you might know, George (Harrison) was one of my oldest and loveliest friends and he taught me a lot about religion…George taught me that nobody will be forgotten as long as you think about him all the time. And I never ever believe that Stuart will be forgotten because as long as I live he will be on my mind and will guide me everyday." (p. 53)

And John felt exactly the same. Indeed, in the words of Alan Clayson and Stu's sister Pauline, "…for as long as [John] lived, so, in spirit, did Stuart." (Backbeat, Stuart Sutcliffe: The Lost Beatle, *178)*

Sources:

Lewisohn, The Beatles: Day by Day, *65.*
Harry, The Ultimate Beatles Encyclopedia, *510 and 635-638.*
Harry, The Encyclopedia of Beatles People, *252.*
Harry, The Beatles, Vol. 4, Beatlemania: The History of The Beatles on Film, *32.*
Lennon, Cynthia, John, *185 and 186-187.*
Lennon, John, "How," 197, *Apple/EMI. On* Imagine.
Miles, The Beatles' Diary, Vol. 1, *205.*
Coleman, Lennon, *254.*

Fallows, Colin and Clough, Matthew H., Stuart Sutcliffe: a retrospective, *53.*

Clayson, Alan and Sutcliffe, Pauline, Backbeat, Stuart Sutcliffe: The Lost Beatle, *178.*

Bedford, Liddypool: Birthplace of The Beatles, *132 and 264.*

Goldman, 173.

Yule, 105.

Schultheiss, 138.

Bicknell, 66.

Friede, Titone, and Wiener, 70.

Help! (film) - WikipediaThis website furnishes additional information on the film, "Help!", including the opening dates for the film.

Meet the Beatles for Real: The Richmond Jazz Festival Sara Schmidt's website furnishes info and rare photos of George and Pattie, John and Cynthia at the Richmond Jazz Festival.

John Lennon Quotes (Author of In His Own Write) (page 4 of 8) (goodreads.com)

https://tinyurl.com/mxytkshw For those wishing to get to know Stu Sutcliffe better, here is a 4-minute collage of photos spanning Stu's life and artwork.
Or use this QR code:

https://www.bing.com/videos/search?q=stuart+sutcliffe&docid=6080514 86694596505&mid=4046B172B11FC7B701BC4046B172B11FC7B701 BC&view=detail&FORM=VIRE
This lovely video/music tribute to the undying friendship between John Lennon and Stuart Sutcliffe helps to explain the lifelong connection John felt to his soulmate.
Or use this QR code:

[2167] Miles, *The Beatles' Diary, Vol. 1*, 205, Harry, *The Beatles, Vol. 4: Beatlemania, The History of The Beatles on Film*, 32, and Help! (film) - Wikipedia. Harry tells us that "Help!" opened in 250 leading cinemas throughout the United States on 11 August." (p. 32)

[2168] Yule, 105.

[2169] Schultheiss, 138.

[2170] Yule, 105.

[2171] Yule, 105.

[2172] Goldman, 173. Goldman accurately states, "Wherever they stayed, the boys lived under strict house arrest."

[2173] Coleman, *Lennon*, 254. Direct quote from John Lennon, according to Ray Coleman.

[2174] Schultheiss, 138.

[2175] Bedford, David. *Liddypool: Birthplace of The Beatles*, 132 and 264. Bedford tells us that at the time that Stu secured his passport in 1960, his family lived at 53, Ullet Road in the Wavertree section of town, near Sefton Park. They moved to the other side of Sefton Park later — to 37 Aigburth Drive, Aigburth. But the first address would have been the one on Stu's 1960 passport. You can see a photo of the Ullet Road home on p. 264 of *Liddypool*.

[2176] Lewisohn, *The Beatles: Day by Day*, 65, Schultheiss, 138, Bicknell, 66, and Meet the Beatles for Real: The Richmond Jazz Festival. The Beatles had been invited to the Richmond Jazz Fest, compliments of Eric Burdon of the Animals. But not long after they arrived, John, Cynthia, George, and Pattie were spotted by the fans, and they hurriedly escaped a Beatlemanic surge. There are excellent photos of John and Cynthia at the festival. Alf Bicknell says that he drove them to the venue, but that is not authenticated.

[2177] John Lennon Quotes (Author of In His Own Write) (page 4 of 8) (goodreads.com) This is a quote from John later in life, which only makes sense since this is a thought that is going through John's mind. Did Stu inspire it? We have no idea.

[2178] John Lennon Quotes (Author of In His Own Write) (page 4 of 8) (goodreads.com)

[2179] John Lennon Quotes (Author of In His Own Write) (page 4 of 8) (goodreads.com)

[2180] Harry, *The Encyclopedia of Beatles People*, 252, Harry, *The Ultimate Beatles Encyclopedia,* 510, and Friede, Titone, and Wiener, 170.

[2181] Lennon, Cynthia, *John*, 187-188. Cynthia, talking about the 1965 European tour states, "Before leaving on tour, [John] confided how much he was looking forward to being at home, a proper dad to Julian, and having time for us as a couple. We agreed that in the future when he went away…Julian and I would go with him, as often as possible." (p. 188) She also states, "[John] was worn out and had reached the point where all he wanted was to be at home, without anyone bothering him." (p. 187)

[2182] Lennon, Cynthia, *John*, 185.

[2183] John Lennon – How? Lyrics | Genius Lyrics How long had he been thinking these things in his head? One never knows. These are not the exact words John expressed in his solo song, "How?", but one can see *how* a lifetime of thoughts like these could one day become quite sincere and poignant lyrics.

[2184] John Lennon – How? Lyrics | Genius Lyrics Again, these are not John's words, but they are the germ of what might emerge.

[2185] John Lennon – How? Lyrics | Genius Lyrics

[2186] John Lennon – How? Lyrics | Genius Lyrics

[2187] John Lennon – How? Lyrics | Genius Lyrics

Early morning, Friday, 13 August 1965
24 Chapel Street
Belgravia[2188]
London

12.30 a.m.

Brian dashed down a sleeping pill with the last draught of Hennessy. He removed his robe and slippers and sat on the edge of the bed, not a bit ready for sleep. In just hours, they'd be off to America again, and after months of tedious preparation, Brian fretted that something had been left undone.

He doused the light and slipped under the sheets, thinking that the boys had no inkling of how much work went into planning their overseas tours. *Instead of appreciating the colossal efforts*, Brian thought, *the boys actually resent being asked to, as the say, "take the show on the road."*

George, especially, was tour-weary and lately, he didn't seem to mind telling reporters about it. "I'm a bit fed up with tourin'," he'd spouted off a few days ago, "particularly in America. I feel sure we won't do another tour of the States for as long as five weeks ever again — it's so exhaustin' and not really satisfyin' for us like that."

Even John, when queried about his penchant for touring, hadn't been bouyant. "It's a drag bein' away from home," he had said, "but if you've got to go anywhere, it might as well be America. I'd sooner be off there than go to Indonesia."[2189]

"Exhausting! A drag!" Brian repeated their words bitterly, tugging the covers under his chin. "I wish they had *this side* of things to navigate! They'd soon see what 'a drag' is!"

For months, Brian, Tony Barrow, and Norm Weiss at General Artists Corporation in New York City[2190] had been neck-deep in negotiations for The Beatles' 1965 North American Tour.[2191]

Bobbing and weaving with the seasoned, savvy promoters representing their ten upcoming venues, NEMS and GAC had artfully wrangled for the most advantageous contract arrangements.

In fact, the dance had started last year on 5 September 1964, when popular Minneapolis deejay Bill Diehl and promoter Ray "Big Reggie" Colihan and his wife had flown to the boys' Chicago International Amphitheatre concert. The trio had made the trip to "the Windy City" not only to see the Fab Four in action, but also to meet Brian — to convince Mr. Epstein that Minneapolis deserved a 1965 tour slot.[2192]

Throughout 1965, the same sort of encounter was repeated over and over again. On 19 January 1965, for example, Brian had returned to New York to consult with Norm Weiss at GAC, to set the wheels in motion for the boys' return to the States,[2193] and in the process, he'd carved out time to hone the particulars of the upcoming Shea Stadium event with Sid Bernstein. Then, Brian had entertained a proposal from Houston's 610 AM program director, C. W. "Bill Weaver," about plans for a concert in the Texas metropolis.[2194]

Whilst the boys were traveling hither and thither, on location for "Help!", Brian had devoted hours to strategy, promotion, and contract negotiations — in person, on the telephone, and via mail, back and forth across the United States and Canada.

Some of the promoters — such as Bob Eubanks, who had successfully engineered the Hollywood Bowl concert in 1964 and was filling that same role again this year[2195] — knew the routine. Others failed to grasp the intricacies of booking The Beatles. And some, battling with rival businessmen, became embroiled in bitter bidding wars that complicated matters.

San Francisco's Paul Catalana, for example — who had successfully hosted the boys in 1964 and held a contract for The Beatles at the Cow Palace on 31 August 1965 — was being challenged by San Francisco's KYA deejays Tom "Big Daddy" Donahue and Bobby "Mighty Mitch" Mitchell, who claimed they had secured a prior verbal agreement with GAC. In fact, the two powerful deejay/promoters complained that, based on their agreement, they had already printed tickets and advertising bills. Neither side was willing to budge.[2196]

Brian realised that he could not afford to deal lightly with such claims. Ultimately, he was accountable for all things tour-connected, and any adverse press — any claims of misconduct or double-dealing — would be damaging for them all. Brian knew that the boys would blame him if anything went awry. These days, the NEMporer hadn't the luxury to blunder; he had to "get it right."[2197]

****

Back in early April, when the boys had found one fleeting free moment to spend with Brian and to review the end-of-summer tour plans, Brian had solicited their opinions on possible opening acts for the North American gigs.

"*I* want the Na-Na guys!"[2198] Paul had piped up, enthusiastically.

"The...Na-Na guys?" Brian had wrinkled his forehead.

"Y' know," Ringo had sung, "naa-na-na-na-naaa, na-na-naa, na-na-naa, na-na-naaa..."

"It's called 'Land of a Thousand Dances,' if y' speaka da English," John had smirked.

"Hannibal...er Cannibal 'n the Headhunters," George had explained. "Somethin' like that."

"They're from L.A., as we say on the Coast," Paul had quipped, in his pseudo-American accent. "I saw them on 'Hullabaloo.'"[2199]

"Yeah, they're all the rage — cannibals." John had flopped onto Brian's new white sofa, purchased to complement his flat's white carpet, white walls, white chairs, and pure white accents.[2200]

But jests aside, John had been right. Mexican-American showstoppers Robert "Rabbit" Jaramillo, Frankie "Cannibal" Garcia, Richard "Scar" Lopez, and Joe "Yo-Yo" Jaramillo had just scored #30 on the *Billboard* charts with their catchy cover song,[2201] originally composed by Chris Kenner.[2202] But the "just-out-of-high-school" teens had restyled the song, appending the "na-na" scat when Garcia had inadvertently forgotten the song's lyrics during a Rhythm Room performance in Fullerton, California.[2203] And the rest, naturally, was now music history.

"All right, then, let me see..." Brian scribbled notes on a thick white pad beside his white telephone. "How do you feel about Brenda Holloway?"[2204]

"Uh, 'gear fab,' as they made me say in the last film," George had wrinkled his nose at the expression.

"*I've* heard you say that," Ringo had mumbled, unconsciously picking at the back of one of Brian's beloved, omolu carved chairs.[2205]

"Yeah, but y' were watchin' the fil-um at the time, Rich," John had explained. He'd pivoted to Brian. "Brenda Holloway, eh? 'Every Little Bit Hurts' Brenda Holloway...that Brenda Holloway?"[2206]

"Yes," Brian had nodded, nervously watching Ringo destroying the finish on his chair, "uh...uhm, a lovely, rising Motown star...and a female solo act that could be nicely juxtaposed between the Headhunters and our own Sounds Incorporated."[2207]

"Ah, Sounds Incorporated!" Paul had nodded once and clicked his cheek. "Our ole Star Club mates!"[2208]

"The Hamburgy boys!" John had seconded.

"Oh, *don't* do that Ringo!"[2209] Brian had finally endured the unintentional destruction of his exquisitely inlaid chair as long as he could. "Please! You'll mess it up!"[2210]

"Oh, sorry." Ringo had quickly dropped his hand, abashed.

Instead of fondly taking the mickey out of the drummer, John had instantly flared into a strong, protective stance, "Drop it, Brian!" he'd demanded quietly. "He had to *buy* the fuckin' thing!"[2211]

Paul eyebrows had shot up. George had clandestinely cut his eyes at Ringo with a short reassuring nod. And a little embarrassed at himself, John had quickly scratched his right sideburn. But rapidly — as if nothing had transpired — Brian had cleared his throat and moved on.

"Not to mention, of course," Brian had stated, "Sounds Incorporated is a NEMS act...and the single most enthusiastic slate of performers I've *ever* witnessed!"

Vamping through mad instrumentals, Sounds Incorporated kept crowds on their feet. They were well-known for glitzy drum solos, wild aerial leaps, violent body-rocks, and Chuck Berry gyrations.[2212] In fact, they were the only group whom Brian could imagine performing prior to the charismatic Beatles. The six-man band was sheer energy.[2213]

"All right, who else?" George had fiddled with the blinds, peering out over the early evening of Belgravia, wishing he could strike for a stroll — alone.

"Well, GAC has selected an excellent performance band," Brian had joined John on the sofa, "one who's not only had several recognizable hits, but who can also serve as a backing group for Brenda Holloway and a new dance act we're considering."[2214]

"'N this performance band is…" John had rolled his hand for Brian to elaborate.

"The King Curtis All-Stars," Brian had said. "Their featured saxophonist, Curtis, is known for a hit called 'Memphis Soul Stew,' but you're probably more familiar with his sax solo in the Coasters' 'Yakety Yak.'"[2215]

"Don't talk back!" John had used the deep parental voice he'd employed on the Cavern stage for The Beatles' beloved rendition of "Youngblood."

"The whole band," Brian had disregarded John, "is quite talented really. They can play anything, or so I've been told. In fact…and I've saved this titbit for last…Curtis played, on occasion, with your Mr. Buddy Holly."[2216]

"*Sold!*" Ringo had lifted a finger in exclamation.

"Right," Paul had smiled. "Good enough for me!"

"'N who is this 'new dance act' to which you refer?" John had leaned back and crossed his arms, as if interviewing some undependable entertainment agent.

"An animated, lively group of assorted discotheque dancers." Brian had flushed. He wasn't one bit sure of this selection. "Five women…one man. All attractive, effervescent…performing various renditions of the latest dances, I understand. You probably experienced something similar last year in the Peppermint Lounge."[2217]

"Ringo's quite good at all those latest dances." George had tossed the drummer a grin.

"Yes, well, Ringo will be occupied, as it were." Brian had waved a dismissive hand in George's direction and moved on. "Now, for accompaniment, the dancers have a highly skilled guitarist, Joe Fasia — and we can provide futher backing by the King Curtis All-Stars, when apropos. So, all in all, this dance group promises to be a…'vivacious act,' designed to keep the crowds mollified until you take the boards."[2218]

"'N the vote is?" John had posed the official question.

All four hands had flown up in unison.

"Seems we have ourselves the rare and contagious germ of a tour, Eppy!" John had pronounced.

And though he'd smiled and nodded, Brian had thought that April afternoon how very little the five of them had accomplished and how very much more he still had to resolve.

****

Throughout April and well into May, Brian and Tony Barrow had put their heads together over the selection of journalists and photographers to accompany The Beatles across the States and Canada. In 1964, a large, permanent press retinue had trekked with the lads for the tour's entirety. This time, however, Barrow had suggested choosing a core group "to stay the course," whilst temporarily adding in local reporters and photographers on location within the ten various cities to which they would travel.

"This would, I anticipate, curry favour with the local press," Barrow had explained, "whilst simultaneously reducing costs for hotels, dinners, incidentals, and so forth."

"Yes, brilliant!" Brian had almost smiled. "Well done, Tony."

And so, a list of the "most-favoured" was carefully prepared, and letters of invitation were issued. Some of those included for the tour's duration were Chris Hutchins, a respected reporter for *New Musical Express* (undeniably, Britain's most influential music publication)[2219] and 22-year-old American radio reporter Larry Kane of WFUN, Miami, who had toured with the group in 1964 and had interviewed the lads in the Bahamas, earlier in the year.[2220] Kane had an excellent rapport with all four Beatles, especially John, and as a young, tireless newsman, Kane energetically fired off press feeds throughout the day, keeping the boys in the public eye.

Brian Epstein, 1 May 1965
Photograph from Wikimedia Commons

This year, the tour's designated photographer would be Australian-born, Robert Whitaker, who had served The Beatles well in that capacity during the 1964 North American Tour.[2221] And at the beginning of the month — in an effort to placate the BBC for the dearth of publicity appearances promoting "Help!" — Brian had invited BBC radio show host Brian Matthew along for the journey.[2222] Since the early days of Beatlemania, when Matthew had hosted the popular *Saturday Club* radio programme,[2223] he'd established a genuine bond with The Beatles. One of the few "press men" the lads enjoyed, Matthew had earned their respect. And when he had launched the new Sunday morning radio programme *Easy Beat*[2224] and then later, *Top Gear*,[2225] the boys had been happy to appear on his première shows and boost his success, just as Matthew had boosted theirs in 1963.[2226]

Now, as host of the weekly radio hit *Top of The Pops*,[2227] Matthew had been asked to join The Beatles in the States until 20 August, when prior commitments would call him back home. Then, U.S. broadcaster Jay Peeples would represent the BBC's Transcription Service in Matthew's absence.[2228] Tony Barrow and Brian Epstein had done everything humanly possible to give the British Broadcasting Corporation top priority.

In 1964, smart and gregarious Ivor Davis had traveled with The Beatles, as a foreign correspondent for the London *Daily Express*[2229] whilst simultaneously serving as ghost writer for George Harrison's travel column. And happily, Davis was returning for the '65 jaunt. He would be joining the troupe for their extended stay in Los Angeles, the two Hollywood Bowl concerts, and the San Diego gig. The boys — especially George, who'd grown quite fond of Davis — were elated to have the erudite, affable Cockney along for the ride.[2230] Ivor was not only sharp and observant; he was trustworthy.

Ivor Davis and George Harrison
Ivor toured with The Beatles
on the 1964 North American Tour,
and would be returning for the 1965 venture.
Photograph used by kind permission of Ivor Davis.

Finally, another veteran of the 1964 Tour, likeable Jim Stagg, whom Larry Kane had dubbed "the interviewer with the golden voice,"[2231] was slated to share in the madness as well.[2232] Stagg was representing WCFL in Chicago, but a native of Birmingham, Alabama, Stagg was brimming with smiles and Southern charm. Everyone liked him.

Working doggedly, Barrow and Epstein had meticulously assembled a distinguished cast of trusted, talented newsmen, radio personalities, and public relations experts. After months of considered preparation, The Beatles would travel with an exceptional "cast and crew."

Of course, crucial to the success of the ten-city North American excursion was the ingenuity and loyalty of The Beatles' inner circle. Brian was thrilled that this year NEMS's senior press officer, Tony Barrow, would actually be traveling with the boys.[2233] Tony had remained in London during the 1964 Tour, overseeing Brian's vast stable and permitting Derek Taylor to work directly with The Beatles.[2234] But this year — facing much larger venues, complicated security risks, and a restive press — Barrow had opted to face the hurdles himself.[2235]

Neil Aspinall and Mal Evans were "musts" for any Fab Four appearance, no matter how large or how small. Neil, their official road manager and closest friend, personally oversaw the boys' venue entrances and exits; he made certain that, day in and day out, the boys' lives comfortable, safe, and protected.[2236] And Mal was not just The Beatles' experienced roadie; he was their assistant, their confidante.[2237] The Beatles depended on Mal and Neil for all things. The duo was indispensable.

On a whim back in May, during the filming of "Help!" on Salisbury Plain, John had asked chauffeur Alf Bicknell along on the "American tour" as well.[2238] Although at first, Brian had been slightly taken aback by John's generous but unsanctioned invitation, Epstein quickly conceded that the more capable "hands on deck," the better. For months, Bicknell had proven himself an expert driver, part-time bodyguard, temporary roadie, and friend. And all of the boys were happy to have him along. Alf, for his part, was elated to be included.[2239]

But these were only a smattering of the issues that had, over the last few months, crossed Brian's desk. As Sid Bernstein in America phrased it, "For months, we've been drawing up battle plans!"[2240] It was true.

GAC's Norm Weiss and Brian had been wrangling with American hotels…to frustrating ends. No longer was it an honour to house the celebrated Merseyside band. Playing host to the Fab Four had become a significant liability, and many of the finest establishments no longer welcomed The Beatles and their heedless, unruly fans.[2241]

With the boys and their retinue in house, no facility felt safe.

Endless screaming precluded sleep for all guests. Lodgers complained; The Beatles complained. No one was happy.[2242] Thus, in 1965, a great many luxury hotels were simply telling Mr. Epstein, "No, thank you."

But the appeals to "meet The Beatles" in person hadn't diminished. Almost every day, Weiss, Barrow, or Epstein himself would receive a persuasively penned note from some politician, celebrity, noted news personality, or president of a Beatles fan club, requesting admittance to a press conference, concert, or even The Beatles' suite. Brian had already been informed that a full retinue of *glitterati* would be fêting the lads after the Shea Stadium show, and Tony Barrow had been busy arranging a *soirée* for the likes of Bob Dylan, the Supremes, members of the Exciters (who had served as one of the boys' opening acts in 1964), and their long-time friend, Del Shannon.[2243]

Because The Beatles could not risk an evening in public as they had in 1964 — not even in an exclusive private club — this pattern was repeating itself in city after city.[2244] Everyone who was anyone wanted to know the Fab Four, to tag along. Admiring strangers wrote daily, seeking admission to The Beatles' hotel suite.

Brian tried to be polite and inclusive of the many stars who sought to call upon John, Paul, George, and Ringo, but the risk of inviting strangers into the boys' private lives was tangible. When people outside "the inner circle" were present, the boys couldn't let down their guard or relax. Marijuana, Brian had preached to all four of them, could never be smoked at such affairs. Drugs were illegal in America and highly frowned upon — especially for a group of young performers who held sway over teenagers.[2245] And it was impossible to know which celebrity might succumb to the lucrative temptation to "tell all." Almost *no one*, Brian believed, could be trusted.

Similarly, Brian had flatly forbidden the boys' espousal of political opinions in any press conference or social setting. "In speaking out, you understand," he expounded sternly, "you'll always offend someone. Furthermore, your sentiments on — well, let's say the American involvement in Vietnam — have nothing to do with your music, your films, or your concerts. Careless dialogue regarding politics is totally irrelevant...and more importantly, it's potentially lethal to your careers."[2246]

But at a private party in their own hotel suite, The Beatles were difficult to constrain. Although Brian had frequently admonished them about smoking in public, the boys still smoked at their parties. And once they had enjoyed a drink or two, The Beatles were deaf to their manager's guidance. Admitting party guests that neither Brian nor Tony knew was a gamble. In fact, these days, everything seemed to hold an element of risk.

At the apex of Fortune's wheel, Brian mulled, *every minor movement is perilous.*

Stadiums, hotels, venues and their promoters, sound systems, recorded shows, celebrities and their complimentary tickets, airport authorities, core reporters, local reporters, youth reporters, radio station competition winners, deejays, TV cameramen, photographers of all stripes, grand and minute expenses, contracts and their riders, transportation on land and in the air, press conferences, stage costumes, security teams, and one secluded rental home with a large and lavish pool...the list of complicated considerations and potential hazards kept accumulating. And to top it all off, Brian sighed, the boys were flatly insisting upon meeting Elvis.[2247]

Sources:

Lewisohn, The Complete Beatles Chronicle, *181 and 200.*
Harry, The Ultimate Beatles Encyclopedia, *105, 213, 353, 394, 443, 598, 614, 653, 687, and 691.*
Harry, The Encyclopedia of Beatles People, *42, 124, 161, 287, 333, and 353.*
The Beatles, The Beatles Anthology, *186.*
Gunderson, Some Fun Tonight!, Vol. 2, *16, 18-19, 20-22, 24-25, 40, 62, 75, 78, 82-83, and 120.*
Kane, Ticket to Ride, *184-189, 195, 202, 209, 213, 220, 246, and 251.*
Miles, The Beatles' Diary, Vol. 1, *206-209.*
Davis, Ivor, The Beatles and Me on Tour, *132, 221, and 224-225.*
Howlett, *14-15, 61, 70, and 72.*
Spitz, *568 and 575.*
Norman, John Lennon: The Life, *368.*
Riley, Lennon, *279-280.*
Badman, *169.*
Womack, The Beatles Encyclopedia, *76-77 and 265-266.*
Coleman, The Man Who Made The Beatles, *219 and 222.*
Bicknell, *43 and 68.*
Barrow, *157 and 159.*

Brown 180 and 188.
Goldman 173 and 181.
Connolly, 202.
Mulligan, 86-87.
Clayton, Leigh and Thomas, Gareth, John Lennon: A Life in Pictures, 102-103.
Robertson, 41.
Schultheiss, 139.
Greenwald, 37-38.
Wiener, 50.

https://www.ivordavisbooks.com/#close This website gives additional information about London Daily Express foreign correspondent Ivor Davis.

Jimmy Staggs - Wikipedia This website gives biographical information on newsman Jim Stagg.

http://america.aljazeera.com/watch/shows/consider-this/Consider-This-blog/2014/2/7/larry-kane-recallshistimeontourwiththebeatles.html This website provides information about Larry Kane's time with The Beatles in 1964 and 1965.

The Beatles | beatlesphotocollection.com | unseen Beatles pictures, Larry Kane: The reluctant Beatles fan - BBC Newshttps://www.robertwhitakerphotography.com/images/the-beatles/ This website shows some of Robert Whitaker's photos of The Beatles in 1965.

https://www.dailymail.co.uk/tvshowbiz/article-2045830/Beatles-Elvis-Presley-Story-meeting-pops-greatest-legends.html This website provides information about Chris Hutchins's role in facilitating the meeting between Elvis and The Beatles.

Chris Hutchins - Wikipedia This is a second website with information about noted journalist Chris Hutchins of New Musical Express.

https://www.youtube.com/watch?v=VZFzKZyyQK0 This video shows Cannibal and The Headhunters performing "Land of 1000 Dances" in 1965. You can see why The Beatles agreed to have them as an opening act...tons of charisma!

https://www.youtube.com/watch?v=FK7gVFBaiNs Here is Brenda Holloway performing her hit, "Every Little Bit Hurts."

https://www.youtube.com/watch?v=7Rx1Glj9K2E&t=20s This is a 2020 telephone interview with Sounds Incorporated, talking about how they met The Beatles and then later, how they recorded the horns for "Good

Morning, Good Morning."

*"EVERYBODY SAID YEAH!" *SOUND INCORPORATED* - YouTube*
This is Sounds Incorporated performing one of their big hits, "Everybody Said Yeah!" Certainly, one can see why Brian wanted this band on the 1965 tour.

https://www.youtube.com/watch?v=0Loy55z4GpA This is a video of King Curtis performing "Memphis Soul Stew."

[2188] Spitz, 568 and Coleman, *The Man Who Made The Beatles*, 219. Brian had recently moved, Spitz tells us, from "the designer flat in William Mews to considerably more glamorous quarters in a Belgravia town house on Chapel Street that he decorated from top to bottom in white furniture…" The address, supplied by Coleman, is 24 Chapel Street, Belgravia. Coleman tells us that Brian spent £40,000 for the new abode.

[2189] The Beatles, *The Beatles Anthology*, 186. Direct quote from John Lennon.

[2190] Harry, *The Ultimate Beatles Encyclopedia*, 394 and 687. Harry describes Norman "Norm" Weiss as an "executive of the prestigious American agency General Artists Corporation" who "dealt with European activities." Weiss heard about The Beatles, initially, from Vic Lewis, a British agent who had witnessed the rise of The Beatles and was impressed with them. Lewis received no commission for securing the boys their first American tour through GAC but was rewarded some time later when Epstein purchased his agency and then put Lewis on the board of NEMS.

[2191] Gunderson, *Some Fun Tonight!, Vol. 2*, 11.

[2192] Gunderson, *Some Fun Tonight!, Vol. 2*, 82-83.

[2193] Gunderson, *Some Fun Tonight!, Vol. 2*, 12, Lewisohn, *The Complete Beatles Chronicle*, 181, Harry, *The Ultimate Beatles Encyclopedia*, 687, and Beatles history - 1965 year (dmbeatles.com)

[2194] Gunderson, *Some Fun Tonight!, Vol. 2*, 62.

[2195] Gunderson, *Some Fun Tonight!, Vol. 2*, 120.

[2196] Gunderson, *Some Fun Tonight!, Vol. 2*, 120.

[2197] Kane, *Ticket to Ride*, 251. Kane observed on the 1965 tour that Brian was "beginning to show visible signs of insecurity." Kane says that while The Beatles never questioned Brian's "authority over The Beatles' empire," it appeared that his "one-on-one relationships with The Beatles weren't as warm as they once had been."

[2198] Gunderson, *Some Fun Tonight!, Vol. 2*, 22. Direct quote from Paul McCartney.

[2199] Gunderson, *Some Fun Tonight!, Vol. 2*, 22. Cannibal and the Headhunters were on the March 1965 "Hullabaloo."

[2200] Spitz, 568.

[2201] Cannibal & the Headhunters - Wikipedia and Richard 'Scar' Lopez dies at 65; founder of East L.A. vocal band Cannibal & the Headhunters - Los Angeles Times (latimes.com)

[2202] Gunderson, *Some Fun Tonight!*, Vol. 2, 22, Cannibal & the Headhunters | Biography & History | AllMusic, and Cannibal & the Headhunters - Wikipedia. AllMusic.com lists Fats Domino as a co-creator of this song.

[2203] Gunderson, *Some Fun Tonight!*, Vol. 2, 22, Cannibal & the Headhunters | Biography & History | AllMusic, and Cannibal & the Headhunters - Wikipedia.

[2204] Gunderson, *Some Fun Tonight!*, Vol. 2, 20-21.

[2205] Coleman, *The Man Who Made The Beatles*, 222.

[2206] https://www.youtube.com/watch?v=FK7gVFBaiNs This is Brenda Holloway performing the song to which John is alluding. This is her hit, "Every Little Bit Hurts."

[2207] Gunderson, *Some Fun Tonight!*, Vol. 2, 21.

[2208] Harry, *The Ultimate Beatles Encyclopedia*, 614.

[2209] Coleman, *The Man Who Made The Beatles*, 222. Direct quote from Brian Epstein.

[2210] Coleman, *The Man Who Made The Beatles*, 222. Direct quote from Brian Epstein.

[2211] Coleman, *The Man Who Made The Beatles*, 222. The words, "He had to buy the fucking thing!" is a direct quote from John Lennon.

[2212] "EVERYBODY SAID YEAH!" *SOUND INCORPORATED* - YouTube Here are Sounds Incoporated gyrating madly as they perform "Everybody Said Yeah!" (Some spell the last word, "Yeh!") No wonder Brian Epstein wanted them on the 1965 North American Tour.

[2213] Gunderson, *Some Fun Tonight!*, Vol. 2, 24-25. Sounds Incorporated, Gunderson tells us, was comprised of Barrie Cameron on organ and saxophone, Alan "Boots" Holmes on saxophone and vocals, Major Griff West on saxophone, John St. John on lead guitar, Wes Hunter on bass, and Tony Newman on drums.

[2214] Gunderson, *Some Fun Tonight!*, Vol. 2, 16. Gunderson tells us "[King Curtis] and his band were selected by GAC..."

[2215] Gunderson, *Some Fun Tonight!*, Vol. 2, 16, Yakety Yak - Wikipedia, and King Curtis - Wikipedia. To hear King Curtis's hit song "Memphis Soul Stew," go to: King Curtis - Memphis Soul Stew - YouTube

[2216] Gunderson, *Some Fun Tonight!*, Vol. 2, 16, Yakety Yak - Wikipedia, and King Curtis - Wikipedia.

[2217] Gunderson, *Some Fun Tonight!*, Vol. 2, 18-19. Gunderson points out that not much is known about The Discotheque Dancers...not even all of their names. Denise Mourges and Dawn Michaels, he says, "were professional dancers. The others, whom [Mourges] remembered only as Steve, Judy, Susan, and Ronnie, were all teachers on summer break." There are several excellent photos of The Discotheque Dancers in Gunderson's incredible book.

[2218] Gunderson, *Some Fun Tonight!*, Vol. 2, 18. Gunderson tells us that Joe Fasia was a gifted guitarist from the popular television program "Hullabaloo."

[2219] Harry, *The Encyclopedia of Beatles People*, 161, Kane, *Ticket to Ride*, 246, Miles, *The Beatles' Diary, Vol. 1*, 208, Davis, Ivor, *The Beatles and Me on Tour*, 221, https://www.dailymail.co.uk/tvshowbiz/article-2045830/Beatles-Elvis-Presley-Story-meeting-pops-greatest-legends.html, and Chris Hutchins - Wikipedia

[2220] Kane, *Ticket to Ride*, 195, Harry, *The Ultimate Beatles Encyclopedia*, 353, Davis,132, Norman, *John Lennon: The Life*, 368, Riley, *Lennon*, 279-280, and Gunderson, *Some Fun Tonight!*, *Vol. 2*, 11.

[2221] Harry, *The Encyclopedia of Beatles People*, 333, Badman, 168, Harry, *The Ultimate Beatles Encyclopedia*, 691, Gunderson, *Some Fun Tonight!*, *Vol. 2*, 75, The Beatles | beatlesphotocollection.com | unseen Beatles pictures, Larry Kane: The reluctant Beatles fan - BBC Newshttps://www.robertwhitakerphotography.com/images/the-beatles/, and http://america.aljazeera.com/watch/shows/consider-this/Consider-This-blog/2014/2/7/larry-kane-recallshistimeontourwiththebeatles.html. You can see a photo of Robert Whitaker taking a photo of Ringo in a mirror on p. 75 of Gunderson's book.

[2222] Howlett, 72. Howlett tells us that Matthew's "on-the-spot tape recordings" of The Beatles in American would "be compiled into *The Beatles Abroad* — a 45-minute documentary for the August [Bank] holiday."

[2223] Harry, *The Ultimate Beatles Encyclopedia*, 574-575 and Howlett, 13-14.

[2224] Harry, *The Ultimate Beatles Encyclopedia*, 213.

[2225] Howlett, 61.

[2226] Harry, *The Ultimate Beatles Encyclopedia*, 443 and Howlett, 15. Howlett identifies *Easy Beat* as "a gentler Sunday morning [radio] show" hosted by Brian Matthew, in comparison to his lively *Saturday Club*. There is a photo of The Beatles on *Easy Beat* on p. 62 of Howlett's *The Beatles at the BBC*.

[2227] Howlett, 70. *Top of the Pops* joined the BBC line-up in October 1964 as "British pop music," Howlett says, "became a very successful export."

[2228] Lewisohn, *The Complete Beatles Chronicle*, 200.

[2229] https://www.ivordavisbooks.com/#close This website gives additional information about journalist Ivor Davis, who toured with The Beatles in 1964 and 1965.

[2230] Davis, 224-225. Ivor explains that in the days prior to The Beatles' arrival in Los Angeles, he "had spent six insane days covering the Watts riots, dodging sniper bullets with *Daily Express* photographer, Harry Benson, who had flown to L.A. on Day 2 of the disaster." But on the evening of 27 August, when Ivor got the call from Mal Evans to "get to the house in an hour" because they were "all going to meet Elvis," Ivor dropped everything and joined The Beatles for the next exciting days.

[2231] Kane, *Ticket to Ride*, 188.

[2232] Kane, *Ticket to Ride*, 209.

[2233] Kane, *Ticket To Ride*, 202 and Jimmy Staggs - Wikipedia Kane calls Barrow "a tough but sensitive press boss." Note: Although Stagg's birth name was Jimmy Pearson Staggs, all of his radio shows were promoted under the name "Stagg." In one of his earliest jobs at WCFL in Chicago, Stagg called his call-in line the "Stagg Line," and he also had a weekly feature known as "Stagg's Starbeat."

[2234] Harry, *The Encyclopedia of Beatles People*, 42. Harry notes that initially, Barrow's main responsibility was "to concentrate on NEMS artists such as Cilla Black and Billy J. Kramer, as Brian employed various other press agents, such as Brian Sommerville and Derek Taylor, to handle The Beatles."

However, in early 1965, Brian acknowledged that he needed Barrow along for the 1965 North American Tour.

[2235] Kane, *Ticket to Ride*, 187, 189, and 202. Kane, who knew Barrow well, calls him "a man of great honor and integrity, who used his prior skills as a journalist to deal exquisitely with press pressures facing The Beatles." (p. 187) Kane goes on to say that in 1965, Barrow was constantly "dealing with the worldwide press swirling around them." (p. 189)

[2236] Kane, *Ticket to Ride*, 186-187, Harry, *The Ultimate Beatles Encyclopedia*, 51, Harry, *The Encyclopedia of Beatles People*, 42, Greenwald, *The Beatles Companion*, 37, and Womack, *The Beatles Encyclopedia*, 76-77.

[2237] Kane, *Ticket to Ride*, 185-186, Harry, *The Ultimate Beatles Encyclopedia*, 232-233, Harry, *The Encyclopedia of Beatles People*, 124, and Womack, *The Beatles Encyclopedia*, 265-266.

[2238] Bicknell, 43, Harry, *The Ultimate Beatles Encyclopedia*, 105, Miles, *The Beatles' Diary, Vol.1*, 209. Bicknell writes in his *Beatles Diary*, "…but the highlight of those three days [on Salisbury Plain] was that John invited me to work on the American tour. It's not something I could have asked, 'Could I come?' When John asks you, that was fine by me!"

[2239] Bicknell, 43.

[2240] Badman, 169. Direct quote from Sid Bernstein.

[2241] Goldman, 173. Goldman notes that hotels "foolish enough to book the group…had to be prepared to withstand every sort of attack, from sneaky infiltrations to all-out rushes against the doors and plate-glass windows."

[2242] Gunderson, *Some Fun Tonight!*, Vol. 2, 78, Harry, *The Encyclopedia of Beatles People*, 287, Harry, *The Ultimate Beatles Encyclopedia*, 598. Gunderson gives the complete listing of the guests. Bill Harry adds additional information about Del Shannon.

[2243] Barrow, 157, Gunderson, *Some Fun Tonight!*, Vol. 2, 40, Kane, *Ticket to Ride*, 213, Bicknell, 68, Miles, *The Beatles' Diary, Vol. 1*, 206, Spitz, 575, Robertson, 41, and Schultheiss, 139. Spitz and Schultheiss include the Ronettes. Barrow, who gave the party, does not include them. They did visit The Beatles at their hotel in New York during the 1964 North American Tour.

[2244] Brown, 180.

[2245] Kane, *Ticket to Ride*, 184. Kane provides a vivid example of a hotel room party in San Francisco, 1965, when John unthinkingly lit up a joint. Brian immediately and covertly insisted John get rid of it, and no one (except Kane) was the wiser. But Kane explains that the situation could have been disastrous.

[2246] Kane, *Ticket to Ride*, 220.

[2247] Barrow, 159. Direct quote from George Harrison.

Now I arsk yew...

   Will The famous Beatles meet the famous
                     Elvis?
   Will Paul convince Brian to reschedule the
          1965 U.K. tour, as it were?
   Will the Liverpool lads be forced to endure yet
   "Another 'Beatles' Christmas Show"? (Dear
                God, I pray not!)
   Will "the boys" (aged 24) be strong-armed into
   making yet another United Artists film in 1966?
         Will John write a solo song entitled
      "Tomorrow" and George, one entitled
                    "Today"?
         Will there be any escape from the hum-
               drudgery of tourin'?
   What will happen in Part 2 of Shades of Life?

Ah, see y' on the flip...

Appendix

Interview with Julia Baird, John Lennon's Sister

From the June 2021 "She Said She Said" podcast
with author of **The Recipe Records Series**, Lanea Stagg,
and Jude Southerland Kessler

Lanea: To quote the one and only John Lennon, "Hello Jadies and Lents!" Welcome to "She Said She Said" as tonight we wind up our significant historical series, "The Beatles Family." The last 14 months have been amazing. We were so blessed to be able to talk with some of the wonderful people who were closest to The Beatles including Roag Best, Chas Newby, and Angie and Ruth McCartney. And this evening our series comes to a close with a truly grand finale...a night to remember! I am your very excited co-host, Lanea Stagg, the author of **The Recipe Records Series,** a four-volume series of great rock'n'roll cookbooks which not only feature delicious and unique recipes, but also offer rock history, fun rock trivia, and marvelous playlists to enjoy with each dish, as you whip them up in the kitchen!

Jude: And I'm telling you, they are *wonderful*!!!! Love, love, love *Recipe Records*!!! Hi guys, I'm Jude Southerland Kessler, the co-host of "She Said She Said." As most of you know, if you've tuned into this podcast regularly, the last 34 years of my life have been given to hours of research every single day in writing **The John Lennon Series**, a 9-volume series of documented historical narratives, telling John's complete life story as if you are actually there...a fly on the wall. And like Lanea, I'm *so* honored to be able to talk this evening with our special guest who knew John as *none other*!!!!

Lanea: You are so right, Jude. And, you know, I met our guest at "Abbey Road on the River" in Louisville, Kentucky several years ago and I was so impressed at how kind and open and friendly she was. She spent time chatting with my daughter and my niece, Abby and Annie, and she was so willing to chat…we took our picture together, and she signed her book for us! Her book was entitled *Imagine This*. It was her second book about John…and we were all "chuffed" to get a signed copy, as they say in Liverpool. That was – as John would have said – a real "red lettuce" day for Abby, Annie, and me. And, Jude, I think you had the same sort of lovely experience.

Jude: Yeah, I think everybody has. People adore meeting our special guest and talking with her. *We* crossed paths the first time in New York City at the 50th anniversary of the Beatles coming to America at the *huge* – and I mean *huge* — party that was hosted by Mark and Carol Lapidos…a really special Fest for Beatles Fans in downtown New York City. It was, coincidentally, the book release event for Volume 3 in **The John Lennon Series**, *She Loves You,* and I was so thrilled to be able to share that book with our guest and to get a signed copy of her book, *Imagine This*, which is a greatly expanded version of another excellent book that she wrote earlier entitled, *John Lennon, My Brother.* (If you have *John Lennon, My Brother,* you still need to get *Imagine This*. They're completely different stories! They're both wonderful!)

Then a few months later, we reconnected at the Los Angeles Fest for Beatles Fans and got a special chance to talk, but since then, she hasn't had too, too many opportunities to frequent the States, not only because of Co-vid, but also because she is the Director for Cavern City Tours and has been involved in a very impressive venture, centering on the site of the real Strawberry Field in Liverpool. This project has tremendously transformed John's beloved neighborhood of Woolton, so we are excited to talk about that project and to welcome to our show one of the people on planet Earth who knew John best and most intimately! Please welcome to "She Said She Said" a teacher, an author, a business director, and now, a city transformer, John Lennon's sister, the one and only Julia Baird. Hey Julia!

Julia: Well, I can't top that as there's nothing to say now!

Jude and Lanea: (Laughing)

Julia: You've picked me up so much I don't know what to say. That's such a wonderful introduction, thank you! I shall record that and take it everywhere with me! (Laughing)

Jude: Well, we're so happy to have you here…it's thrilling. And I'm going to try to maintain my calm and quiet and let Lanea take the ball for a while, but honestly, we're thrilled to have you, Julia. We are.

Julia: That's lovely. Thank you, Jude. Thank you very much.

Lanea: Well, we're just delighted to have you, Julia. It's so special, and I know that it's late in Liverpool for you, but we're so excited to share this conversation with all of our listeners!

So, 60 years after the fact, the world, as you know, is still very much in love with The Beatles, and their songs are still the soundtrack of millions of lives. You knew all of them so well and played such a vital role in their story.

But now, after years of working as a special education teacher in Chester and after writing two books about your life and your brother's life, you've taken on a *new role* that honors John, who penned that magical song, "Strawberry Fields Forever." You are the Director of Cavern City Tours. And furthermore, you've been working with the Strawberry Field Project! In fact, in 2018, I donated to the project and secured a commemorative brick from the original Strawberry Field building for Jude.

Julia: Oh, well thank you so much, Lanea. Thank you!

Lanea: (Laughing) That was *very* special.

Julia: Lovely, 'cause it's a way for you to be a part of it, 'cause I'm assuming that you haven't actually been to Strawberry Fields yet. Is that right?

Jude: I have.

Lanea: Not since the project has taken shape. Have you, Jude?

Jude: No, not since then…to the original building, but not since you've reshaped it.

Julia: Of course, the lockdown has closed everything, hasn't it? You know, with the dread and the trauma of the Corona virus. It [Strawberry Field] had only just opened, and it had to close for the first lockdown. It had just got going again – then, the second lockdown! It had just ramped up again…then, the third lockdown! So, you know, it has been like some big mallets have come down on the business's head every time it, sort of, opened up. But the building is *absolutely* stunning. I call it Battlestar Galactica 21ˢᵗ Century!

Jude: (Laughing)

Julia: You go in, and it's like you almost feel as if you're in "Star Wars." You're going to take off and zoom into the stratosphere! It's stunning!

The building itself is absolutely beautiful: floor to ceiling windows, a little outside area to catch the sun, to sit. There's a café; there's a shop. There's a museum and an exhibition there with some very original things, believe me...including the "Imagine" piano which was only installed this year...the *original* "Imagine" piano from George Michael's estate.

But the main thing of all...you did say, Jude, that I was a special needs teacher, which I was. But when I started out many, many years ago (about like the 17ᵗʰ Century, it feels like!), I was a languages teacher. Mainly French and English and a bit of math and a bit of Spanish, but mainly French and English. That was my core stuff.

And then, when I went back after my third child, I just took a different route and went into special needs, and I found it the most challenging and rewarding time of my career! That was the last 15 years.

I went straight into The Cavern from there, and then Strawberry Fields came up. Now this time, instead of dealing with EBD, which was my specialism in education, which is "emotional and behavioral difficulties," I was working in a unit, running the unit. But this isn't the same.

What Strawberry Fields has opened for is to train young people with mild to moderate learning disabilities...into life. When I say "into life," I mean to take them out of exclusion and seclusion and loneliness and maybe their bedroom on a screen and to help them, to guide them to join *in the world* normally by some form of employment.

And I'm not talking about a "9 to 5," a mortgage, you know...these students, from 16 to about 25, have mild to moderate learning difficulties, which means they can be Down's syndrome or various abilities of Down's syndrome. Additionally, they've had "various difficulties" all their lives. They've never been mainstream. They've never been "on the main train track."

And they're just *so* lovely and just let me give you one little story. We had a range of talks set up for business people...you know, to [interest them in] sponsor[ing] the students at Strawberry Field and to take an interest in them....(and this is on-going on...even throughout lockdown, the school hasn't stopped. It's *so important!*)

And [at one of these talks]...we asked, "Would anyone like to say anything?" I had given a talk to...explain the program, and the room was full. Absolutely packed! Lots of businessmen, lots of potential sponsors [who] were very interested in these people [and] we *need* them to take an interest!

And this one girl said, "I don't mind saying something." I said, "It only has to be one or two words." She said, "All right, then." And she's very, very retiring, coy, quiet...no confidence *whatsoever*. And so, I'd given my talk, and she went and just stood there, and we just looked at her, and I thought, "She's not going to say anything!"

[Then] the chairman, who was very good, looked at her and said, "What do you think the course has done for you?" (Because this lovely girl had actually been through it.) And she said, "Before, I was no one, and now I'm not."

Jude: (Sigh)

Lanea: Oh gosh, that's so precious!

Julia: I'll *never* forget it – never, never, never. That's exactly what she said.

Lanea: Wow.

Julia: And for all my blabbering and what I'd said and all that the chairmen had said...she *nailed it* in that one little phrase!! She had nailed the entire purpose of the program! The [entire purpose of the] training program for these students!

And so far, there's probably about between eight or ten [students] in every group. I think 60 kids have gone through [altogether, thus far]. I keep calling them "children" because I was a teacher, but they're students, aren't they? And they're all doing bits of things.

Now, in Liverpool...because we have a massive Beatles industry, if you go into the Beatles Café, there's one of our students there doing a bit of work experience. If you go into the Beatles Museum, there's another one there! If you come into The Cavern when we re-open, there will be one student there. You know...The Beatles industry *certainly* is going to take them on...when we "get back"!

My job was to network, to find places that I could put them in for work experience, to give them a chance to show their worth, because no one else had given them that chance. We now have a department networking to find places for these students. One of them – I have spoken to Bill [Heckle of The Cavern Club]...we're going to put [that student] on the Magical Mystery Tour bus. He'll be able to chat into the microphone, so we can find places for [these young people], and I hope – *desperately hope* – within five years that *everywhere you go in Liverpool*, there will be a Strawberry Field graduate!

Jude: Yeah. That is amazing. Can I jump in for one second, Lanea?

Julia: Oh, please – I've said my thing now about Strawberry Field.

Jude: No, no – I just want to say –

Julia: The training program, that is the focal point!

Jude: It's so perfect – Strawberry Field...because of that line in John's song: "No one, I think, is in my tree. I mean, it must be high or low." And *that* has to be the feeling that these kids have: "No one's sitting on the limb I'm sitting on. Either they're high above me or they're low." That's the whole motto; that's the whole focus of what you're doing!

Julia: You've got it exactly! You've got it completely! That is *exactly* it! And then, [there's] this fabulous building with these fabulous gardens [which] will become their second home, which is their forever home. Once they've been through the course (and they do) they're in the café all day...They bring their whole family because they have found somewhere that actually cares about them!

Lanea: Wow. Julia, that is an absolutely stunning story that you've shared about your help with those children and your brother, John, would be so proud of you.

Julia: It's not me; it's the Salvation Army! Well, the Salvation Army has actually set it up...I had no idea until it was actually all underway, and then they asked me to come on board, and I talk to people – potential sponsors...

I jumped in with two feet because it was a wonderful project! But believe me, the entire idea of the training school was *all* the Salvation Army! They just invited me to come in, and I'm privileged enough to be able to step in and out…do bits, chat to them.

I did a poetry session with [the students] about lockdown, and I wrote some poems…not good ones, just poems, about lockdown: locked up, locked in, locked out, locked anyway… we're just locked up, you know? And the [students] loved it, and I said, "Right, I want you to do some stuff now, and they wrote their own feelings…And I said [to one student in her 20s], "What did lockdown mean to you?" And she said, "I thought I was going to die."

Lanea: Yeah.

Julia: So, the school has kept going the whole time with a dedicated staff of coaches and staffers and they are…they're funny, they're witty…as you have to be in Liverpool and as you just are!

Jude and Lanea: (Laughing)

Julia: And they get "into" the students, and there's a loyalty zinging around all over the place! It's a *very* privileged thing to be doing, but it was not my idea. I was just invited to jump in and I did.

Lanea: Wow. You are so inspirational, and you're doing *incredible, incredible* work, touching those lives of those precious children and young adults. And your brother would be extremely proud of the work that you're doing! I can feel, you know, the love through you and the same kind of love for humankind that John had as well, so –

Julia: Well, I'm sure *he* would've been there! We would've had him in there doing guitar lessons!

Jude and Lanea: (Laughing)

Lanea: So, Julia, is it possible to see videos? Like a video tour or anything of the facility?

Julia: I think so. I think if you'll go to the website: https://www.StrawberryFieldLiverpool.com

Lanea: Okay, perfect, perfect.

Julia: And I think you'll be able to do a tour around the exhibition and truly, it has great things in it! It's got a mellotron that you can actually play! I think it's the only one in any of the museums you can actually put the headphones on as you play a tune.

Lanea: Wow!

Julia: It's got the actual "Imagine" piano, which is wonderful that John actually composed and recorded "Imagine" on...so...you know, that was a bit cool! And we got that back in October actually, so that's big! And we just got all that and ready to do *big* splashes and we were locked down. I mean...it's been exasperating!

Lanea: Yeah, absolutely, absolutely. Well, we hope that we can push through it and put it behind us and I cannot *wait* to go. I can't wait for Jude and I to make it to Strawberry Field as soon as it's safe.

Julia: Oh do! Let me know if you're coming over, and I'll make sure that I'm there. If I'm in the country, I'll make sure I'm there.

Jude: Oh, that's so exciting!! We'd love it!

Lanea: Fantastic, fantastic! So, Julia, I'm going to kind of switch gears here and I'm sure that all of our listeners realize that you were named in honor of your incredible mother...of course, John's mother also – Julia Stanley Lennon.

Now Beatles fans know about Julia from the books we've read and films that we've seen, but of course, you know the many sides of Julia that no book can convey. So tell us about this very special woman and about whom John wrote, "Half of what I say is meaningless, but I say it just to reach you, Julia." To inspire a lifetime of devotion and hundreds of songs that changed the world, she must have been extremely amazing, indeed.

*The interview continues here with Julia's very tender and lovely words about her mother. She talks about her mother's musical talent and how she shared that gift with John. Julia also discusses each of The Beatles and recalls John's best friend, Stu Sutcliffe, as well. In **great personal stories**, she shares what they each meant, in her life. To hear this 30-minute segment, please go to:* <u>SheSaidSheSaid talks with John Lennon's Sister, Julia Baird (podbean.com)</u>

Or use the QR code at the end of this segment.

Now, we'll pick the interview up again as the topic turns to Julia Stanley Lennon's second child, Victoria…and to the way in which the loss of Victoria played a crucial role in the loss of John to Mimi Smith.

Jude: Julia, if it's okay with you, I want to read an excerpt from your book, *Imagine This* and then, ask you to talk about it. It's an emotional excerpt, but you say that one of your earliest memories was seeing your mother sitting and listening to a particular record that reminded her of John, and this is what you wrote about that moment.

You said although you didn't see John much in those earliest days, *"John was the ghost in our house. I realise now that my mother was grieving as well as living. She went on loving us and smiling and hugging with such warmth while the life was being squeezed right out of her bones."*

So, tell us what was going on at that time when John was living with Mimi, apart from all of you, and what had transpired to make things the way they were.

Julia: …Really, you've got to read the book [*Imagine This*] to understand it. I mean, it took a book to get that onto paper! So, it's a very difficult thing.

But in a very short, sort of, concise way, John's father, Alfred [Lennon], and my mother had been married a good few years before they had John, and he went to sea. He had always wanted to go to sea. He refused to be a land lubber. You know, he just did *not* want to be at home. He was in the Merchant Navy; he was traveling to and fro to the States mainly…And he disappeared in America.

…My mother had been getting money because they were married, and they had a child. She had been getting eight shillings a week from his money that was given to her because he was away. And she went down to get this money at the Seaman's Mission one time and was just told, "You can't have any money. He's gone AWOL. He's gone missing."

There are many, many stories about what happened to him, you know, and as it turned out, he might've been in prison – *I don't know* because I wasn't in America, and I haven't met anyone to corroborate properly any of the stories. So I think I've said this *might* have happened and that *might've* happened, but what definitely *did* happen was back in Liverpool, my mother was left with a child and no financial support whatsoever!

And Alfred just disappeared. She didn't hear from him at all for 18 months. And she met someone, got pregnant, and had [a baby], Victoria, that I didn't know anything about until 1985, believe it or not.

Jude: Wow.

Julia: It was never, never talked about. You know, most families have some form of skeleton in the cupboard, and you may go your whole life even if you live 'til 90 never knowing about it! Well, unfortunately, our skeleton – our cupboard – dusty cupboard – has been opened, and all the skeletons have been brought out so that *everyone* can have a little word about them! And often the people who are, sort of, critical don't know that their own cupboard is right behind them. Be careful.

So, you know, my mother had [the] baby, [Victoria]. My grandfather and Mimi insisted that she wasn't keeping the baby. It was a shameful thing. Even though Alfred disappeared, and [my mother] got no money…it was totally irrelevant to them. It was all about "middle class morality" and "keeping up with the Joneses." You know, keeping everything "smart on the outside." All rubbish. So, Victoria was adopted and then [my mother] met my father.

But when my mother had Victoria, I *now know* that she had gone into what we would now call "postnatal depression." Now, my aunt told me about it, and earlier, Jude, you mentioned about my doing *two* books. Now, I did [the first book,] *John Lennon, My Brother* in response to a documentary in 1985 that was *totally* wrong that was supposed to be commemorating five years since John had died. There were so many factual errors in it that I couldn't believe it.

I was grieving. I was getting on with my job. I was raising three children. You know, I was working full time – so, I hadn't looked at what was going on, but this documentary came on, and it was on the BBC which is supposed to be well-respected, so everyone watched it. Julian wasn't even *mentioned*. He wasn't even in it at all!

Jude: Ugh.

Julia: So, I got in touch with the *Liverpool Echo*, spoke to the editor, and he's the one that told me about Victoria. I did not know.

So, I then started finding out about things, but what I now know, I know because Nanny – my mother's middle of five sisters and the one I became closest to in my adult life…She told me in the last 18 months before she died.

She died in 1997 [but]…the last couple of years [before that] she started to talk to me and I said, "Nanny, these are the things I've been asking you for years." She said, "I know they are. I'm telling you now." And I said, "Why are you telling me?" She said, "Because you're the only one that's ever been interested."

I was asking her all the time: "What about this? What about that? What about this? Tell me this, tell me that." And in the end, she said, "You're the only one that's *ever* asked these questions. I'm telling you now. Just listen." And she would tell me the stories again and again, and it changed everything.

She said after Victoria, my mother was ill. I mean, *took to her bed* when the baby had gone because she was allowed to look after her for six weeks. Not allowed to – *made to*. With the adoptive parents waiting to take her away! But *this* is what happened. This is what happened…So, she was ill afterwards, and I said to Nanny, "Would you call that postnatal depression?" And, of course, she was, like 86 or 87 and she said, "I don't know what you'd call it. Your mother was very ill."

Jude: Right.

Julia: …So, Mimi just took advantage of that. It's as simple as that. [Mimi] was an opportunist, and she took advantage of that. And then, when my mother went to get John back, I put this in the book – John was six [years old]. And Mimi threw John behind her and said, "Get out! Get out! Get out! You're *not* having him!" And my cousin was there at the time. She told me about that. So, I haven't made any of that up! It's all from, you know…it's all from other people.

…John was a victim. And he…didn't know any of this. That's the saddest thing. He *did not* know.

Jude: I think it would've changed everything, had he known.

Julia: Of course, it would. Of course, it would.

Jude: …his heart was so broken, and he could not figure out why. "Why does my mother keep her two daughters but she didn't keep me? It must be *me*. She loves children, you know?"

Julia: He said that to me. "You've a mother, and I didn't. You had her, and I didn't."

Jude: Right. And so he *blamed himself.* And all through the rest of his life, he's singing these songs to her, to Julia, you know, but it would've changed *everything* had he known for sure that she wanted him.

Julia: Well, he didn't know. It was only because I was like somebody with a pickaxe [that *I* found out]. I wasn't giving up until I dug the foundations for the building…which was the book. I wasn't giving up!

Jude: Yeah. I so wish I had known these things when I wrote *Shoulda Been There*. I portrayed Julia as heartbroken – *heartbroken* when Mimi finally found a way to get [John]. She'd sent Social Services over [to Julia's house] before. And she finally [got] her way, but had I known – and I intend to go back and completely revise [that book] with all of this new information – had I known…But at that time, we didn't know [any of] this, you know?

Julia: No, nobody knew it. This is the thing. Nobody – *Nobody knew it.* You know, I've spoken to Philip Norman, and he said, "What you have said makes my book ridiculous and rubbish." And I said, "We didn't know the story at the time."

…He wanted to write a book with me. He said, "Let's us write the book together." And I said, "No, Philip – it's got to be me. This is something I have to do by myself."

But…in the national press when *Imagine This* came out, he said, "Well, we can all stop [writing now]. Julia's done it! We can all stop now."

Jude: Right. Your book, *Imagine This*, is beautiful. It's so beautiful and it's *so hard to read.* But it's so worth the effort.

Let me encourage everyone to read Imagine This. *It tells the story you have just read in a way that will touch your heart. If you're a John Lennon fan, it's a crucial part of his history!*

At this point, the discussion turned to those halcyon days when teen John was coming over regularly to 1 Blomfield Road, learning to play the banjo and learning rock'n'roll songs from Julia's records. Julia shares so many wonderful stories that you don't want to miss!

Then…

Jude: And, of course, it's during that time – that pivotal moment... Oh, what I would give to be there when your mother told John that secret...that he had "music in his bones"!!! And she begins to teach him to play those instruments and all the great rock'n'roll songs... What do you remember about that?

Julia: Well, my father came in with "Hound Dog." That's the first one, isn't it? The first Elvis one and said, "Is this what you wanted?"

We had the old record player, and they were all jiving in the living room. That was my mother and my father, John, Stan, and Leila. It was all big excitement, and then they started to listen to Gene Vincent, Eddie Cochran, Buddy Holly...they were all Buddy Holly fans! And then Lonnie Donegan and "Rock Island Line" and it was...it wasn't just The Beatles then, was it? The Quarry Men or *anything* that John was in! It was everyone in the Western world.

Jude: And really, it all starts with Julia Stanley Lennon. I mean, it's *her love* of rock'n'roll, *her belief* that he has "music in his bones" that she instills in him...[She convinces him] that he's destined to form a band...it just is *unbelievable* the difference that she made in the world. She changed everything. She really did.

One episode that I love in both your books is this account of seeing John on the stage for the very first time at what all authorities really consider to be the Quarrymen's first *big gig*. They had others, but this was "the big one," the Rosebery Street Festival. So, tell us about that great day.

Julia: Well, we [Jackie and I] had gone to the Sunday school. You know, our lives, sort of, revolved around church, didn't they? And we had gone to the Sunday school outing – annual outing. We got back on the coach that had taken us over. We were all dropped back at the church, the church community center. And my mother was waiting there to take us off the bus with all the other mothers. And we only lived over the road and we expected to go home, you know, have tea, have a bath, go to bed...what would normally happen.

But we didn't. We went over the road, and we got the bus into town, and it was great excitement! You know, that was a special treat for us! And we went to the Rosebery Street Festival! [John's band was supposed to perform] on the back of a coal lorry, and I can tell you that it had *not* been cleaned properly! I can tell you!

Jude: (Laughing)

Julia: And [Jackie and I] got on the back of that [lorry] with John, and we got off it very quickly because it was…absolutely filthy with coal…small bits of coal everywhere!

My mother went into one of the houses because one of the mum's had made tea and sandwiches for everybody. So, my mother had gone in there, and the shirts that [The Quarrymen] wore, my mother had bought at the market about two weeks before. I had been with her when we had gone down to the local market, and she bought real genuine American – *ha-ha* – cowboy shirts!

Jude: (Laughing)

Julia: And they loved those shirts! John [had] his on…Anyway, a gang came, and we were all aware of it, and there was a bit of an argy-bargy going on…there was about to be a punch-up! You know…teenagers [saying], "Get that Lennon!" And we were escorted by a policeman to the local bus stop to make sure we left.

Here, Julia tells so many wonderful stories about the early years of Beatlemania…especially the night of the Liverpool Première of "A Hard Day's Night," and about her visits to Kenwood in 1964-1965. Then…

Jude: As the years went along through Beatlemania, did you ever get a chance to reconnect in any way with John?

Julia: Yes, because he would turn up at home. He would turn up in Woolton, and he would just turn up…he didn't just disappear. He only disappeared when he went to America.

Jude: Right.

Julia: And…I had gone to Ireland then. I got married in August in 1968, and I had gone to Ireland and didn't come back. You know, [I] was living there in…June 1968. And then, John was doing all the stuff with Yoko. This is when everything went, sort of…when the family stuff dissipated.

I was growing up, and he was moving on. If he had stayed in England…if he had stayed in the U.K., I believe… (She trails off.) You know, I'm not sure about this, but I have heard that there were two alternatives. One was [for John and Yoko] to live in New York, and the other one was to live in Paris. Now, if he had lived in Paris, we'd never have lost touch!

Jude: Right.

Julia: But it was New York! It was America!

Jude: Yeah, yeah. But did you talk to him. You talked to him on the phone, I know, several times.

Julia: Yeah, yeah, oh lots! We talked on the phone a lot. And wrote letters. And I last spoke to him in 1980 on November the 17th because it was Nanny's – the aunt that I [was close to] – it was her birthday and [I] had gone down to see her on her birthday, and John phoned to wish Nanny a "Happy birthday!", and we had a long chat then. Yeah.

Lanea: Well Julia, Jude and I…feel so privileged that you were kind enough to share your beautiful memories with us…Hopefully, we can see you in person at Strawberry Field. We so hope that our listeners check out the wonderful Strawberry Field training programs   at https://www.StrawberryFieldLiverpool.com and Julia, please also let our listeners know where they can buy copies of your book.

Julia: Yeah, okay. So, that's https://www.JuliaBaird.co.uk. That's all they've got to do. **JuliaBaird.co.uk**, and you can get my book! You'll get the copy of the CD interview that I did with Paul McCartney as well. We sat in his office all afternoon just chatting and recorded it. And he gave it to me, and he said, "Good luck!"

He knew that I was doing it for the backbone for the first book and, of course, I've used it for the backbone of the second book because this is literally "straight from the horse's mouth" and, of course, nobody has contradicted anything because they know it's true! It is true because Paul was telling me what was going on!

So, the interview is there; the book is there; and a fabulous, fabulous Cavern wall poster that my friend did for me as a 50th birthday present, and I've had it put onto linen grained [paper]. It's a fabulous poster of the Cavern wall!...you have to look at it. And's it's all free, [when you buy the book].

Jude: Well, Julia, thank you from our hearts for being here tonight! It's very late in Liverpool, and we thank you for staying up past midnight and into the wee hours or "the small hours" as you'd say. And we thank you *mostly* for being such an important part of our lives.

I appreciate your setting the record straight about what *really* happened with your mother and for letting us know because so much of the story has been distorted.

And please know that from my heart – I will live out the rest of my life telling John's story from this end, tooo. I really hope that the world *always remember*s the great gift that your mother gave us through what she taught John to believe! So thank you for sharing your memories with us.

Julia: Well, thank you, Jude, and thank you, Lanea. Thank you very much.

Lanea: Thank you so much, Julia. We send you our best.

Julia: You too. And – well, the next time I see you hopefully will be in Strawberry Field.

Jude and Lanea: We will look forward to it! We really will!

This is just one small portion of a 90-minute interview with Julia Baird in which she discussed her life in Blomfield Road and her relationship with her brother, John. It is a sincere, touching interview that can be heard in its entirety at
https://shesaidshesaid.podbean.com/e/shesaidshesaid-talks-with-john-lennons-sister-julia-baird/
Or listen via this QR code below:

To learn more about the wonderful work being done at **Strawberry Field** and to help support the excellent training provided to so many worthy students, please go to:
https://www.StrawberryFieldLiverpool.com

To learn more about **Julia Baird** and her book, *Imagine This*, please go to: https://www.JuliaBaird.co.uk

Follow Julia on Facebook at:
https://www.facebook.com/julia.baird.374
Follow Julia on Twitter at:
@imaginethis4

Scouse Glossary

The first afternoon that I spent in Liverpool, in 1993, I discovered that a road map was called an "A to Zed," that "ta" was "thank you," and that a "nudger" wasn't a jab in the ribs, but a fantastic hard bread roll.

Liverpool's Scouse vernacular is a rich language all its own. During my seven trips to Liverpool, I studied and learned the lingo to avoid saying repeatedly, "Excuse me?" or more currently, "Wait, what?!"

If you want to learn more about Scouse and how to "speak it proper," you may want to purchase the four books below. (And I might add, they are great fun to read!)

Lern Yerself Scouse, Volume One. Frank Shaw, with notes and translations by Fritz Spiegl and a pome [sic] by Stan Kelly. Scouse Press, Liverpool, 1965.

Lern Yerself Scouse, How to Talk Proper in Liverpool, Volume Two. Linacre Lane. Edited by Fritz Spiegl. Scouse Press, Liverpool, 1966.

Lern Yerself Scouse, Wersia Sensa Yuma? The Third Volume of the Scouse Press Thesaurus of Merseyside Words and Phrases. Brian Minard. Scouse Press, Liverpool, 1972.

Lern Yerself Scouse, The Language of Laura Norder, Volume Four of the Great Liverpool Tetralogy of Scouseology edited by Fritz Spiegl. Scouse Press, Liverpool, 1989.

And you'll also enjoy this quite "colourful" Scouse website: https://www.redandwhitekop.com/forum/index.php?topic=11561 5.0

The following are my own definitions – not as vivid as might be found in these more exhaustive works – but as my father's friend Cleo Polk always commented, "That'll do."

A to Zed - the street atlas or road map booklet

A long string of misery - a pain, a person who's always down and glum (As in, "Y'er a long string of misery, now aren't you?")

"Absofuggin'lutely!" - "Absolutely!" Scousers liberally insert "fuggin'" into the middle of words or expressions. (As in, "efuggin'nough!" or "absofuggin'lutely!")

All in - tired, worn out

All Mutt 'n Jeff - "deaf and dumb." Used when someone won't pay attention to you or listen to you (or "refuses to crack on"). You might derisively say of that person, "Ah, he's all Mutt 'n Jeff." This phrase is also used when someone isn't talking at all.

"(It's) all shite!" - "It's all a load of crap!"

Anyroad - anyway (As in, "Ah, but y'er doin' it anyroad, aren't you?")

Ascloseasthis [sic] - A term used to describe a couple who is very much in love and always together. (From Tony Barrow's book, *John, Paul, George, Ringo & Me*. Tony, if you recall, grew up in Liverpool.)

Aspero - aspirin

At one another - fighting, bickering

Avvy - afternoon, as in "He'll be 'round thisavvy." The "avvy" is connected to the "this" and said as one word.

"Awright?" - "Are you okay?" Or really, "How's it going?"

Baird - girl or girlfriend, also "gerl"...also, *Julia* Baird, of course!

Bedsit - the equivalent of an American efficiency apartment, a one-room apartment where you're obliged to sit on the bed instead of a sofa.

Bent - different, having unusual tendencies (As in, "The Marquis de Sade...now, he's a bit bent!")

Bevvied - drunk, also "lushed"

Bevvy - beverage, usually an alcoholic beverage

(A) Bice - a bite to eat

(A) Birrova - a bit of a (As in, "Y'er a birrova crank, aren't yer?")

"(He's a) Birrova Beatle!" - "He's a diva!" or "He thinks he's something else!" Can also mean: "He can play a little guitar."

Bombay crud - diarrhea

Browned off - ticked off, pissed off, angry

"Buggeroff!" - "Leave me alone! Get away!"

"Bushwa!" - "Bullshit!"

Butty - a Scouse sandwich, often open-faced, that features toast, butter, jam, and if you're splurging, bacon. You can have a "jam butty" or a "bacon butty."

(The) Buzzer went - The doorbell rang.

Cadge - borrow

"(I) Can't hear a blind word he says!" - "I'm ignoring him."

"Cheeky!" - "Aren't you impudent!"

Chuffed - thrilled or delighted (also "jacked) (Used with "dead" to mean "very")

Cig - (also "fag" or "ciggie") cigarette

Clean mennal - completely crazy, mad (As in, "She's gone clean mennal!")

"(The) Clergy's all here!" - "All the important people are present!"

(A) complete tip - a gigantic mess or foul-up.

Cop On - Catch on, get it. When someone fails to understand what you're saying, you remark, "He won't cop on."

Crack On - Most often, "catch on" or "understand" or in some cases, "listen" (As in, "He won't crack on," meaning, "He's ignoring us.") Also, see "cop on."

Craggy bastard - a serious person, often scholarly, who doesn't take part in the fun

Creased - tired

"Cummoffit!" - "Get off that subject!"

Cuppa - a cup of tea

Daft - crazy, insane (This word generally accompanies "gone" as in: "He's gone daft.")

Dead - very, as in "dead creased"

Dead creased - extremely tired

Diary - schedule (As in, "Brian filled The Beatles' diary with gigs and venues.")

(A) Do - a gala or party, a celebration

"(I'll) Do the same for you when I'm carryin'." - "I'll buy you a round when I have some money."

"Don't be at it!" - "Stop! Quit! Give up the nagging!"

"Don't go ter bits!" - "Don't have a breakdown." or "Don't fall apart!"

"Don't take a blind bit o' notice..." - "Pay no attention to..."

Doorstep - follow, hound, surround (As in, "We're bein' doorstepped by the press, aren't we?") or in the case of the chorus in "Help!", to follow something closely, to overlap

"(My) Dream is out!" - "You read my mind!"

"Eck! Eck!" - This is a warning cry meaning "Watch out!" or "Beware!"

"Efuggin'nough!" - "Stop it! I've had enough!"

Fag - a cig, ciggie, or cigarette (However, John Lennon did use the term "fag-ass" when referring to Larry Kane's apparel when he sees Kane for the first time on the 1964 North American Tour, and John wasn't using "fag" to refer to cigarettes, in that instance.)

"Fanfuggin'tastic!" - "Great!"

Fave Rave - favourite thing to do, or simply "favourite"

For a big clock - for anything (As in, "I wouldn't do that for a big clock.")

Frazzled - tired or weary, with a side of confused

Gear - fantastic (This is a term they rarely used in conversation, but The Beatles use it in the 1965 *Playboy* interview with Jean

Shepard.)

"Gerroff!" - "Bug off!"

"Get stuck!" - "Get screwed!"

"(Y'er) Gettin' on me wick!" - "You're getting on my nerves!" or "You're aggravating me!"

"Give over!" - "Cut it out! Stop that!"

"Give the boy a coconut!" - a tongue-in-cheek expression said to someone who has said or done something stupid

(To) Give (someone) the short shrift - give them the brush-off

Go ter bits - get flustered or crack up (As in, "Calm yerself. Don't go ter bits!")

Goes a bomb - ignites, goes over in a big way, is a hit

Goin' Bismarck - exploding in anger

Goin' crackers - going mad

Gorra - got a (As in, "I've gorra bit of...")

(Someone's) Got rabies - (Someone's) in a terrible mood

"(Y'er) Great to come with!" - "(You're) welcome to accompany us."

(The) Griff - the scoop, the news, or variantly, "the issue at hand"

Have done - Get over with, as in "Let's have done with it!"

Havin' nowt to do with - having nothing to do with

Havin' you (us) on - teasing you, or "takin' the mickey out of you"

(A) Head on - a hangover (As in, "I've got a head on.")

Helps - encouragements, as in "Me girl whispered helps to me as I prepared to take the stage."

"H' orta!" - "He oughta!" (Meaning, "He owes it to us!" or "He certainly should!")

Himself - the boss, the person in charge, as in "Ah, here comes Himself in all his glory!"

(In) Hospital - in the hospital. This isn't really a Scouse expression, *per se*. Rather, it is a British expression, as in, "in university" But, just for clarification purposes, I included it for American readers.

"Isthasso?" (or "Thasso?") - "Is that right? Is that correct?"

It had just gone - (in reference to time) it had just turned, as in, "It had just turned midnight."

Jacked - thrilled, also "chuffed"

Jumper - sweater

Just - only. Instead of saying "only a shadow," Scousers would say "a shadow, just."

Kecks - trousers, slacks

Knackered - same as "dead creased," tired, worn out

Knockin' off a baird - Having sex with a female (Used in the *Playboy* interview with Jean Shepard, 1965)

(A) Larf - a joke

Larkin' about - having fun, doing nothing in particular

Loo - bathroom

Loosie - a single cig

Lost the run of himself (herself, yourself) - lost control of himself (herself, yourself)

(To) Make heavy weather - to complain

Makey-up - make-believe, fantasy.

(A) Marred kid - spoiled brat

Maths - math classes or the math curriculum

Mickey-takin' - teasing someone, picking at them

Mizzle off - wander away or lose focus

"Muck in!" - "Eat up!"

Muzzied - witless, ignorant

'N - and (and in the middle of a sentence, it appears as: 'n)

Nick - steal

Nobut (or Nobbut) - nothing but. Can also be used as "No, but…"

Norra - not a (whatever), as in "I've norra care in the world."

Norra bit - not a bit, not at all

"(Y'er) Not werth a light!" - "(You're) of no value at all!"

Nudger - a hard, crusty roll with a soft center

Nutters - mad, crazy (As in, "He's gone nutters.")

On about - as in "What're y' on about?" meaning, "What are you raving on about?" or "What are you going on and on about?"

On the flip - on the other side, tomorrow

PAFO - Pissed And Fell Over (drunk)

Packet o' fags - carton of cigs (cigarettes)

Potty - slightly crazy

Prezzie - a gift or present

Punters - fans, ticket-holders, or attendees at a Liverpool concert or club

Queen Mary on front 'n Queen Mury Ann on back - someone or something shallowly pretentious…someone putting on a show

Queen o' the Midden - stuck up female, conceited girl or woman

"Rambullon!" - "Keep talkin'!" (As in, "Rambullon, I'm not listenin!'")

(A) Rigour - an extreme fit of temper

Rill fax - the truth, the real facts (As in, "Givvus the rill fax" or "Tell us the whole story.")

Roolya broolya - a to-do, an upset…in some instances, a fight

Rumbled - found out, discovered

Rumbler - fast-paced, rocking song

Scarper (away or home) - to escape to a place you're anticipating

Set upon - hounded by, surrounded by (As in, "The lads were set upon by the press.")

"S'even!" - "It's heaven!"

"Shirrup!" - "Shut up!"

Shite - Shit, or really, stuff, as in "We'll not be havin' any more of that shite."

(The) Short Shrift - a dearth of attention or caring, as in, "When the press tried to doorstep me, I gave 'em the short shrift."

Skint - broke, usually accompanied by "dead." If you are dead skint, you're penniless indeed!

Skive off - play hooky or escape one's duties for something better.

(A) Snug - In a pub, a cosy, often tiny back-room set apart from the main area

(To) Strike for - to set out to get something (Fred Lennon tells Cynthia in this book that he never really wanted to "strike for a vocation.")

"(I'll or we'll) Sort you out." - "(I'll or we'll) find out what's wrong with you." It can also imply that we'll find a way to get you in a better mood

Spot of kip - a nap

Stand for - buy, purchase (As in, "stand for the next round.")

"(That will) Stand me in good" - "(That will) show me in a good light."

"(I'll) Stand you a round." - "(I'll) buy a round of drinks."

Straight away - right now (As in, "We'd better do it straight away, before Brian notices.")

Stung - to have one's feelings hurt

Suit - a businessman (a derogatory expression)

"Ta!" - "Thank you!"

Takin' the mickey out (of someone) - teasing them, kidding them

Teacher's best boy - Teacher's pet

"That sorts it!" - "That explains it!"

Thisavvy - this afternoon

Throw one's eyes to the ceiling (or the heavens) - Roll one's eyes

Tissarah (or T' rah) - goodbye

(To) Take the piss out - to tease

Tsart - girl, girlfriend, or "baird" (pronounced "bird")

Turned to - got down to work (originally, a military expression)

"'Ullo dur!" or ("'Ullo dere!") - "Hello, there!"

"Up the 'Pool!" - "Hurrah for Liverpool!"

Wack - person, man

(To) warn someone off (of something) - to advise them strongly against (something)

Werth - worth (As in "Y' aren't werth a light!")

Wet the kettle - put the kettle on. This is an Irish phrase, but a very large portion of Liverpool's population is Irish.

"We've done with…" - "We're fed up with…" or "We've had enough of…"

"When I'm carryin'…" - "When I have money on me…"

Whinge - Complain, whine

Won't Crack On - Won't try to understand. (As in, "He won't crack on." This means he won't listen and comprehend what someone is saying. It also often implies that this is intentional.)

"(I) Wouldn't do that for a big clock!" - "(I) wouldn't do that for anything!" (The "big clock" referred to in this expression is the clock on the Liver Building, situated on Liverpool's dock and overlooking the Mersey River.)

Yeahbut - yes, but…as opposed to "nobut"

Yer - your, and sometimes, "you"

Y'er - you're

"Yerrokay." - "Yeah, okay."

"Y' don't want to believe…" - "You shouldn't believe…" As in, "You don't want to believe those lies about me!"

Yew - You (Used for emphasis, as in, "Who did this? Was it *yew*!?")

Yew 'n yer ilk - You and your kind (meaning your friends, your family, your cohorts, etc.)

Yob - a hick, a greenhorn

You lot - you guys, all of you

"Zing, you!" - "Sing!" (a demand shouted to a member of a band)

Bibliography

Aldridge, Alan. **THE BEATLES ILLUSTRATED LYRICS.** Macdonald and Co Publishers, London, U.K., 1969. ISBN 0-395-59426-X.

Babiuk, Andy. **BEATLES GEAR.** Outline Press, London, U.K., 2001. ISBN 0-87930-731-5.

Badman, Keith. **THE BEATLES: OFF THE RECORD.** Omnibus Press, New York, NY, 2000. ISBN 978-1-84772-101-3.

Baird, Julia. **IMAGINE THIS.** Hodder & Stoughton, London, U.K., 2007. ISBN 978-0-340-83924-9.

Baird, Julia. **JOHN LENNON: MY BROTHER.** Jove, New York, NY, 1988. ISBN 0-515-10250-4.

Barrow, Tony. **JOHN, PAUL, GEORGE, RINGO & ME: THE REAL BEATLES STORY.** Thunder's Mouth Press, New York, NY, 2005. ISBN 1-56025-882-9.

Barrow, Tony. **MEET THE BEATLES.** Souvenir Press, London, U.K., 2014. ISBN 978-0-28564-289-8.

Beatles, The. **THE BEATLES ANTHOLOGY.** Chronicle Books, San Francisco, CA, 2000. ISBN 0-8118-2684-8.

Bedford, David. **THE COUNTRY OF LIVERPOOL.** Dalton Watson Fine Books Limited, Liverpool, U.K., 2020. ISBN 978-1-8383062-1-2.

Bedford, David. **LIDDYPOOL.** Dalton Watson Fine Books, Deerfield, IL, 2009. ISBN 978-185443-237-7.

Belmo and Garry Marsh. **THE BEATLES' CHRISTMAS BOOK: EVERYWHERE IT'S CHRISTMAS.** GC Publishing, Ontario, Canada, 2011. ISBN 978-1926592251.

Best, Pete and Patrick Doncaster. **BEATLE! THE PETE BEST STORY.** Plexus Publishing, London, 1985. ISBN 0-85965-077-4.

Bicknell, Alf. **ALF BICKNELL'S PERSONAL BEATLES DIARY.** Jack Edwards Productions, 1995. No ISBN.

Borack, John M. **JOHN LENNON: LIFE IS WHAT HAPPENS.** F+W Media, Iola, WI, 2010. ISBN 979-1-4402-1391-5.

Boyd, Pattie and Penny Junor. **WONDERFUL TONIGHT.** Three Rivers Press, New York, NY, 2007. ISBN 978-0-307-40783-2.

Bramwell, Tony. **MAGICAL MYSTERY TOURS: MY LIFE WITH THE BEATLES.** Thomas Dunne Books, New York, NY, 2005. ISBN 0-312-33043-X.

Braun, Michael. **LOVE ME DO: THE BEATLES' PROGRESS.** Penguin Books, New York, NY, 1964. ISBN 0-14-002278-3.

Brown, Craig. **100 GLIMPSES OF THE BEATLES.** Farrar, Straus and Giroux, New York, NY, 2020. ISBN 978-0-374-10931-8.

Brown, Peter and Steven Gaines. **THE LOVE YOU MAKE.** McGraw-Hill, New York, NY, 1983. ISBN 0-07-008159-X.

Burns, Kathy. **THE GUITAR'S ALL RIGHT AS A HOBBY, JOHN.** Self-published, 2014. ISBN 978-1-4949-6868-7.

Burrows, Terry. **GUITAR FAMILY TREES.** Apple Publishing, 2011. ISBN 978-1845434236.

Burrows, Terry. **JOHN LENNON: A STORY IN PHOTOGRAPHS.** Thunder Bay Press, San Diego, CA, 2000. ISBN 1-57145-469-1.

Buskin, Richard. **THE COMPLETE IDIOT'S GUIDE TO THE BEATLES.** Alpha Books, New York, NY, 1998. ISBN 0-02-862130-1.

Buskin, Richard. **JOHN LENNON: HIS LIFE AND LEGEND.** Crescent, New York, NY, 1991. ISBN 0-517-03590-1.

Cain, Alex and Terry McCusker, **RINGO STARR AND THE BEATLES BEAT.** Matador Publishing, Leicestershire, U.K., 2016. ISBN 978-1-78589-955-3.

Carlin, Peter Ames. **PAUL McCARTNEY: A LIFE.** Touchstone, New York, NY, 2009. ISBN 978-1-4165-6209-2.

Carr, Roy and Tony Tyler. **THE BEATLES: AN ILLUSTRATED RECORD.** Harmony Books, New York, NY, 1975. ISBN 0-517-52045-1.

Carr, Roy. **BEATLES AT THE MOVIES.** HarperPerennial, New York, NY, 1996. ISBN 0-06-273437-7.

Clayson, Alan and Pauline Sutcliffe. **BACKBEAT: STUART SUTCLIFFE: THE LOST BEATLE.** Pan Books Limited, London, U.K., 1994. ISBN 0-330-3358004.

Clayson, Alan. **PAUL McCARTNEY.** Sanctuary Publishing, London, UK, 2003. ISBN 1-86074-482-6.

Clayson, Alan. **RINGO STARR: A LIFE.** MPG Books, London, U.K., 2003. ISBN 1-86074-647-0.

Clayson, Alan and Spencer Leigh. **THE WALRUS WAS RINGO: 101 BEATLES MYTHS DEBUNKED.** Chrome Dreams, Surrey, U.K., 2003. ISBN 1-84240-2056.

Coleman, Ray. **LENNON.** McGraw-Hill, New York, NY, 1984. ISBN 0-07-011786-1.

Coleman, Ray. **THE MAN WHO MADE THE BEATLES: AN INTIMATE BIOGRAPHY OF BRIAN EPSTEIN.** McGraw-Hill, New York, NY, 1989. ISBN 0-07-011789-6.

Connolly, Ray. **BEING JOHN LENNON: A RESTLESS LIFE.** Pegasus Books: New York, NY, 2018. ISBN 978-1-64313-053-8.

Creasy, Martin. **BEATLEMANIA! THE REAL STORY OF THE BEATLES U.K. TOURS 1963-1965.** Omnibus Press, New York, NY, 2010. ISBN 978-1-84938-659-3.

Davies, Hunter. **THE BEATLES: THE AUTHORIZED BIOGRAPHY.** McGraw-Hill, New York, NY, 1968. No ISBN.

Davies, Hunter. **THE JOHN LENNON LETTERS.** Little, Brown and Company, New York, NY, 2012. ISBN 0-316-20080-6.

Davies, Hunter. **THE QUARRYMEN.** Omnibus Press, New York, NY, 2001. ISBN 0-7119- 8526-X.

Davis, Andy. **THE BEATLES FILES.** CLB/Bookham Project, LTD., New York, NY, 1988. ISBN 978-1858338576.

Davis, Ivor. **THE BEATLES (AND ME) ON TOUR.** Cockney Kid Publishing, Ventura, CA, 2014. ISBN 978-0-9903710-7-6.

DeWitt, Howard. **THE BEATLES: UNTOLD TALES.** Horizon Books, Fremont, CA, 1985. ISBN 0-938840-03-7.

DuNoyer, Paul. **WE ALL SHINE ON: THE STORIES BEHIND EVERY JOHN LENNON SONG, 1970-1980.** Carlton Books, New York, NY, 1997. ISBN 0-06-273491-1.

Edmondson, Jacqueline. **JOHN LENNON: A BIOGRAPHY.** Greenwood Press, Santa Barbara, CA, 2010. ISBN 978-0-313-37938-3.

Egan, Sean, ed. **THE MAMMOTH BOOK OF THE BEATLES.** Running Press, London, U.K., 2009. ISBN 978-0-7624-3627-9.

Epstein, Brian. **A CELLARFUL OF NOISE.** Pierian Press, Ann Arbor, MI, 1984. ISBN 0-87650-169-2.

Evans, Mike. **THE BEATLES: BEATLEMANIA FOR FANS OF THE FAB FOUR.** Igloo Press, Sywell, U.K., 2012. ISBN 978-0-85734-797-8.

Evans, Mike, ed. **THE BEATLES: PAPERBACK WRITER: 40 YEARS OF CLASSIC WRITING.** Plexus, London, U.K., 2012. ISBN 978-0-85965-465-4.

Everett, Walter. **THE BEATLES AS MUSICIANS: THE QUARRY MEN THROUGH RUBBER SOUL.** Oxford University Press, Oxford; New York, NY, 2001. ISBN 978-0-19-514105-4.

Fallows, Colin and Clough, Matthew H., eds. **STUART SUTCLIFFE: A RETROSPECTIVE.** University of Liverpool Press, Liverpool, U.K., August 2008-January 2009. ISBN 978-1-84631-176-5.

Freeman, Robert. **THE BEATLES: A PRIVATE VIEW.** Mallard Press, New York, NY, 1990. ISBN 0792-445282-8.

Freiman, Scott. **DECONSTRUCTING THE BEATLES:** "A Hard Day's Night" and "Help!" Double DVD set.

Friede, Goldie, Robin Titone, and Sue Wiener, **The Beatles: A to Z.** Methuen, Inc., New York, NY, 1980. ISBN 0-416-00781-3.

Frontani, Michael R. **THE BEATLES: IMAGE AND THE MEDIA.** University Press of Mississippi, Jackson, MS, 2007. ISBN 978-1-57806-966-8.

Fulpen, H. W. **THE BEATLES: AN ILLUSTRATED DIARY.** Plexus, London, U.K., 1982. ISBN 0-85965-070-7.

Geller, Debbie. **IN MY LIFE: THE BRIAN EPSTEIN STORY.** St. Martin's Press, New York, NY, 2000. ISBN 0-312-26564-6.

Gentle, Johnny and Ian Forsyth. **JOHNNY GENTLE & THE BEATLES: FIRST EVER TOUR, SCOTLAND 1960.** Merseystock Publications Liverpool, U.K., 1998. ISBN 0-9532989-0-6.

Geppetti, Marcello. **THE BEATLES IN ROME 1965.** Manic D Press, San Francisco, CA, 2007. ISBN 978-1-933149-12-7.

Goldman, Albert. **THE LIVES OF JOHN LENNON.** William Morrow and Company, New York, NY, 1988. ISBN 0-688-0472-1.

Goldsmith, Martin. **THE BEATLES: COME TO AMERICA.** John Wiley and Sons, Hoboken, NJ, 2004. ISBN 0-471-46964-5.

Goodden, Joe. **RIDING SO HIGH: THE BEATLES AND DRUGS.** Pepper and Pearl, Cardiff, U.K., 2017. ISBN 9781999803308.

Gould, Jonathan. **CAN'T BUY ME LOVE: THE BEATLES, BRITAIN, AND AMERICA.** Harmony Books, New York, NY, 2007. ISBN 978-0-307-35337-5.

Greenwald, Ted. **THE BEATLES COMPANION: THE FAB FOUR IN FILM, PERFORMANCE, RECORDING, AND PRINT.** Friedman Book Group, New York, NY, 1992. ISBN 0-8317-0717-8

Gunderson, Chuck. **SOME FUN TONIGHT!: THE BACKSTAGE STORY OF HOW THE BEATLES ROCKED AMERICA: THE HISTORIC TOURS OF 1964-1966, VOLS. 1 AND 2.** Gunderson Media, San Diego, CA, 2013. ISBN 978-0-615-88162-1.

Hammack, Jerry. **THE BEATLES RECORDING REFERENCE MANUAL, VOLUME 2.** CreateSpace Independent Publishing, North Charleston, SC, 2017. ISBN 9781983704550.

Harrison, Louise. **MY KID BROTHER'S BAND, A.K.A. THE BEATLES.** Acclaim Press, Morley, MO, 2014. ISBN 978-1-938905-52-0.

Harry, Bill. **THE BEATLES, VOL. 4: BEATLEMANIA, THE HISTORY OF THE BEATLES ON FILM.** Avon Books, New York, NY, 1984. ISBN 0-380-89557-9.

Harry, Bill. **THE ENCYCLOPEDIA OF BEATLES PEOPLE.** Blandford Publishing, London, U.K., 1997. ISBN 0-7137-2606-7.

Harry, Bill. **THE JOHN LENNON ENCYCLOPEDIA.** Virgin Publishing, London, U.K., 2000. ISBN 0-7535-0404-9.

Harry, Bill. **LIVERPOOL: BIGGER THAN THE BEATLES.** Trinity Mirror NW, Liverpool, U.K., 2009. ISBN 978-1-906802-04-2.

Harry, Bill. **THE ULTIMATE BEATLES ENCYCLOPEDIA.** Hyperion, New York, NY, 1992. ISBN 1-56282-814-2.

Hertsgaard, Mark. **A DAY IN THE LIFE: THE MUSIC AND ARTISTRY OF THE BEATLES.** Delacorte Press, New York, NY, 1995. ISBN 0-385-31377-2.

Hill, Tim. **THE BEATLES: A LIFE IN PICTURES.** Metro Books, New York, NY, 2004. ISBN 978-0-7607-5613-3.

Hill, Tim, and Allison Guantlett, Gareth Thomas, and Jane Benn. **THE BEATLES: THE ILLUSTRATED BIOGRAPHY.** Trans-Atlantic Press. Croxley Green, Hertfordshire, U.K., 2008. ISBN 978-1-9071760-6-7.

Hill, Tim. **THE BEATLES: UNSEEN ARCHIVES.** Parragon, Bath, U.K., 2000. ISBN 0-75500-041-2.

Hill, Tim. **IMAGES OF THE BEATLES.** Parragon Books, Bath, U.K., 2006. ISBN 1-40548-934-0.

Hill, Tim. **JOHN, PAUL, GEORGE & RINGO: THE DEFINITIVE ILLUSTRATED CHRONICLE OF THE BEATLES, 1960-1970.** Metro Books, New York, NY, 2007. ISBN 978-1-4351-1007-6.

Hoffmann, Dezo and Norman Jopling. **THE FACES OF JOHN LENNON.** McGraw-Hill, New York, NY, 1986. ISBN 0-07-029306-6.

Howlett, Kevin. **THE BEATLES AT THE BBC: THE RADIO YEARS, 1962-7.** BBC Books, London, U.K., 1996. ISBN 0-563-38770-X.

Howlett, Kevin. **THE BEATLES: THE BBC ARCHIVES 1962-1970.** Harper Design, New York, NY, 2013. ISBN 978-0-06-228853-0.

Jackson, Andrew Grant. **THE MOST REVOLUTIONARY YEAR IN MUSIC: 1965.** Thomas Dunne Books, New York, NY, 2015. ISBN 978-1-250-05962-8.

Kane, Larry. **LENNON REVEALED.** Running Press, Philadelphia, PA, 2005. ISBN 0-7624-2364-1.

Kane, Larry. **TICKET TO RIDE.** Running Press, Philadelphia, PA, 2003. ISBN 0-7624-1592-4.

Kane, Larry. **WHEN THEY WERE BOYS.** Running Press, Philadelphia, PA, 2013. ISBN 978-0-7624-4014-6.

Kenny, Francis. **THE MAKING OF JOHN LENNON: THE UNTOLD STORY OF THE RISE AND FALL OF THE BEATLES.** Luath Press, Ltd., Edinburgh, U.K., 2014. ISBN 978-1-910745-24-3.

Lennon, Cynthia. **JOHN.** Crown Publishers, New York, NY, 2005. ISBN 0-307-33855-X.

Lennon, Cynthia. **A TWIST OF LENNON.** Avon Books, New York, NY, 1978. ISBN 0-380-45450-5.

Lennon, John. **A SPANIARD IN THE WORKS.** Simon and Schuster, New York, NY, 1965. No ISBN.

Lennon, Pauline. **DADDY COME HOME.** Angus and Robertson, London, U.K., 1990. ISBN 0-207-16996-9.

Lewisohn, Mark. **ALL THESE YEARS, VOL. 1, TUNE IN (Extended Special Edition).** Little, Brown, London, U.K., 2013. ISBN 978-1-0478-3.

Lewisohn, Mark. **THE BEATLES: DAY BY DAY.** Harmony Books, New York, NY, 1987. ISBN 0-517-57750-X.

Lewisohn, Mark. **THE BEATLES RECORDING SESSIONS: THE OFFICIAL ABBEY ROAD STUDIO SESSION NOTES 1962-1970.** Harmony Books, New York, NY, 1988. ISBN 0-517-57066-1.

Lewisohn, Mark. **THE COMPLETE BEATLES CHRONICLE.** Harmony Books, New York, NY, 1992. ISBN 0-517-58100-0.

Lewisohn, Mark and Kevin Howlett. **IN MY LIFE: JOHN LENNON REMEMBERED.** BBC Books, London, U.K., 1990. ISBN 0-563-36105-0.

MacDonald, Ian. **REVOLUTION IN THE HEAD: THE BEATLES' RECORDS AND THE SIXTIES.** Henry Holt and Company, New York, NY, 1994. ISBN 0-8050-2780-7.

Margotin, Philippe and Jean-Michelle Guesdon, **ALL THE SONGS: THE STORY BEHIND EVERY BEATLES RELEASE.** Black Dog, New York, NY, 2013. ISBN 978-1-57912-952-1.

Marion, Larry. **THE LOST BEATLES PHOTOGRAPHS: THE BOB BONIS ARCHIVE, 1964-1966.** Harper Collins, New York, NY, 2011. ISBN 978-0-06-196078-9.

Martin, George. **ALL YOU NEED IS EARS.** St. Martin's Press, New York, NY, 1979. ISBN 0-312-11482-6.

McCabe, Peter and Robert Schonfeld. **JOHN LENNON: FOR THE RECORD.** Bantam Books, New York, NY, 1984. ISBN 0-553-24802-2.

McCartney, Angie. **MY LONG AND WINDING ROAD.** ROK Books, Wolverhampton, England, 2013. ISBN 978-0-9575029-0-1.

McCartney, Angie. **YOUR MOTHER SHOULD KNOW.** Probabilistic Publishing, Sugar Land, Texas, 2019. ISBN 978-1-941075-09-8.

McCartney, Michael. **REMEMBER: RECOLLECTIONS AND PHOTOGRAPHS OF THE BEATLES.** Henry Holt and Company, New York, NY, 1992. ISBN 0-8050-2283-X.

McKinney, Devin. **MAGIC CIRCLES: THE BEATLES IN DREAM AND HISTORY.** Harvard University Press, Cambridge, MA, 2003. ISBN 0-674-01202-X.

Mellers, Wilfrid. **TWILIGHT OF THE GODS: THE MUSIC OF THE BEATLES.** Schirmer Books, New York, NY, 1973. ISBN 670-73598-1.

Miles, Barry. **THE BEATLES' DIARY, VOLUME 1: THE BEATLES YEARS.** Omnibus Press, London, U.K., 2001. ISBN 0-7119-8308-9.

Miles, Barry. **JOHN LENNON: IN HIS OWN WORDS.** Quick Fox, London, U.K., 1981. ISBN 0-8256-3953-0.

Miles, Barry. **PAUL McCARTNEY: MANY YEARS FROM NOW.** Henry Holt and Company, New York, NY, 1997. ISBN 0-8050-5249-6.

Monaco, James. **HOW TO READ A FILM: MOVIES, MEDIA, AND BEYOND.** Oxford University Press, U.K., 2009. ISBN 0-1953-2105-7.

Mulligan, Kate Siobhan. **THE BEATLES: A MUSICAL BIOGRAPHY.** Greenwood, Santa Barbara, CA, 2010. ISBN 978-0-313-37686-3.

Norman, Philip. **JOHN LENNON: THE LIFE.** Ecco, New York, NY, 2008. ISBN 978-0-06-075401-3.

Norman, Philip. **SHOUT!** MJF Books, New York, NY, 1981. ISBN 1-56731-087-7.

O'Donnell, Jim. **THE DAY JOHN MET PAUL.** Penguin Books, New York, 1994. ISBN 0-14-025301-7.

Pawlowski, Gareth. **HOW THEY BECAME THE BEATLES: A DEFINITIVE HISTORY OF THE EARLY YEARS: 1960-1964.** E. P. Dutton, New York, NY, 1989. ISBN 0-525-24823-4.

Prelutsky, Jack. **THE RANDOM HOUSE BOOK OF POETRY FOR CHILDREN.** Random House, New York, NY, 1983. ISBN 0-394-85010-6.

Rayl, A.J.S. **BEATLES '64: A HARD DAY'S NIGHT IN AMERICA.** Doubleday, New York, NY, 1989. ISBN 0-385-24583-1.

Riley, Tim. **LENNON: THE MAN, THE MYTH, THE MUSIC.** Hyperion Books, New York, NY, 2011. ISBN 978-1-4013-2452-0.
Riley, Tim. **TELL ME WHY.** Vintage Books, New York, NY, 1988. ISBN 0-679-72198-3.

Robertson, John. **LENNON.** Omnibus Press, New York, NY, 1995. ISBN 0-7119-4981-6.

Robertson, John. **THE MUSIC OF JOHN LENNON.** Omnibus Press, New York, NY, 1993. ISBN 0-8065-1438-8.

Robustelli, Anthony. **I WANT TO TELL YOU: THE DEFINITIVE GUIDE TO THE MUSIC OF THE BEATLES, VOL. 1: 1962/1963.** Shady Bear Productions, New York, NY, 2014. ISBN 978-0-9915191-0-1.

Rodriguez, Robert, and Peter Braunstein, Philip Carpenter, Anthony O. Edmonds, David Farber, Michael S. Foley, Jeffrey C. Sanders, and Bradley G. Shreve. **THE SIXTIES CHRONICLE.** Legacy Publishing, Lincolnwood, IL, 2004. ISBN 1-4127-1009-X.

Ruhlmann, William. **JOHN LENNON.** Smithmark, Greenwich, CT, 1993. ISBN 0-8317-5253-X.

Russell, Jeff. **THE BEATLES COMPLETE DISCOGRAPHY.** Universe Publishing, New York, NY, 2006. ISBN 0-7893-1373-1.

Salewicz, Chris. **McCARTNEY.** St. Martin's Press, New York, NY, 1986. ISBN 0-312-90451-7.

Sawyers, June Skinner, ed. **READ THE BEATLES.** Penguin Books, New York, NY, 2006. ISBN 0-14-3037832-3.

Schaffner, Nicholas. **THE BEATLES FOREVER: HOW THEY CHANGED OUR CULTURE.** MJF Books, New York, NY, 1978. ISBN 1-56731-008-7.

Schultheiss, Tom. **THE BEATLES: A DAY IN THE LIFE, THE DAY-BY-DAY DIARY 1960-1970.** Quick Fox, New York, NY, 1981. ISBN 0-8256-3229-3.

Schwensen, Dave. **THE BEATLES AT SHEA STADIUM.** North Shore Publishing, Vermillion, OH, 2014. ISBN 978-0-9791030-25.

Sheff, David. **ALL WE ARE SAYING: THE LAST MAJOR INTERVIEW WITH JOHN LENNON AND YOKO ONO.** St. Martin's Press, New York, NY, 1981. ISBN 0-312-25464-4.

Sheff, David. **THE *PLAYBOY* INTERVIEWS.** Playboy Press, New York, NY, 1980. ISBN 0-87223-705-2.

Shotton, Pete and Nicholas Schaffner. **JOHN LENNON: IN MY LIFE.** Stein and Day, Briarcliff Manor, NY, 1983. ISBN 0-8128-2916-6.

Solt, Andrew and Sam Egan. **IMAGINE.** Macmillan, New York, NY, 1988. ISBN 0-02-630910-6.

Spignesi, Stephen J. and Michael Lewis. **100 BEST BEATLES SONGS: AN INFORMED FAN'S GUIDE.** Tess Press, New York, NY, 2004. ISBN 978-1-60376-191-8.

Spitz, Bob. **THE BEATLES.** Little, Brown and Company, New York, NY, 2005. ISBN 0-316-80352-9.

Spizer, Bruce. **THE BEATLES ARE COMING!** 498 Productions, LLC, New Orleans, LA, 2003. ISBN 0-9662649-8-3.

Spizer, Bruce. **THE BEATLES FOR SALE ON PARLOPHONE RECORDS.** 498 Productions, LLC, New Orleans, LA. ISBN 0-9832957-0-0.

Spizer, Bruce. **THE BEATLES STORY ON CAPITOL RECORDS, VOL. 2.** 498 Productions, LLC, New Orleans, LA. ISBN 0-9662649-2-4

Staggs, Jim and Jim Pollson. **THE BEATLES WITH JIM STAGGS: BEHIND THE SCENES ON THEIR FIRST U.S. TOUR, 1964.** Jim Staggs, Staggstarbeat.com, 2008. Book on CD.

Stannard, Neville. **THE BEATLES: THE LONG & WINDING ROAD, A HISTORY OF THE BEATLES ON RECORD.** Avon Books, New York, NY, 1982. ISBN 0-380-85704-9.

Stark, Steven D. **MEET THE BEATLES: A CULTURAL HISTORY OF THE BAND THAT SHOOK YOUTH, GENDER, AND THE WORLD.** Harper, New York, NY, 2005. ISBN 0-06-000893-8.

Starr, Michael Seth. **RINGO: WITH A LITTLE HELP.** Backbeat Books: Milwaukee, WI, 2015. ISBN 9789-1-61713-657-3.

Stokes, Geoffrey. **THE BEATLES, A ROLLING STONE PRESS BOOK.** New York Times Books, New York, NY, 1980. ISBN 0-8129-0928-3.

Taylor, Alistair. **YESTERDAY: MY LIFE WITH THE BEATLES.** Pioneer Books, Las Vegas, NV, 1991. ISBN 1-55698-292-5.

Taylor, Derek. **AS TIME GOES BY: LIVING IN THE SIXTIES.** Popular Culture, Inc., Ann Arbor, MI, 1973. ISBN 1-56075-007-3.

Taylor, Derek. **IT WAS TWENTY YEARS AGO TODAY: AN ANNIVERSARY CELEBRATION OF 1967.** Simon and Schuster, New York, NY, 1987. ISBN 0-671-64201-4.

Thomas, Gareth. **JOHN LENNON: THE ILLUSTRATED BIOGRAPHY.** Transatlantic Press, Croxley Green, Hertfordshire, U.K., 2008. ISBN 978-0-9557949-3-5.

Tremlett, George. **THE JOHN LENNON STORY.** Futura Publications, Ltd., Bungay, Suffolk, U.K., 1976. ISBN 0-8600-7294-0.

Trynka, Paul, ed. **THE BEATLES: TEN YEARS THAT SHOOK THE WORLD.** DK Books, London, U.K., 2004. ISBN 0-7566-0670-5.

Turner, Steve. **A HARD DAY'S WRITE: THE STORIES BEHIND EVERY BEATLES SONG.** Little-Brown/Carlton, New York, NY, 1994. ISBN 0-316-91212-3.

Ward, Ed, Geoffrey Stokes, and Ken Tucker. **ROCK OF AGES: THE *ROLLING STONE* HISTORY OF ROCK'N'ROLL.** Rolling Stone Press/Summit Press, New York, NY, 1986. ISBN 0-671-63068-7.

Wiener, Allen J. **THE BEATLES: THE ULTIMATE RECORDING GUIDE, 3rd REVISED EDITION.** Bob Adams, Inc., Holbrook, MA, 1994. ISBN 1-55850-414-1.

Wenner, Jann. **LENNON REMEMBERS.** Popular Library, New York, NY, 1971. No ISBN.

Wells, Simon. **THE BEATLES: 365 DAYS.** Getty Images, Abrams, New York, NY, 2004. ISBN 0-8109-5911-9.

Williams, Allan and William Marshall. **THE MAN WHO GAVE THE BEATLES AWAY.** Coronet Books, London, U.K, 1975. ISBN 0-340-21016-8.

Winn, John C. **LIFTING LATCHES.** Multiplus Books, Sharon, VT, 2005. ISBN 0-978362-2-5.

Winn, John C. **WAY BEYOND COMPARE.** Three Rivers Press, New York, NY, 2003. ISBN 978-0-307-45157-6.

Womack, Kenneth. **THE BEATLES ENCYCLOPEDIA, VOLS. 1 AND 2.** Greenwood Press, Santa Barbara, CA, 2014. ISBN 978-0-313-39171-2.

Womack, Kenneth. **JOHN LENNON 1980.** Omnibus Press, New York, NY, 2020. ISBN 078-1-787601-36-9.

Womack, Kenneth. **LONG AND WINDING ROADS: THE EVOLVING ARTISTRY OF THE BEATLES.** Continuum Press, New York, NY, 2007. ISBN 978-0-8264-1746-6.56

Womack, Kenneth. **MAXIMUM VOLUME: THE LIFE OF BEATLES PRODUCER, GEORGE MARTIN, VOL. 1.** Chicago Review Press Incorporated, Chicago, IL, 2017. ISBN 978-1-61373-188-5.

Wooton, Richard. **JOHN LENNON: AN ILLUSTRATED BIOGRAPHY.** Haughter and Stoughton, London, U.K., 1984. ISBN 0-340-35875-0.

Yule, Andrew. **THE MAN WHO FRAMED THE BEATLES: A BIOGRAPHY OF RICHARD LESTER.** Donald Fine, Inc., New York, NY, 1994. ISBN 1-55611-390-0.

INTERVIEWS

Interview with **Julia Baird,** John's sister, in February 2021 about growing up with John and about the time she spent in Kenwood with John and Cynthia. Here is the link from the "She Said She Said" podcast with co-host, Lanea Stagg, of **The Recipe Records Series**: SheSaidSheSaid talks with John Lennon's Sister, Julia Baird (podbean.com)

Interviews with **Angie and Ruth McCartney** about their time in the Bahamas with The Beatles during the making of "Help!" Here is the link from the "She Said She Said" podcast, with co-host Lanea Stagg of The Recipe Records Series: Angie and Ruth McCartney Rock "She Said She Said" (podbean.com)

Interview with **Freda Kelly,** The Beatles' Fan Club Secretary and trusted employee of Brian Epstein at NEMS for 12 years. (Chicago Fest for Beatles Fans, 2013 and on "The John Lennon Hour," *BeatlesARama* radio, 2013)

Interview with **Charlie Lennon,** John's uncle, who talked about the rift between Fred Lennon and his brothers, and the role that Mimi Smith played in Fred's absence in John's life. (The Grapes, Liverpool, March, 1995)

Interview with **Bob Wooler,** who discussed the incident at Paul McCartney's birthday party that caused John Lennon to hit him. Bob did not tell me the exact words he said to John that night. (Lark Lane, Liverpool, March, 1995)

Interview with **Larry Kane,** who travelled with The Beatles on the 1964 and 1965 North American Tours as an "on the scene reporter" from WFUN, Miami, FL, and who also flew to the Bahamas to interview The Beatles in early 1965. (Philadelphia, March 2010)

Interviews and conversations with **Ivor Davis,** who toured with The Beatles in 1964 and 1965 and was one of only two journalists to go into Elvis's home in Beverly Hills with The Beatles. (Numerous interviews, e-mails, and phone conversations throughout 2014-2021)

Interview with **Louise Harrison,** sister of George Harrison, about her time with The Beatles in the Bahamas, 1965. (Kansas City, 1993)

Interview with **Bob Eubanks,** entrepreneur who booked The Beatles in The Hollywood Bowl, 1964 and 1965, during the North American Tour. (Chicago Fest for Beatles Fans, 2014)

Interview with **Sid Bernstein** regarding his concept of booking The Beatles at Shea Stadium, 1965, and the process it took to make this dream into a reality. (BEATexpo, 2009)

Interview with **Helen Anderson,** John's Liverpool College of Art friend, "Heloon," about John's college days and how they impacted The Beatles. We also discussed her friendship with Cynthia Lennon throughout The Beatlemania years. Here is the link to that "She Said She Said" podcast with co-host, Lanea Stagg, "The Coolinary Chef" and author of **The Recipe Records Series**: https://shesaidshesaid.podbean.com/e/shesaidshesaid-interview-with-john-lennons-friend-and-artist-helen-anderson/

Telephone consultation with **Chuck Gunderson,** author of *Some Fun Tonight!, The Backstage Story of How The Beatles Rocked America: The Historic Tours of 1964-1966, Vols. 1 and 2.*

Telephone consultation with **Steve Marinucci,** who also interviewed Sid Bernstein for Beatles Examiner, to compare notes on the information we gleaned from our conversations with Sid.

Interview with **Bettie Westmoreland Birdsall,** head stewardess on board the Electra II aircraft owned by American Flyers in which

The Beatles traveled throughout the 1964 North American Tour. She returned as head stewardess for the 1965 North American Tour and will appear in *Shades of Life, Part 2*. I also interviewed Bettie (via Facetime link) at the 2018 Beatles at the Ridge Festival in Walnut Ridge, AR.

Beatles Books and Merchandise

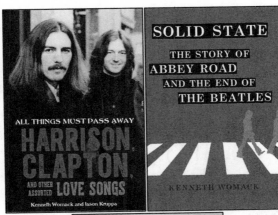

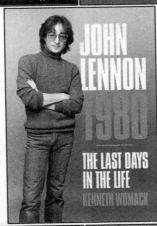

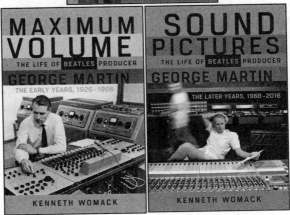

**Learn more about Kenneth Womack's books
and work at:
everythingfabfour.com**

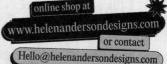

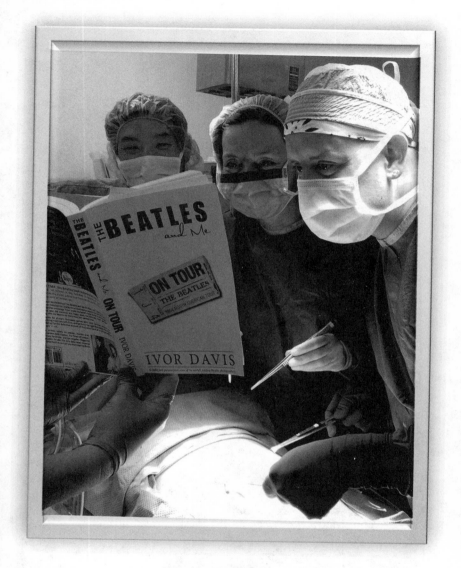

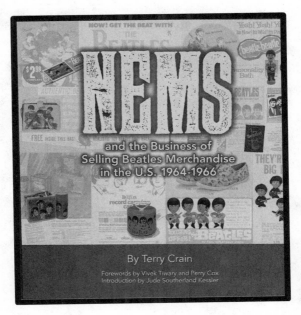

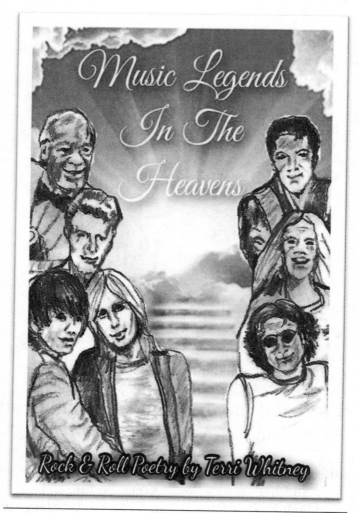

Music Legends In The Heavens

Music icon history from as early as the 1950s.
"Richie Valens" to "Aretha Franklin" to "John Lennon"
50 great musicians that not only gave us memorable music,
but inspired other musicians as well.
"A tribute to them all!"
Also available from Terri Whitney for all Beatle lovers,
"Any Rhymer At All"
https://therockinrhymer.com/

https://www.beatlesarama.com/
24-Hour Beatles Radio!

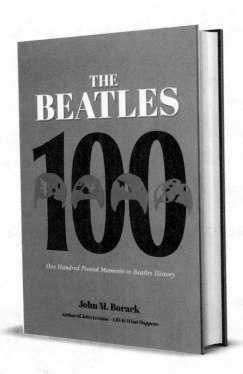

*Was John Lennon meeting Paul McCartney more
significant than John Lennon meeting Yoko Ono?
Rubber Soul or Revolver?
Which Wings album was Paul McCartney's solo
pinnacle?*

**In 100 brief chapters, John M. Borack discusses and ranks the
greatest moments in Beatles history.**

OUT NOW WHEREVER GOOD BOOKS ARE SOLD

$35.00 | RAREBIRDLIT.COM

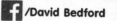
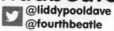 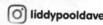

Dear Beatle People: The Story of the North American Beatles Fan Clubs

by Sara Schmidt
(Scheduled release in the Fall of 2021)

For the first time ever, read the story of The Beatles Fan Clubs in North America!

Sara is also the author of
Happiness is Seeing The Beatles
and creator of the website
Meet The Beatles....for Real

The book includes: previously unknown stories of fan club members that met the Beatles in person; the story of when The Beatles threatened to sue their fans about the very first Beatles convention; previously unseen Beatles photos, memorabilia, and much more! Be the first to know when it is available by going to
Dear Beatle People: The Beatles North American Fan Clubs 1963-1972.